LITER $= 1000$ cm^3

KDR

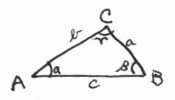

LAW of COSINES

$$a^2 = b^2 + c^2 - 2bc \cos a$$
$$b^2 = a^2 + c^2 - 2ac \cos \beta$$
$$c^2 = a^2 + b^2 - 2ab \cos \gamma$$

$$\cos a = \frac{b^2 + c^2 - a^2}{2bc}$$

$$\cos \beta = \frac{a^2 + c^2 - b^2}{2ac}$$

$$\cos \gamma = \frac{a^2 + b^2 - c^2}{2ab}$$

The Elements of Physics

THE ELEMENTS
OF PHYSICS

Alpheus W. Smith

PROFESSOR OF PHYSICS, EMERITUS
THE OHIO STATE UNIVERSITY

John N. Cooper

PROFESSOR OF PHYSICS
U.S. NAVAL POSTGRADUATE SCHOOL

SIXTH EDITION

1957

New York   Toronto   London

McGRAW-HILL BOOK COMPANY, INC.

Preface

The impact of physics in modern society is so great that no active person can fail to utilize many physical phenomena every day. His life is far richer if he understands the principles which underlie these phenomena. The central aim of this book is to introduce the student to physics in such a way that he develops a capacity for seeing relationships between physical phenomena and for applying universal physical principles. In this revision the junior author has tried to maintain the emphasis on the physics of everyday experience which Dean Smith has incorporated in previous editions. Although much material from the fifth edition has been deleted to make room for recent developments in physics, there remain a large number of applications of physics to engineering, biology, agriculture, and everyday life.

In order to maintain appropriate attention to the principles of electricity, the author has used only the practical units. While there is an undeniable convenience to using the electrostatic system of units for some problems and electromagnetic units for others, this convenience has been sacrificed to avoid the inevitable confusion associated with mastering three different systems of units. In mechanics both the British engineering system and the mks system are emphasized. Although the gram and the centimeter are used freely as submultiples of the basic units, the general development follows the mks pattern.

The practice of printing illustrative material, minor topics, and some advanced material in fine print has been continued to differentiate them from the fundamental concepts and principles. In an abbreviated course these sections may be omitted without loss of continuity. Alternatively, it is possible to elect to omit certain entire chapters without seriously weakening the background for subsequent material.

The junior author gratefully acknowledges his indebtedness to many of his former colleagues at the Ohio State University. In particular he is indebted to Prof. Robert A. Oetjen who participated actively in the early stages of this revision. Many of the problems were prepared by Pro-

fessor Oetjen and his influence permeates much of the text.   Acknowl-
edgment is also made of the special help of Dr. Harvey Hanson who
read critically the section on mechanics.

Corrections, criticisms, and suggestions from those who use this book
will be greatly appreciated.   Dean Smith provided a wealth of material
and contributed many valuable ideas and discussions, but all errors,
failings, and weaknesses of this edition are the sole responsibility of the
junior author.

John N. Cooper

Contents

PART IV. LIGHT

PART V. ELECTRICITY

PART VI. ELECTRONICS

PART VII. ATOMIC AND NUCLEAR PHYSICS

OPTICAL SPECTRA

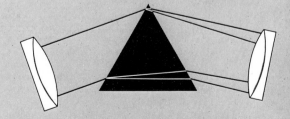

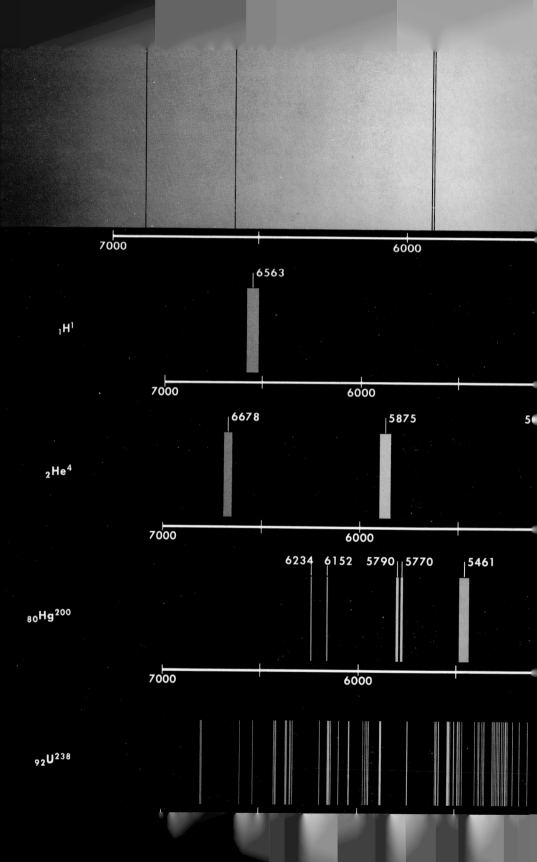

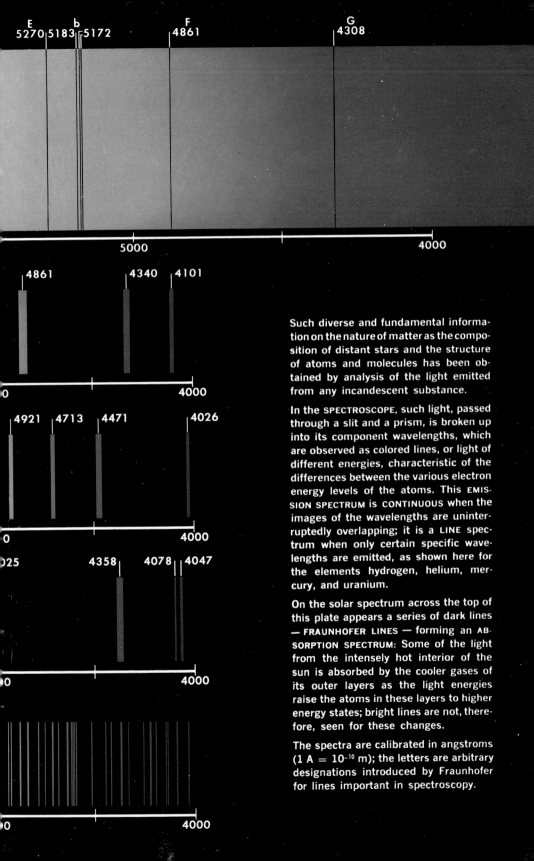

Such diverse and fundamental information on the nature of matter as the composition of distant stars and the structure of atoms and molecules has been obtained by analysis of the light emitted from any incandescent substance.

In the SPECTROSCOPE, such light, passed through a slit and a prism, is broken up into its component wavelengths, which are observed as colored lines, or light of different energies, characteristic of the differences between the various electron energy levels of the atoms. This EMISSION SPECTRUM is CONTINUOUS when the images of the wavelengths are uninterruptedly overlapping; it is a LINE spectrum when only certain specific wavelengths are emitted, as shown here for the elements hydrogen, helium, mercury, and uranium.

On the solar spectrum across the top of this plate appears a series of dark lines — FRAUNHOFER LINES — forming an ABSORPTION SPECTRUM: Some of the light from the intensely hot interior of the sun is absorbed by the cooler gases of its outer layers as the light energies raise the atoms in these layers to higher energy states; bright lines are not, therefore, seen for these changes.

The spectra are calibrated in angstroms (1 A = 10^{-10} m); the letters are arbitrary designations introduced by Fraunhofer for lines important in spectroscopy.

PART I

Mechanics

CHAPTER 1

Physics and Measurement

1.1. What Is Physics? In its broadest sense physics is that branch of knowledge which describes and explains the material world and its phenomena. In terms of this sweeping definition all the other physical sciences may be regarded as branches of the basic science *physics*, which a century ago was known as natural philosophy. At present, it is customary to use *physics* in a more restricted sense. The boundaries between physics and the related physical sciences such as chemistry, geology, and astronomy are not definite. Sharp distinctions between these sciences are neither necessary nor desirable. There are certain aspects of nature, however, which are ordinarily regarded as clearly in the special domain of physics. For convenience, they may be grouped under the headings: mechanics, sound, heat, light, electricity, and atomic structure. In addition, several broad areas of knowledge where the science of physics overlaps related sciences are described by such names as astrophysics, biophysics, chemical physics, and geophysics. Of course, these fields are not distinct, for they merge into one another.

In all ages men of intelligence have endeavored to explain what went on in the world about them. There has been a never-ending struggle to formulate a systematic set of conceptions about the world in which we live. In part, men have been driven by curiosity—an urge to learn "why?" In part, they have been motivated by the conviction that their efforts to understand natural phenomena would inevitably lead to the possibility of controlling these phenomena. Thousands upon thousands of men have contributed to build up the vast store of knowledge and information which constitute the physics of today. Thousands more are actively working now to add new facts to this body of knowledge and to organize the facts already known into logical patterns. Physics is growing at an unprecedented rate. It is a science full of life and of vigor.

As our knowledge of physics has grown, we have learned how to use the laws of nature in ways which have revolutionized our mode of life. In the eighteenth century physicists learned what heat is and how it can be controlled and used. This knowledge led to the development of various forms of heat engines—the steam engine, the gasoline engine, and the jet engine. In the nineteenth century physicists learned about the laws of electricity. Applications of these laws led to the use of electrical energy for light, for heat, for radio and television, and for the electric motors which operate washing machines, refrigerators, and modern locomotives. The discovery of x-rays and of radioactivity near the end of the nineteenth century paved the way for revolutionary advances in diagnosis and treatment of diseases.

In the twentieth century physicists have studied the structure of atoms and their nuclei with the consequence that we now know how to release vast quantities of energy through nuclear reactions. We have only begun to exploit the many possible uses of nuclear energy. Applications of physical knowledge have led to revolutionary improvements in aircraft. Today the principles of physics are being invoked to produce artificial satellites to circle the earth, to develop nuclear power plants for electric power and for aircraft, to construct guided missiles to defend our nation against possible attack, and to improve our highways, our appliances, and our homes.

Progress in physics brings with it progress in commerce and industry, in medicine, and in the related sciences. Much of the difference between the way we live in the United States and the way the Indians lived 500 years ago is associated with our greater knowledge of physical phenomena and how they may be controlled.

1.2. Physics as a Branch of Knowledge. In physics and related sciences the facts and laws are expressed in precise language. For the most part the terms used in physics are defined in a detailed and unambiguous way, so that scientists all over the world mean exactly the same thing by the same term. In order to formulate valid relationships between physical quantities, accurate measurements must be made. Thus, physics is a quantitative science. In 1883, Lord Kelvin emphasized this quantitative aspect in the following words:

> I often say that when you can measure what you are speaking about, and express it in numbers, you know something about it; but when you cannot measure it, when you cannot express it in numbers, your knowledge is of a meager and unsatisfactory kind. It may be the beginning of knowledge, but you have scarcely, in your thoughts, advanced to the stage of science, whatever the matter may be.

In making measurements of physical quantities, we ordinarily perform a series of operations which involve the comparison of an unknown quantity with an accepted standard of the same kind. Thus, when we say that a table is 10 feet (ft) long, we mean that a standard of length called a "foot" must be applied to it ten times in succession in order to cover its entire length. Similarly, a body is said to have a mass of 25 kilograms (kg) if its mass is twenty-five times as great as the mass of a standard kilogram.

1.3. Standards of Length and Mass. It is convenient to measure all quantities in mechanics in terms of three fundamental units; one for length, one for mass, and the third for time. Precise standards have been set up for measuring these quantities.

At one time the length of a king's foot or the span of his hand served as an adequate standard of length and a selected stone as a standard of mass. However, as commerce between countries increased and as scientists began to make more and more accurate measurements, established standards of length and mass became of increasing importance. The French took the lead in adopting a system of weights and measures which is now almost universally used in scientific work. French scientists chose as their standard of length one ten-millionth of the distance from the North Pole to the equator measured on a quadrant through Paris and they fabricated a platinum bar of this length. This bar, known as the *Meter of the Archives*, was adopted by the French government as the national standard of length.

As a standard mass the French scientists prepared a platinum cylinder which had a mass as near as they could make it to the mass of 1,000 cubic centimeters (cm³) of water at maximum density. This platinum cylinder, known as the *Kilogram of the Archives*, was adopted as the French standard of mass.

In 1875, representatives from most of the civilized countries met in Paris to discuss international standards of measurement. It was generally agreed that the French units were most suitable and that copies should be made for nations which wished to adopt the metric system of units. Some thirty bars were made of an alloy of platinum (90 per cent) and iridium (10 per cent). On these bars there were ruled transverse, fine lines separated as nearly as possible by the distance equal to the length of the Meter of the Archives. These new standards were made in 1880 and in 1889 they were distributed to the governments participating in the convention of 1875. The United States obtained two of these standard "meters" of which bar No. 27 is the primary standard of length for the United States. Bar No. 6 was most nearly equal to the Meter of the Archives and it was declared the International Standard Meter. It is kept at the International Bureau of Weights and Measures at Sèvres near Paris.

At the same time, 40 standard kilograms were constructed from the platinum-iridium alloy with masses as nearly as possible equal to that of the Kilogram of the Archives. The new mass which agreed most closely with the Kilogram of the Archives is now the International Mass Standard, while the primary mass standard of the United States is kilogram No. 20, one of the two received by the United States. Figure 1.1 shows the national standards of length and of mass.

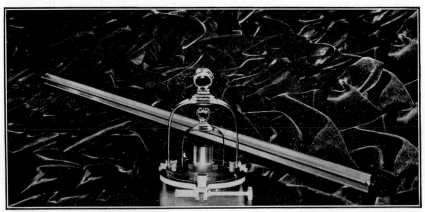

Fig. 1.1. The national standards of mass and of length are the kilogram and the meter. The distance between two parallel lines engraved on the meter bar is the primary standard meter. (*Courtesy of the National Bureau of Standards.*)

In the United States the yard is defined as 3,600/3,937 m.

The American yard does not agree exactly with the British imperial yard, which is the distance at 62°F between two lines ruled on a bronze bar preserved in London. Comparison of the international standard meter with the British yard yields the result that 39.370147 British in. equal 1 m. Modern machinery is made so precisely that many parts made in British inches are not interchangeable with those in United States inches.

The fundamental unit of mass of the United States is the *kilogram*. The International Standard Kilogram is a metal cylinder, made of a platinum-iridium alloy, almost 39 mm in diameter and 39 mm in height. Although it was originally intended to duplicate the mass of 1,000 cm³ of air-free, distilled water at maximum density, subsequent measurements have shown that it requires a volume of 1000.027 cm³ of water at maximum density for a mass of 1 kg. This volume is known as the *liter*.

In the United States the pound mass is defined as 0.4535924277 kg. The British pound mass is, by definition, the mass of a piece of platinum kept in London. The British and American pounds do not agree exactly.

1.4. Units of Time. In both English and metric systems of units the *second* is the fundamental unit of time. This unit is defined in terms of the rotation of the earth in the following manner: The time from the instant the center of the sun is on the meridian plane (the meridian plane of an observer is a plane determined by the axis of the rotation of the earth and the point at which the observer is located on the earth's surface) until the sun is centered on the meridian the following day is called a *solar day*. For several reasons solar days are not all of identical duration. The average is called the *mean solar day;* this period is divided into 24 hr, each hour into 60 min, and each minute into 60 sec. Thus, the mean solar day contains 86,400 sec and the second is 1/86,400 part of a mean solar day.

1.5. Choice of Units. In measuring any physical quantity, the choice of units is ordinarily dictated by convenience and by the habits of the observer. In addition to the units for measuring length previously mentioned, men have used the barleycorn, the cubit, the span, the hand, the fathom, the rod, and many others. In most scientific work metric units are used. These units are truly international. Further, the larger and smaller units are related in terms of powers of ten to the fundamental units. Thus the kilometer is 1,000 m, and the centimeter is $\frac{1}{100}$ of a meter. Table 1 lists the prefixes which are used with metric units to indicate multiples and submultiples of standard units.

Table 1

Factor	Prefix	Abbreviation	Example
10^3	kilo-	k	kilogram (kg), kilometer (km)
10^6	mega- (or meg-)	M	megohm (MΩ); million electronvolts (Mev)
10^{-2}	centi-	c	centimeter (cm)
10^{-3}	milli-	m	millimeter (mm), milligram (mg)
10^{-6}	micro-	μ	microgram (μg), micron (μ) $= 10^{-6}$ m

Other prefixes: deka- (10), hecto- (100), deci- (0.1).

We live in a country where most of the everyday measurements are made in the English system, but much scientific work involves metric units. Therefore, it is desirable to be able to transform from one system to another, since any one who has to deal with scientific phenomena in the United States is essentially forced to learn to use both the British and the metric systems.

In converting a quantity from one unit to another, it is convenient to set up the conversion in the form of the examples below. Note that one can cancel units just as though they were algebraic quantities. Note further that the factors by which one multiplies are always basically unity.

Example. Convert 60 mi/hr to the corresponding speed in feet per second and meters per second.

$$60 \frac{\text{mi}}{\text{hr}} = 60 \frac{\text{mi}}{\text{hr}} \times \frac{1 \text{ hr}}{3,600 \text{ sec}} \times \frac{5,280 \text{ ft}}{1 \text{ mile}}$$

$$= \frac{60 \times 5,280}{3,600} \frac{\text{mi hr}}{\text{hr sec mi}} \frac{\text{ft}}{} = 88 \frac{\text{ft}}{\text{sec}}$$

$$= 88 \frac{\text{ft}}{\text{sec}} \times \frac{12 \text{ in.}}{1 \text{ ft}} \times \frac{1 \text{ m}}{39.37 \text{ in.}} = 26.8 \frac{\text{m}}{\text{sec}}$$

Example. The density of aluminum is 2.7 g/cm³. Convert this density to kilograms per cubic meter and to pounds per cubic foot.

$$2.7\,\frac{g}{cm^3} = 2.7\,\frac{g}{cm^3} \times \frac{(100\ cm)^3}{1\ m^3} \times \frac{1\ kg}{1,000\ g}$$

$$= 2,700\,\frac{kg}{m^3}$$

$$= 2,700\,\frac{kg}{m^3} \times \frac{1\ lb}{0.454\ kg} \times \frac{(1\ m)^3}{(39.37\ in.)^3} \times \frac{(12\ in.)^3}{(1\ ft)^3}$$

$$= 160\,\frac{lb}{ft^3}$$

In reporting the measurement of any quantity, it is important to list not only the number of times the standard unit was included, but also to state what this standard unit is. For example, the height of a man might be 6 ft, 72 in., 2 yd, or 190 cm. The number which describes the height is quite meaningless unless the units which go with the number are specified.

1.6. Derived Units. All quantities in mechanics can be expressed in terms of length, mass, and time. Combinations of these fundamental dimensions may be used as dimensions for other quantities. The units for area may be written as the square of units of length. Thus, we express areas in square feet, square meters, square centimeters, and so forth. Similarly, the dimensions for volume are lengths cubed, cubic centimeters, cubic feet, etc.

Speed. The average speed of a body may be defined as the ratio of the distance it traverses to the time required to pass over that distance. Thus, speed is obtained by dividing a length by a time. Appropriate units of speed are meters per second, feet per second, miles per hour, etc. The speeds of ships and aircraft are often measured in *knots*. One knot is one nautical mile (6,080 ft) per hour.

Example. A track star runs a measured mile in 3 min 56 sec. Find his average speed.

$$\text{Average speed} = \frac{\text{distance}}{\text{time}} = \frac{5,280\ ft}{236\ sec}$$

$$= 22.4\ ft/sec$$

Density. The density of a body is defined as the ratio of its mass to its volume. This definition may be written in the form of an equation

$$d = \frac{m}{V} \tag{1.1}$$

where d is the density, m the mass, and V the volume. Among the familiar units for density are kilograms per cubic meter, pounds per cubic foot, and grams per cubic centimeter.

Example. A quantity of mercury has a mass of 2.04 kg and occupies a volume of 150 cm³. What is its density?

$$d = \frac{m}{V} = \frac{2.04 \text{ kg}}{150 \text{ cm}^3} = 0.0136 \text{ kg/cm}^3$$
$$= 13.6 \text{ g/cm}^3 = 13{,}600 \text{ kg/m}^3$$

Example. Find the mass of air in a room which is 3 by 8 by 6 m. The density of the air is a 1.29 kg/m³.

$$m = dV = 1.29 \text{ kg/m}^3 \times 144 \text{ m}^3$$
$$= 186 \text{ kg}$$

In addition to the mass density defined above, the term *density* is often used in conjunction with certain other words to suggest the amount of some quantity for a given amount of some other quantity. For example, we use the term *population density* to describe number of people per unit area. In electricity the term *charge density* means the ratio of electric charge to volume and *surface charge density* is the ratio of the electric charge to surface area. The ratio of the *weight* of an object to its *volume* is called its *weight density*. The ratio of the mass of a rope to its length is sometimes called its *linear density*. Whenever the word *density* appears in this text in any sense other than that of *mass per unit volume*, it will be qualified by an additional word.

1.7. Measurement of Angles. Degrees, minutes, and seconds are familiar units in which angles are measured. A degree is the angle subtended at the center of a circle by an arc of length ⅟₃₆₀ of the circumference of the circle (Fig. 1.2). A minute is ⅟₆₀ of a degree and a second is ⅟₆₀ of a minute.

For measuring the angle turned through by a rotating wheel, we are likely to use the *revolution* as measure of the angle. The angle subtended by the full circumference is one revolution.

Still another unit which is often convenient for measuring angles is the radian. *A radian is the angle subtended at the center of a circle by an arc of length equal to the radius.* Thus, the magnitude of the angle AOC of Fig. 1.2 is 1 radian, since the arc length AC is equal in length to radius

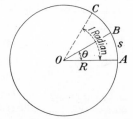

Fig. 1.2. Measurement of angles. The angle AOC is 1 radian, since $AC = OA$.

OA. In general, the angle θ (AOB) is AB/R radians, where AB represents the length of the arc and R the radius of the circle. Since the circumference of a circle is 2π times the radius, it follows that there are 2π radians in a revolution. Hence,

$$360° = 2\pi \text{ radians} = 1 \text{ revolution}$$

1.8. Force. One of the most important concepts in physics is that of *force.* For the moment, we may think of a force as a *push* or a *pull* which is exerted upon some object. The most familiar forces are those which we experience through our own muscular activities. More generally, a force is an action exerted by one body on another that tends to change the state of motion of the body acted upon. Thus, a loaded wagon is drawn by a tractor.   When a man throws a baseball, he exerts a force upon it which changes its state of motion.   We shall later define force explicitly in terms of effects on the motions of objects.

We know that every body on the surface of the earth is pulled toward the earth by gravitational attraction, which we shall now use to define units of force.   The pull of the earth on a standard kilogram mass at 45° latitude and mean sea level is called the kilogram-weight (kg-wt).   By means of standard masses a well-designed spring balance can be made to read forces with rather high precision.   Similarly the pound-force (lb) is defined as the pull of the earth on a standard one-pound mass at a speci-fied location on the surface of the earth.   The force units pound (lb) and kilogram-weight (kg-wt) are called *gravitational* units because they are defined in terms of the pull of the earth on a standard mass *at a specified location*.

Fig. 1.3.   The weight of a body is the force due to the pull of gravity on the body.

Another very important force unit in the metric sys-tem is the *newton*.   The newton is defined in terms of its effect on the motion of a one-kilogram mass in a way which is *independent of the location of this mass*.   For this reason the newton is called an *absolute* unit of force. The definition of force in terms of the effects on motion is developed in Chap. 5.   For the moment, it is suffi-cient to observe that 9.807 newtons = 1 kg-wt or 1 newton = 0.2248 lb.

1.9. Weight and Mass.   The weight of an object is defined as the gravitational force of attraction of the earth for the object (Fig. 1.3).   Its value depends on the location.   If a good spring balance were calibrated at 45° latitude and mean sea level and then transported to vari-ous points on the earth's surface, it would be found that the pull of the earth on a 1-kg mass would be more than 1 kg-wt at the North Pole, but less than 1 kg-wt at the equator or on top of a high mountain.   The weight of a body is slightly different on top of Pike's Peak than in New York City.   These changes in weight are not large, but they can be detected readily with sensitive instruments.   In principle, we could reduce the weight of a body to almost zero by taking it sufficiently far off in space, as we shall see in Chap. 6.

On the other hand, the *mass of a body at rest is the same at all points in the universe*.   This is one reason that the concept of mass is so important in physics.   It is sometimes said that the mass of a body is the "quantity of matter in the body," a property of the body which does not change. An object has mass whether or not it is near enough to the earth to have observable weight.   The mass of a body reveals itself as inertia—the tendency of matter to resist any change in its state of motion.   This important attribute of mass is discussed further in Chap. 5.

The larger the mass of a body, the harder the earth pulls on it.   Indeed, the weight of a body at any place is directly proportional to its mass, and the mass of a body is often determined by comparing the pull of the earth on it with the pull on a standard mass at the same place.

PROBLEMS

1. The elevation of Pike's Peak is 4,293 m above sea level.   What is the elevation expressed in feet?   *Ans.* 14,100 ft

2. The Washington Monument is 555 ft high.   Find its height in meters.

3. Mount McKinley is the highest mountain in North America with an elevation of 20,300 ft.   Find the altitude in kilometers.   *Ans.* 6.19 km

4. The highest point in the United States is Mount Whitney with an altitude of 14,496 ft above sea level.   Find the altitude in meters.

5. Five miles is equivalent to how many kilometers?   *Ans.* 8.05

6. It is 1,290 km from Laredo, Tex., to Mexico City by the National Railways of Mexico.   How far is it in miles?

7. One of the events in the Olympics is the 100-m dash.   To how many yards does 100 m correspond?   *Ans.* 109 yd

8. The standard meter was selected originally as 1/10,000,000 of the distance from the North Pole to the equator along the quadrant of the earth's surface through Paris. Assuming that the earth is spherical, find the radius of the earth in kilometers and in miles.

9. A rectangular lot has sides 50 ft and 200 ft long.   Find the area in square meters.   *Ans.* 929 m²

10. Calculate the number of square feet in 1 m².

11. A circle has a diameter of 2 m.   What is its area in square feet?   *Ans.* 33.8 ft²

12. A rectangular lot has sides of length 75 ft and 160 ft.   Find the area in square meters.

13. A gallon occupies 231 in.³   Express this in liters.   *Ans.* 3.79 liters

14. How many cubic inches are there in 1 liter?

15. A tourist in Mexico fills his gasoline tank by buying 40 liters.   To how many gallons does this correspond?   *Ans.* 10.6

16. The gasoline tank of an automobile holds 18 gal.   If 1 gal is 231 in.³, find the volume of the tank in cubic feet.

17. A curve on a railroad track is 650 ft long and subtends an angle of 22° at the center of the circle of which it is a part.   What is the radius of the curve?   *Ans.* 1,700 ft

18. A circle is 8 ft in radius.   How many radians are subtended at the center by an arc of length 6 ft?

19. A projectile is fired at an angle of 47° above the horizontal.   Express this angle in radians.   *Ans.* 0.82 radians

20. In going around a sharp curve the driver of an automobile turns the steering wheel through an angle of 5 radians.   Through how many degrees did it turn? Through how many revolutions?

21. The effective radius of the wheel of an automobile is 15 in.   Find through what angle in radians the wheel rotates in going a distance of 1 mile.   *Ans.* 4,224 radians

22. The angle subtended by the sun's diameter at the surface of the earth is 0.5°.

Find the approximate diameter of the sun if it is at a distance of 93,000,000 miles from the earth.

23. An electric motor rotates 1,800 rev/min. Find its angular speed in radians per second.   *Ans.* 188 rad/sec

24. If 1 gal is 231 in.³, find the volume in gallons of an aquarium 3 ft by 2 ft by 2 ft in dimensions. If a cubic foot of water weighs 62.4 lb, what weight of water does the tank hold when full?

25. How many tons of water fall on 1 square mile of land during a 1-in. rain if 1 ft³ of water weighs 62.4 lb?   *Ans.* 72,400 tons

26. An automobile is moving 90 mi/hr. Find its speed in feet per second.

27. To how many meters per second does a speed of 50 km/hr correspond?
                                                                                Ans. 13.9 m/sec

28. The speed of sound is 330 m/sec. Find the speed in kilometers per hour.

29. To how many yards per second does a speed of 50 mi/hr correspond?
                                                                                Ans. 24.4 yd/sec

30. A swimmer wins the 100-yd event with a time of 45 sec. Find his speed in miles per hour.

31. An aircraft has a speed of 600 knots. Find its speed in miles per hour and in meters per second.   *Ans.* 690 mi/hr; 309 m/sec

32. The flow of oil in a pipe line is maintained at the rate of 8.5 ft/sec. Find how many miles the oil travels in 1 day.

33. A liter of air under standard conditions weighs 1.3 g-wt. Find the weight of a cubic yard in pounds.   *Ans.* 2.2 lb

34. Find the volume of a block of aluminum that weighs 1 ton. The weight density of aluminum is 168 lb/ft³.

35. Assuming an average density of 1 g/cm³ for the human body, find the volume occupied by a person weighing 80 kg-wt.   *Ans.* 80 liters, or 2.82 ft³

36. Solid carbon dioxide has a density of 1.53 g/cm³. How much volume would be occupied by 5 cm³ after evaporation to gas with a density of 0.0019 g/cm³?

Vector Quantities

2.1. Displacement. When a body moves from one location to another, it is said to undergo a *displacement*. Suppose, for example, that a helicopter takes off, flies due east 12 miles, and lands. It has undergone a displacement of 12 miles east. If the helicopter takes off again and flies 25 miles in a straight line before landing, how far is it from its original starting point? A specific answer to this question cannot be given until we have one *additional* piece of information; in what direction is this second displacement? From the information now available we can only be sure that it lies somewhere on a circle with a center at B and a radius of 25 miles (Fig. 2.1). *A displacement is completely specified only when we state both its magnitude and direction*. The magnitude consists of a numeral and a unit.

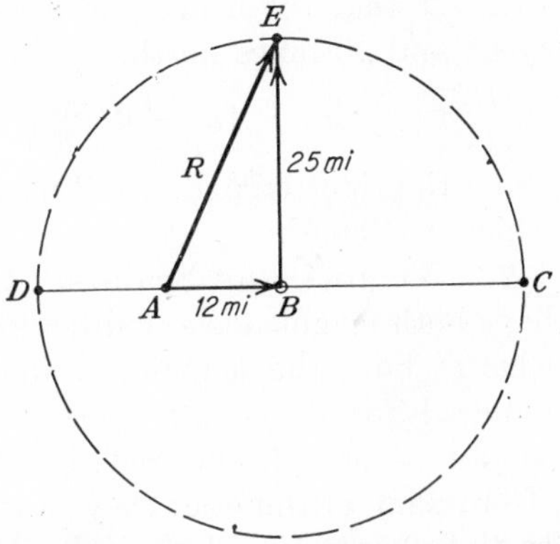

If the second displacement is in the same direction as the first, the helicopter is at point C and the total displacement is $12 + 25 = 37$ miles east. If the second displacement is in the direction opposite to the displacement AB, the helicopter is at D and the displacement is 13 miles

Fig. 2.1. Consecutive displacements of 12 miles east and 25 miles in an arbitrary direction could bring a helicopter to any point on the circle *DEC*. If the 25-mile displacement is to the north, the helicopter is at *E*.

west. If the displacement is due north, the helicopter is at E and its distance from the starting point is $R = \sqrt{(25)^2 + (12)^2} = 27.7$ miles.

Let us now specify the 25-mile displacement to be at an angle of 53°N of E (Fig. 2.2). In our figure we represent each displacement by an arrow pointed in the direction of the displacement and of length proportional to

13

the displacement. One possible way of determining the distance from the starting point to the final position is by making a scaled drawing and measuring the distance with a ruler. However, in most cases it is easier to solve a problem of this type analytically than graphically. We observe that the displacement BP of 25 miles at an angle of 53°N of E takes the helicopter a distance BG to the east and a distance GP to the north. By definition (Appendix A) we know that _in any right triangle the sine of an angle is the ratio of the side opposite the angle to the hypotenuse,_ while _the cosine is the ratio of the side adjacent to the angle to the hypotenuse._ (A table of sines and cosines may be found in Appendix A.)

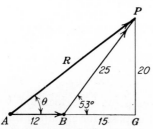

Therefore $BG/25 = \cos 53° = 0.6$ and $BG = 15$ miles. Similarly $GP/25 = \sin 53° = 0.8$ from which $GP = 20$ miles. Thus, a displacement of 25 miles at an angle of 53°N of E is equivalent to a displacement of 15 miles east plus a displacement of 20 miles north. We can, if we like, replace our

Fig. 2.2. The vector **R** is the resultant of the displacements 12 miles east and 25 miles 53°N of E.

25-mile displacement by the displacements BG and GP. We observe from Fig. 2.2 that the helicopter is now 27 miles east of its original starting point and 20 miles north. The distance AP is therefore given by

$$AP = \sqrt{(27)^2 + (20)^2} = 33.6 \text{ miles}$$

From the right triangle AGP we see that $\sin \theta = 20/33.6 = 0.596$, from which $\theta = 36.6°$.

2.2. Vectors and Scalars. Quantities such as displacements which have both magnitude and direction are called _vector quantities_. A knowledge of both the magnitude and the direction of a vector quantity is required for its complete description. Vectors in different directions cannot be added, subtracted, multiplied, and divided by the methods of ordinary arithmetic; they must be treated by geometrical techniques. In this chapter we shall deal with three types of vector quantities: displacements, velocities, and forces. In later chapters, many more vector quantities such as acceleration, momentum, torque, angular velocity, and angular acceleration will be introduced.

There are many quantities in physics, such as mass, time, and volume, which have only a magnitude and which can be completely specified by a numeral and a dimension. They do not involve any idea of direction. Such quantities are called _scalars_. They obey the ordinary laws of addition, subtraction, multiplication, and division. If 10 gal of gasoline are added to a tank which originally contained 4 gal, the tank contains 14 gal. If a 10-g mass is removed from the pan of a balance which holds

80 g, the mass remaining on the pan is 70 g. These are illustrations of the addition and subtraction of *scalar quantities*.

Vectors are often denoted in print by boldface type, such as **F** for force, **v** for velocity, and so forth. Whenever a boldface symbol is used in text or a formula, it indicates that direction as well as magnitude is of importance. Italic type is used for scalar quantities and for the magnitude of vectors.

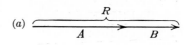

(a)

2.3. The Graphical Addition of Vectors. A vector quantity can always be represented by an arrow in the direction of the vector and of length proportional to the magnitude of the vector. If we wish to add two vectors **A** and **B**,

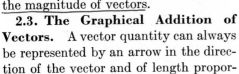

(b)

Fig. 2.3. Resultant of two displacements: (*a*) in the same direction; (*b*) in opposite directions.

we may represent each of them by arrows of scaled length and add them (Figs. 2.3 to 2.5) by placing the tail of the second arrow at the point of

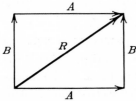

Fig. 2.4. Resultant of two vectors at right angles to each other.

$$\mathbf{A} + \mathbf{B} = \mathbf{R} = \mathbf{B} + \mathbf{A}$$

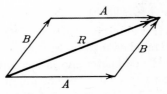

Fig. 2.5. Resultant of two vectors not at right angles to each other.

$$\mathbf{A} + \mathbf{B} = \mathbf{R} = \mathbf{B} + \mathbf{A}$$

the first. Alternatively, we might start with the second vector and add the first, as shown in Figs. 2.4 and 2.5. This gives rise to the "vector parallelogram." The vector sum is given by the diagonal **R**. If the graphical representation of the vectors **A** and **B** is carefully done, the resultant vector **R** can be measured with considerable accuracy. It is customary to call the result of vector addition the *resultant* of the vectors rather than the sum to emphasize the geometrical nature of the addition. To subtract one vector from another, we need only take the vector we wish to subtract, reverse its direction, and add this negative vector to the first. This is shown schematically in Fig. 2.6.

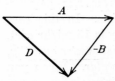

Fig. 2.6. To subtract vector **B** of Fig. 2.5 from vector **A**, we add −**B** to **A** to obtain the vector difference **D**.

There is no limit to the number of vectors which may be added graphically. If we have four vectors to add together, we may add the third vector to the resultant of the first two, the fourth vector to the resultant of the first three, etc. For example, suppose that an object has four forces acting upon it: 8 lb east, 5 lb 30°N of E, 7 lb 37°W of N, and 3 lb due south, as shown in Fig. 2.7. The resultant is given by the vector **R**. Note that the order in which the vectors are added makes no difference in determining the resultant. We shall calculate the value of **R** in Sec. 2.7.

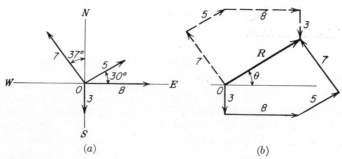

(a)   (b)

Fig. 2.7. The four forces shown in (a) act upon a body at O. The resultant **R** is shown in (b). Note that the resultant is independent of the order in which the vectors are added.

2.4. Velocity.

Suppose you take an automobile ride. The distance you travel as read by the odometer is a scalar quantity. If at the end of 3 hr the odometer shows you have traveled a distance of 150 miles, your average speed has been 50 mi/hr. Suppose that at this point you are due east 45 miles from your starting point (Fig. 2.8). Then your displacement is 45 miles east. _Displacement_ is a vector quantity. It is not necessarily related in any simple way to the total _distance_ traversed. The _average velocity_ during the trip is _the ratio of the displacement to the time_. In this case the average velocity is 15 mi/hr east. Note that _velocity is a vector quantity_, while _speed is a scalar_. When you return to your starting point, the average velocity is zero since the _displacement_ is zero. On the other hand, the average speed is something very different from zero.

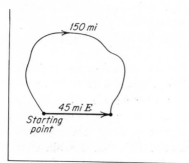

Fig. 2.8. Displacement is a vector quantity while distance is a scalar quantity.

Example. On a transcontinental trip a family begins to drive at 6 A.M. and stops finally at 5 P.M. In this period the car has gone 495 miles and is 350 airline miles southwest of its starting point. Find the average speed and average velocity for the day.

$$\text{Av speed} = \frac{\text{distance}}{\text{time}} = \frac{495 \text{ mi}}{11 \text{ hr}} = 45 \text{ mi/hr}$$

$$\mathbf{v_{av}} = \frac{\text{displacement}}{\text{time}} = \frac{350 \text{ mi southwest}}{11 \text{ hr}} = 31.8 \text{ mi/hr southwest}$$

In this chapter we shall add velocities, confining ourselves to cases in which the velocity is *uniform* (i.e., in which equal displacements are traversed in equal times). In later chapters we shall consider other types of motion in which the velocity varies with time in some known way.

2.5. Frame of Reference. When we deal with velocity and displacement, we must always refer these quantities to some frame of reference. With few exceptions we refer them to a frame fixed on the earth. When we say an object is at rest, we mean it is at rest relative to the earth. Relative to the sun it is moving through space at a speed of 19 mi/sec by virtue of the orbital motion of the earth (and at a speed, which depends on latitude, due to the spin of the earth on its axis). A passenger seated in a train traveling 60 mi/hr is at rest relative to the car and the other passengers. If he walks forward in the car with a speed of 4 mi/hr, his speed referred to the earth is $60 + 4 = 64$ mi/hr. An airplane flying with an air speed of 300 mi/hr is traveling only 250 mi/hr relative to the earth if it is flying into a 50 mi/hr head wind.

Whenever we refer to the displacement or velocity of a body, we are always by implication referring these measurements to some other body or framework of lines which must be regarded as fixed. Such a framework is called the frame of reference. Some problems can be greatly simplified by the choice of a suitable frame of reference. For almost all the problems which we shall meet it is convenient to refer all quantities to a system of axes fixed in the earth.

2.6. Rectangular Components of a Vector. Consider a vector 5 units in length and directed at an angle of 37°N of E (Fig. 2.9). This displacement is exactly equivalent to displacements of 4 units east and 3 units north. In any problem in which this 5-unit vector occurs, we may always replace it by vectors of 4 units east and 3 units north. These two vectors, which are perpendicular to each other, are called the *rectangular components* of the vector. By replacing a vector by its rectangular components, we can always reduce any problem in vector addition to a situation in which we are dealing with component vectors, all of which lie either along one line or perpendicular to this line. Thus, the replacement of a vector by suitable components results in a possibility of handling vector additions with a minimum of mathematical complexity.

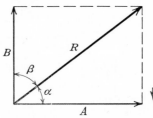

Fig. 2.9. The resolution of a vector into its rectangular components.

$$\frac{A}{R} = \cos \alpha$$

$$\frac{B}{R} = \cos \beta = \sin \alpha$$

If we wish to obtain the rectangular components of a vector in any mutually perpendicular directions, we proceed as follows: We place the

origin of our rectangular coordinate system at the tail of the vector which
we wish to resolve and then drop perpendiculars from the point of the
vector to each of the coordinate axes.   *The component in any direction is
given by the length of the vector multiplied by the cosine of the angle between
the vector and the axis along which we seek the component.*

Example.   A 50-lb weight rests on an inclined plane (Fig. 2.10) making an angle of
30° with the horizontal.   Find the components of the weight parallel and perpendicular to the plane.

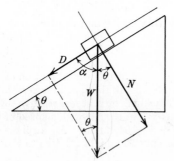

We place the origin of a system of axes at the
body with its x axis parallel to the plane.   Next
we drop perpendiculars from the end of the **W** vector to find the lengths of D and N.

$$D = W \cos \alpha = W \sin \theta = 50 \text{ lb} \sin 30° = \textbf{25 lb}$$
$$N = W \cos \theta = 50 \text{ lb} \cos 30° = \textbf{43.3 lb}$$

Consider a canalboat as indicated in Fig. 2.11
and let a cable pull on it in the direction BC.
This force produces two distinct effects on the
boat.   It moves the boat forward and it also
pulls it to the bank.   Two separate forces BA
and BD might have been applied with the same
result.   These two forces that would produce
the same effect as BC are the components of BC.

Fig. 2.10. The resolution of the
weight of an object into components parallel to and perpendicular to an inclined plane.

The components of this force are represented by
the sides of a rectangle of which the original force is the diagonal.   In Fig. 2.12
the force due to the wind acting on a sailboat is resolved into components perpendicular and parallel to the sail, and the force perpendicular to the sail is
then resolved into components perpendicular and parallel to the axis of the
boat.   The force perpendicular to the axis produces little effect because of the
shape of the boat.

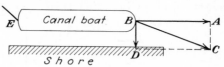

Fig. 2.11. Components of the force BC exerted on a canalboat by a cable.

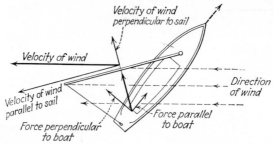

Fig. 2.12. Resolution of the wind velocity into components and the resolution of the
force exerted on the sail into components parallel to and perpendicular to the keel of a
sailboat.

2.7. The Analytical Addition of Vectors. In adding vectors analytically it is desirable first to make a rough sketch of the vectors to be added.   Then we choose a set of mutually perpendicular axes which appear to be convenient for the problem in question.   Usually, this involves a choice of the east-west and north-south axes or vertical and horizontal axes.   However, in some cases it may be more convenient to choose a set of mutually perpendicular axes which are oriented in some special way. Next, we find the components of all the vectors along the axes chosen. We then ignore the vectors and work only with the components.   We can readily add together all the vector components whose arrows are in the direction of each of the axes and then find their resultant by the use of the Pythagorean theorem.   The following examples will show how these steps may be followed.

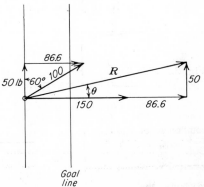

Example. In a football game two linemen are assigned to open a hole by blocking a guard.   One of them exerts a force of 150 lb straight toward the goal line (Fig. 2.13) and the other exerts a force of 100 lb at an angle of 60° with the goal line.   Find the resultant force.

Fig. 2.13. To find the resultant force **R**, we find its components parallel to and perpendicular to the goal line.

The component of the 100-lb force toward the goal line is 100 cos 30° = 100 sin 60° = 86.6 lb.   The component parallel to the goal line is 100 cos 60° = 50 lb.   The net force toward the goal line is 150 + 86.6 = 236.6 lb, while the net force parallel to the goal line is 50 lb.

$$R = \sqrt{(236.6)^2 + (50)^2} = \sqrt{58,500} = 242 \text{ lb}$$

and the angle θ between **R** and the 150-lb force is given by sin θ = 50/242 = 0.207; then θ = 12°.

Example.   Find the resultant of the four forces shown in Fig. 2.7.

First we find the east and north components of each force and list them in the table at the right.   For the 5-lb force the east component is

5 cos 30° = 4.33 lb

and the north component is

5 sin 30° = 2.5 lb.

For the 7-lb force the east component is

−7 sin 37° = −4.2 lb

and the north component is 7 cos 37° = 5.6 lb.

Force, lb	Components	
	East	North
8 E	8	0
5 30°N of E	4.33	2.5
7 37°W of N	−4.20	5.6
3 S	0	−3.0
R	8.13	5.1

The components of the resultant are 8.13 lb east and 5.1 lb north.   The resultant R is given by

$$R = \sqrt{(8.13)^2 + (5.1)^2} = \sqrt{92.1} = 9.6 \text{ lb}$$

and the angle between $\mathbf{R}$ and the east is given by

$$\sin \theta = \frac{5.1}{9.6} = 0.53$$

so that $\theta = 32°$N of E.

Example.   An airplane cruises at a speed of 300 mi/hr relative to the surrounding air.   If the wind is blowing from the southwest at 40 mi/hr, find the direction in which the pilot must point the airplane if he wishes to go due east.   What is the velocity of the airplane relative to the ground?

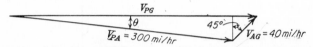

Fig. 2.14. To fly due east when the wind is blowing from the southwest, the pilot must have a velocity relative to the air at an angle θ south of east.

The pilot must fly at an angle θ (Fig. 2.14) south of east such that the southward component of $\mathbf{V}_{PA}$ (velocity of plane relative to air) is exactly equal to the northward component of $\mathbf{V}_{AG}$ (velocity of air relative to ground).

$$300 \sin \theta = 40 \cos 45° = 28.3$$
$$\sin \theta = \frac{28.3}{300} = 0.0943$$
$$\theta = 5°25'\text{S of E}$$

The velocity $\mathbf{V}_{PG}$ of the airplane relative to the ground is

$$\mathbf{V}_{PG} = 300 \cos \theta + 40 \sin 45°$$
$$= 298.7 + 28.3 = 327.0 \text{ mi/hr due east}$$

PROBLEMS

1. An automobile is driven 12 miles west and then 16 miles north in going from one city to another.   How far apart are the two cities?   *Ans.* 20 miles

2. What is the magnitude of the single displacement that is equivalent to successive displacements of 144 m and 60 m, the direction of the second displacement being perpendicular to that of the first one?

3. Two vectors of 25 cm and 10 cm have an angle of 90° between them.   What is the magnitude and direction, with respect to the 25-cm vector, of the resultant?
                                                            Ans. 27.0 cm; 21.8°

4. A body is displaced 5 miles toward the east and 12 miles toward the south. What is the magnitude and direction of the resultant displacement?

5. A horizontal force of 5 kg-wt acts on a body while the earth attracts it with a vertical force of 15 kg-wt.   What is the magnitude and the direction with respect to the vertical of the resultant of these two forces?   *Ans.* 15.8 kg-wt; 18.4°

6. Calculate the horizontal and vertical components of a vector which has a magnitude of 15 ft and makes an angle of 25° with the horizontal.

7. Find the horizontal and vertical components of a force of 15 lb acting at an angle of 30° with the vertical direction.   *Ans.* 7.5 lb; 13.0 lb

8. A force of 25 lb makes an angle of 45° with the vertical direction.   Find the horizontal and vertical components of this force.

9. Find components along north-south and east-west lines of a displacement of 10 miles, 28°E of N.   *Ans.* 8.83 miles; 4.69 miles

10. An airplane flies 160 miles in a direction 40°E of N.   Find the components of its displacement toward the north and toward the east.

11. Find components along north-south and east-west lines of a displacement of 27 m, 13°S of W.   *Ans.* 6.08 m; 26.3 m

12. A boat has a velocity of 30 mi/hr 40°E of N.   What is its velocity component toward the east?   toward the north?

13. Forces are exerted on a body through two strings attached to the body.   One is a horizontal force of 20 kg-wt toward the right.   The other is a force of 40 kg-wt which acts upward and toward the left, making an angle of 60° with the horizontal.   Find the magnitude and direction of the one force that could replace these two.
                          Ans. 34.6 kg-wt upward

? 14. The current in a river flows north at a rate of 3 mi/hr.   A man rows a boat west at a rate of 4 mi/hr relative to the water.   Find the speed of the boat relative to the land.

15. Find the magnitude and direction of the resultant of the three displacements 1 km east, 2 km north, and 3 km west.   *Ans.* 2.83 km; 45°N of W

16. Find the magnitude and direction of the resultant of the three displacements 3 miles west, 4 miles north, and 6 miles south.

17. Find the magnitude and direction of the resultant of the five displacements: 1 ft southwest, 3 ft northwest, 5 ft northeast, 7 ft southeast, and 9 ft southwest.
                          Ans. 6.40 ft; 6.3°W of S

18. Find the magnitude and direction of the resultant of the five displacements: 2 cm northeast, 4 cm northwest, 6 cm southwest, 8 cm southeast, and 10 cm northeast.

19. Find the magnitude and direction of the resultant of the two forces, 10 kg-wt downward and 5 kg-wt which makes an angle of 45° above the horizontal.
                          Ans. 7.37 kg-wt; 61.4° below horizontal

20. Calculate the magnitude of the resultant of two displacements that make an angle of 60° with each other, if one of the displacements is 10 ft and the other is 6 ft.

21. Find the magnitude and direction of the one displacement that is equivalent to the two displacements 5 ft 20°N of W and 10 ft northwest.   *Ans.* 14.7 ft; 36.7°N of W

22. Find the magnitude and direction of the one displacement that is equivalent to the two displacements 12 m southeast and 12 m 30°E of S.

23. An automobile is driven 7 km north, then 3 km northeast, then 5 km northwest, and then 5 km west.   How far and in what direction is it from the starting point?
                          Ans. 14.2 km; 26.8°W of N

24. A body is subject to a vertical force of 80 lb upward and to a horizontal force of 50 lb.   What are the magnitude and the direction of the resultant?

25. Add the following four displacements: 6 m east; 3 m south; 2 m west; 2 m south.
                          Ans. 6.403 m; 51°20′S of E

26. Two forces at right angles have a resultant of 300 lb.   If one of the forces is 200 lb, what must the other one be?

27. A body is moved 17 cm along a line making an angle of 30° with the horizontal.   Determine the horizontal and vertical components of this displacement.
                          Ans. 14.7 cm; 8.5 cm

28. Find the resultant of the following three forces: a force of 20 lb making an angle of 30° with the +x axis; a force of 30 lb making an angle of 135°; and a force of 40 lb making an angle of 240° with the +x axis.

29. A body is moved 19 m eastward, and then 42 m northeastward.   Determine the magnitude and direction of the resultant displacement.   *Ans.* 57.1 m; 31°20′N of E

30. Find the components and the resultant of two forces, one having a magnitude of 50 lb and making an angle of 30° with the vertical and the other having a magnitude of 20 lb and making an angle of −60° with the vertical.

31. A rope attached to the sled makes an angle of 40° with the ground. With what force must the rope be pulled to produce a horizontal component of 10 kg-wt?

Ans. 13.1 kg-wt

32. Three forces are acting on a body as follows: (a) 400 lb directly north, (b) 200 lb northwest, and (c) 300 lb southeast. Find the magnitude and direction of the resultant.

33. To overcome friction and keep a wagon in uniform motion requires a horizontal force of 35 lb. If two people pulled with equal forces on horizontal ropes, each making an angle of 45° with the direction of travel, what force would each need to exert? Draw a diagram showing components of these forces.   *Ans.* 24.7 lb

34. Two boys are pulling on a sled. One boy pulls forward with a force of 20 lb at an angle of 30° with the horizontal and the other boy pulls backward with a force of 10 lb at an angle of 45° with the vertical. Find the horizontal and vertical components of the resultant force on the sled.

35. A man pushes along the handle of a lawn mower which makes an angle of 25° with the horizontal ground. One component of the 35-lb force he exerts drives the lawn mower along the ground; another component pushes the lawn mower against the ground. Calculate the component forces parallel to and perpendicular to the ground.

Ans. 31.8 lb; 14.8 lb

36. A sled and a boy together weigh 80 lb. The sled is pulled forward by means of a rope that makes an angle of 30° with the horizontal. If the rope exerts a force of 30 lb on the sled, what is the forward pull on the sled and with what force does the sled press against the horizontal ground?

37. The pilot of an airplane is trying to keep it on a "beam" toward an airport due east. The air speed of this plane is 250 mi/hr. If the wind is blowing from the north at 30 mi/hr, in what direction must he head the plane?   *Ans.* 6.9°N of E

38. A pilot steers an airplane due north. If the plane has a speed of 200 mi/hr with respect to still air and the wind is blowing from the southeast with a speed of 50 mi/hr, what is the speed of the airplane with respect to the ground?

39. An automobile is driven 3 km east, then 4 km north, and then 2 km east in 20 min. Determine the distance traveled, the displacement, the average speed, and the average velocity.

Ans. 9 km; 6.40 km, 38.7°N of E; 27 km/hr; 19.2 km/hr, 38.7°N of E

40. A ball is thrown from a moving car in a direction perpendicular to the motion of the car. If the velocity of the car is 50 ft/sec and that of the ball is 30 ft/sec, what is the velocity of the ball with respect to the ground?

41. A boy walks 500 m west, 1,500 m south, and then 1,000 m east in 40 min. Determine the distance traveled, the displacement, the average speed, and the average velocity.   *Ans.* 3,000 m; 1,581 m, 18.4°E of S; 4,500 m/hr; 2,372 m/hr, 18.4°E of S

42. An airplane is flying toward the north with a velocity of 400 mi/hr relative to the ground. A wind is blowing from east to west with a velocity of 60 mi/hr. Find the air speed of the airplane and the direction in which it is flying relative to the air.

43. In 1 min a motorcyclist makes 10 trips around a circular course of radius 100 ft. Calculate the distance traveled, the displacement, the average speed, and the average velocity.   *Ans.* 6,283 ft; 0; 105 ft/sec; 0

44. A ferry boat goes straight across a river in which there is a current of 4 mi/hr. If the speed of the boat relative to the water is 8 mi/hr, find the direction in which it is pointed. What is its velocity relative to the earth?

45. A steamboat (Fig. 2.15) is moving eastward with a speed of 10 mi/hr relative to the earth. The wind is blowing from north to south with a speed of 6 mi/hr. Find the velocity of the smoke relative to the boat.   *Ans.* 11.7 mi/hr at 59°W of S

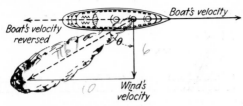

Fig. 2.15

46. A steamboat (Fig. 2.15) is moving eastward with a speed of 12 mi/hr. The wind is blowing out of the north with a speed of 8 mi/hr. Find the speed of the smoke relative to the boat.

47. A man drives 4 miles, 30°E of N, then 4 miles west and then 2 miles, 30°E of S in 15 min. Determine the distance traveled, the displacement, the average speed, and the average velocity.
        Ans. 10 miles; 2 miles, 30°W of N; 40 mi/hr; 8 mi/hr, 30°W of N

48. A man rows a boat at the rate of 8 km/hr across a stream having a current flowing at 5 km/hr. What is the velocity of the boat with respect to land if the man points his boat perpendicular to the current?

49. In what direction would the boat in Prob. 48 have to be pointed for the course of the boat to be perpendicular to the current? How long would it require to cross if the width is 5 km?
        Ans. Upstream, making an angle of 51.3° with the current; 48 min

50. The velocity of an aircraft relative to the air is 300 mi/hr north. The wind is blowing 50 mi/hr from the south and west with the wind velocity making an angle of 37° with north. Find the velocity of the aircraft relative to the ground.

51. A steam locomotive is traveling north at a speed of 40 mi/hr. The wind blows from the west at a speed of 20 mi/hr. In what direction does the line of smoke from the train lie?   *Ans.* 26.5°E of S

52. An airplane with an air speed of 200 mi/hr is to fly due eastward. The wind has a speed of 40 mi/hr from 40°N of E. In what direction should the aircraft be pointed? What is its ground speed?

53. A boat moves east at a speed of 10 km/hr. The wind is blowing from the northwest at 15 km/hr. In what direction does the trail of smoke from the boat lie?
        Ans. 3.3°E of S

54. Two trains leave stations at different times traveling toward each other. One of them travels at a speed of 60 mi/hr, the other at a speed of 50 mi/hr. The stations are 120 miles apart. How much later should the faster train start in order that the two trains meet halfway between the stations?

Statics and Equilibrium

3.1. Force and Motion. The idea of a force as a push or pull is a familiar one. From our everyday experience we know that we must exert forces on bodies whenever we wish to change their state of motion. It is our objective to obtain an understanding of the quantitative relationships between forces and motions, a subject which is called *dynamics*. But first, it is desirable that we examine the conditions which must be satisfied in order that a body be at *rest*. This study is known as *statics* and it is here that we begin our formal development of mechanics.

3.2. Concurrent Forces. When two or more forces act upon a body and the lines of action of all these forces pass through a common point, the forces are said to be *concurrent*. By the line of action of a force we mean simply the line along which the force acts, extended indefinitely in both directions.

Consider an iron ball suspended by a cord as shown in Fig. 3.1. When the ball is hanging at rest, there are two forces acting on it—the pull of the earth downward on the ball and the pull of the cord upward on the ball. The force exerted on the ball by the earth is, of course, its weight **W**. The two forces in question are concurrent, since they act along lines which pass through a common point. How great is the tension **T** in the cord if the ball remains at rest? Accurate measurements reveal that it is exactly as common sense suggests—the upward force **T** is equal to the downward force **W**. If we wish to lower the ball, we would expect to start it downward by reducing **T** so that it is smaller than **W**; if we wish to raise the ball, we start it upward by making **T** greater than **W**.

Suppose now that someone were to push on the ball with a force of 5 lb to the right and you wish to keep the ball at rest. What must you do? Clearly, you must push with a force of 5 lb in the opposite direction (Fig. 3.2). In general, if we wish to keep the ball at rest, we must balance any force applied in any given direction by an equal force in the opposite direction. (Of course, we can replace any force by its rectangular components!)

24

A body that remains at rest or moves with constant velocity is said to be in a state of equilibrium (equal balance). In order that a body be in equilibrium under the influence of any number of concurrent forces, *the vector sum of the forces acting on the body must be zero.* If we draw a vector

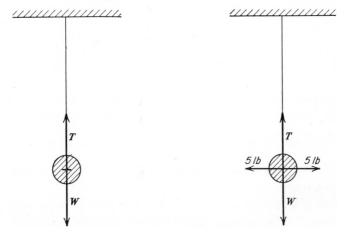

Fig. 3.1. When a ball hangs at rest, its weight is exactly balanced by the upward force exerted by the cord.

Fig. 3.2. If a force is exerted to the right on the ball, an equal force to the left is required to keep the ball at rest.

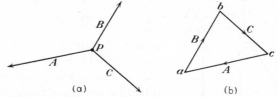

(a)   (b)

Fig. 3.3. If three forces act on a point mass at P, the vector sum of the forces must be zero if the mass is in equilibrium.

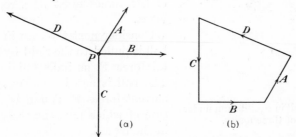

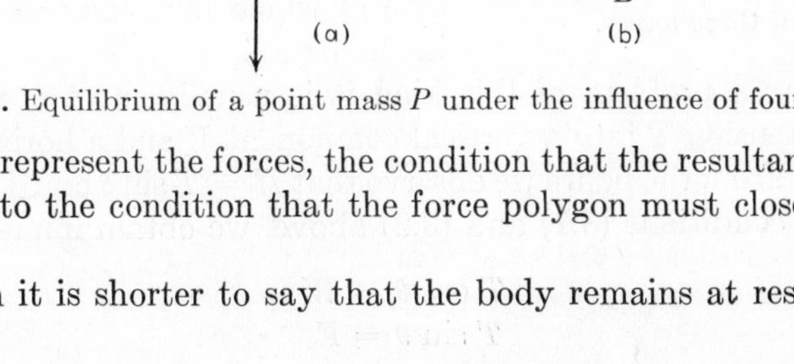

(a)   (b)

Fig. 3.4. Equilibrium of a point mass P under the influence of four forces.

diagram to represent the forces, the condition that the resultant be zero is equivalent to the condition that the force polygon must close (Figs. 3.3 to 3.5).

Although it is shorter to say that the body remains at rest when the vector sum of the forces acting on it is zero, it is often more convenient in working problems to resolve the forces into components in mutually perpendicular X and Y (and Z, if necessary) directions. Usually, but not

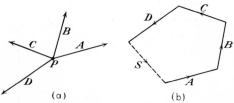

(a) (b)

Fig. 3.5. Four forces acting on a point mass P do not produce equilibrium when the polygon does not close, i.e., when the vector sum of the forces is not zero.

always, it is desirable to choose vertical and horizontal axes. In this case:

1. *The sum of all upward force components is equal to the sum of all downward force components.*

2. *The sum of all force components to the right is equal to the sum of all force components to the left.*

In mathematical shorthand these conditions may be written in the form:

$$\Sigma F_{up} = \Sigma F_{down} \qquad (3.1)$$
$$\Sigma F_{right} = \Sigma F_{left} \qquad (3.2)$$

where Σ (Greek capital sigma) is a standard abbreviation for "the sum of." Clearly, if the components in any direction are exactly equal to those in the opposite direction, the vector sum of the forces must be zero, and vice versa.

Consider next the case in which the ball is pulled to the right by a horizontal force F, as indicated in Fig. 3.6. The ball is acted upon by three concurrent forces F, T, and W, the vector sum of which must be zero, as shown in the figure.

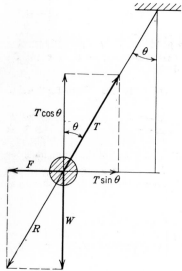

Fig. 3.6. A ball in equilibrium under the influence of three forces.

In treating a problem of this kind it is usually most convenient to resolve the tension T into a vertical component V and a horizontal component H. From the figure we observe that $H = T \sin \theta$ and $V = T \cos \theta$. If we apply conditions (3.1) and (3.2) above, we obtain immediately

$$T \cos \theta = W$$
$$T \sin \theta = F$$

Example. If $W = 10$ lb and $\theta = 30°$, find F and T.

$$T \cos \theta = W \qquad\qquad T \sin \theta = F$$
$$0.866T = 10 \qquad\qquad 0.5 \times 11.55 = F$$
$$T = 11.55 \text{ lb} \qquad\qquad F = 5.77 \text{ lb}$$

In Fig. 3.6 the resultant of **W** and **F** is indicated as **R**. Note that **T** is equal to **R** and in the opposite direction. A force which is equal to and opposite to the resultant of two or more forces is called the *equilibrant*. Figure 3.7 shows the resultant and equilibrant of two forces **P** and **Q** which are not mutually perpendicular.

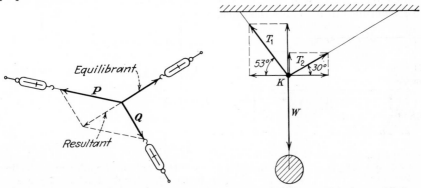

Fig. 3.7. Resultant and equilibrant of two forces not at right angles to each other.

Fig. 3.8. The knot K is in equilibrium under the influence of the three forces **T**₁, **T**₂, and **W**.

Example. A weight of 40 lb is supported as shown in Fig. 3.8. Find the tension in each rope.

The lower rope supports the 40-lb weight so the tension in it is 40 lb. Now let us consider the knot K at which the ropes meet to be the body in equilibrium. It is acted upon by three forces as shown.

The vertical component of **T**₁ is $T_1 \sin 53° = 0.8 \, T_1$ and the horizontal component is $T_1 \cos 53° = 0.6 T_1$. The vertical component of **T**₂ is $T_2 \sin 30° = 0.5 T_2$ and the horizontal component is $T_2 \cos 30° = 0.866 T_2$. Applying the force conditions (3.1) and (3.2) yields

$$0.8 T_1 + 0.5 T_2 = 40 \text{ lb}$$
$$0.866 T_2 = 0.6 T_1$$

$\longleftarrow$ (solve simotaneously)

from which $T_1 = 34.9$ lb and $T_2 = 24.2$ lb. Note that the larger force is exerted by the shorter rope in this case.

3.3. Torque. If two boys who weigh 50 and 60 lb, respectively, sit on opposite ends of a horizontal teeter-totter 12 ft long (Fig. 3.9), we know that the teeter-totter will not remain horizontal; the 60-lb boy will move downward and the 50-lb boy upward. This occurs even though the upward force exerted by the support is equal to 110 lb (plus the weight of the teeter-totter, which we assume for the moment is negligible). A glance at the figure reveals that the forces are not concurrent and that the conditions required for a body to be at rest under the influence of concurrent forces are not enough to keep the teeter-totter at rest. The weight of the 60-lb boy acts to produce a rotation about the fulcrum clockwise, while the weight of the 50-lb boy acts to produce a rotation in the opposite direction.   When both boys are at the ends of the teeter-totter, the two rotational tendencies do not balance each other and there is a resultant clockwise rotation.   We all know from our experience that the two boys can sit on the teeter-totter and keep it at rest, provided the heavier boy sits closer to the fulcrum.   This sug-gests that the tendency to produce rotation depends not only on the force acting but also on a distance.

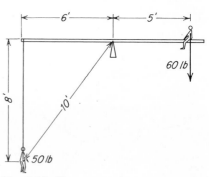

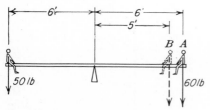

Fig. 3.9. The teeter-totter is not in rota-tional equilibrium when the 60-lb boy is at *A*; equilibrium is established if he moves to *B*.

Fig. 3.10. The torque about the fulcrum depends on the product of the force and the distance from the fulcrum to the line along which the force acts.

A simple experiment shows that if the 50-lb boy sits 6 ft from the fulcrum and the 60-lb boy 5 ft from the fulcrum, the teeter-totter is balanced.   We observe that $60 \times 5 = 50 \times 6$.   This suggests that the tendency to produce rotation depends on the product of force and dis-tance.   We must, however, inquire more closely into how this distance factor is to be determined.   Suppose that our teeter-totter is elevated and that the 50-lb boy is suspended from a rope 8 ft long hanging from the end of the teeter-totter (Fig. 3.10).   His distance from the fulcrum is then $\sqrt{8^2 + 6^2} = 10$ ft.   Will the teeter-totter still be balanced?   Yes, indeed.   An experiment would show that moving the 50-lb boy to this position had no effect on the balance.   Thus, it is clear that it is *not* the distance from the point at which the forces are applied to the fulcrum which is important; rather, it is the *perpendicular distance from the fulcrum to the line along which the force acts*.   This distance is known as the *lever arm*.   *The lever arm for any axis is the perpendicular distance from the axis to the line along which the force acts* (Fig. 3.11).

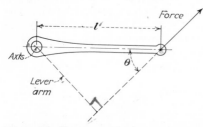

Fig. 3.11. The torque is the product of the force and the lever arm.   The lever arm is the distance from the axis to the line along which the force acts.

The product of the force and the lever arm is the torque (or the moment of the force). Torque is a vector quantity. The direction associated with a torque is the direction in which a right-handed screw would advance if it were turned by the torque (Fig. 3.12). In describing torques, we shall refer to torques as clockwise if they act to produce a rotation in the direction in which the hands of a clock move, and counterclockwise if they act in the opposite direction.

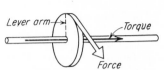

In the case of the teeter-totter we see that it will be in balance if the clockwise torque about the fulcrum is balanced by the counterclockwise torque. *If the vector sum of all torques acting on a body is zero for one axis, it is zero for any parallel axis whatsoever.*

Fig. 3.12. Torque is a vector quantity with direction given by the direction in which a right-handed screw would advance if it were turned by the torque.

For example, if the weight of the teeter-totter itself is negligible, Eq. (3.1) requires that the fulcrum exert an upward force of 110 lb. If we choose an axis through the left end of the teeter-totter, we have a counterclockwise torque of $110 \times 6 = 660$ lb-ft and a clockwise torque of $60 \times 11 = 660$ lb-ft.

As a further illustration of the importance of the lever arm in computing the torque, consider the operation of a bicycle. If a boy pushes down on the pedal with his full weight (Fig. 3.13), the rotational effect produced depends on the location of the pedal. If it is straight down, no rotational effect is produced. The torque in this case is zero, because the lever arm is zero. The maximum torque occurs when the pedal is in the position marked A, since in this position the lever arm is equal to the radius of the pedal. When the pedal is in position B, the lever arm is reduced from R to X.

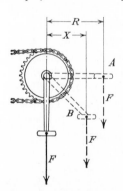

3.4. Center of Gravity. Every particle of an extended body possesses weight, so that the pull of the earth on the body is composed of a large number of forces directed toward the center of the earth. For a body of ordinary size these forces are essentially parallel to one another. The body can, however, be supported in equilibrium by a single upward force, provided its line of action passes through a point called the *center of gravity* of the body. This point can be located as follows.

Fig. 3.13. When a bicycle pedal is straight down, no torque is produced by a vertical force. The torque is maximum for a vertical force when the pedal is in position A.

If we suspend the body from a single point, it comes to rest with a definite orientation. Let us determine a line through the body directed vertically downward from the point of suspension (Fig. 3.14). Next, let us suspend the body from several other points on its surface and in each case determine the position of the line through the point of support and directed vertically downward. We find that all the lines determined in this way intersect at a point, which is the *center of gravity* of the body.

The center of gravity of a uniform sphere, cube, or rod is at its geometrical center. The center of gravity of an axe or hammer is nearer the head than the handle. The center of gravity of a telephone pole or a baseball bat lies on the axis, but is closer to the thicker end. The center of gravity of a ring or of a tire is at the geometrical center, which, of course, does not lie in the material of the object. Although the center of gravity is a point fixed relative to the body, it does not necessarily lie within the body.

Since an extended body can be at rest when supported by a single upward force whose line of action passes through the center of gravity, the sum of the clockwise torques due to the individual forces on the particles of the body must be equal to the sum of the counterclockwise torques about an axis through the center of gravity. For any axis the torque due to the weight of the body acting at the center of gravity is equal to the sum of the torques of the forces of gravity on all the various parts of the body (Fig. 3.15). When we are dealing with the extended body, we may consider all the weight of the body as concentrated at the center of gravity and we

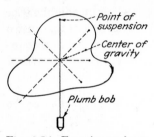

Fig. 3.14. Experimental procedure for finding the center of gravity of a body.

may thus replace the individual forces acting on the many particles of the body by a single force equal to the weight. This is true not only for an axis determined by the center of gravity, but for any axis. *The center of gravity of an object is that point at which we can consider the entire weight of the object to be concentrated for the purpose of computing torques.*

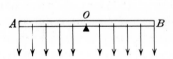

Fig. 3.15. Center of gravity of a uniform bar.

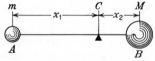

Fig. 3.16. Center of gravity of two spheres connected by a rod of negligible mass.

Example. Find the center of gravity of two spheres of masses 50 and 200 g connected by a light (negligible mass) rod 20 cm long (Fig. 3.16).

If the center of gravity is at a point C, the clockwise torque due to the larger mass M about an axis through C is just equal to the counterclockwise torque due to the smaller mass m. Let w and W be the weights of m and M, respectively. Then

$$wx_1 = Wx_2$$

Since $x_1 + x_2 = 20$ cm,

$$(50 \text{ g-wt})(x_1 \text{ cm}) = (200 \text{ g-wt})(20 - x_1) \text{ cm}$$
$$x_1 = 16 \text{ cm}$$

3.5. Equilibrium. Thus far we have been considering the conditions which must be satisfied in order that a body remain at rest. Exactly the same conditions apply to a body which is in motion with constant velocity. Most of us have had the experience of sitting in a train in a station with another train on an adjacent track. If we watch this second train when our train begins to pull out at a constant speed, it is impossible to tell from this observation alone whether we are moving or the other train is moving in the opposite direction. The forces which act upon us are exactly the same whether we are at rest or traveling with constant velocity. The most careful experiments verify the fact that the forces exerted on a body which is traveling with constant velocity have a resultant of zero. Thus, the conditions which we have described for bodies at rest apply equally well to bodies in motion with constant velocity.

The condition that the vector sum of the torques on a body be zero in order that there be no rotation for a body at rest can be extended to include rotating bodies as follows: *If the vector sum of the torques acting on a rigid body is zero, the rotational velocity of the body is constant. A body which has a constant linear velocity and a constant rotational velocity is in a state of equilibrium.* Statics involves a special case of equilibrium, namely, the case in which both the linear velocity and the rotational velocity have the constant value *zero*.

3.6. The Conditions for Equilibrium. In order that a rigid body be in equilibrium, two conditions must be satisfied:

1. The resultant of all forces acting on the body must be zero.
2. The resultant of all torques *about any axis* must be zero.

The first condition for equilibrium guarantees that the center of gravity (more accurately the center of mass) of the body moves with constant velocity. The second condition guarantees that the rotational velocity of the body remains constant. In applying the second condition, there is no restriction as to what axis is chosen. It may be through the center of gravity of the body, through one end of the body, or at any convenient place.

In actual practice, it is usually convenient to use the conditions of equilibrium in a slightly different form, but one which is equivalent to the briefer statements above. If we replace forces by their vertical and horizontal components, we may write the conditions for equilibrium in the form:

1. The sum of all upward forces is equal to the sum of all downward forces.

The sum of all forces to the right is equal to the sum of all forces to the left.

2. The sum of all clockwise torques *about any axis* is equal to the sum of all counterclockwise torques *about the same axis.*

If we introduce once more the symbol Σ to represent "the sum of," we may write these conditions

$$\Sigma F_{\text{up}} = \Sigma F_{\text{down}} \tag{3.1}$$
$$\Sigma F_{\text{right}} = \Sigma F_{\text{left}} \tag{3.2}$$
$$\Sigma \text{ torques}_{\text{clockwise}} = \Sigma \text{ torques}_{\text{counterclockwise}} \tag{3.3}$$

These equations are written for the case in which we are dealing with forces acting in a plane. The extension to three-dimensional systems is not difficult in that all we need do is (1) to add to the first condition of equilibrium that the sum of all components perpendicular to the plane determined by the first two axes add to zero, and (2) to apply the torque condition for another axis chosen perpendicular to the first axis. It is not necessary that we choose vertical and horizontal axes for applying the conditions for equilibrium, but in the vast majority of cases this is the most convenient choice.

In working equilibrium problems it is imperative that *all* forces acting on the body in question be considered and *only* those forces. The first thing one must do is to decide what body is to be dealt with. Then it is usually helpful to make a rough sketch of this body, showing all forces acting on the body by suitably placed arrows. Next, one resolves all those forces which are neither horizontal nor vertical and replaces them by their components. At this point he is ready to apply the conditions for equilibrium.

Example. It is found by weighing that the front wheels of a truck support 3,000 lb and the rear wheels 5,400 lb. If the wheel base (distance between axles) is 18 ft, find the weight of the truck and the location of the center of gravity (Fig. 3.17).

By Eq. (3.1),

$$3,000 + 5,400 = W$$
$$W = 8,400 \text{ lb}$$

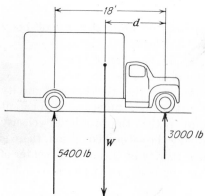

Fig. 3.17. The center of gravity of a truck.

Let d be the distance from the front wheels to the center of gravity and find torques about the front axle as axis. By Eq. (3.3),

$$Wd = 5,400 \times 18$$
$$8,400d = 5,400 \times 18$$
$$d = 11.6 \text{ ft}$$

Example. A uniform ladder weighs 60 lb and is 25 ft long. It leans against a smooth (frictionless) wall at a point 20 ft above the ground (Fig. 3.18). A 150-lb man stands 0.4 the way up the ladder. Find the force exerted on the ladder by the wall. Find the horizontal and vertical components of the force exerted on the ladder by the ground. (Note that it is 15 ft from the base of the ladder to the wall.)

The object in equilibrium is the ladder and the forces *exerted on* the ladder are shown in the figure, where H and V are the components of the force exerted by the ground.

By Eq. (3.1), $\qquad\qquad V = 150 + 60 = 210$ lb

By Eq. (3.2), $\qquad\qquad H = F$

If we take the base of the ladder as axis, we obtain, by Eq. (3.3),

$$(150 \times 6) + (60 \times 7.5) = F \times 20$$
$$F = 67.5 \text{ lb} \qquad \text{and} \qquad H = 67.5 \text{ lb}$$

Note that we may choose *any axis* for applying Eq. (3.3). For example, if we pick the

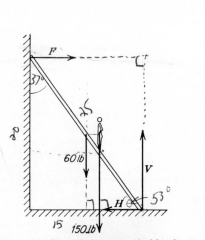

Fig. 3.18. Equilibrium of a ladder leaning against a smooth wall.

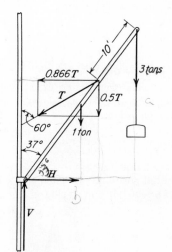

Fig. 3.19. Equilibrium of a derrick boom.

point at which the ladder touches the wall as axis, we have

$$15V = 20H + (150 \times 9) + (60 \times 7.5)$$
$$(15 \times 210) = 20H + 1{,}350 + 450$$
$$H = 67.5 \text{ lb} \qquad \text{(as before)}$$

(It may be instructive to try other axes such as one through the center of the ladder to assure yourself that we may indeed choose *any axis*.)

Example. A derrick (Fig. 3.19) has a uniform boom 30 ft long which weighs one ton. A load of 3 tons is suspended from the end. The boom is hinged to a vertical mast and held up by a cable which makes an angle of 60° with the mast and which is fastened 10 ft from the end of the boom. If the boom makes an angle of 37° with the mast, find the tension in the cable and the force exerted on the boom by the hinge.

First, we resolve the tension into its horizontal and vertical components which are $T \sin 60° = 0.866T$ and $T \cos 60° = 0.5T$, respectively. Next let H and V represent the components of the force exerted on the boom by the hinge.

By Eq. (3.1), $\qquad\qquad\qquad V = 3 + 1 + 0.5T$
By Eq. (3.2), $\qquad\qquad\qquad H = 0.866T$

If we choose the hinge as the axis, Eq. (3.3) yields

$$(9 \times 1) + (0.5T \times 12) + (3 \times 18) = (0.866T \times 16)$$
$$T = 8.02 \text{ tons}$$

whence $V = 8.01$ tons and $H = 6.95$ tons.

Note that we have replaced the force T by its components and then computed the torque due to each component. The resultant of the torques due to the components is equal to the torque due to the original force.

3.7. Types of Equilibrium. The equilibrium of a body may be *stable, unstable,* or *neutral* (Fig. 3.20). When a body returns to its original position after being slightly disturbed, the equilibrium is said to be *stable*. A cone standing on its base (Fig. 3.21) is an illustration of this type of equilibrium. When this cone is tilted slightly, it returns to its original position on being released.

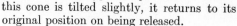

Fig. 3.20. Neutral, stable, and unstable equilibrium.

If the cone rests on its vertex, it can be in equilibrium only when its center of gravity lies directly above the vertex. If it is slightly displaced, the cone falls over. A cone balanced on its vertex is in *unstable* equilibrium. A body in unstable equilibrium does not return to the original equilibrium position when slightly displaced, but rather moves farther away. Lastly, a billiard ball resting on a horizontal table is said to be in *neutral* equilibrium. When it is slightly displaced, it neither returns to its former position nor does it go farther away from the initial position. It remains in any position in which it finds itself. A cylinder or a cone lying on its side on a horizontal surface is also in neutral equilibrium.

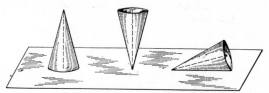

Fig. 3.21. Stable, unstable, and neutral equilibrium of a cone.

The position of the center of gravity is of paramount importance in determining the stability of a body. The lower the center of gravity, the greater the stability of the body and the more difficult it is to overturn. The body becomes unstable as soon as the vertical line through the center of gravity falls outside its base. The leaning tower of Pisa remains in stable equilibrium because in spite of its leaning the line of action of the weight falls inside the base.

3.8. The Stability of Aircraft. An airplane flying horizontally at constant speed is in equilibrium under the influence of four generalized forces: the lift, the weight, the drag, and the thrust (Fig. 3.22). The weight of the airplane may, of course, be regarded as concentrated at the center of gravity. The lift forces, which arise from the pressure differences on the wing, fuselage, and tail sections of the aircraft, may be replaced in a similar way by a resultant lift vector.   The friction resulting from the passage of air over the surface of the aircraft gives rise to a net retarding force known as the drag, while the aircraft engine, whether it be propeller or jet, provides thrust to overcome this drag.

For the aircraft to be longitudinally stable, the resultant of the torques about a transverse axis through the center of gravity must be zero.   Note that the conditions for equilibrium must be satisfied over a wide range of speeds and loadings. This can be accomplished by moving aileron, wing, or elevator surfaces in such a way as to keep the lift equal to the weight and the center of lift appropriately placed relative to the center of gravity.   When the speed of an aircraft approaches the speed of sound, there may be radical changes in the way in which air flows over the aircraft surfaces.   Such changes introduce sudden shifts in the position

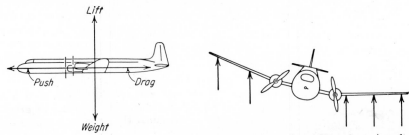

Fig. 3.22. An aircraft in stable equilib-   **Fig. 3.23.** Lateral stability of an aircraft.
rium.

of the center of lift and thereby introduce large and sudden torques on the aircraft.   For this and other reasons, it is dangerous to fly any type of aircraft above a maximum speed which depends upon the design.

Not only must the airplane be stable longitudinally, but also laterally.   One way of achieving lateral stability is by having the center of gravity of the aircraft well below the center of lift.   Another device which increases the lateral stability is to make the dihedral angle between wing surfaces less than 180° (Fig. 3.23).   In this case, when the airplane tilts, the lowered wing has more lift than the raised one, because it presents a greater horizontal area to the air.   As a consequence, there is a torque in the direction to restore the aircraft to its stable position.

PROBLEMS

1. A horizontal force of 10 lb acts upon a small object which weighs 5 lb.   What single additional force will hold the object at rest?

Ans. 11.2 lb at 26.5° with the horizontal

2. Forces of 30 kg-wt east and 45 kg-wt south act upon a small body.   What is the magnitude and direction of the force that will produce equilibrium?

3. A 5-kg body is supported by two cords, each of which make an angle of 45° with the horizontal.   What is the tension in each cord?   *Ans.* 3.54 kg-wt

4. In Prob. 3, the angle between the cords is 90°.   To what value would this angle need to be changed in order that the tension in each cord be 5 kg-wt?

5. A picture is supported by two wires fastened to the ends of the upper edge of the picture frame which is horizontal.   Each of the wires makes an angle of 60° with the vertical.   What is the tension in each wire if the picture weighs 8 lb?   *Ans.* 8 lb

6. A pendulum bob with a mass of 3 kg is hung on a cord 1.6 m long. A horizontal force is applied to the bob, sufficient to bring the cord to an angle of 30° with the vertical. Find the horizontal force and the tension in the cord.

7. A bird weighing 3 lb alights on a weightless wire (Fig. 3.24) midway between two poles 200 ft apart. Because of the weight of the bird, the wire, which was initially essentially horizontal, sags 3 in. What is the tension in the wire due to the weight of the bird?

Ans. 600 lb

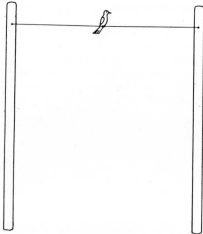

Fig. 3.24

8. A bird weighing 1 lb alights on a telephone wire (Fig. 3.24) midway between poles which are 200 ft apart. Assume that the wire between the bird and the poles forms two straight lines. If the center of the wire is 6 in. below its level at the poles and if the weight of the wire is neglected, calculate the tension in the wire due to the weight of the bird.

9. A square is acted upon by forces of 2, 5, 9, and 11 g-wt, respectively, along the four sides. The forces all act to produce rotation in the same direction. If the length of the side of the square is 0.5 m, what is the resultant torque acting to rotate the square about an axis through its center?

Ans. 6.75 g-wt-m

10. A wheel whose diameter is 25 cm has an axle whose diameter is 4 cm. If a force of 16 kg-wt is exerted along the rim of the wheel, what is the smallest force exerted on the outside of the axle which will result in zero net torque?

11. A beam 12 m long is supported at its ends by two walls. Find the forces exerted on the supports when a 75-kg man stands on the beam at a distance of 4 m from one end. Neglect the weight of the beam.

Ans. 25 and 50 kg-wt

12. A beam 18 ft long weighs 100 lb and is supported at its ends by two walls. Find the reactions of the walls against the beam when a man weighing 200 lb stands on the beam at a distance of 8 ft from one end.

13. Weights of 250, 500, 750, and 1,000 g are located, respectively, at 25-, 50-, 75-, and 100-cm marks on a meter stick whose weight is negligible. What is the magnitude and location of the single upward force which will balance the system?

Ans. 2,500 g-wt at the 75-cm mark

14. A pole, which is 14 ft long and weighs 80 lb, can be balanced at a point 6 ft from the thicker end. If it were to be supported at its ends, how much force would be needed at each end?

15. A rod 80 cm long with negligible mass has attached to it weights of 2 kg at one end, 10 kg at the other end, and 8 kg in the middle.   Find the position of the center of gravity.   *Ans.* 56 cm from the 2-kg weight

16. A uniform rod which is 15 ft long and weighs 80 lb is supported at one end and a point 3 ft from the other end.   Where can a weight of 50 lb be attached to the rod so that the total force on each support will be the same?

17. A telegraph pole is placed on a two-wheeled truck located 2 m from the thicker end, and an upward force of 15 kg-wt at the thinner end is required to keep it horizontal.   The pole is 6 m long and has a mass of 115 kg.   Where is the center of gravity?
                                       Ans. 2.52 m from the thicker end

18. A uniform bar a yard long has fastened to it at one end a weight of 4 lb, and at the other end a weight of 5 lb.   The bar itself weighs 2 lb,.   Where could a single force be applied to balance the system, and how great would the force have to be?

19. When the front wheels of an automobile are run on a platform scale, the scale balances at 2,000 lb and when the rear wheels are run on the scale it balances at 1,200 lb.   What is the weight of the automobile and how far is its center of gravity in front of the rear axle?   The distance between axles is 125 in.   *Ans.* 3,200 lb; 78.1 in.

20. A rod 120 cm long has a mass of 2 kg.   It has attached to it a mass of 3 kg at one end, a mass of 10 kg at the other end, and a mass of 8 kg in the middle.   Find the position of the center of gravity.

21. A uniform rod which is 12 ft long and weighs 60 lb is supported at one end and at a point 3 ft from the other end.   Where can a weight of 40 lb be attached to the rod so that the total force on each support will be the same?
                                       Ans. 9.75 ft from unsupported end

22. If weights A, B, C, D, and E are, respectively, located at distances a, b, c, d, and e from one end of a light bar, use the two conditions for equilibrium to show that the center of gravity is located a distance y from that end of the bar, where

$$y = \frac{Aa + Bb + Cc + Dd + Ee}{A + B + C + D + E}$$

23. To a thin circular disk whose radius is 50 cm, there is attached another circular disk of the same material whose radius is 25 cm.   Find the center of gravity of the combination if the smaller disk has one point on its circumference at the center of the larger disk.
         Ans. 5 cm from the center of the larger disk, on the line between the centers

24. From a circular disk whose radius is 10 cm there is cut out a circle whose diameter is 5 cm.   Find the center of gravity of the remainder of the disk if the circular hole is in contact with the circumference of the disk at one point.

25. From a circular disk whose radius is 50 cm there is cut a circular hole whose radius is 25 cm.   Find the center of gravity of the remainder of the disk if the hole has one point on its circumference at the center of the disk.
Ans. 8⅓ cm from the center of the disk, on the extension of the line between the center of the disk and the center of the hole

26. A bar of uniform cross section is carried by two boys, one at either end of the bar.   If the bar weighs 80 lb and is 15 ft long, where must a load of 70 lb be hung from the bar so that one boy will carry twice as much as the other?

27. A uniform bar has a mass of 30 kg and is 3 m long.   From one end is suspended a 15-kg mass, and from the other end a 20-kg mass.   At what point must the bar be suspended in order that it be in equilibrium?
                                       Ans. 1.62 m from end having 15-kg mass

28. A cart standing on an inclined plane that makes an angle of 5° with the horizontal is kept from rolling down hill by a force of 90 lb applied in a direction parallel to the plane. What is the weight of the cart?

29. A bar of uniform cross section is carried by two boys, one at either end of the bar. If the bar has a mass of 40 kg and is 5 m long, where must a load of 35 kg be hung from the bar so that one boy will carry twice as much as the other boy?

Ans. 0.71 m from boy carrying the heavier load

30. The end of a horizontal electric-transmission line in which there is a tension of 1,000 lb is fastened to the top of a vertical pole and also to a guy wire which can sustain a tension of 2,500 lb. What is the smallest angle which the guy wire can make with the pole if there is to be no lateral force on the pole?

31. A uniform rod 10 ft long supports two loads, 80 lb at a distance 1 ft from one end and 30 lb at a distance 2 ft from the other end. If the rod balances at a point 3 ft from the end that supports the 80 lb, what is the weight of the rod?

Ans. 5 lb

32. A frictionless car rests on an inclined plane that makes an angle of 30° with the horizontal. The car weighs 150 lb. What force must be exerted to keep it from sliding down the plane, if the force is applied in such a way that it makes an angle of 45° downward with the horizontal?

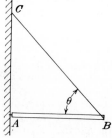
Fig. 3.25

33. The horizontal bar AB in Fig. 3.25 is supported by the cord BC at one end and by the wall AC at the other end. If the bar is of uniform cross section, weighs 25 lb, and is 5 ft long, and if θ is 45°, what is the tension in the cord? *Ans.* 17.7 lb

34. In Fig. 3.25 the uniform horizontal bar 5 ft long weighs 60 lb and the angle θ is 60°. What is the tension in the cord?

35. The horizontal bar AB in the Fig. 3.25 is non-uniform, being 10 ft long, having its center of gravity 4 ft from the wall and weighing 100 lb. In addition, a 70-lb weight is suspended on the bar 8 ft from the wall. The angle θ is 60°. What is the tension in the cord BC? *Ans.* 111 lb

36. The horizontal bar AB in the Fig. 3.25 is nonuniform, being 8 m long, its center of gravity being 3 m from the wall. The bar has a mass of 40 kg. A 20-kg mass is suspended at the end B of the bar. What is the tension in the supporting cord if the angle θ is 30°?

37. The uniform ladder shown in Fig. 3.26 is 4 m long and weighs 20 kg-wt. If the angle between the ladder and the vertical direction is 30°, what are the magnitudes of the forces X, Y, and R?

Ans. 5.77 kg-wt; 20 kg-wt; 5.77 kg-wt

38. The uniform ladder shown in Fig. 3.26 is 20 ft long and weighs 80 lb. If the angle between the ladder and the vertical direction is 20°, what are the magnitudes of the forces X, Y, and R?

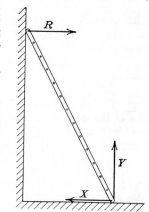
Fig. 3.26. R is force exerted on the ladder by the wall, while X and Y are the horizontal and vertical components of the force exerted on the ladder by the earth.

39. The ladder shown in Fig. 3.26 is smaller at the top than at the bottom. It is 18 ft long, has its center of gravity 8 ft from the bottom, and weighs 70 lb. A man weighing 160 lb stands 2 ft from the top. The angle θ between the ladder and the vertical direction is 25°. Find the magnitudes of the forces X, Y, and R.

Ans. 81.0 lb; 230 lb; 81.0 lb

40. The ladder shown in Fig. 3.26 is **7** m long, has its center of gravity 3 m from the lower end, and weighs 50 kg-wt. A boy weighing 40 kg-wt stands on the ladder 1 m from the upper end. The angle θ between the ladder and the vertical direction is 22°. Find the magnitudes of the forces X, Y, and R.

41. A 20-ft ladder weighing 40 lb rests against the smooth side of a house so that it makes an angle of 60° with the ground. A 60-lb boy stands on the ladder 5 ft from the bottom. A 160-lb man stands on the ladder at its center. (*a*) What is the horizontal force pushing against the house? (*b*) What is the force pushing down toward the ground? Assume the ladder is uniform. *Ans.* 66.4 lb; 260 lb

42. A ladder weighing 50 lb makes an angle of 30° with the vertical. The length of the ladder is 20 ft. A man weighing 180 lb is at a point 15 ft from the lower end of the ladder. What horizontal force is required at the foot of the ladder to keep it from slipping? Neglect frictional forces of wall on ladder.

43. A 5-kg block rests on a frictionless plane inclined 20° with the horizontal. It is connected to a weight X by a rope of negligible weight. The rope runs parallel to the plane and passes over a pulley so the weight X hangs vertical. What must be the magnitude of the weight if the system is in equilibrium? *Ans.* 1.71 kg-wt

44. A horizontal bar 8 ft long has a downward force of 80 lb at its center. Upward forces of 30 and 50 lb, respectively, are exerted at the ends. Is the bar in equilibrium? Calculate the torque about one end, about the center, and a point 10 ft from one end of the bar. Under what conditions is the torque not the same about any arbitrarily chosen axis?

45. Two vehicles are crossing a bridge 100 ft long. A passenger car weighing 3,500 lb is 10 ft from one end. A truck weighing 6,500 lb is 30 ft from the same end. If the bridge is symmetrical with respect to the center and weighs 20 tons, what is the force on the two supports at the ends of the bridge? *Ans.* 27,700 lb; 22,300 lb

46. A ladder weighing 50 lb makes an angle of 60° with the ground and is leaning against a smooth wall. The ladder is 15 ft long and of uniform density along its length. Calculate the force on the ladder exerted by the wall and the horizontal and vertical components of the force exerted by the ground.

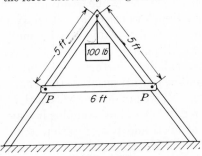

Fig. 3.27

47. A simple light A frame (Fig. 3.27) is held together by pins. It supports a load of 100 lb from its apex. If the sides make an angle of 37° with the vertical, find the forces exerted on the top pin by each side member and the horizontal force exerted by the pins P if the ground upon which the frame rests is smooth so that it exerts no horizontal force. *Ans.* 62.5 lb; 37.5 lb

48. A derrick similar to that of Fig. 3.19 has a uniform boom 20 ft long which weighs 1,500 lb. A load of 4,000 lb is suspended from one end. Find the tension in the supporting cable if it makes an angle of 50° with the vertical mast when the boom makes an angle of 30° with the mast.

CHAPTER 4

Linear Motion

4.1. Types of Motion. As we saw in Chap. 3, the linear velocity of a body is constant when the vector sum of the forces acting on the body is zero. This fact immediately suggests that if the resultant force is not zero, the velocity of the body must be changing. Before we relate this change in velocity to the force, it is important that we develop some of the equations of *kinematics*, the science of motion. In this chapter we deal with some of the simpler but relatively important problems of linear motion. (In order to treat advanced problems in kinematics, it is necessary to use *calculus*, a branch of mathematics developed by Newton and Leibnitz to solve such problems.)

In the motion of an automobile chassis along a straight road or of an elevator up and down in its shaft, all points of the body move along parallel lines. Any object which moves in this way is said to have a motion of pure *translation*, or a linear motion. On the other hand, a merry-go-round and the flywheel of a stationary engine revolve about stationary axes. Such a body is said to have a motion of *pure rotation*, or an angular motion. All points in the object describe concentric circles about the axis. We shall defer further consideration of rotational motion to Chap. 13, and confine our attention in this chapter to several types of translational motion. If we are dealing with a rigid body, we can always resolve its motion, regardless of how complex it may be, into pure translation of the center of mass and pure rotation about the center of mass. The motion of the wheel of a train, or of a boomerang flying through the air, may be regarded as a combination of translational and rotational motions.

4.2. Instantaneous Velocity. In dealing with the motion of an object, we shall be concerned with how its displacement and velocity change in time. Suppose that we are interested in the motion of an automobile. Let s_0 be the displacement at the instant we start our stop watch, which hereafter reads the time t. We use a subscript zero to indicate the value of any quantity measured at the time $t = 0$. A time t sec

40

later let the displacement be **s**. We have already defined the average velocity as

$$\mathbf{v}_{av} = \frac{\mathbf{s} - \mathbf{s}_0}{t} \tag{4.1}$$

More often than not we shall choose to measure our distances from the point where the automobile is when $t = 0$. Then $\mathbf{s}_0 = 0$, and

$$\mathbf{v}_{av} = \frac{\mathbf{s}}{t} \tag{4.1a}$$

The velocity of the automobile may well be changing. If so, we may be interested in how fast (and in what direction) it is moving at a given instant—a quantity which we call the *instantaneous velocity*. If we want to know the velocity at a given instant as the car passes a telephone pole, we may proceed as follows: We measure the average velocity of the car in the block containing the telephone pole by dividing the length of the block by the time required to cover the block. This will almost surely be closer to the velocity at the instant of passing than would the average velocity over some longer period. We might come closer to the instantaneous velocity by determining where the car was 1 sec before it reached the pole and 1 sec after it passed the pole, but this still gives us an average velocity over a 2-sec interval. To get closer to the instantaneous velocity, we measure the displacement over shorter and shorter time intervals. Let $\Delta\mathbf{s}$ represent the displacement of the car during a short time interval Δt. (Here we are using the Greek letter Δ as mathematical shorthand to mean "a small change in"). The ratio $\Delta\mathbf{s}/\Delta t$ gives us the average velocity during the time interval Δt. As we make Δt shorter and shorter, this average velocity comes closer and closer to the instantaneous velocity. We define the instantaneous velocity **v** as the limit approached by $\Delta\mathbf{s}/\Delta t$ as Δt becomes smaller and smaller, approaching zero as a limit. We may write this in the form of an equation.

$$\mathbf{v} = \lim_{\Delta t \to 0} \frac{\Delta\mathbf{s}}{\Delta t} \left(= \frac{d\mathbf{s}}{dt} \right) \tag{4.2}$$

The instantaneous speed is the magnitude of the instantaneous velocity. The speedometer of an automobile is designed to read instantaneous speed.

4.3. Acceleration. When an automobile is driven in city traffic, its velocity is continually changing. It is zero while the car is waiting for a red light to change; when the traffic light goes green, the velocity is increased for a while, and then varies up and down as traffic conditions require until the car is again brought to rest. Figure 4.1 shows a possible pattern for such a motion. Notice that after the first stop light the car picked up speed rapidly, while after the second it gained velocity slowly.

The ability to pick up speed quickly is a prized characteristic of modern automobiles.

In treating motion in which the velocity is changing, it is convenient to introduce a new technical term, *acceleration*. *Acceleration is the time rate of change of velocity*. The word *deceleration* is often used to mean negative acceleration. The average acceleration over any period of time t is the change in velocity divided by the corresponding change in time.

$$\mathbf{a}_{av} = \frac{\mathbf{v} - \mathbf{v}_0}{t} \qquad (4.3)$$

In the rather complex motion shown in Fig. 4.1 the acceleration varies, and we proceed to define instantaneous acceleration $\mathbf{a}$ as

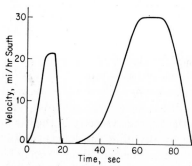

Fig. 4.1. Plot of velocity as a function of time for an automobile in a city.

$$\mathbf{a} = \lim_{\Delta t \to 0} \frac{\Delta \mathbf{v}}{\Delta t} \qquad (4.4)$$

From the definition of acceleration we see that it has the units of velocity divided by time, since it tells us how much the velocity changes per unit of time. For example, acceleration may be expressed in feet per second per second (ft/sec²). For discussing the motion of an automobile, we might measure the change in velocity in miles per hour and the change in time in seconds. Then the acceleration would be in miles per hour per second. If an automobile decelerates from 30 mi/hr to 10 mi/hr in 5 sec, the average acceleration is -20 mi/hr divided by 5 sec, or -4 mi/hr-sec. In metric units we shall most often measure acceleration in meters per second per second.

Example. An automobile manufacturer advertises that his product can start from rest and reach 60 mi/hr (88 ft/sec) in less than 11 sec. What minimum average acceleration is required?

$$a_{av} = \frac{v - v_0}{t} = \frac{88 \text{ ft/sec}}{11 \text{ sec}} = 8 \text{ ft/sec}^2$$

The mathematical treatment of motions in which the acceleration varies irregularly is beyond the scope of this text. We shall confine our discussion to several very important types of motion in which the acceleration is either constant or varies in some relatively simple way. We begin by considering the case in which the acceleration is constant and the motion takes place along a straight line.

4.4. Uniformly Accelerated Rectilinear Motion. If a ball is dropped and its velocity measured as a function of time, it is found that the velocity is 3.2 ft/sec 0.1 sec after release, 6.4 after 0.2 sec, 9.6 after 0.3 sec, and so forth. The velocity and displacement vary with time after release as shown in Fig. 4.2. Each tenth of a second the velocity increases 3.2 ft/sec; each second it increases 32 ft/sec.

The acceleration of a freely falling body at mean sea level and 45° latitude is 32.174 ft/sec², or 9.80665 m/sec². It varies slightly from place to place for reasons which are discussed in Chap. 6. By a freely falling body we mean one for which the air resistance is negligible. Obviously, a feather does not fall through the air with this large an acceleration because of the substantial air friction, but if it is released in an evacuated tube, it has the same acceleration as a steel ball (Fig. 4.3). When a body is falling freely through the air, the effect of

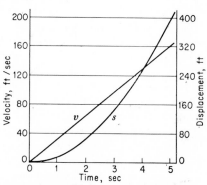

Fig. 4.2. Velocity and displacement of a freely falling body as a function of time.

air friction depends on the velocity, size, shape, density, and surface of the falling object. This friction naturally reduces the acceleration somewhat. In our problems on falling bodies, we shall take the acceleration due to gravity as 32 ft/sec² or 9.80 m/sec², thus making the arithmetic of the problems a little easier. (It should be noted that if a ball is thrown upward, air friction increases the downward acceleration on the way up, decreases it on the way down.) We represent the acceleration due to gravity by the symbol g.

When the acceleration is constant, the average velocity during any time interval is given by

$$v_{av} = \frac{v + v_0}{2} \qquad (4.5)$$

If a ball is released from rest and falls for 3 sec, its initial velocity is 0 and its final velocity is 96 ft/sec. During these 3 sec the average velocity is $(96 + 0)/2 = 48$ ft/sec. Similarly, if an automobile is *uniformly accelerated* from 20 mi/hr to 60 mi/hr, the average velocity during the acceleration is 40 mi/hr. Equation (4.5) together with the equations defining average velocity and acceleration are the three fundamental equations for uniformly accelerated motion. If we measure displacement from the position of the body at $t = 0$,

Fig. 4.3. A feather and a steel ball fall with the same acceleration in a vacuum.

$$v_{av} = \frac{s}{t} \qquad (4.1)$$

$$a = \frac{v - v_0}{t} \tag{4.3}$$

$$v_{\text{av}} = \frac{v + v_0}{2} \tag{4.5}$$

These basic equations may be combined in many ways; two of the possibilities are of particular usefulness. They are

$$s = v_0 t + \tfrac{1}{2} a t^2 \tag{4.6}$$
$$v^2 = v_0^2 + 2as \tag{4.7}$$

Equation (4.6) may be obtained by combining Eqs. (4.1), (4.3) and (4.5) as follows:

$$s = v_{\text{av}} t \qquad\qquad \text{by Eq. (4.1)}$$

$$= \frac{v + v_0}{2} t \qquad\qquad \text{by use of Eq. (4.5)}$$

$$= \frac{v_0 + at + v_0}{2} t \qquad \text{by use of Eq. (4.3)}$$

$$= v_0 t + \tfrac{1}{2} a t^2$$

Equation (4.7) may be derived by multiplying $s = [(v + v_0)/2]t$ by $a = (v - v_0)/t$ which gives $as = (v^2 - v_0^2)/2$ or $2as = v^2 - v_0^2$.

In the relations developed above, it is important to observe that s is the displacement of the body and not the total distance traversed. For example, if we throw a body up into the air with a speed of 96 ft/sec and ask what the displacement is at the end of 5 sec, the relations above will

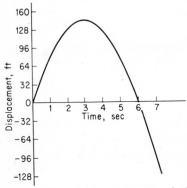

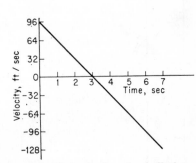

Fig. 4.4. The displacement of a body thrown upward at $t = 0$ with a velocity of 96 ft/sec as a function of time.

Fig. 4.5. The velocity of a ball thrown upward at $t = 0$ with a velocity of 96 ft/sec as a function of time.

provide the answer, which is 80 ft. Figure 4.4 shows the displacement measured upward as a function of time and the velocity of the ball is plotted as a function of time in Fig. 4.5. During the 5 sec the ball traverses a much greater distance. Indeed, at the end of 3 sec it is at the height of 144 ft.

A second caution has to do with the fact that displacement, velocity, and acceleration are *vector* quantities and due regard must be given to direction.   Which direction one elects to choose as positive is his own free choice, but once it is decided that upward is positive, any vector quantity which is downward must be given a negative sign.   If we return once more to the problem of throwing a ball upward with a speed of 96 ft/sec, we may decide to choose upward as the positive direction.   If we do, $v_0 = 96$ ft/sec, but $a = -32$ ft/sec^2.   An alternative choice would be to call downward positive.   Then v_0 becomes -96 ft/sec, and $a = +32$ ft/sec^2.

Although displacement, velocity, and acceleration are vector quantities, Eqs. (4.5) to (4.7) are *not* valid vector equations.   They apply only when s, v, v_0, and a are all along the same straight line.

Example.   A baseball is dropped from the top of the Washington Monument which is 555 ft high.   Find how long it takes to reach the ground, its velocity when it hits, and the average velocity during the fall.

Let us take downward as positive.   Then $a = 32$ ft/sec^2, $s = 555$ ft, and $v_0 = 0$.

By Eq. (4.6),
$$s = v_0 t + \tfrac{1}{2}at^2$$
$$555 \text{ ft} = 0 + \tfrac{1}{2}(32 \text{ ft/sec}^2)t^2$$
$$t^2 = \frac{555 \text{ ft}}{16 \text{ ft/sec}^2} = 34.7 \text{ sec}^2$$
$$t = 5.9 \text{ sec}$$

By Eq. (4.7),
$$v^2 = v_0^2 + 2as$$
$$= 0 + 2 \times 32 \text{ ft/sec}^2 \times 555 \text{ ft}$$
$$= 35{,}520 \text{ ft}^2/\text{sec}^2$$
$$v = 188 \text{ ft/sec}$$

By Eq. (4.1),
$$s = v_{av}t$$
$$555 \text{ ft} = v_{av} \times 5.9 \text{ sec}$$
$$v_{av} = 94 \text{ ft/sec}$$

Check: By Eq. (4.5),
$$v_{av} = \frac{v_0 + v}{2} = \frac{188}{2} \text{ ft/sec}$$

Example.   A ball is thrown upward from a bridge with a speed of 48 ft/sec.   It misses the bridge on the way down and lands in the water 160 ft below.   Find how long the ball rises, how high it goes, how long it is in the air, and its velocity when it strikes the water.

Let us take upward as positive.   Then $v_0 = 48$ ft/sec, and $a = -32$ ft/sec^2.   The ball rises until $v = 0$.

By Eq. (4.3),
$$a = \frac{v - v_0}{t}$$
$$-32 \text{ ft/sec}^2 = \frac{0 - 48 \text{ ft/sec}}{t}$$
$$t = \frac{48 \text{ ft/sec}}{32 \text{ ft/sec}^2} = 1.5 \text{ sec}$$

During this 1.5 sec

$$v_{av} = \frac{v + v_0}{2} = \frac{0 + 48}{2} = 24 \text{ ft/sec}$$

and
$$s = v_{av}t = 24 \text{ ft/sec} \times 1.5 \text{ sec} = 36 \text{ ft up}$$

By Eq. (4.6),
$$s = v_0 t + \tfrac{1}{2}at^2$$
$$-160 = 48t + \tfrac{1}{2}(-32)t^2 \quad \text{(Note } s \text{ is negative)}$$
$$t^2 - 3t - 10 = 0$$
$$t = +5 \text{ sec (or } -2 \text{ sec)}$$

(Clearly we want the positive answer here. The negative answer tells us how much before we threw the ball we would have had to fire it upward from the water to have it pass the bridge going 48 ft/sec at $t = 0$.)

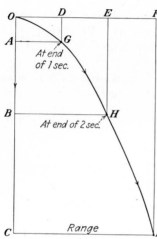

Fig. 4.6. Path of a body projected horizontally. The horizontal component of the velocity remains constant, while the vertical component increases uniformly.

By Eq. (4.3) $\qquad a = \dfrac{v - v_0}{t}$

$$-32 = \frac{v - 48}{5}$$

$$v = -112 \text{ ft/sec}$$

(The − minus sign means downward.)

Check: $\qquad s = v_{av}t = \dfrac{v + v_0}{2}t$

$$-160 = \frac{(-112 + 48)}{2}\,5$$

$$= -160 \text{ ft}$$

4.5. Path of a Projectile Fired Horizontally. If a body is projected horizontally from the top of a tower of height h (Fig. 4.6) with a velocity v_x, it continues to move with the same horizontal velocity it had at the beginning of its path (any decrease caused by the resistance of the air is neglected). At the same time the body falls because of the attraction of the earth.

Hence at any instant, the velocity of the projectile has two components: a horizontal component which remains constant and a downward component which increases with the time. The horizontal component of the velocity and the horizontal displacement are independent of whether or not the body is falling. Similarly, the vertical components of the displacement, velocity, and acceleration are independent of whether or not the body is moving horizontally.

If a bullet is fired horizontally with a velocity of 2,000 ft/sec, it falls 16 ft in 1 sec, 64 ft in 2 sec, and so forth, just exactly as would a bullet which was simply dropped from the end of the gun. In this case the vertical velocity of the body after t sec is given by $v_y = gt$. The horizontal component of the velocity remains constant, so that the resulting velocity, which is tangent to the path of the body, is $v = \sqrt{v_x^2 + v_y^2} = \sqrt{v_x^2 + g^2t^2}$. The horizontal displacement s_x of the body in time t is equal to $v_x t$, while the distance the body falls in the same time is $s_y = \frac{1}{2} gt^2$.

When an aircraft flying in a horizontal direction (Fig. 4.7) at height h above the ground releases a bomb, the bomb is moving forward with the same velocity as the airplane and travels forward with a constant horizontal velocity until it strikes a target. When the bomb is released, it has no downward velocity component. The downward velocity component increases in time because of the acceleration of gravity. The bomb does not strike the ground at a point directly below the release point. In order to hit the target, the bomb must be released some time before the aircraft is directly above the target. The time of release is determined by the velocity of the aircraft and its height above the ground.

Example. A ball is thrown horizontally with a velocity of 50 ft/sec from a tower 100 ft high. Find the time of flight, the horizontal range, and the speed of the ball just before it strikes the ground.

Let us choose downward as positive. For the vertical motion, $a_y = 32$ ft/sec², $v_{0y} = 0$, and $s_y = 100$ ft.

By Eq. (4.6),
$$s_y = v_{0y}t + \tfrac{1}{2}a_y t^2$$
$$100 = 0 + \tfrac{1}{2}(32)t^2$$
$$t = 2.5 \text{ sec}$$

The horizontal range s_x is the horizontal velocity (which is constant at 50 ft/sec) multiplied by the time of flight.

$$s_x = v_x t = 50 \times 2.5 = 125 \text{ ft}$$

Just before hitting, $v_x = 50$ ft/sec and, by Eq. (4.3),

$$v_y = a_y t = 80 \text{ ft/sec}$$
$$v = \sqrt{v_x^2 + v_y^2} = \sqrt{(80)^2 + (50)^2} = \sqrt{8{,}900} = 94.3 \text{ ft/sec}$$

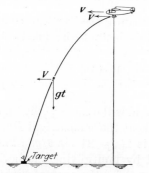

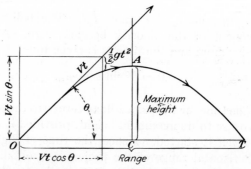

Fig. 4.7. The path of a bomb released from an aircraft flying horizontally.

Fig. 4.8. Path of a projectile fired at an angle θ to the horizontal.

4.6. Projectile Fired at an Angle with the Horizontal. If a projectile is fired at an angle θ with the horizontal, it traces out a parabolic path, as indicated in Fig. 4.8. A punted football, a batted baseball, or thrown basketball follows a similar path. In treating problems of this kind, we shall assume that the air friction is negligible and that the horizontal component of the velocity remains constant. This is an approximation which is not entirely justified in most practical situations. Everyone knows that a punter can kick a football farther with the wind than against it—clear evidence that air friction is not negligible. Similarly, air friction is important for golf balls, baseballs, and for projectiles of other kinds.

The first step in analyzing the motion of a projectile fired at an angle with the horizontal is to resolve the velocity of projection into vertical and horizontal components. If the velocity of projection V makes an angle θ with the horizontal, the horizontal component is $v_x = V \cos \theta$, the vertical component $v_y = V \sin \theta$. The horizontal velocity remains constant, but the vertical component changes. After time t the vertical

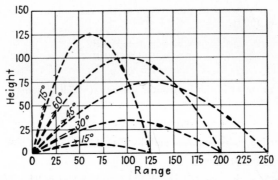

Fig. 4.9. Range of projectiles with the same initial speed but fired at different angles.

component $v_y = V \sin \theta - gt$. The ball rises until the vertical component of the velocity becomes zero. At this instant the height is maximum and the time t_m is given by

$$0 = V \sin \theta - gt_m, \quad \text{or} \quad t_m = \frac{V \sin \theta}{g}$$

The time for the projectile to return to the ground is the same as the time to rise to its maximum height, provided it ends at the same height from which it started. Hence, the time of flight is $2t_m = 2V \sin \theta/g$. The horizontal range of the projectile is obtained by multiplying the horizontal component of the initial velocity ($V \cos \theta$) by the time of flight. For a given initial speed, maximum range is obtained for $\theta = 45°$ if air friction is negligible (Fig. 4.9). Note that under these conditions the range is the same for any two complementary angles.

Figure 4.10 shows a V-2 rocket being accelerated upward by its rocket motor. Once the fuel is exhausted the rocket becomes a ballistic (freely falling) missile. Figure 4.11 plots the trajectory of a typical V-2 rocket flight.

Example. A punter kicks a football with a velocity of 80 ft/sec at an angle of 37° with the horizon. Find the time the ball rises, how high it goes, and the length of the kick (from punter's toe to receiver's hands).

The vertical component of the initial velocity is 80 sin 37° = 48 ft/sec and the horizontal component 80 cos 37° = 64 ft/sec. If we choose upward as positive for the vertical motion, v_{0y} = 48 ft/sec and a_y = −32 ft/sec². At the top of the path v_y = 0; thus, by Eq. (4.3),

$$-32 \frac{\text{ft}}{\text{sec}^2} = \frac{0 - 48 \text{ ft/sec}}{t}$$

$$t = 1.5 \text{ sec}$$

On the way up, the average velocity is $(48 + 0)/2$ = 24 ft/sec. Since $s_y = v_{av}t$, we have s_y = 24 ft/sec × 1.5 sec = 36 ft, which is how high the ball goes.

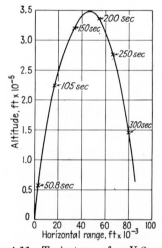

Fig. 4.10. A V-2 rocket fired at White Sands Proving Grounds. (*Photograph by U.S. Army Signal Corps.*)

Fig. 4.11. Trajectory of a V-2 rocket flight.

It takes as long for the ball to come down as it did to go up, so that the total time in the air is 3 sec. In this time the horizontal velocity is constant at 64 ft/sec, so that

$$s_x = 64 \text{ ft/sec} \times 3 \text{ sec} = 192 \text{ ft, or } 64 \text{ yd}$$

Example. A stone is thrown from the edge of a cliff with a velocity of 50 ft/sec at an angle of 30° above the horizontal. Four seconds later it strikes the ocean below. Find the height of the cliff above the ocean and the horizontal range of the stone.

The vertical component of the initial velocity is 50 sin 30° = 25 ft/sec upward. If we choose upward as positive, v_{0y} = +25 ft/sec and a_y = −32 ft/sec². The height of the cliff is then given by

$$s_y = v_{0y}t + \tfrac{1}{2}at^2$$
$$= (25 \times 4) + \tfrac{1}{2}(-32)16$$
$$= +100 - 256$$
$$= -156 \text{ ft}$$

The horizontal range s_x is

$$s_x = v_x t$$

since v_x is constant.

$$v_x = 50 \cos 30° = 43.3 \text{ ft/sec}$$
$$s_x = 43.3 \text{ ft/sec} \times 4 \text{ sec}$$
$$= 173.2 \text{ ft}$$

PROBLEMS

1. A uniformly accelerated body is moving with a velocity of 12 m/sec north and 5 sec later it has a velocity of 32 m/sec north. What is the acceleration?

Ans. 4 m/sec² north

2. A uniformly accelerated body is moving with a velocity of 12 m/sec east and 5 sec later it has a velocity of 32 m/sec west. What is the acceleration?

3. An airplane starting from rest has a uniform acceleration of 6 ft/sec² south. What is its velocity at the end of 1 min if this acceleration is maintained?

Ans. 360 ft/sec south

4. During an interval of 40 sec a train on a straight track changes its velocity from 15 to 25 mi/hr. Determine the acceleration and the average velocity during that period, assuming that the change occurred uniformly.

5. If a train has an acceleration of 3 ft/sec² in a direction opposite that of the motion of the train, how long will it require the train to stop if it is initially going 30 mi/hr (44 ft/sec)?

Ans. 14.7 sec

6. Find the time required for a locomotive traveling at the rate of 40 ft/sec to come to rest if the brakes are applied to produce a negative acceleration of 2 ft/sec².

7. A stone is dropped (starting from rest) from a high bridge. How far (in meters) does it fall in 10 sec? What velocity does it attain in that time?

Ans. 490 m; 98 m/sec downward

8. Solve Prob. 7 using English units.

9. An automobile is moving with a speed of 10 mi/hr at 10:00 A.M. one day. At 10:15 A.M. the same day, the car is moving in the same direction with a speed of 30 mi/hr. If the acceleration is constant, how far does the car travel during the 15-min interval? What is the magnitude of the acceleration? *Ans.* 5 miles; 1.33 mi/hr-min

10. A freight train starts from rest and travels 300 ft in 30 sec; find the acceleration, the average speed, and the final speed. (Assume constant acceleration.)

11. A ball is dropped from a bridge. If it requires 5 sec for the ball to strike the ground below, how high is the bridge?

Ans. 400 ft

12. The ball in Prob. 11 is thrown so that it has an initial velocity in the downward direction. It requires 4 sec for the ball to strike the ground. What must have been its initial velocity?

13. A ball thrown from a tower with an initial velocity of 30 ft/sec downward falls freely for 3 sec. (a) What is its speed at the end of this interval? (b) How far does it travel?

Ans. (a) 126 ft/sec; (b) 234 ft

14. A small object has an initial downward velocity of 12 m/sec. (a) What is its velocity if it falls freely for 7 sec? (b) What is the displacement from its initial position?

15. If a free object has an initial velocity of 12 m/sec upward, what is its velocity after 7 sec? What is the displacement from its initial position?

Ans. 56.6 m/sec downward; 156 m down

16. A balloon ascending with a velocity of 3.2 ft/sec releases a bag of sand at a height of 300 ft from the surface of the ground. Find the time for the bag to reach the earth.

17. A ball is thrown upward from the roof of a building. It has an initial velocity of 60 ft/sec. How high is the building if on its downward flight it just misses the thrower and falls to the ground 6 sec after it is thrown? With what speed does it strike the ground?

Ans. 216 ft; 132 ft/sec

18. How long does it take a freely falling body which starts from rest to fall 200 ft? What is its velocity when it has fallen that far?

19. A balloon is 1.5 km (approximately 1 mile) above the earth. How long does it require for an object dropped from the balloon to strike the earth? What is its velocity immediately before landing?   *Ans.* 17.5 sec; 172 m/sec downward

20. A sled is started with an initial velocity of 10 ft/sec down a hill on which it accelerates 8 ft/sec². How far will it go in 6 sec?

21. With what initial velocity will a body moving along a vertical line have to be thrown if after 5 sec it is 100 m below its starting place? *Ans.* 4.5 m/sec upward

22. With what initial velocity will a body moving along a vertical line have to be thrown if after 5 sec it is 100 ft below its starting place?

23. A ball is thrown straight up and returns to the level of the thrower in 3 sec. How high does the ball travel? What are its velocity and acceleration at the top of its flight? What are its initial and final velocities?

Ans. 36 ft; 0 ft/sec and 32 ft/sec² downward; 48 ft/sec upward and 48 ft/sec downward

24. The maximum deceleration which the tires of an automobile can produce on a certain pavement is 25 ft/sec². Find the minimum distance in which a car traveling 100 ft/sec (68 mi/hr) can be stopped, measuring from the point at which the brakes are first applied.

25. A naval aircraft is to be launched by a catapult from a carrier. If the catapult acts over a distance of 300 ft, find the minimum average acceleration which will give the aircraft a speed of 150 ft/sec at launching.   *Ans.* 37.5 ft/sec²

26. If an aircraft lands at a speed of 180 mi/hr (264 ft/sec) and the maximum deceleration which the braking system can produce is 6 ft/sec², find the minimum distance in which the plane can be stopped on level ground.

27. The speed of a baseball pitched by Bob Feller was once determined to be 145 ft/sec. What average acceleration must Feller have given the ball if this speed was produced over a distance of 8 ft?   *Ans.* 1,315 ft/sec²

28. In a football game a passer throws the ball with a speed of 60 ft/sec. If he produces speed by moving the ball over a distance of 4 ft along a straight line, find the average acceleration during the throwing operation.

29. When an aircraft lands on a carrier, it is arrested by a restraining cable which is engaged by a tail hook as the aircraft passes the cable. If the cable produces an average deceleration of 2.5 g's (80 ft/sec²), find how far the aircraft moves after it engages the cable at a speed of 120 ft/sec.   *Ans.* 90 ft

30. The deck of an aircraft carrier is 600 ft in length. Find the minimum average deceleration which an aircraft landing at a speed of 150 ft/sec must have if it is to stop in the length of the flight deck.

31. A streamlined body is dropped from an airplane flying horizontally 10,000 ft above level ground at the rate of 300 ft/sec. Ignoring the resistance due to air, what is the horizontal component of the displacement when the body strikes the ground?
Ans. 7,500 ft

32. A body is thrown in a horizontal direction from the top of a tower that is 300 ft high with a velocity of 60 ft/sec. Find its range.

33. If a baseball is thrown with an initial horizontal velocity of 100 ft/sec from the top of the Washington Monument which is about 555 ft high, how far from the base of the monument will the ball land?   *Ans.* 590 ft

34. A ball is projected upward from the bottom of a tower that is 400 ft high, and, at the same instant, another ball is dropped from the top of the same tower. If the balls meet at a point halfway between the top and the bottom of the tower, with what initial velocity was the ball projected upward?

35. A boy kicks a soccer ball off the ground, giving it a speed of 40 ft/sec at an angle of 37° with the horizontal.   Find how long the ball is in the air, how high it goes, and the horizontal distance it traverses before it strikes the ground   *Ans.* 1.5 sec; 9 ft; 48 ft

36. If the ball in Prob. 35 had been kicked with a speed of 40 ft/sec at an angle of 53° with the horizontal, find the time in the air, how high the ball went, and the distance it traversed.

37. A ball is batted so that its initial velocity makes an angle of 45° with the level ground.   If the horizontal component of the initial velocity is 80 ft/sec, determine the distance from the batter to the place where the ball is caught.   *Ans.* 400 ft

38. A ball is thrown at an angle of 45° with the horizontal.   Its initial speed is 64 ft/sec.   Find the time which will elapse before the ball returns to the ground, if it is assumed that the ground is level.

39. A tourist stands at the top of a canyon through which a river is flowing.   If the river is 1,600 ft below and 500 ft to one side of the tourist, with what initial velocity in a horizontal direction toward the nearest part of the river would he need to throw a stone so that it would land in the water?   *Ans.* 50 ft/sec

40. With what speed would a projectile have to be fired from the surface of the earth at an angle of 45° in order that it land 5,000 miles away?   (Assume that the earth is flat, that the acceleration due to gravity is 32 ft/sec² throughout the path, and that air resistance is negligible.   Of course, none of these assumptions is warranted for the problem in question.   What is the direction of the error introduced by each of these assumptions?)

41. From a bridge, a stone is thrown upward with an initial velocity of 29.4 m/sec. On falling, the stone misses the bridge and falls into the river 10 sec after being thrown.   (*a*) How high does the stone rise?   (*b*) How far is the bridge above the river?
Ans. (*a*) 44.1 m; (*b*) 196 m

42. Find the range of a shell fired from a cannon with a muzzle velocity of 1,200 ft/ sec, when the shell is fired at an angle of 30° with the horizontal.

CHAPTER 5 Important

Force and Motion

5.1. Newton's First Law of Motion. It is a familiar fact that the motion of a body is intimately related to the forces which act upon it. However, for many centuries the exact way in which force and motion are related eluded the philosphers who speculated about the relationship. Aristotle expressed the idea that a body in motion comes to rest unless it has a force acting upon it continuously. For centuries men wondered what it was that pushed the planets around in the sky and what made the moon go around the earth. Although brilliant minds worked on the problem, no consistent and acceptable relationship between force and motion was established until the seventeenth century.

Galileo (1564–1642) performed a number of careful experiments on the motions of bodies and it is largely to his work that we owe the equations of kinematics in the last chapter. Galileo studied accelerated motion both by dropping bodies and by rolling balls up and down inclined planes. He observed that, when friction was very small, a ball would roll for a great distance on a horizontal plane without stopping. Eventually, he became convinced that a ball on a perfectly frictionless horizontal plane would persist forever in its motion at constant speed. This revolutionary idea was one which was to prove most fruitful in developing an understanding of motion. Galileo discovered that bodies do not fall with constant speed; rather they have a *constant acceleration*. This suggested that the pull of the earth produced not the motion itself, but the change in the state of motion.

Isaac Newton (1642–1727) accepted Galileo's conclusions and formulated this idea as his first law of motion, which may be stated in the form:

Every body continues in its state of rest or of uniform velocity in a straight line unless it is compelled to change that state by the application of some unbalanced external force.

No actual body is ever completely free from external forces, but there are situations in which it is possible to make the resultant force approximately zero. In those cases we find that the body behaves in accord

53

with the first law of motion.   Since we can never eliminate friction completely in our experiments and since our efforts to compensate for it are imperfect, we must recognize that Newton's first law is an idealization. However, it is an idealization which provided the key for building a consistent and understandable theory of motion.   There are, of course, many ways in which this great principle may be enunciated.   Another statement is the following:

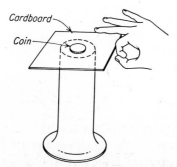

A body at rest remains at rest, and a body in motion remains in motion with constant velocity along the same straight line unless acted upon by some external unbalanced force.

Because a body at rest remains at rest in the absence of an unbalanced force, we can snap a card from under a coin, pull a tablecloth from under a glass, or snap a nickel under a pile of nickels without upsetting the pile (Fig. 5.1), so long as we do not bring any substantial frictional forces into play.   We depend on Newton's first law to put the head of a hammer onto the handle (Fig. 5.2).

Fig. 5.1. A body at rest remains at rest unless acted upon by some external unbalanced force.

5.2. Inertia.   In Newton's first law of motion an important property of matter appears.   It is known as inertia—that property of matter by which it maintains a constant velocity in the absence of an unbalanced external force.   When an automobile is suddenly stopped, the passengers obey Newton's first law and continue in motion with constant velocity until some external force changes their state of motion. Seat belts in an automobile can provide such an external force—one much preferred to that exerted by the windshield or dashboard.   A man running on an icy sidewalk finds it difficult to stop suddenly because friction is inadequate to provide the necessary external force. When a baseball leaves the pitcher's hand, it continues to move with es-

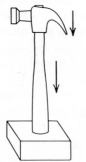

Fig. 5.2. A body in motion remains in motion with constant velocity unless acted upon by some external unbalanced force.

Fig. 5.3. When the downward force is slowly increased, the string breaks above the ball; but if a sudden force is applied, the lower string breaks.

sentially constant velocity until it reaches the catcher's glove.   No force is required to keep it moving.   Of course, the ball is slowed down slightly by air resistance and is pulled toward the earth by its weight.

If a heavy ball is suspended from a string (Fig. 5.3) and an identical string is fastened below, the upper string breaks under a slowly increasing steady pull from below. But if a sudden jerk is applied to the lower string, it breaks. The inertia of the ball is so great that it isolates the upper string from the jerk.

All matter has inertia. The amount of inertia is not, however, the same for all bodies. The concept of mass was introduced by Newton as a measure of inertia. At any point on the earth the inertia of any body is proportional to its weight, but if the body were in interplanetary space where it no longer had observable weight, it would still have inertia. It would still take the same force of toe on ball to give a football a specified acceleration. If the football were filled with mercury, its inertia would be greatly increased. To kick such a football (Fig. 5.4) would be just as painful in a rocket ship as on the earth, even though the mercury-filled ball might have no weight.

Fig. 5.4. It would be just as painful to kick a mercury-filled football in a rocket ship where it has negligible weight as on the earth. Inertia is independent of location.

5.3. Newton's Second Law. If no external unbalanced force acts upon a body, it maintains a constant velocity. What happens if there is an external unbalanced force? To answer this question quantitatively, let us consider a set of idealized experiments.

1. Suppose that we have a perfectly level and frictionless table along which we can accelerate a mass of several kilograms. (We could make the friction very small by using small wheels with roller bearings.) If we

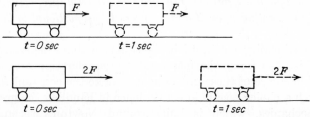

Fig. 5.5. The acceleration of a given body is directly proportional to the unbalanced force acting on the body.

now take an accurately calibrated spring balance and exert a net force **F** on the mass, a certain acceleration is produced. Let us measure this acceleration. Next, let us exert exactly twice as great an unbalanced force and again measure the acceleration (Fig. 5.5). We find the acceleration to be exactly double the first acceleration. If we again double the unbalanced force, the acceleration doubles once more and is thus four times the first acceleration. By measuring the acceleration for a large number of different unbalanced forces, we find that (within experimental error) the *acceleration* of our chosen mass *is directly proportional to the unbalanced force* **F** and its direction is that of the unbalanced force.

2. Next suppose that we choose an unbalanced force of 0.1 kg-wt and measure the acceleration it produces in a mass of 1 kg. Then let us keep the force constant, but make the mass accelerated 2 kg (Fig. 5.6). We find the acceleration is half as great as it was the first time. If we increase the mass accelerated to a 3 kg and measure the acceleration, we find it is one-third as great. If this experiment is performed for a number

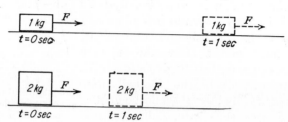

Fig. 5.6. For a given unbalanced force the acceleration is inversely proportional to the mass accelerated.

of different masses, we find that the data is consistent with the idea that *the acceleration* **a** *is inversely proportional to the mass accelerated.*

If we combine the results of these two series of experiments, we conclude that

$$\mathbf{a} = \frac{k\mathbf{F}}{m} \tag{5.1}$$

This equation is a statement (in restricted form) of Newton's second law of motion. *The acceleration of a body is directly proportional to the unbalanced force acting upon it and is inversely proportional to the mass of the body.*

The proportionality constant k in the equation above depends upon the units in which the force, the mass, and the acceleration are measured. By a suitable choice of these units one can make the constant k equal to unity. Such a choice results in convenience in handling the great structure of mechanics, which is built around Newton's second law of motion. Unfortunately, many different schemes of making $k = 1$ have been devised and have had some use. Each has certain advantages and certain disadvantages. In our work with Newton's second law and its consequences, we shall use two of the many possible choices—one for working in the metric system and a very different one for the English system.

5.4. The Newton. In the metric system we have already defined the fundamental units of mass (the kilogram), length (the meter), and time (the second). We shall retain these basic units. In order to be able to write Newton's second law in the form

$$\mathbf{F} = m\mathbf{a} \qquad (5.2)$$

we define a new unit of force which we call the *newton*. *The newton is that force which will produce an acceleration of one meter per second per second in a mass of one kilogram.*

The newton is the basic force unit in the mks system of units; its value is about 0.225 lb. One kilogram-weight corresponds to 9.80665 newtons. In dealing with tiny forces in the metric system of units, the dyne is often used; 1 dyne* is equal to 10^{-5} newton. The newton is a so-called absolute unit of force because its definition is made without any reference to the earth or its pull. From $\mathbf{F} = m\mathbf{a}$, we see that 1 newton is equivalent to 1 kg-m/sec².

Example. An automobile has a mass of 1,600 kg. Find what force is required to give this automobile an acceleration of 1.2 m/sec² if there are frictional retarding forces totaling 200 newtons.

By Newton's second law,

$$F = ma$$
$$= 1{,}600 \text{ kg} \times 1.2 \text{ m/sec}^2$$
$$= 1{,}920 \text{ newtons}$$

This gives us the *net*, or unbalanced, force on the automobile. The total force is

$$1{,}920 + 200 = 2{,}120 \text{ newtons}$$

5.5. Gravitational Units of Force. For the British engineering system of units an entirely different approach has been adopted. The constant k in Newton's second law of motion is made equal to unity by choosing not a new unit of force, but a new unit of mass.†   In this system the basic unit chosen for acceleration is the foot per second per second and the basic force unit is the pound, which is the gravitational attraction of the earth for a 1-lb mass at a place where the acceleration due to gravity has the value 32.17398 ft/sec².   This force unit is known as a *gravitational unit*, since it is defined in terms of the pull of the earth on a standard object.   Once we have chosen such a force unit and acceleration unit, the only way we can make k equal to unity is by choosing a new unit of mass. This unit, called the *slug*, is defined as follows: *One slug is the mass of a body which experiences an acceleration of one foot per second per second when acted upon by an unbalanced external force of one pound.*

* The dyne was originally defined as the force required to produce an acceleration of one centimeter per second per second in a mass of one gram.

† An alternative method of handling the British system of units is to retain the pound as a unit of mass and define a new unit of force called the *poundal*. The poundal is that force which produces an acceleration of one foot per second per second in a mass of one pound.

A force of 1 lb will give a 1-lb mass an acceleration of 32.174 ft/sec² and it will give a one-slug mass an acceleration of 1 ft/sec². Therefore, the slug has a mass slightly more than 32 times that of the standard pound mass. In the British engineering system, forces are measured in pounds, masses in slugs, and accelerations in feet per second per second.

When the unbalanced force acting on a body is its weight $\mathbf{W}$, the resulting acceleration is $\mathbf{g}$, the acceleration due to gravity. For this case $\mathbf{F} = m\mathbf{a}$ becomes

$$\mathbf{W} = m\mathbf{g} \tag{5.3}$$

If we divide Eq. (5.2) by Eq. (5.3), we obtain $\mathbf{F}/\mathbf{W} = \mathbf{a}/\mathbf{g}$, or

$$\mathbf{F} = \frac{W}{g}\, \mathbf{a} \tag{5.4}$$

a form in which it is often convenient to put Newton's second law.

Example. A 160-lb man stands in an elevator. Find the force exerted on the man by the floor of the elevator (a) when the elevator has an upward acceleration of 4 ft/sec², (b) when the elevator has a downward acceleration of 4 ft/sec², and (c) when the elevator has a constant downward velocity of 4 ft/sec.

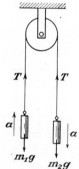

(a) $F = ma = \dfrac{W}{g}\, a$

$$F = \frac{160\ \text{lb}}{32\ \text{ft/sec}^2} \times 4\ \text{ft/sec}^2 = 20\ \text{lb}$$

This is the *unbalanced force* on the man. If E is the force exerted by the elevator, $F = E - W$, $20 = E - 160$ or $E = 180$ lb upward.

(b) The unbalanced force is now 20 lb downward so that E is 20 lb less than W.

$$E = 160 - 20 = 140\ \text{lb}$$

(c) If the velocity is constant, $a = 0$ and the unbalanced force is zero. The elevator exerts a force just equal to the man's weight.

$$E = W = 160\ \text{lb}$$

Fig. 5.7. At-wood's machine.

5.6. Applications of Newton's Second Law. Consider two masses m_1 and m_2 (Fig. 5.7) suspended by a flexible string that passes over a weightless pulley. Such an arrangement is known as Atwood's machine. Assume that m_2 is greater than m_1. To find the acceleration of the system and the tension in the string, let T be the tension and a the acceleration of the system. Applying Newton's second law of motion to each mass separately, we have

$$m_2g - T = m_2a$$
$$T - m_1g = m_1a$$

If $m_1 = 1.2$ kg and $m_2 = 1.8$ kg, these equations become

$$(1.8 \times 9.8) - T = 1.8a$$
$$T - (1.2 \times 9.8) = 1.2a$$

lbs = forces
kg -- mass

If we add the second equation to the first, we have

$$17.64 - 11.76 = 3a$$
$$a = 1.96 \text{ m/sec}$$
whence $$T = 14.1 \text{ newtons}$$

As a second illustration of the application of Newton's second law of motion, consider a mass M sliding along a smooth horizontal table (Fig. 5.8) with a second mass m fastened to it by means of a flexible string that passes over a weightless pulley.

Let T be the tension in the string and a be the acceleration of the system. Applying Newton's second law of motion to each mass separately, we have

$$T = Ma$$
$$mg - T = ma$$

If M weighs 8 lb and m 2 lb, these equations become

$$T = \tfrac{8}{32}a$$
$$2 - T = \tfrac{2}{32}a$$

from which $a = 6.4$ ft/sec² and $T = 1.6$ lb.

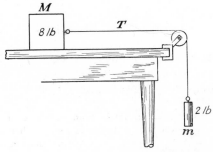

Fig. 5.8. Newton's second law of motion applies to the system as a whole and also to each of the masses independently.

5.7. Newton's Third Law of Motion.

When you hold this book in your hand, you exert an upward force *on the book*. At the same time the book exerts a downward force *on your hand*. These two forces are exactly equal and opposite. The wheels of an automobile in motion push backward on the road, but the road pushes forward on the wheels with an equal force. *Whenever one body exerts a force upon a second body, the second body exerts an equal and opposite force on the first.* This is a statement of *Newton's third law of motion.*

Whenever a force acts *upon* a body, there always exists an equal and opposite force exerted *by* this body (Figs. 5.9 to 5.11). If, for example, a

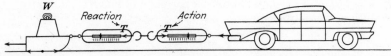

Fig. 5.9. Action and reaction are equal. This is Newton's third law of motion.

man pulls on a rope with a force of 40 lb, the rope pulls back on the man's hand with a force of 40 lb. A train pulls back the locomotive with a force which is exactly as great as the force which the locomotive exerts forward on the train. A helicopter pushes downward on the air with a force equal to that which the air exerts upward on the helicopter. The sun pulls on the earth and the earth pulls on the sun with equal and opposite forces.

Newton stated his third law in the form: *"to every action there is an equal and contrary reaction."* Here the term "action" is used to imply force.

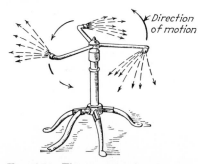

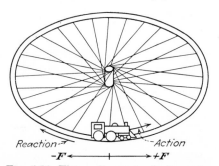

Fig. 5.10. The water pushes forward on the nozzle with a force exactly equal and opposite to the one which the nozzle exerts on the water.

Fig. 5.11. The engine pushes back on the track with a force equal to that with which the track pushes forward on the engine.

5.8. Momentum and Newton's Second Law. In Sec. 5.3 we introduced Newton's second law in a somewhat restricted form. In order to express this law in a more general form, we introduce linear *momentum.* The linear *momentum* of a body *is the product of the mass and the linear velocity.* Momentum is a *vector* quantity which has the direction of the velocity.

Example. A fullback with a mass of 90 kg is running with a velocity of 8 m/sec due north. Find his momentum.

$$\text{Momentum} = \text{mass} \times \text{velocity}$$
$$= 90 \text{ kg} \times 8 \text{ m/sec north} = 720 \text{ kg-m/sec north}$$

A force changes the momentum of a free mass upon which it acts. The rate at which the momentum of the body changes is directly proportional to the force. Indeed, Newton's second law may be written in the form: *The time rate of change of the momentum of a body is proportional to the net force acting upon the body and is in the direction of this resultant force.* As an equation, we may write

$$\mathbf{F} = \frac{\Delta(m\mathbf{v})}{\Delta t} \qquad (5.5)$$

If we are dealing with a single simple mass and a velocity small compared with that of light, the mass is constant, and we may write the equation above $\mathbf{F} = m \, \Delta\mathbf{v}/\Delta t = m\mathbf{a}$. However, at a velocity near the speed of light, the mass of a body changes with velocity, and we must use Newton's law in its more general form [Eq. (5.5)]. Similarly, if we consider the case in which a sailor pulls a rope along the deck from a large coil, the mass in motion is constantly increasing and the problem of calculating the acceleration again requires the use of Newton's law in the form $\mathbf{F} = \Delta(m\mathbf{v})/\Delta t$.

One of the most important situations in which the mass of an accelerated object changes is that of rocket propulsion. The rocket carries its own fuel and burns it rapidly. As the hot gases are exhausted, the mass of the rocket decreases. If the thrust of the rocket motor remains constant, the acceleration of the rocket increases as the mass decreases.

5.9. Impulse and Momentum. Suppose that an unbalanced force $\mathbf{F}$ acts on an automobile for a time t sec. By Newton's second law

$$\mathbf{F} = \frac{\Delta(m\mathbf{v})}{\Delta t} = \frac{m(\mathbf{v} - \mathbf{v}_0)}{t}$$

from which
$$Ft = m\mathbf{v} - m\mathbf{v}_0 \qquad (5.6)$$

The right side of this equation is just the momentum at time t minus the initial momentum, or the change in momentum of the automobile. The quantity on the left side of the equation, *the product of the force and the time the force acts, is called the impulse.* From Eq. (5.6) we see that *the impulse is equal to the change in the momentum.*

In many types of collisions the force acting on a body is not constant, but varies during the reaction. For example, when a football is kicked off, the toe of the kicker exerts zero force on the ball until it comes in contact and the force increases rapidly as the ball is distorted (Fig. 5.12). As the ball returns to its initial shape, the force diminishes. A picture of the force as a function of time might be that

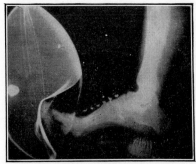

Fig. 5.12. High-speed radiograph of a kicked football. (*Courtesy of C. M. Slack, Westinghouse Electric Corp.*)

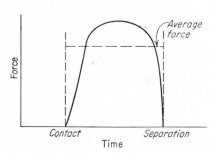

Fig. 5.13. Schematic diagram of the force on the football of Fig. 5.12 as a function of time.

of Fig. 5.13. In this case the impulse is given by the area under the force-as-a-function-of-time curve. Alternatively, we can express the impulse as the product of the average force and the time. The average force is indicated by the dashed line of the figure.

In many situations the force varies so rapidly that it is not practical to know what the force is at any particular instant, but the change in the momentum of the body is equal to the total impulse. If we know how long the impulsive force acts, we can calculate the average value of the force even though we cannot know the instantaneous value, i.e., the exact shape of the force curve. We have impulsive forces in play when a pitched ball is hit by a bat, when a bullet is fired from a rifle, and when two billiard balls collide.

Example. A baseball of mass 0.145 kg is thrown by the pitcher with a speed of 30 m/sec. The bat is in contact with the ball for 0.01 sec and gives it a speed of 40 m/sec in a direction straight toward the pitcher. Find the impulse and the average value of the force.

$$
\begin{aligned}
\text{Impulse} &= \text{change in momentum} \\
&= 0.145[30 - (-40)] \\
&= 10.1 \text{ kg-m/sec} \\
&= 10.1 \text{ newton-sec} \\
F_{av} &= \text{impulse/time} \\
&= 10.1 \text{ newton-sec}/0.01 \text{ sec} \\
&= 1{,}010 \text{ newtons}
\end{aligned}
$$

5.10. The Conservation of Momentum. Consider a freely suspended rifle, cocked and ready to fire (Fig. 5.14). When the trigger is pulled, a force F_b is exerted on the bullet. By Newton's third law, if the gun exerts a force F_b on the bullet, the bullet exerts an equal and opposite force F_g on the gun. We may therefore write $F_b = -F_g$. By Newton's

Fig. 5.14. The momentum of the system bullet plus rifle is zero before the trigger is pulled. The momentum given the bullet by the charge is equal and opposite to that given the rifle, so that the resultant momentum remains zero.

second law $F_b = m_b v_b/t$ and similarly $F_g = M_g V_g/t$, since the initial velocities were both zero. Clearly, the forces F_b and F_g act for exactly the same length of time and the impulses for the gun and the bullet are equal in magnitude and opposite in direction. Therefore,

$$
m_b v_b = -M_g V_g
$$

The momentum gained by the bullet in one direction is equal in magnitude and opposite in direction to that received by the gun. We recall that momentum is a vector quantity. If we wish to add these two, we must do it geometrically. The resultant of the momenta is zero, just as it was before the trigger was pulled. The momentum of the system composed of the gun and the bullet has not changed.

It follows directly from Newton's second and third laws of motion that *If two or more bodies interact, the momentum after the interaction is equal to the momentum before the interaction.*

This important principle is known as the *law of conservation of momentum.* It may be stated in the form: *The total momentum of any system of bodies is unchanged by any actions which occur between the different members of the system.*

When a battleship fires a broadside, the shells are given a large momentum in one direction. The battleship recoils with an equal momentum in the opposite direction. When two billiard balls collide, momentum is transferred from one ball to the other, but the resultant momentum after the collision is equal to the momentum before the collision. When two football players collide in mid-air, the law of conservation of momentum determines which way they fall.

Consider one aircraft chasing another of about the same maximum speed. If the pursuing craft opens fire, the bullets are given forward momentum and the plane loses an equal momentum. On the other hand, when the pursued craft opens fire, the bullets have momentum toward the rear and this aircraft gains speed.

Example. An 80-kg halfback dives over the line of scrimmage at a velocity of 7 m/sec. He is met in mid-air by a 100-kg linebacker going 5.4 m/sec in the opposite direction. If they fall together, find their velocity.

$$\text{Momentum before} = \text{momentum after}$$
$$(80 \text{ kg} \times 7 \text{ m/sec}) - (100 \text{ kg} \times 5.4 \text{ m/sec}) = (180 \text{ kg})v$$
$$20 \text{ kg-m/sec} = (180 \text{ kg})v$$
$$v = {}^{20}\!/_{180} = 0.11 \text{ m/sec in direction of halfback}$$

PROBLEMS

(Use the approximate values $g = 32$ ft/sec² $= 9.8$ m/sec² for these problems.)

1. What resultant force is required to accelerate a 3,200-lb automobile 5 ft/sec²?
Ans. 500 lb

2. What resultant force is required to give an airplane of mass 20,000 kg an acceleration of 2 m/sec²?

3. What total force is required to produce an upward acceleration of 3 m/sec² in a mass of 5 kg? *Ans.* 64 newtons

4. What retarding force must be exerted on a 100-lb body to permit it to fall with an acceleration of 8 ft/sec²?

5. A man weighing 160 lb slides down a rope that can sustain only 145 lb. What is the smallest acceleration the man can have without breaking the rope? *Ans.* 3 ft/sec²

6. A man weighing 150 lb slides down a rope that serves as a fire escape. The maximum force that can be applied to the rope without breaking it is 100 lb. Find the least acceleration that the man can have without breaking the rope.

7. An elevator and its load weighs 6 tons. It is suspended by means of a cable that will sustain a load of 8 tons. What is the greatest upward acceleration that the elevator may be given without breaking the cable? *Ans.* 10.7 ft/sec²

8. A porter carries a bag weighing 16 lb into an elevator. What force must he exert on the bag in order to hold it when the car is started with an upward acceleration of 4 ft/sec²?

9. A string that can sustain a tension of 25 newtons is fastened to a mass of 2 kg lying on a smooth horizontal table. What is the largest acceleration that can be imparted to the mass without breaking the string? *Ans.* 12.5 m/sec²

10. If the cable which supports an elevator exerts an upward force of 4.6 tons on an elevator which weighs 5 tons, what is the acceleration of the elevator? Neglect frictional forces.

11. The car of an elevator and its contents exert a force of 3 tons on the cables when at rest. How great is the force when an upward acceleration of 4 ft/sec² is being given to the elevator? when the acceleration is numerically the same but downward?
Ans. 6,750 lb; 5,250 lb

12. A man weighing 160 lb is ascending in an elevator that has an upward acceleration of 6 ft/sec². What force is exerted on the floor of the elevator?

13. Two bodies are suspended by means of a flexible string that passes over a weightless pulley. If one body weighs 18 lb and the other 14 lb, what is the acceleration of the system and the tension in the string?   *Ans.* 4 ft/sec²; 15.75 lb

14. A baseball has a mass of 0.145 kg. Find the resultant force required to give this baseball an acceleration of 200 m/sec².

15. A football has a mass of 0.42 kg. What unbalanced force is required to produce an acceleration of 150 m/sec² on this football?   *Ans.* 63 newtons

16. A catapult for launching aircraft from a carrier produces an acceleration of 3 *g*'s (96 ft/sec²) on a 64,000-lb aircraft. Find the unbalanced force required to produce this acceleration.

17. A large helicopter weighs 16,000 lb. Find the total force exerted on the helicopter by the air when it has an upward acceleration of 2 ft/sec². What is the force when the helicopter has a constant upward velocity of 4 ft/sec?

Ans. 17,000 lb; 16,000 lb

18. If the frictional forces on a 3,200-lb automobile add up to 100 lb retarding force, what would be the deceleration of the car coasting to a stop on a level road? How far would it coast from an initial speed of 50 ft/sec?

19. Find how many seconds it would take an unbalanced thrust of 10,000 lb to give a 50,000-lb rocket a speed of 600 mi/hr (880 ft/sec), assuming that the mass of the rocket is not changed significantly during this period.   *Ans.* 138 sec

20. A force of 6 newtons acts continuously on a mass of 15 kg during a period of 2 min. What velocity does the body acquire if it was originally at rest?

21. An elevator weighs 1,500 lb. A counterweight of 1,500 lb is attached to it; the cable between the two passes over a pulley. A person weighing 200 lb steps onto the elevator. If all other forces are neglected, what would be the acceleration of the system?   *Ans.* 2 ft/sec²

22. A 20-lb body rests on a smooth table. It is fastened by means of a flexible cord which passes over a frictionless pulley to a weight of 3 lb which hangs freely. Find the acceleration of the system.

23. A 6-kg block rests on a smooth table. A string passes over a pulley and a 3-kg body is attached at *F* as indicated in Fig. 5.15. (*a*) What is the acceleration of the

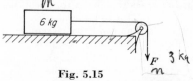

Fig. 5.15

block? (*b*) What is the acceleration of the block if a person pulls on the string at *F* with a force of 3 kg-wt? (*c*) In each case what is the tension in the string?

Ans. 3.27 m/sec²; 4.90 m/sec²; 2 kg-wt; 3 kg-wt

24. A 10-lb body rests on a smooth horizontal table. It is fastened to another body of weight 6 lb by means of a flexible string that passes over a weightless pulley. What is the acceleration of the system and the tension in the string?

25. Each car of a toy train weighs 2 lb. The engine weighs 6 lb. In a train containing four cars and the engine, the engine pulls on the first car with a force of 1.4 lb. If the acceleration of the train is 4 ft/sec², with what force does the first car pull on the engine? What is the unbalanced force on the first car? What is the total frictional force on the four cars?   *Ans.* 1.4 lb; 0.25 lb; 0.4 lb

26. A wire will sustain a maximum tension of 250 lb without breaking. It is used to impart an acceleration to a 180-lb body.   If there are no other forces acting on the body, what is the maximum acceleration that can be produced without breaking the wire?

27. A mass of 18 kg rests on a smooth inclined plane that makes an angle of 30° with the horizontal.   It is fastened to a mass of 12 kg by means of a flexible string that passes over a weightless pulley.   Find the acceleration of the system and the tension in the string.   *Ans.* 0.98 m/sec²; 106 newtons

28. The brakes of an automobile that weighs 4,000 lb can exert a retarding force of 600 lb.   Find the distance the car will move before stopping, if it is traveling at the rate of 40 mi/hr when the brakes are applied.

29. A box resting on a plane inclined 30° with the horizontal slides a distance of 4.5 ft down the plane.   How long does it take the box to travel this distance if friction is neglected?   *Ans.* 0.75 sec.

30. A bullet of mass 25 g is projected from a gun of mass 15 kg with a velocity of 350 m/sec.   What is the velocity with which the gun recoils?

31. A 2-g bullet is fired from a 3-kg rifle with a velocity of 300 m/sec north.   Find the momentum of the bullet and the recoil velocity of the rifle, assuming that no other bodies are involved.   *Ans.* 0.60 kg-m/sec north; 0.2 m/sec south

32. Find the recoil velocity of a rifle weighing 9 lb when it projects a 0.5-oz bullet with a velocity of 2,400 ft/sec.

33. A machine gun fires eight bullets per second into a target.   The mass of each bullet is 3 g and the velocity 1,000 m/sec.   Find the average force required to hold the gun in position.   *Ans.* 24 newtons

34. A 160-lb swimmer dives from a 240-lb rowboat initially at rest.   If the swimmer leaves the boat with a horizontal speed of 6 ft/sec, find the recoil speed of the boat, neglecting the transfer of momentum to the water.

35. A pitcher exerts an average resultant force of 5 lb for 0.12 sec on a baseball weighing 0.32 lb.   Find the average acceleration, the impulse, the speed of the ball, and the magnitude of the momentum.

Ans. 500 ft/sec², 0.6 lb-sec; 60 ft/sec; 0.6 slug-ft/sec

36. An 0.32-lb baseball approaches a batter with a speed of 100 ft/sec.   The batter lines the ball directly back at the pitcher with a speed of 150 ft/sec.   Find the change in momentum and the impulse.   If bat and ball were in contact for 0.01 sec, find the average force exerted on the ball during this period.

CHAPTER 6

Uniform Circular Motion
and Gravitation

6.1. Ptolemy's Theory of the Universe. When Newton formulated his laws of motion, he was particularly interested in explaining the movements of the moon, the planets, and other heavenly bodies. These motions had fascinated men since the beginning of history. In Greek mythology the daily journey of the sun was attributed to the god Apollo driving a flaming chariot across the sky. In the third century B.C. Ptolemy developed the theory that the stars, the sun, the moon, and the

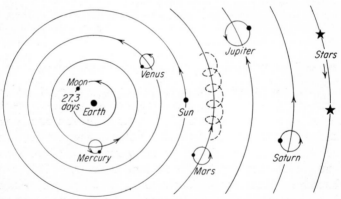

Fig. 6.1. In the Ptolemaic system the earth is the center of the universe.

planets all revolved about the earth (Fig. 6.1). In his theory one could think of the stars as mounted on a great transparent sphere which rotated at a constant rate around the earth at its center. The sun and the moon were mounted on similar, but smaller, spheres which rotated about the earth at rates different from that of the stars. To explain the motions of the planets (*planet* means "wanderer"), which move most of the time in the same direction as the stars but occasionally retrogress, the Ptolemaic theory assumed that each planet moved in a small circular path about a center, which in turn followed a much larger circular path about the earth. Small circles superimposed on a large circle were called *epi-cycles*.

6.2. Copernicus, Galileo, Brahe, and Kepler.   In 1543, Nicholas Copernicus, a Polish monk, published the results of some 35 years of patient study in a celebrated book which showed that the need for epi-cyclic paths of planets and many of the other complications of the Ptolemaic theory disappeared if one took the sun as the center of the universe (Fig. 6.2).   The idea of a heliocentric (*helios* means "sun") system as opposed to the Ptolemaic geocentric (*geos* means "earth") system was a great stimulus to the field of astrophysics.   Supporting evidence for the Copernican theory grew over the next century.

Galileo constructed a telescope shortly after a Dutch spectacle maker discovered in 1608 that he could use two spectacle lenses to form an

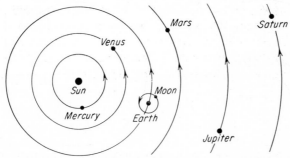

Fig. 6.2. In the Copernican system the sun is the center of the solar system.

enlarged image of distant objects.   With his telescope Galileo dis-covered four of Jupiter's moons, that there were mountains on the surface of the moon, that Saturn had rings, and that the sun had dark spots moving across its disk which gave evidence that the sun itself was in rota-tion.   Some of these discoveries were readily explained on the basis of the Copernican theory, but not by the Ptolemaic theory.   Galileo became one of the major supporters of Copernicus, but he soon suffered persecu-tion and imprisonment because his views differed from those held by certain high officials of the church.

The Danish astronomer Tycho Brahe (1546–1609) devoted most of his professional life to making extraordinarily accurate measurements on the positions of stars and planets.   His data were analyzed by the mathe-matical physicist Johan Kepler (1571–1630).   Kepler found that the motions of the planets did not always agree exactly with those predicted by the Copernican theory of circular paths.   After many years of work he was able to show that the motions of the planets could be understood in terms of three assumptions, which we now know as *Kepler's laws*.

1. The orbit of each planet is an ellipse with the sun at one focus.

2. The speed of the planet varies in such a way that the line joining the planet and the sun sweeps out equal areas in equal times (Fig. 6.3).

3. The cubes of the semimajor axes of the elliptical orbits are proportional to the squares of the times for the planets to make a complete revolution about the sun.

Although the general motion of the planets about the sun occurs in elliptic orbits, the motion of the earth around the sun and of several of the other planets can be reasonably well described by circular orbits, as can the motion of the moon around the earth. Since the geometrical complexity of circular motion is substantially less than that of general elliptic motion, and since the physical ideas involved in both types are equivalent, we shall focus our attention on circular motion and leave elliptic

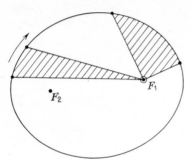

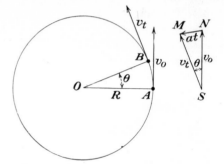

Fig. 6.3. The line joining a planet and the sun sweeps out equal areas in equal time intervals.

Fig. 6.4. In uniform circular motion the magnitude of the velocity remains constant, but the direction changes. The acceleration is toward the center of the circle.

motion to more advanced treatments. We observe that the circle may be regarded as a limiting case of the ellipse, namely, that in which the two foci merge into one.

6.3. Uniform Circular Motion. When a body moves in a circular path in such a way that it always passes over equal distances in equal intervals of time, it is said to describe *uniform circular motion*. The magnitude of the velocity is constant, but the direction is always changing. A body describing uniform circular motion has an acceleration, illustrated in Fig. 6.4. By the definition of acceleration, $\mathbf{a} = (\mathbf{v}_t - \mathbf{v}_0)/t$, or $\mathbf{v}_t - \mathbf{v}_0 = \mathbf{a}t$. In Fig. 6.4 the vector difference $\mathbf{v}_t - \mathbf{v}_0 = \mathbf{a}t$ is shown. Note that the vector $\mathbf{a}t$ is directed almost toward the center of the circle. Indeed, if we draw a vector diagram similar to that of Fig. 6.4 for the case in which the angle θ approaches zero, the acceleration is directed toward the center of the circle. The acceleration is constant in magnitude throughout the circular path, but it varies in direction.

To calculate this acceleration, we proceed as follows: Suppose that the particle passes over the arc AB with constant speed v in the time t. The distance passed over is $AB = vt$. In the case that θ is a small angle, the chord AB is essentially equal in length to the arc AB. If we consider the velocity vector triangle of Fig. 6.4, we observe that the angle between v_t and v_0 is θ (since the velocity of uniform circular motion is always perpendicular to the radius). Therefore, the triangles OAB and SNM are similar, from which we conclude that $vt/r = at/v$, and

$$a = \frac{v^2}{r} \qquad (6.1)$$

The acceleration of a body describing uniform circular motion is always directed toward the center of the circle and has the magnitude v^2/r.

6.4. Centripetal Force. If a body has an acceleration toward the center of the circle, there is a net force in that direction by Newton's second law. This force is called the *centripetal force*. To find its magnitude, we recall that $\mathbf{F} = m\mathbf{a}$ and that $a = v^2/r$, whence

$$F = ma = m\frac{v^2}{r} \qquad (6.2)$$

Consider for a moment a model airplane constrained to move in a horizontal circle by a control wire (Fig. 6.5). The wire pulls on the airplane toward the center of the circle. By Newton's third law, if the wire exerts a force towards the center of the circle on the airplane, the airplane must exert an equal force away from the center on the

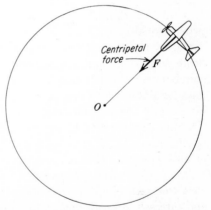

Fig. 6.5. The control wire pulls toward the center of the circle in which the model airplane is flying.

wire. This force, away from the center of the circle and *acting on the wire*, is known as the *centrifugal force*.

Note carefully that the force *on the airplane is toward the center* of the circle. If this force were suddenly removed and no unbalanced force acted on the airplane, it would move along a tangent to the circular path. No force acts upon the airplane outward along the radius. The airplane does exert a force outward on the restraint, which in this case is the control wire. This outward force on the restraint is the centrifugal force; it is the reaction to the centripetal force which acts inward on the body describing circular motion.

6.5. Newton's Law of Universal Gravitation. Let us now, follow-ing Newton, apply these ideas and equations to the motion of the moon about the earth. Imagine for the moment that the earth itself is fixed rigidly in space. If we assume that the path of the moon is circular, the moon has an acceleration toward the earth (the center of the circle) given by $a = v^2/r$. To produce this acceleration there must be an unbalanced centripetal force $F = mv^2/r$. This is the force acting upon the moon which keeps it traveling with uniform circular motion.

For a circular orbit the semimajor axis is equal to the radius r. The magnitude of the velocity is given by the circumference $2\pi r$ divided by the period T. Therefore, the centripetal force is

$$F_c = m \frac{4\pi^2 r^2}{T^2} \frac{1}{r} = \frac{4\pi^2 m r}{T^2} \qquad (6.3)$$

By Kepler's third law, we know that the period T (the time for one complete revolution) of the moon is such that T^2 is proportional to A^3, where A is the semimajor axis. If T^2 is to be proportional to r^3, the cen-tripetal force F_c must be inversely proportional to r^2. Furthermore, if the proportionality constant for the moon and all the planets is to be the same, F_c must be proportional to the mass of the body describing the orbit, so that the mass cancels out of Eq. (6.3). Otherwise the relation-ship between the period and the semimajor axis would have to involve the mass of the rotating heavenly body. If the mass of one of the bodies is involved in the attractive force between the two, it seems reasonable that the mass of the central body should be involved in a similar way. After much reasoning along these general lines, Newton proposed his great law of universal gravitation.

Between every two bodies in the universe there is a force of gravitational attraction which is proportional to the product of the masses of the two bodies and inversely proportional to the square of the distance between their centers of mass. This force, which acts along the line joining the two bodies, is given by

$$F = G \frac{m_1 m_2}{r^2} \qquad (6.4)$$

where G is the universal gravitational constant. Its value has been measured and is 6.67×10^{-11} newton-m^2/kg^2.

If we have two identical lead spheres of mass 1 kg with their centers 1 m apart, the force of attraction between these spheres is only 6.67×10^{-11} newton. The gravitational forces between two ordinary man-sized objects are detectable only under the most favorable of conditions. When one or more of the bodies involved is a star or a planet, the mass involved is so very great that the forces become observable and in many cases exceedingly large.

Evidence for the validity of Newton's law of gravitation is obtained from

astronomical observations.   By application of the law, it is possible to calculate
and to predict with great accuracy the motions of the planets and their satellites
many years in advance.   Such accurate long-term predictions are a severe test
of the law.

**6.6. The Determination of the Gravitational Constant and the Mass
of the Earth.**   The gravitational constant G was first measured by Cavendish
in the eighteenth century.   He used a torsion balance (Fig. 6.6) in which two
spheres of mass m were fixed to the end of a light rod which was suspended by a
long, fine wire so that it could turn easily.   When two heavy lead balls are placed
at the positions marked M, the rod carrying the two small balls is turned into a
new position.   If the lead balls are placed at M_1, the light rod with the small
spheres is turned in the opposite direction.   By measuring the elastic constant
of the suspending wire, it becomes possible to determine the attractive force
between the movable spheres and the balls.

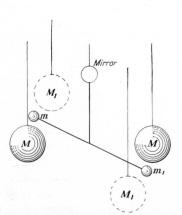

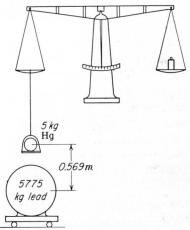

Fig. 6.6. Schematic diagram of the apparatus with which Cavendish measured the universal gravitational constant.

Fig. 6.7. Jolly's method of measuring
the universal gravitational constant.

A method of measuring G which is simple to understand was developed by
Jolly. A spherical vessel containing 5 kg of mercury was attached to one arm of
a sensitive balance and the balance put in equilibrium (Fig. 6.7).   Then a lead
sphere of mass 5,775 kg (over 6 tons) was rolled beneath the mercury flask with
its center about 0.57 m below the center of mass of the mercury.   The gravitational attraction between the lead and the mercury was found to be such that a
mass of 0.589 mg on the left pan was able to restore equilibrium.   All the quantities in Eq. (6.4) were thus known except for G, the value of which was calculated.

Once the value of the gravitational constant is known, it is possible to calculate
the mass of the earth m_E.   Consider for the moment the earth to be a perfect
sphere of radius $r = 6.4 \times 10^6$ m.   The force which the earth exerts on a mass of
1 kg at its surface is 1 kg-wt = 9.81 newtons.   Therefore, from $F = Gmm_E/r^2$

$$9.81 \text{ newtons} = 6.67 \times 10^{-11} \frac{\text{newton-m}^2}{\text{kg}^2} \frac{1 \text{ kg} \times m_E}{(6.4 \times 10^6 \text{ m})^2}$$

from which $m_E = 6 \times 10^{24}$ kg.

We may also find the mass of the sun M_s. The earth revolves around the sun in an elliptical path which is fairly close to a circle of radius 93,000,000 miles (1.5×10^{11} m). The centripetal force for the earth is provided by the gravitational attraction between the earth and the sun. Thus,

$$F = G\frac{M_s m_E}{r^2} = m_E\frac{v_E^2}{r} \qquad (6.5)$$

and

$$M_s = \frac{v_E^2 r}{G} = \frac{(2\pi r)^2 r}{T^2 G} = \frac{(2\pi)^2(1.5 \times 10^{11})^3}{(365.26 \times 86,400)^2 \times 6.67 \times 10^{-11}}$$

$$= 2 \times 10^{30} \text{ kg}$$

Table 1 gives important data about the solar system.

Table 1
DATA ON THE SOLAR SYSTEM

Body	Mass, kg	Radius,* km	g at surface, m/sec²	Sidereal period, days	Radius of orbit,† km
Moon..........	7.35×10^{22}	1,738	1.67	27.3	3.8×10^5
Sun............	1.97×10^{30}	695,000	274.4		
Mercury........	3.28×10^{23}	2,570	3.92	88	5.8×10^7
Venus..........	4.82×10^{24}	6,310	8.82	245	1.08×10^8
Earth..........	5.98×10^{24}	6,370	9.80	365.26	1.50×10^8
Mars...........	6.37×10^{23}	3,430	3.92	687	2.28×10^8
Jupiter.........	1.88×10^{27}	71,800	26.46	4,333	7.78×10^8
Saturn..........	5.62×10^{26}	60,300	11.76	1.08×10^4	1.43×10^9
Uranus..........	8.62×10^{25}	26,700	9.80	3.07×10^4	2.87×10^9
Neptune.........	1.0×10^{26}	2,490	9.80	6.02×10^4	4.5×10^9
Pluto...........	....	......	......	9.09×10^4	5.9×10^9

* Bodies are not exactly spheres.
† Orbits are actually elliptical; the values quoted are mean distances.

6.7. Artificial Satellites. Men have long dreamed of "space stations" circling the earth at a height of a few hundred miles. Such artificial satellites can now be launched. Let us consider such a station 600 km above the earth's surface and therefore some 7,000 km from the center of the earth. For this satellite the gravitational attraction of the earth provides the required centripetal force. If m_s is the mass of the satellite,

$$G\frac{m_s m_E}{r^2} = m_s\frac{v^2}{r}$$

or

$$6.67 \times 10^{-11}\frac{\text{newton-m}^2}{\text{kg}^2}\frac{6 \times 10^{24}\text{ kg}}{(7 \times 10^6\text{ m})^2} = \frac{v^2}{(7 \times 10^6\text{ m})}$$

$$v = 7,600 \text{ m/sec}$$

or about 17,000 mi/hr.

At this speed the satellite would require a time of $2\pi \times 7 \times 10^6$ m/7,600 m/sec = 5,600 sec = 1.6 hr to encircle the earth. To achieve such a speed, the satellite must be accelerated by a multistage rocket.

If the only force on the satellite were the gravitational force, the satellite would encircle the earth indefinitely.   Actually air friction and other small forces gradually reduce the speed of the object so that eventually it approaches the earth, and dissipates its energy in the earth's atmosphere.

6.8. Variation of Weight with Position.   If the earth were at rest and were a perfect sphere of radius r, the weight of an object would be the same at all points on the earth's surface.   Actually, the earth is somewhat flattened at the poles.   Consequently, a body at one of the poles is closer to the center of the earth than an identical body at the equator. This leads to a somewhat greater weight at the poles than at the equator.

Another factor which also works in the direction of making the weight less at the equator is the rotation of the earth.   At the equator a portion of the gravitational pull is used to supply the centripetal force to keep the body moving with uniform circular motion.   Therefore, the force which must be applied to the body to prevent it from falling to the earth is smaller at the equator. The total variation from equator to pole is approximately 0.5 per cent.

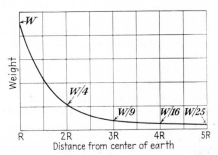

Fig. 6.8. The weight of an object decreases as its distance from the center of the earth increases.

The weight of a body varies not only with latitude, but also with altitude.   The weight is somewhat less atop Pike's Peak than it is in Death Valley.   As we go above the earth, the weight of a body of mass m decreases gradually as r increases.   Figure 6.8 shows how the weight of a body varies with its distance from the center of the earth, neglecting effects arising from the rotation of the earth.   Of course, the weight is given by mg.   Table 2 shows how g differs from place to place.

Table 2

ACCELERATION OF GRAVITY g AT VARIOUS LOCATIONS

Place	Elevation, m	g, m/sec²
Equator.................	0	9.78039
Panama Canal............	5	9.78243
Latitude 45° (Standard)........	0	9.80665
North Pole..............	0	9.83201
Boston, Mass.............	22	9.80395
Chicago, Ill..............	182	9.80277
Denver, Colo.............	1,638	9.79608
Pike's Peak, Colo..........	4,293	9.78953
San Francisco, Calif.........	114	9.79965

In prospecting for oil and for heavy masses of ore below the surface of the earth, very careful measurements of g are commonly made at selected points over a fairly large area. Modern gravimeters are sufficiently sensitive so that a change in g of a few parts in one hundred million can be readily detected. The variation in g over a region is plotted on a map and experts can frequently locate places where drilling for oil or ore is most likely to be successful.

The variations in the acceleration of gravity at different places on the earth's surface are small enough so that they may be neglected in ordinary activities. However, if man develops his rocket ships to the point where travel to the moon or to Mars becomes feasible, he would find that the pull of these objects would be very different from that of the pull of the earth. On the surface of the moon his weight (force with which the moon would hold him to its surface) would be only one-sixth of that on the earth. Indeed, the gravitational pull on the moon is so small that gas molecules escape readily and therefore the moon has no atmosphere. On the planet Jupiter a man would be pulled down by a force 2.6 times as great as his weight on the earth. Under these circumstances it would be difficult for him to walk about.

6.9. The Formation of Tides. One of the familiar and important phenomena which is explained by gravitational attraction is that of the tides. It is easy to see how the moon raises the tide (Fig. 6.9) on side A nearest to it, since water flows readily and is subjected to an extra force due to the gravitational attraction of the moon. To understand why there is a tide on the opposite side of the earth at the same time, one must recall that the moon does not rotate about a fixed earth, but rather the two bodies rotate about their common center of gravity. As a consequence, the center of the earth performs essentially uniform circular motion about the center of gravity of the earth-moon system. Since the resultant force on a kilogram of water at point C is less than that on a kilogram at the center of the earth B or on the side A, it has a smaller

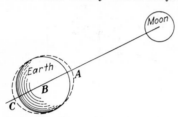

Fig. 6.9. Oversimplified diagram showing the formation of tides by the moon.

acceleration toward the center of gravity of the earth-moon system, and hence water piles up on this side also. Lunar tides have their greatest heights twice in a period of 1 day and 51 min. The inertia of the water, forces of friction, and other causes produce lags in the motion of the water and otherwise complicate the picture, so that high tide does not coincide with the time when the moon is directly overhead.

The sun produces tides as well as the moon, but the solar tides are much smaller. They, of course, have their greatest height twice in the period of 24 hr. The resulting tide is a combination of the large lunar tide and the relatively small solar tide. When the sun, moon, and earth are all in line, unusually large tides are formed.

6.10. Applications of Centripetal Force. When an automobile goes around a curve (Fig. 6.10) on a perfectly level road, friction between the tires and roadway is required to provide the necessary centripetal force mv^2/r. If the road is coated with ice, this frictional force may be too small to provide the necessary centripetal acceleration and the car may slide off the road. Note carefully that there is no force pulling the car outward along the radius. By Newton's first law, the car would continue to move indefinitely with constant velocity in the absence of any force. If there is a force toward the center of the circle which is inadequate to provide the full centripetal force, the car is accelerated toward the center of the curve, but not enough to keep it on the road.

If the road is suitably banked, the car may go around the curve without requiring any frictional force at all. If friction between tires and roadway is absent, the road pushes on the car only in the direction perpendicular to the surface. If the vertical component of this normal

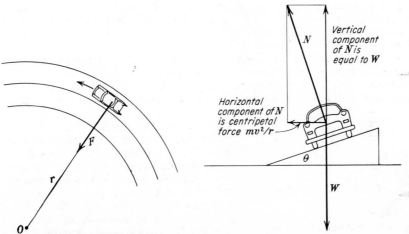

Fig. 6.10. When an automobile goes around a curve on a perfectly level road, friction between tires and road must provide the necessary centripetal force.

Fig. 6.11. A curve is perfectly banked for a given speed v when the force exerted by the road perpendicular to its surface has a vertical component equal to the weight and a horizontal component equal to the centripetal force mv^2/r.

force (Fig. 6.11) is exactly the weight of the vehicle and if the horizontal component is just mv^2/r, the automobile goes around the curve without skidding. We observe that to satisfy these conditions the angle θ must be such that

$$\tan \theta = \frac{mv^2/r}{mg} = \frac{v^2}{gr} \tag{6.6}$$

The ideal angle at which the road should be banked depends on the speed, but not on the mass, of the car.

The centrifuge, which is widely used in the separation of liquids of unequal densities, depends for its operation on centripetal force. One type of centrifuge (Fig. 6.12) consists of a wheel that rotates in a horizontal plane. To this wheel are attached buckets that are vertical when the wheel is at rest. However, when the wheel is revolving rapidly, the buckets assume a position so that their axes are almost horizontal. If a mixture of liquids of unequal densities is introduced into the buckets and the wheel is revolved rapidly, the liquids separate, the heavy liquids farther from the axis of rotation and the lighter liquids nearer to it.

Fig. 6.12. A small hand-operated centrifuge.

This means that the heavier liquids are at the bottom of the buckets when the centrifuge is stopped. The forces developed in a high-speed centrifuge may be very large (Fig. 6.13). The cream separator works on the same principle as the centrifuge.

Fig. 6.13. Even rigid metal cannot withstand the large forces developed by high-speed centrifuges. (*Courtesy of J. W. Beams, University of Virginia.*)

6.11. Centripetal Forces in Aviation. When an aircraft makes a turn in a horizontal plane, it banks in such a way that the vertical component of the forces on the wings is equal to the weight of the aircraft, while the horizontal component provides the necessary centripetal force. Very high-speed aircraft cannot make exceedingly sharp turns because it is not feasible to provide the necessary centripetal force.

When an aircraft pulls out of a steep dive, very large forces must be exerted by the wings. More than one pilot has pulled the wings off his aircraft when he has tried to pull out of a dive too quickly. Consider an aircraft which is coming down at the rate of 800 ft/sec and tries to pull out of the dive, in a circle of radius 2,000 ft (Fig. 6.14). The centripetal acceleration becomes

$$a = \frac{v^2}{r} = \frac{800 \times 800}{2,000} = 320 \ \text{ft/sec}^2$$

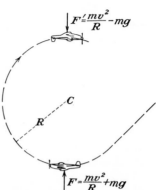

or ten times the acceleration due to gravity. Thus, the *unbalanced upward force* required on the aircraft is ten times the weight. At the bottom of the circle the wings must not only provide this centripetal acceleration, but overcome the pull of the earth on the aircraft. They must provide $10 \times 32 \ \text{ft/sec}^2 = 10 \ g$'s centripetal acceleration plus $1 \ g$ to take care of the pull of the earth on the aircraft—a total of $11 \ g$'s. The wings of most aircraft are not designed for such heavy loading. A typical fighter aircraft is designed to take accelerations of the order of 8 or 9 g's, while passenger aircraft, bombers, and

Fig. 6.14. Forces exertea on an aircraft at the upper and lower extremities of a circular loop.

transports are designed for much lower g loadings. At the top of the circular path (Fig. 6.14) the pull of gravity helps to provide the centripetal acceleration and the net force exerted by the wings is $mv^2/r - mg$.

Not only does the aircraft itself have to stand these accelerations, but so do all the objects in the aircraft, including the organs of the pilot's body. Consider a gram of blood in a pilot's brain when the aircraft is performing a 6-g turn. The total force on this gram of blood must be six times the ordinary force exerted. The blood may rush out of the pilot's brain, which results in his "blacking out." If the heart is unable to pump hard enough to get the blood to the brain, the blood accumulates in the legs and the lower body. Considerable research has been done to develop techniques which allow pilots to take large g loadings without losing consciousness.

PROBLEMS

1. A 3,200-lb automobile traveling 90 ft/sec (61 mi/hr) goes around a curve of radius 1,000 ft. Find the centripetal acceleration and the centripetal force.

Ans. 8.1 ft/sec²; 810 lb

2. If the maximum centripetal acceleration available is 16 ft/sec², find the maximum speed at which an automobile can safely negotiate a curve of 100 ft radius.

3. A ball is whirled in a vertical circle on the end of a string 2 ft long. At what speed will the tension in the string be zero at the top of the circle? *Ans.* 8 ft/sec

4. Assuming 12 ft/sec² as the largest sidewise acceleration which is safe for a certain car, what is the smallest circle on which it can travel at the rate of 15 mi/hr?

5. A boy weighing 60 lb is swinging in such a way that he describes an arc of 10 ft radius. If the horizontal speed at the lowest point of the swing is 4 ft/sec, what is the total force which the ropes of the swing must sustain at that instant? *Ans.* 63 lb

6. A stone whirling on the end of a string 4 ft long has a horizontal acceleration of 36 ft/sec² toward the center of the circle. What is the velocity of the stone?

7. An airplane pulls out of a dive at 300 mi/hr (440 ft/sec) in a circle of radius

1,210 ft.   Find the centripetal acceleration and the total force exerted by the plane on a 160-lb pilot at the bottom of the arc.   *Ans.* 160 ft/sec²; 960 lb

8. A thread 30 in. long which cannot support a force greater than 10 lb is used to whirl a 2-lb stone in a horizontal circle.   How fast will the stone be moving when the thread breaks?   Consider only horizontal force.

9. At what angle should a curve of 100 ft radius be banked if no frictional forces are to be required for a speed of 40 ft/sec?   *Ans.* 26.5°

10. A curve of 200 ft radius is banked at 10°.   At what speed must an automobile go around this curve if no frictional forces are to be used to keep the automobile on its circular path?

11. What is the speed of an airplane that is making a loop with a radius of 800 ft when objects in the plane at the top of the loop begin to drop to the earth?
Ans. 160 ft/sec

12. When a sphere of lead is placed 30 cm from another sphere of lead with a mass of 2.5 kg, the attraction of one for another is found to be 1×10^{-7} newton.   What is the mass of the first sphere?

13. How many revolutions per minute would the earth have to make in order that the weight of a body at the equator become zero?   *Ans.* 0.012 rev/min

14. A body moving in a circle with a radius of 2 ft requires a force of 5 lb to keep it in its circular path when making 18 rev/min.   Find the weight of the body.

15. What is the angle at which a circular speedway must be banked for cars running at 90 mi/hr, if the radius of the track is 900 ft?   *Ans.* 31°

16. The governor of an engine has arms which are 25 cm long and which stand at an angle of 60° with the vertical when the governor is in constant rotation.   Find the angular speed of the shaft of the governor.

17. Calculate the attractive force of the earth for the moon.
Ans. 2.0×10^{20} newtons

18. The mass of the earth is 80 times that of the moon and its radius is 3.66 times that of the moon.   What would be the weight of a kilogram of gold on the moon?

19. What is the centripetal acceleration of the moon in its orbit around the earth?
Ans. 0.0027 m/sec²

20. A body weighs 200 lb on the surface of the earth.   Find its weight 1,000 miles above the surface of the earth.   Assume the radius of the earth to be 4,000 miles.

21. It is proposed to put a space station in a circular orbit at a distance of one earth's radius above the earth's surface.   What would be the acceleration due to gravity at this station?   Find the speed which this station must have if it is to go around the center of the earth in a circular orbit.   How long will it take to make one complete revolution?   *Ans.* 2.45 m/sec²; 5,600 m/sec; 1.4×10^4 sec

22. Find the value of the acceleration of gravity on Mars, if the mass of Mars is one-tenth that of the earth and the radius of Mars is one-half that of the earth.

23. What centripetal force is necessary to keep the earth in its orbit?   What would have to be the area of a steel cable with a strength of 10^9 newtons/m² in order to sustain this force?   *Ans.* 3.6×10^{22} newtons; 3.6×10^{13} m²

CHAPTER 7 *Important - especially collisions and momentum*

Work and Energy

7.1. Work. The word *work* is a familiar one, used in many everyday senses. In physics, however, it is used in a highly restricted and carefully defined manner. When a force acts upon a body to produce a displacement, the *work done by the force is defined as the product of the displacement and the component of the force in the direction of the displacement.* If the angle between the displacement vector and the force vector is θ (Fig. 7.1), the component of the force in the direction of the displacement is $F \cos \theta$ and work is defined by the equation:

$$\text{Work} = Fs \cos \theta \qquad (7.1)$$

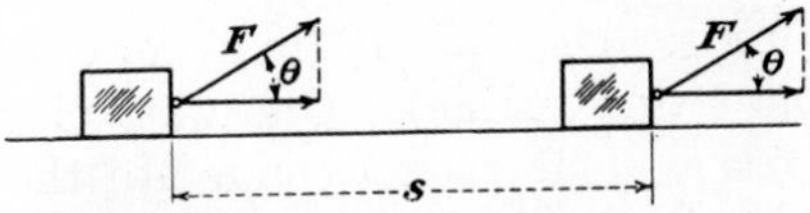

If the force does not produce a displacement, no work is done in the sense in which *work* is used in physics. A man holding a 10-lb weight at rest does no work on it. A desk or cement post could hold the weight indefinitely without any difficulty. Although the man holding the weight does *no work on it*, the muscles in his arm do stretch and contract and thus some work is done internally which may result in fatigue.

Fig. 7.1. The work done by a force **F** acting at an angle θ with the displacement s produced is $Fs \cos \theta$.

7.2. Units for Work. Since work is measured by the product of force and displacement, its units involve a unit of force multiplied by a unit of length. In the British engineering system the force is ordinarily measured in pounds and the displacement in feet; the resulting unit of work is the *foot-pound.* *One foot-pound is the work done when a force of one pound acts through a distance of one foot.*

In the metric system the basic units of force and distance are the newton and the meter. Work is measured in newton-meters. This unit has been named the *joule* in honor of James Prescott Joule, a distinguished British physicist whose work on the relation between heat and mechanical work was of great importance. *One joule is the work done when a force of one newton acts through a distance of one meter.*

79

There are many other units in which work may be measured. For example, large amounts of work are sometimes reported in ton-miles. Small amounts in the metric system are sometimes measured in ergs; 1 erg is equal to 10^{-7} joule.

Example. How many joules of work are done by a force in lifting a mass of 2 kg upward a distance of 3 m?

$$\text{Work in joules} = \text{force in newtons} \times \text{distance in meters}$$
$$F = mg = 2 \text{ kg} \times 9.8 \text{ m/sec}^2 = 19.6 \text{ newtons}$$
$$\text{Work} = 19.6 \text{ newtons} \times 3 \text{ m} = 58.8 \text{ joules}$$

Example. A force of 10 lb is used to move a box across a horizontal floor for a distance of 5 ft. If the force makes an angle of 30° with the floor, how much work is done?

$$\text{Work} = Fs \cos \theta$$
$$= 10 \text{ lb} \times 5 \text{ ft} \times 0.866$$
$$= 43.3 \text{ ft-lb}$$

7.3. Power. In physics, *the time rate of doing work is called power.* Thus, power P is equal to work divided by time.

$$P = \frac{\text{work}}{t} \tag{7.2}$$

An engine which produces a large amount of power can do work rapidly. In the metric system power is measured in joules per second, which in turn is called the *watt* (in honor of James Watt, an important developer of the steam engine). One watt of power is expended when one joule of work is done each second. In the British engineering system power is sometimes measured in foot-pounds per second, but more often it is expressed in *horsepower* (hp); 1 hp is equal to 550 ft-lb/sec. The origin of this strange number is of interest. When James Watt tried to sell his steam engines to British coal mines, the question arose: How many horses would one of these new engines replace? Watt spent some time at a mine and found that, on the average, the horses were doing about 550 ft-lb of work per second; he called this unit of power the horsepower. He found the rate at which his steam engines could work and thus rated them in terms of "horsepower." One horsepower is equivalent to 745.7 watts.

Example. A building crane lifts a 1,500-lb steel beam to a height of 44 ft in 10 sec. Find the power developed.

$$P = \frac{\text{work}}{t} = \frac{1,500 \text{ lb} \times 44 \text{ ft}}{10 \text{ sec}} = 6,600 \text{ ft-lb/sec}$$
$$= 6,600 \frac{\text{ft-lb}}{\text{sec}} \times \frac{1 \text{ hp}}{550 \text{ ft-lb/sec}} = 12 \text{ hp}$$

Example. An electric motor exerts a force of 400 newtons on a cable and pulls it a distance of 30 m in 1 min. Find the power supplied by the motor.

$$P = \frac{\text{work}}{\text{time}} = \frac{400 \text{ newtons} \times 30 \text{ m}}{60 \text{ sec}} = 200 \text{ joules/sec}$$
$$= 200 \text{ watts}$$

When a constant force acts on a body in the direction of the body's motion, the power can be expressed in the form: $P = \text{work}/\text{time} = Fs/t$. Since $s/t = v$,

$$P = Fv \qquad (7.3)$$

This equation is fundamental in the design of aircraft or in determining how many diesel units to put on a railroad train to pull it at a certain speed.   If one wishes to make the velocity of an airplane greater, there are basically two things he can do; increase the power or decrease the retarding forces, which in the case of level constant-speed flight is the drag due to air friction.

Example.   An aircraft has four 2,000-hp engines and flies 300 mi/hr (440 ft/sec) when all engines are delivering rated power.   Find the drag.

$$P = Fv$$

$$8,000 \text{ hp} \times \frac{550 \text{ ft-lb/sec}}{1 \text{ hp}} = F \times 440 \text{ ft/sec}$$

$$F = 10,000 \text{ lb drag}$$

7.4. Energy and Its Conservation.   *Energy is defined as the ability or capacity to do work.*   It occurs in many forms.   A swinging hammer can do work by virtue of its motion; energy associated with motion is known as *kinetic energy*.   A raised pile driver can do work by virtue of its elevated position; it has what we call *potential energy*.   When we buy gasoline, we buy chemical energy.   The food we eat provides energy for our living.   We purchase electrical energy so our electric motors can do work for us.   Energy may exist in the form of electromagnetic radiation; indeed, the earth's primary source of energy lies in the radiation it receives from the sun.   Much of physics involves the relationships between the many forms of energy and the transformations from one form to another.

The study of the various forms in which energy may occur and of the transformation of one kind of energy into another has led to the statement of a very important principle, known as the *law of conservation of energy:*

Energy cannot be created or destroyed; it may be transformed from one form into another, but the total amount of energy never changes.

This principle is one of the great generalizations of physical science.

As an example of the transformations through which energy may go, consider radiation coming to the earth from the sun.   Some of this energy may fall on plants where it is transformed into chemical energy through photosynthesis. The energy stored in the plant may be converted eventually into coal or oil, or the plant may be eaten by some animal which utilizes the energy to carry on its existence.   Part of the radiant energy from the sun goes into evaporating water from the surface of the ocean.   The water vapor, lifted high above the earth by solar energy, has potential energy by virtue of its position.   Eventually, it returns to the earth in the form of rain which may be trapped behind a dam.   The water thus stored has potential energy by virtue of its position.   The water may be led through a giant turbine where the potential energy is converted into energy of motion, and this energy in motion in turn converted into electrical energy in a generator. Electrical energy is distributed to houses where it may be converted into heat or light, or be used to perform work through an electric motor. Throughout all these transformations, the total energy remains constant.

Early in the twentieth century it was found that mass itself could be converted into energy, and we now regard mass as one of the forms of energy. We know that the sun's mass is decreasing because mass energy is converted into radiant energy in the sun. In atomic bombs and nuclear reactors mass is converted into energy. The theoretical physicist Einstein showed that, whenever mass is converted into another form of energy (or vice versa), the equivalence could be expressed by the equation

$$E = mc^2 \tag{7.4}$$

where E is the amount of some other form of energy appearing or disappearing, m is the mass disappearing or appearing, and c is the speed of light. If c is expressed in meters per second and m in kilograms, E is in joules.

Example. What is the total energy in a gram of matter at rest?

$$m = 10^{-3} \text{ kg}$$

The velocity of light c is 3×10^8 m/sec and

$$c^2 = 9 \times 10^{16} \text{ m}^2/\text{sec}^2$$
$$E = mc^2 = 9 \times 10^{13} \text{ kg-m}^2/\text{sec}^2 = 9 \times 10^{13} \text{ joules}$$

This energy is sufficient to lift a mass of 1 million kg through a distance of 9,000 km against the action of gravity!

Energy is an important commodity in economics and commerce. It is bought and sold in many forms, for example, as coal, petroleum products,

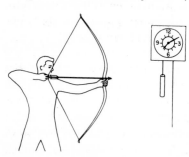

Fig. 7.2. Examples of potential energy.

food, and electrical energy. Energy is used to operate automobiles, refrigerators, stoves, washing machines, and television sets. In the past century the amount of energy consumed per person has undergone a remarkable increase. Primitive man used energy only for his food and warmth; modern man has hundreds of appliances which transform energies for his entertainment, comfort, and convenience.

7.5. Potential and Kinetic Energy. In mechanics it is natural that we should be concerned primarily with the various mechanical forms of energy. It is convenient to distinguish between two types—*potential energy* and *kinetic energy.*

The energy that a body has by virtue of its position or configuration is called potential energy (Fig. 7.2). When a mass has been lifted above the surface of the earth, it has energy because of its position. When a spring has been compressed or a bow has been bent, potential energy has been stored up.   Other examples of potential energy are found in the mainspring of a watch and in a stretched rubber band.   In these cases the material of the spring or the rubber band is in a state of strain; because of this strain, the body possesses potential energy.

The measure of the potential energy which a body has because of its position is the work done against gravity in lifting the body.   The upward force required is equal to the weight of the body W and the work done in lifting the body through a height h is given by the product Wh; therefore,

$$\text{Potential energy} = Wh = mgh \qquad (7.5)$$

In the English system we ordinarily measure potential energy in foot-pounds, in the metric system in joules (newton-m).

Example.   A block weighing 3 lb is lifted 6 ft against gravity.   What potential energy is stored?

$$\text{Potential energy} = Wh = 3 \text{ lb} \times 6 \text{ ft}$$
$$= 18 \text{ ft-lb}$$

Example.   Find the potential energy given to the 50-kg hammer of a pile driver when it is raised 4 m.

$$\text{Potential energy} = mgh = 50 \text{ kg} \times 9.8 \text{ m/sec}^2 \times 4 \text{ m}$$
$$= 1{,}960 \text{ joules}$$

Kinetic energy is the energy a body possesses by virtue of its motion.   Any body in motion can set other bodies in motion by colliding with them. The moving head of an axe can do work in splitting a log.   The bullet leaving the muzzle of a gun has kinetic energy and can do work in penetrating a board.

To find the kinetic energy which a body possesses, we consider the work which must be done on the body in order to give it its speed.   When the body is stopped, it gives up this amount of energy.   By definition, this is its kinetic energy.   Consider a mass m initially at rest, upon which a constant force F is applied through a displacement s in the direction of the force.   The work done on the body is Fs.   By Newton's second law, $F = ma$; thus the work is equal to mas.   Since the acceleration of the body is constant, Eq. (4.7) is applicable.   Therefore, $v^2 = 2as$, since $v_0 = 0$.   If we replace as by $v^2/2$ and recall that the work done appears as kinetic energy, we have

$$\text{Kinetic energy} = \tfrac{1}{2}mv^2 \qquad (7.6)$$

In metric units we express the kinetic energy in joules (or the equivalent $kg\text{-}m^2/sec^2$), while in the British system the kinetic energy is given in foot-pounds (or the equivalent $slug\text{-}ft^2/sec^2$).

Example. If an automobile weighing 3 tons is moving with a velocity of 30 ft/sec, what is its kinetic energy in foot-pounds?

$$\text{Kinetic energy } = \frac{1}{2} mv^2 = \frac{1}{2} \frac{W}{g} v^2$$
$$= \frac{6,000 \text{ lb} \times (30 \text{ ft/sec})^2}{2 \times 32 \text{ ft/sec}^2} = \frac{3,000 \text{ lb} \times 900 \text{ ft}^2/\text{sec}^2}{32 \text{ ft/sec}^2}$$
$$= 84,000 \text{ ft-lb}$$

Example. What force is required to stop a bullet that has a mass of 15 g and a velocity of 400 m/sec in a distance of 20 cm?

$$\text{Force} \times \text{distance} = \text{change in kinetic energy}$$
$$(0.20 \text{ m}) F = \frac{1}{2}(0.015 \text{ kg})(400 \text{ m/sec})^2$$
$$= 1,200 \text{ kg-m}^2/\text{sec}^2 \text{ (or joules)}$$
$$F = \frac{1,200 \text{ kg-m}^2/\text{sec}^2}{0.2 \text{ m}} = 6,000 \text{ kg-m/sec}^2 = 6,000 \text{ newtons}$$

7.6. Transformation of Potential and Kinetic Energy.

The potential energy of a body due to its position depends upon its height h and this in turn depends on what one wishes to call the zero for height. A book on a table has no potential energy relative to the table top, but it does have potential energy relative to the floor and relative to mean sea level. If the book weighs 2 lb and the table top is 3 ft above the floor, the potential energy of the book is 6 ft-lb relative to the floor. Potential energy is always determined *relative* to some level or position which is assigned the value of zero. The choice of this level is at the disposal of the person who is working the problem.

In many situations we have a simple transformation of potential into kinetic energy with no other forms of energy involved. For example, when a pile driver is lifted into position, it is given potential energy. This potential energy is transformed into kinetic energy before the hammer strikes the pile upon which it is to do work. Similarly, consider water going over a dam (Fig. 7.3). Just above the dam the water has potential energy and, if its velocity is negligible, no significant kinetic energy. As the water falls, its potential energy decreases and its kinetic energy increases. Upon striking the bottom, part of this kinetic energy is transformed into heat.

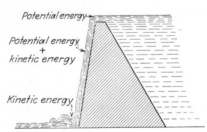

Fig. 7.3. The potential energy of the water at the top of the dam is converted to kinetic energy at the bottom.

The swinging of a pendulum illustrates the way in which potential energy may be transformed into kinetic energy and then back to potential energy (Fig. 7.4). When a pendulum is pulled to one side, the mass has no velocity and no kinetic energy, but it does have potential energy.

When the mass is released, it swings downward, acquiring kinetic energy and losing potential energy. At the bottom of the swing the pendulum bob has maximum kinetic energy. As it swings upward, this kinetic

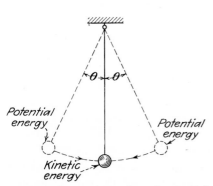

Fig. 7.4. A transformation of potential energy into kinetic energy and then back to potential energy.

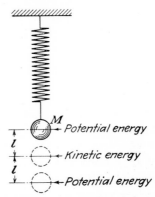

Fig. 7.5. The sum of the potential and kinetic energies does not change as the mass on the end of an ideal spring moves up and down.

energy is retransformed into potential energy. A very similar transformation of energy can be traced in the case of a mass on the end of the spring (Fig. 7.5).

Example. A pendulum bob is pulled over to one side until its center of gravity has been raised 10 cm above its equilibrium position. Find the speed of the bob as it swings through the equilibrium position.

Potential energy at top = kinetic energy at bottom
$$mgh = \tfrac{1}{2}mv^2$$
whence
$$v^2 = 2gh$$
$$= 2 \times 9.8\,\text{m/sec}^2 \times 0.1\,\text{m} = 1.96\,\text{m}^2/\text{sec}^2$$
$$v = 1.4\,\text{m/sec}$$

7.7. Energy in the Human Body. The human body is capable of doing work. The energy necessary for the performance of this work comes from the burning of carbohydrates, fats, and proteins, which also provide energy for maintaining the body temperature and for carrying on its internal vital functions. The pumping of blood through the veins and arteries is an illustration of the internal work performed in the body. This work is done by the heart muscle. For a man at rest the heart normally beats about 70 times per minute and develops a power of about 1.3 watts. An average working man uses about 10 million joules of energy per day, of which about half goes into maintaining temperature and carrying on internal functions. The remainder is available for the performance of external work.

7.8. Collisions between Bodies. When two bodies collide with one another, the laws of conservation of momentum and of conservation of energy are both always applicable. However, in some collisions part of the kinetic energy of the bodies is transformed into some nonmechanical form of energy, such as heat or sound. In this case the application of the law of conservation of energy to the problem becomes exceedingly difficult, because many kinds of energy may be involved, some of which are difficult to measure.

If a bullet is fired into a block of wood sitting on a fence post, the bullet sticks in the block and they remain together indefinitely. Such a collision is called a *perfectly inelastic* one. The bodies are permanently deformed and never separate.

In another type of collision the bodies spring apart after the collision. If a steel ball is dropped on a steel plate, the ball and plate are distorted during the action of the impulsive forces, but they return to their original shape and the ball springs away from the plate. In this case the bodies are only temporarily deformed and they regain their original shape immediately after collision. Figure 7.6 shows a collision in which a golf ball is distorted during impact. Bodies which return to their original shape after collision are said to be *elastic*.

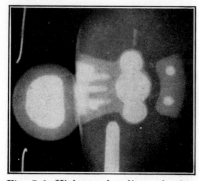

Fig. 7.6. High-speed radiograph of a club striking a golf ball. (*Courtesy of C. M. Slack, Westinghouse Electric Corp.*)

In a perfectly elastic collision kinetic energy is conserved as well as momentum. Such an ideal situation is never achieved with large-scale objects; thus, we have no perfectly elastic collisions of macroscopic bodies. However, collisions between atomic nuclei, atoms, molecules, and electrons are often perfectly elastic. Collisions between billiard balls or between a basketball and the floor are *imperfectly elastic*.

Although the bodies spring apart, the kinetic energy of the system after collision is less than it was before the collision. *Momentum is always conserved.*

It is convenient to divide all types of two-body collisions into three classes: (1) inelastic, in which the bodies stick together; (2) perfectly elastic, in which both momentum and kinetic energy are conserved; and (3) imperfectly elastic, in which the bodies separate, but some kinetic energy is lost by transformation to heat, sound, or some other form of energy. In the paragraphs below we shall consider these types of collisions in greater detail. In each case we shall treat "head-on" collisions between two bodies of masses m and M (Fig. 7.7) which have velocities v_0 and V_0, respectively, before collision and v and V after collision. Before we write equations, we recall that velocities are vector quantities;

therefore, we shall need to concern ourselves with directions as well as magnitudes. In the equations which follow we shall adopt the convention that velocities to the right are positive and velocities to the left negative.

1. *Perfectly Inelastic Collisions.* In an inelastic collision the two bodies stick together after they have made contact. As a consequence, the two bodies have the same final velocity. In such a collision a substantial fraction of the kinetic energy may be transformed into heat or some other kind of energy. The law of conservation of momentum

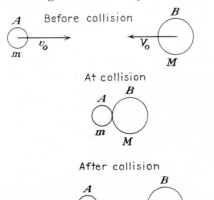

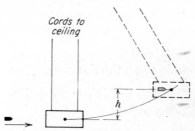

Fig. 7.7. Head-on collision between two bodies showing meanings of symbols used in text. Velocities to the right are taken as positive, to the left as negative.

Fig. 7.8. The speed of a bullet may be found by firing it into the bob of a ballistic pendulum and finding how much the center of gravity of the bob is raised at the end of its swing.

alone is adequate to permit us to compute the final velocity if the masses and initial velocities are known.

$$mv_0 + MV_0 = (m + M)V \qquad (7.7)$$

Example. A 2-g bullet is fired into a 2.398-kg block (Fig. 7.8) of wood suspended from a long cord. The bullet is embedded in the block and the two start off together with a speed of 0.7 m/sec. Find the velocity of the bullet before collision.

$$(0.002 \text{ kg})v_0 + (2.398 \text{ kg} \times 0) = 2.4 \text{ kg} \times 0.7 \text{ m/sec}$$
$$v_0 = 840 \text{ m/sec}$$

Figure 7.9 shows a ballistic pendulum designed to measure the velocity of a spring-fired ball by catching it in the bob of the pendulum. Since the collision is inelastic, Eq. (7.7) is applicable to the collision between ball and pendulum bob. The velocity V of the ball plus bob immediately after collision is determined by measuring how much the center of gravity of the system is raised in the upward swing of the pendulum. If the center of gravity is raised a distance h, conservation of energy yields $(m + M)gh = \frac{1}{2}(m + M)V^2$, where m and M are the masses of ball and pendulum bob, respectively.

2. *Perfectly Elastic Collisions.* In a perfectly elastic collision both momentum and kinetic energy are conserved. If two bodies in question

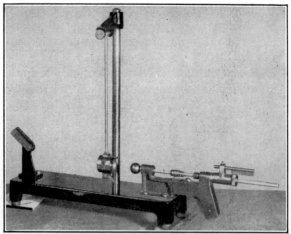

Fig. 7.9. Ballistic pendulum for studying inelastic collisions.　*(Central Scientific Co.)*

collide along the line connecting the centers, we may write

$$mv_0 + MV_0 = mv + MV \qquad \text{conservation of momentum} \qquad (7.8)$$

and

$$\tfrac{1}{2}mv_0^2 + \tfrac{1}{2}MV_0^2 = \tfrac{1}{2}mv^2 + \tfrac{1}{2}MV^2 \qquad \text{conservation of energy} \qquad (7.9)$$

These equations may be rewritten

$$m(v_0^2 - v^2) = M(V^2 - V_0^2) \qquad \text{and} \qquad m(v_0 - v) = M(V - V_0)$$

If we divide the first by the second, we obtain $v_0 + v = V + V_0$, or

$$v_0 - V_0 = V - v = -(v - V) \qquad (7.10)$$

Note that $v_0 - V_0$ is the *velocity of approach*, or the velocity of the smaller mass relative to the larger one before the collision, while $v - V$ is the *velocity of separation*, or the velocity of the smaller mass relative to the larger after the collision.　In a perfectly elastic collision the velocity of approach is equal in magnitude to the velocity of separation, but reversed in direction.

Example.　A 40-g ball traveling east with a speed of 5 m/sec has a "head-on" collision with a 60-g ball traveling 3 m/sec west (Fig. 7.7).　If the collision is elastic, find the velocities after the collision.

Let us choose east as the positive direction.

By Eq. (7.8),

$$(0.04 \text{ kg} \times 5 \text{ m/sec}) + (0.06 \text{ kg} \times -3 \text{ m/sec}) = (0.04 \text{ kg})v + (0.06 \text{ kg})V$$
$$v + 1.5V = 0.5 \text{ m/sec} \qquad (A)$$

By Eq. (7.10),
$$5 \text{ m/sec} - (-3 \text{ m/sec}) = V - v$$
$$-v + V = 8 \text{ m/sec} \qquad (B)$$

Adding Eqs. (A) and (B) yields

$$2.5V = +8.5$$
$$V = +3.4 \text{ m/sec}$$

and
$$v = -4.6 \text{ m/sec}$$

The minus sign means the 40-g ball is moving westward.

3. *Imperfectly Elastic Collisions.* In a perfectly elastic collision kinetic energy is conserved and the velocity of approach is equal to the velocity of separation in magnitude and opposite in direction. In an inelastic collision the velocity of separation is zero, since the two bodies remain together. Imperfectly elastic collisions lie between these two extremes. Newton studied collisions between many types of spheres and concluded that in general the velocity of separation was equal to a constant times the velocity of approach.

$$-(v - V) = e(v_0 - V_0) \quad (7.11)$$

where for a given pair of materials e is a constant which always lies between zero and one. This constant is called the *coefficient of restitution.* It is zero when the materials stick together and approaches unity for highly elastic materials. If the coefficient of restitution is known, the use of Eqs. (7.8) and (7.11) is sufficient to find the final velocities of the two bodies. Figure 7.10 shows imperfectly elastic collisions of a steel ball and a hardened steel

Fig. 7.10. Imperfectly elastic collisions of a hollow steel ball filled with tungsten powder dropped on a hardened steel plate. (*Walter V. Johnson Engineering Co.*)

plate. Since the plate is fastened to the earth, M is essentially infinity and $V_0 = V = 0$. Hence, $e = -v/v_0$.

Example. If the ball of Fig. 7.10 is initially dropped from a height of 40 cm and if the coefficient of restitution is 0.8, find the height attained on the first bounce.

By conservation of energy $mgh = \frac{1}{2}mv_0^2$ or $v_0^2 = 2gh$. Therefore, the velocity v_0 for the first collision is $\sqrt{2 \times 9.8 \times 0.4} = 2.8$ m/sec. By Eq. (7.11), $-v = ev_0$, since V and V_0 are essentially zero.

$$-v = 0.8v_0 = 2.24 \text{ m/sec}$$

This initial upward speed will carry the ball to a height h_1 such that $v^2 = 2gh_1$ or

$$h_1 = \frac{(2.24)^2}{2 \times 9.8} = 0.256 \text{ m} = 25.6 \text{ cm}$$

PROBLEMS

1. A horizontal force of 50 lb is required to pull a 300-lb box along a floor. How much work is required to move the box 40 ft across a level floor?   *Ans.* 2,000 ft-lb

2. To what height can a piece of structural steel weighing 0.5 ton be lifted if work amounting to 100,000 ft-lb is done on it?

3. One kilowatt-hour is enough energy to lift how large a load from a basement to an attic which is 10 m above?   *Ans.* 360,000 newtons

4. A cylindrical standpipe 80 ft high has an internal diameter of 10 ft. How much work would be required to fill the standpipe with water (*a*) if the water were pumped in at the bottom; (*b*) if it were pumped in at the top?

5. In driving a 3,500-lb automobile 8,000 ft, the car is elevated 400 ft. What is the increase in the potential energy of the car?   *Ans.* 1,400,000 ft-lb

6. A crank 15 in. long is turned by hand at the rate of 100 rev/min, a force of 6 lb applied tangent to the circle described by the handle being required. Calculate the horsepower applied.

7. An 80-kg man is lifted by an elevator through a distance of 200 m in 40 sec. What is the increase in his potential energy? What power is expended in raising him?
Ans. 156,800 joules; 3,920 watts

8. A boat is moving through the water at the rate of 25 ft/sec. Its engines develop 70 hp. Find the resistance overcome in moving the boat through the water.

9. A man pushes a lawn mower 100 ft in 10 sec by exerting a force of 20 lb at an angle of 53° with the horizon. Find the work done and the average power expended.
Ans. 1,200 ft-lb; 0.22 hp

10. The locomotive of a freight train exerts a force of 20,000 lb on the train as it pulls it along on a level track at a speed of 30 mi/hr (44 ft/sec). Find the power developed by the engine and the work done on the train in a distance of 1 mile.

11. An airplane requires 660 hp to keep it in level flight at 360 mi/hr (528 ft/sec). Find the drag.   *Ans.* 687.5 lb

12. A man wheels a wheelbarrow containing 100 lb of dirt up 8 ft every 3 min. At what rate is he expending energy? Neglect friction.

13. If a 0.1-kg mass is dropped through 2.5 m so that all of its potential energy is changed to kinetic energy, calculate its final velocity. Verify this by calculating the velocity of a body that falls freely through 2.5 m.   *Ans.* 7 m/sec

14. A 70-kg man climbs to the fourth floor of a building. If he rises 15 m in 30 sec, how many joules of work has he done? How much power has he expended?

15. A boy, starting from rest, slides down a hill 100 ft high on a sled. If friction is negligible, find the speed of the sled at the bottom.   *Ans.* 80 ft/sec

16. An automobile weighing 3,200 lb has a speed of 30 mi/hr along a level road. The clutch is thrown out and the car is allowed to coast until it comes to rest. If it coasts 200 ft before coming to rest, find the average retarding force. What horsepower was developed while the automobile was traveling 30 mi/hr?

17. A boy throws a 0.25-lb stone from the top of a 96-ft cliff with a speed of 40 ft/sec. Find its energy and speed when it lands in a river below.
Ans. 30.25 ft-lb; 88 ft/sec

18. Neglecting frictional forces, find the horsepower necessary to give an automobile weighing 2,800 lb an acceleration of 6 ft/sec² when it has a velocity of 30 mi/hr.

19. A cake of ice weighing 400 lb slides down an inclined plane which is 50 ft long and makes an angle of 30° with the horizontal. Neglecting the force of friction, what is the speed of the block of ice when it reaches the bottom of the inclined plane?
Ans. 40 ft/sec

20. Three men using a block and tackle are lifting a safe weighing 2,200 lb to a height of 30 ft. If each man develops ¼ hp, how long will it take to do the work?

21. A 64-lb boy on a swing is pulled backward and upward until his center of gravity has been raised 4 ft. What is his potential energy? If the swing is released, what will be his maximum speed?   *Ans.* 256 ft-lb; 16 ft/sec

22. A pendulum bob has a mass of 60 g. It is suspended by a cord 100 cm long which is pulled back through an angle of 30°. Find its maximum potential energy and its potential energy when the cord makes an angle of 15° with the vertical. Find its maximum speed and its speed when the cord makes the angle of 15° with the vertical.

23. A freight car weighing 40 tons runs into another freight car having the same weight. If one car were stationary and the other running at the rate of 15 mi/hr (22 ft/sec) and if the cars move off together after collision, with what velocity do they move?   *Ans.* 11 ft/sec

24. A bullet weighing 5 g is fired horizontally into a block of wood with a velocity of 250 m/sec. The block of wood weighs 12 kg. The bullet is embedded in the block and the two move off together. What is their velocity?

25. If the small steel ball in Fig. 7.11 has a mass of 100 g and the large one a mass of 200 g, find the recoil velocity of each ball if the smaller one is pulled out and released in such a way as to have an elastic collision when it is moving 50 cm/sec.
Ans. −16.7 cm/sec; 33.3 cm/sec

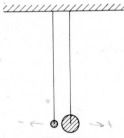

Fig. 7.11

26. A 15-lb body moving with a velocity of 6 ft/sec strikes a 6-lb body moving in the same direction with a velocity of 2 ft/sec. Find the velocity after impact, assuming that the masses are perfectly inelastic.

27. A 4-g bullet is fired into a 1,996-g block suspended by a long cord. The bullet remains in the block, which swings until its center of gravity is raised by 1.6 cm. Find the speed of the block and bullet as they leave the equilibrium position of the block. What was the initial speed of the bullet?   *Ans.* 0.56 m/sec; 280 m/sec

28. Two perfectly elastic balls, one of mass 5 lb and the other of mass 4 lb, are moving in opposite directions with velocities of 8 and 15 ft/sec, respectively. Find their velocities after impact.

29. A 20-g bullet is fired horizontally into a 2-kg block of wood suspended from a cord 1.5 m long. The block swings because of the impact, deflecting the cord to a position 30° from the vertical. Find the initial speed of the bullet. *Ans.* 202 m/sec

30. A bullet having a mass of 15 g is fired into a suspended wooden block that has a mass of 6,000 g. The block swings through an arc such that its center of gravity rises 2 cm. What was the initial velocity of the bullet?

31. A machine gun fires 300 bullets each minute with a velocity of 1,800 ft/sec. If the mass of each bullet is 0.025 lb, what horsepower is developed by the gun?
Ans. 11.5 hp

32. Two ivory balls, each weighing 200 g, are suspended by two cords 50 cm in length so that the balls are in contact when they are at rest. One ball is displaced until the angle between the cords is 30° and is then released. Find the velocity of each ball after impact.

33. In Fig. 7.11 the smaller ball has a mass of 200 g and the larger one of 400 g. If the smaller one is pulled back and released so that it has a velocity of 0.3 m/sec just before collision, the velocities of the two balls just after collision are −0.06 m/sec and 0.18 m/sec. What is the coefficient of restitution?   *Ans.* 0.8

34. If the coefficient of restitution for a golf ball dropped on a cement sidewalk is 0.75, find the height to which the ball returns if it is dropped from a height of 4 ft.

CHAPTER 8 important - especially AMA, IMA, eff, pulleys, inclined planes - and combinations of the last two.

Friction and Simple Machines

8.1. Friction. When a heavy block of wood is pushed along the top of a table, resistance is encountered. This resistance is called *friction*. The amount of frictional resistance depends on the surface of the table, the surface of the block, how clean the surfaces are, and several other factors. No matter what the nature of the surfaces in contact, there is always some resistance to the motion, whatever the direction. In some situations friction is undesirable and elaborate means are employed to make it as small as possible.

Friction has advantages as well as disadvantages. Except for friction between the shoes and the floor, a person would have the greatest difficulty in moving about. When the pavement is covered with ice, friction is small and walking is difficult. Because of friction, belts cling to pulleys and drive machinery. Without friction the acceleration and the braking of an automobile would require entirely different operations. Screws and nails hold their places in objects into which they are driven by means of friction.

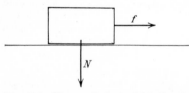

Fig. 8.1. The coefficient of friction is the ratio of the force f required to overcome friction to the force N pressing the surfaces together.

8.2. Kinetic Friction. When an object is sliding over a surface, the direction of the frictional force is always parallel to the surface and opposite to the direction of motion (Fig. 8.1). Let us denote by a lower-case f the force which is just necessary to overcome the frictional force and to keep a body moving with constant speed across the surface. It is found experimentally that the force necessary to overcome friction is proportional to the force pressing the surfaces against one another. This fact may be expressed by the equation

$$f = \mu_k N \qquad (8.1)$$

where N is the force pressing the surfaces together and μ_k is a constant called the *coefficient of kinetic* (or sliding) *friction*. *The coefficient of kinetic friction is the ratio of the force required to overcome friction between two surfaces to the normal force pressing the surfaces together when one surface is sliding over the other at constant speed.*

If the force perpendicular to the surface remains the same, the friction usually does not depend on the area of the rubbing surfaces.   The frictional force is sometimes independent of the velocity, but in other cases it varies with velocity.   For wood rubbing on wood, for brass on iron, or for iron on steel, the frictional force increases with the velocity in such a way that the coefficient of kinetic friction is roughly proportional to the logarithm of the speed.   However, for rubber tires on cement pavement the coefficient of friction decreases as the speed goes up.

It should be noted that these statements about friction are worded in a guarded way.   This is desirable because the rules which govern friction are only good working approximations.   Friction is a very complex phenomenon.   Even the smoothest surface is composed of hills and valleys from the microscopic point of view.   Surfaces may have significant elastic properties and change when the pressure changes.   If the surfaces are made as smooth as humanly possible, friction is likely to increase because of the greater significance of intermolecular attractions.   More molecules are in intimate contact.   Some substances melt and flow under the influence of frictional forces.   Such a behavior is called *plastic flow* and the flowing of the softer material may have the effect of lubricating the surface.

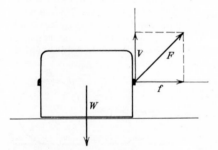

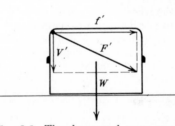

Fig. 8.2. The upward component of the applied force reduces the force pressing the surfaces together.

Fig. 8.3. The downward component of the applied force increases the force pressing the surfaces together.

It is important to observe that the force N pressing two surfaces together is not necessarily the weight of the sliding object.   Suppose that you wish to move a heavy trunk across a rough floor.   One possibility might be to pull on the handle as indicated in Fig. 8.2.   Then we may resolve the force **F** into two components; the horizontal component f is the force which is useful in overcoming the friction, while the vertical component V reduces the force pressing the surfaces together.   In this case $N = W - V$, where W is the weight of the trunk.   If you tried to move the trunk by pushing downward with the force **F'** as indicated in Fig. 8.3, the force N pressing the surfaces together would be $W + V'$, where V' is the downward component of **F'**. Thus, it takes a substantially greater force to move the trunk by pushing downward than by pulling upward.

8.3. Reducing Friction.   If a layer of liquid is introduced between two surfaces, the liquid flows over the surfaces and adheres to them. Instead of

having friction between two solids, there is friction between layers of the liquid. When oil is poured into the bearings of a machine, it forms layers and the sliding takes place primarily between layers of oil. Since the friction between oil layers is much less than between metal surfaces, the frictional force is much decreased. Oil is usually preferred to water as a lubricant, not because there is less friction between oil layers than between water layers, but because oil films have the property of staying between the metal surfaces, while water layers are readily squeezed out. The subject of friction in fluids is discussed in more detail in Chap. 12.

Fig. 8.4. Roller bearings reduce friction. (*New Departure Division, General Motors Corp.*)

When frictional forces cannot be reduced sufficiently by lubrication, it is customary to substitute rolling friction for sliding friction. The friction of a solid rolling on a surface is far less than the friction of a solid sliding over the surface. For this reason, automobiles and railroad trains operate on wheels rather than on runners and often use ball bearings or roller bearings (Fig. 8.4) at the axles. When a car wheel rolls on a level track, it makes a slight depression (Fig. 8.5) in the track and the wheel is somewhat flattened. As the wheel rolls, it is forced continually to climb out of this depression. This is one reason that even rolling wheels require a force to overcome friction. The amount of the depression depends on the nature and areas of the surfaces in contact.

8.4. The Coefficient of Static Friction.   If a body is at rest on a surface, it requires a larger force to overcome the friction and put the body

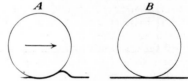

Fig. 8.5. The deformation of surfaces by rolling bodies.

in motion than it requires to keep the body in motion at constant speed. If we let f_s represent the force necessary to overcome friction in starting the body, we find that this force is also proportional to the force N pressing the surfaces together. Thus

$$f_s = \mu_s N \tag{8.2}$$

where μ_s is called the *coefficient of static friction*. *The coefficient of static friction between two surfaces is the ratio of the force required to overcome friction to the normal force pressing the surfaces together when the surfaces are at rest relative to one another.* Since the force necessary to overcome static friction is always greater than the force necessary to overcome sliding friction, the coefficient of static friction is always greater than the coefficient of kinetic friction.   Table 1 lists the coefficient of kinetic and static friction for several types of surfaces.

Table 1

APPROXIMATE COEFFICIENTS OF FRICTION

Surface	μ_k	μ_s	Surface	μ_k	μ_s
Steel on			Rubber tire on		
Steel..............	0.15	0.20	Dry concrete, low speeds....	0.7	0.9
Ice................	0.01	0.02	Dry concrete, high speeds...	0.35	0.6
Oak on oak..........	0.4	0.5	Wet concrete, low speed....	0.5	0.7
Greased surfaces.......	0.05	0.06			

Because static friction is always greater than kinetic friction, a good automobile driver is careful not to keep wheels locked when he is braking to a stop.   Rather, he keeps his wheels moving over the pavement as slowly as possible.   Once the wheels have stopped revolving, the tires slide over the pavement and the coefficient of kinetic friction is in effect.   As long as the point of contact between tire and pavement is at rest relative to the pavement, the coefficient of static friction is applicable.

If a body is at rest on a surface, the frictional force is just large enough to permit the conditions for equilibrium to be satisfied.   If the body is resting on a horizontal surface and no horizontal forces act, the frictional force is zero.   If the surface is tilted slightly, the frictional force becomes just great enough to prevent the body from sliding.   Thus the force of friction can be computed by the relation $f_s = \mu_s N$, only when the body is just at the point of sliding.   The product $\mu_s N$ gives the maximum value of the friction when the body is at rest.   In many cases the frictional force may be substantially less than this.

8.5. Friction on an Inclined Plane.   In Fig. 8.6 a block of weight W rests on a plane inclined at an angle θ with the horizontal.   Let the angle θ be varied until the block will just slide down the plane with uniform velocity when once started.   We represent this angle by θ_k. Let D represent the component of the weight down the plane and N be the component of the weight at right angles to the plane.   The force of friction between the block and plane is parallel to the plane and in the direction opposite to D, that is, up the plane.   Since the block experiences no acceleration, the frictional force up the plane is equal to

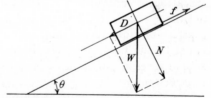

Fig. 8.6.   Friction holds a block in equilibrium on an inclined plane if θ is sufficiently small.

the component of the weight parallel to the plane, thus $D = f_k = W \sin \theta_k$. The force pressing the surfaces together is just the component of weight perpendicular to the plane which is $W \cos \theta_k$.   By definition, the coefficient of kinetic friction is

$$\mu_k = \frac{f_k}{N} = \frac{W \sin \theta_k}{W \cos \theta_k} = \tan \theta_k \qquad (8.3a)$$

The tangent of the angle at which the block slides down the plane with uniform velocity is equal to the coefficient of kinetic friction.

If the angle θ is varied until it is the largest angle at which the block will remain at rest on the plane, the component of the weight parallel to the plane ($W \sin \theta_s$) is equal to the force f_s necessary to overcome static friction, while the force pressing the surfaces together is equal to $W \cos \theta_s$, the component of the weight perpendicular to the plane. The angle θ_s at which we have satisfied these conditions is known as the *angle of repose*.

$$\mu_s = \frac{f_s}{N} = \frac{W \sin \theta_s}{W \cos \theta_s} = \tan \theta_s \qquad (8.3b)$$

8.6. Simple Machines. A machine is a device for overcoming a resisting force at one point by the application of a force at some other point. (In some machines, such as the automobile transmission, one torque may be exchanged for another torque.) Let us consider a specific

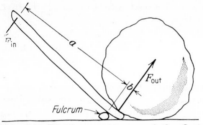

example: Suppose a primitive man wished to move a very large boulder, which was too large to shove. He would find a strong stick and use it to move the boulder, as shown in Fig. 8.7. If he pulls on one end of the stick with a force F_in, a very much larger force F_out is exerted on the boulder. When the stick is in equilibrium, the torque condition

Fig. 8.7. The lever was one of the first simple machines to be used by man.

gives the relation $F_\text{in} a = F_\text{out} b$. If a is 20 times b, F_out is 20 times F_in. By using this lever, our primitive man could exchange an input force F_in for an output force F_out 20 times as great.

At first glance it might seem that this violates the principle of conservation of energy, but a little further consideration shows that this is not the case. In order to move the boulder 1 in., the input force must be exerted for a distance a/b in. The work done by the man on the stick is equal to the work done on the boulder by the stick. By the use of a simple machine, *it is possible to exchange a small force acting through a large distance for a large force acting through a small distance.*

There are many kinds of simple machines. Among them are levers, inclined planes, pulleys, gear wheels, screws, wheels and axles, the wedge, and the differential pulley. Very complicated machines, such as the automobile or the mechanical cotton picker, are composed of a large number of interconnected simple machines.

8.7. Mechanical Advantage and Efficiency. As we have seen, a simple machine is a device for providing some output force in return for an input force. *The ratio of the output force F_out to the input force F_in is the actual mechanical advantage (AMA) of the machine.*

$$\text{AMA} = \frac{F_{out}}{F_{in}} \tag{8.4}$$

In defining the actual mechanical advantage of the machine, we concern ourselves only with the magnitudes of the forces and not with their directions.

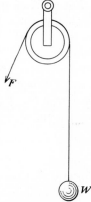

In our example of a primitive man moving a boulder, we had a lever which had a large mechanical advantage. It is by no means true that all useful machines have large mechanical advantage.   The simple pulley (Fig. 8.8) has a mechanical advantage of essentially unity and serves only to change the direction of the force.   However, if we are trying to lift some mortar to the top of a building, it is convenient to be able to stand on the ground and pull downward on the rope to lift the mortar.   Some of our most useful machines have mechanical advantages of less than one.   Consider the human forearm (Fig. 8.9) where the output force exerted by the hand is very much smaller than the input force exerted by the muscles. Here we have a mechanical advantage which is much less than unity.   In such a machine we have a smaller output force moving through a greater distance than does the input force.

Fig. 8.8. A simple pulley changes only the direction of the applied force.

In real machines friction opposes the motion and work must be done to overcome this friction.   In addition, it may be necessary to raise some

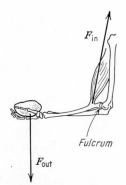

Fig. 8.9. The human forearm is a lever with mechanical advantage much less than unity.

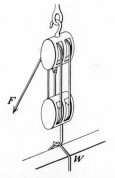

Fig. 8.10. In raising the load W, work must be done to lift the lower pulley block and to overcome friction.

part of the machine which gives us no useful work output.   For example, in Fig. 8.10 the lower pulley block must be raised when we lift the load W.   The work done against friction and in lifting parts of the machine does not appear as useful work output.   Therefore, in any real machine the useful work output is less than the work input.   The *efficiency* (*Eff*) *of a machine is the ratio of the useful work output to the work input.*

$$\text{Eff} = \frac{\text{work}_{\text{out}}}{\text{work}_{\text{in}}} \tag{8.5}$$

For an ideal machine, with no friction and massless moving parts, the efficiency would be 100 per cent.   The mechanical advantage of an ideal machine is called the *ideal mechanical advantage* (IMA).   Let d_{out} be the distance moved by the output force and d_{in} the distance moved by the input force.   For an ideal machine the efficiency is 100 per cent and $\text{work}_{\text{out}} = \text{work}_{\text{in}}$; hence, $F_{\text{out}}d_{\text{out}} = F_{\text{in}}d_{\text{in}}$.   Therefore, *the mechanical advantage* $F_{\text{out}}/F_{\text{in}}$ *for an ideal machine is* $d_{\text{in}}/d_{\text{out}}$.   This ratio is the *ideal mechanical advantage*, which we abbreviate IMA.

$$\text{IMA} = \frac{d_{\text{in}}}{d_{\text{out}}} \tag{8.6}$$

For any real machine the ideal mechanical advantage is greater than the actual mechanical advantage.   Indeed, the efficiency can be seen to be equal to the ratio of the actual mechanical advantage to the ideal mechanical advantage by observing that

$$\text{Eff} = \frac{\text{work}_{\text{out}}}{\text{work}_{\text{in}}} = \frac{F_{\text{out}}}{F_{\text{in}}}\frac{d_{\text{out}}}{d_{\text{in}}} = \frac{\text{AMA}}{\text{IMA}}$$

8.8. Types of Simple Machines. The concepts of actual mechanical advantage, ideal mechanical advantage, and efficiency may be applied to all

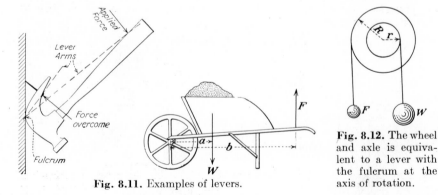

Fig. 8.11. Examples of levers.

Fig. 8.12. The wheel and axle is equivalent to a lever with the fulcrum at the axis of rotation.

types of simple machines.   Among the many kinds of simple machines some of the more important are the following:

1. *The Lever.*   The lever is one of the most efficient machines.   It may take many different forms and have a wide variety of applications in both physical and biological systems.   Two examples are illustrated in Fig. 8.11.

2. *The Wheel and Axle.*   A wheel and axle (Fig. 8.12) consists of a large wheel and a small wheel fastened together on the same axle.   The small wheel may

itself be the axle.   This simple machine may be looked upon as a lever with the axis of the wheel as the fulcrum.

3. *The Pulley.*   A pulley consists of a wheel with a grooved rim, called a *sheave*, which is free to move about an axis which is mounted in a frame known as a *block*.   A flexible rope passes over the groove in the rim of the wheel.   Fixed and movable pulleys may be combined in a variety of ways.   It is common to use a single fixed block and a single movable block, both of which have two or more sheaves.   Typical examples are shown in Fig. 8.13.

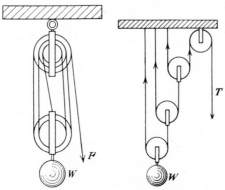
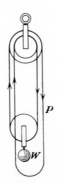

Fig. 8.13. Examples of pulley arrangements.   **Fig. 8.14.** A differential pulley with an endless chain.

4. *The Differential Pulley.*   Where heavy loads are to be lifted, use is often made of the differential pulley (Fig. 8.14).   This pulley consists of a movable block with a single sheave and a fixed block with two sheaves of different diameters *fastened rigidly together*.   An endless chain passes over the sheaves.   Teeth-like projections extend from the rim of the sheaves and the links of the chain fit over the teeth so that the chain cannot slip.

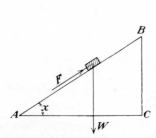
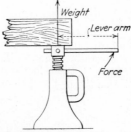

Fig. 8.15. An inclined plane as a simple machine.

Fig. 8.16. The jackscrew combines the principle of the lever with that of the inclined plane.

5. *The Inclined Plane.*   If a heavy object must be raised or lowered, an inclined plane is frequently used.   When a body rests on an inclined plane (Fig. 8.15), its weight may be resolved into two components, a force $W \sin \theta$ parallel to the plane and $W \cos \theta$ pressing the body against the plane.   The force required to move the body up the plane is equal to $W \sin \theta$ plus any frictional force f which must be overcome.   The output force is just the weight to be lifted.

The wedge used to split a log and the head of an axe are examples of the inclined plane used in special operations.

6. *The Jackscrew.* When large forces must be exerted, a jackscrew is often useful (Fig. 8.16). It has a high mechanical advantage and ordinarily a very low efficiency. The screw is essentially an inclined plane wrapped around a cylinder. The pitch P of a screw is the distance between successive threads. If the input force is rotated through one complete revolution, the output force moves through a distance equal to the pitch.

8.9. Rotating Systems. In the automobile transmission and in other rotating machinery one torque is exchanged for another. For a rotating system the actual mechanical advantage is the torque output divided by the torque input,

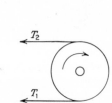

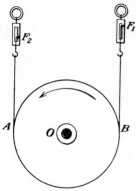

Fig. 8.17. The frictional force between the belt and the pulley is $T_1 - T_2$.

Fig. 8.18. A Prony brake in which the power output of an engine is dissipated by doing work against the net frictional force ($F_1 - F_2$).

while the ideal mechanical advantage is given by the angle turned through by the input torque divided by the corresponding angle turned through by the output torque.

When a pulley is being driven by a belt (Fig. 8.17), the tensions in the straight parts of the belt are not equal. They differ by the friction that is exerted between the belt and the pulley. Let T_2 be the tension in that part of the belt which is moving toward the pulley, T_1 the tension in that part which is moving away from the pulley, and V the velocity with which the belt is moving. The net frictional force between the belt and the pulley is $T_1 - T_2$ and the power delivered to the pulley is $(T_1 - T_2)V$.

Example. The tension on one side of a belt is 350 lb and that on the other side is 150 lb. The belt is moving 300 ft/min. Find the horsepower delivered to the pulley.

$$
\begin{aligned}
\text{Power} &= (350 - 150)\ \text{lb} \times (300\ \text{ft/min}) \\
&= \frac{200\ \text{lb} \times 300\ \text{ft/min}}{60\ \text{sec/min}} \times \frac{1\ \text{hp}}{550\ \text{ft-lb/sec}} \\
&= 1.8\ \text{hp}
\end{aligned}
$$

Engines and motors are rated in terms of the brake horsepower which they develop. This may be measured by using the engine to drive a shaft like that of Fig. 8.18. Such an arrangement is known as a *Prony brake.* The power output is dissipated in heat by friction. The power is determined by measuring the net frictional force F and the linear speed v of a point on the surface of the shaft and is given by the product Fv.

PROBLEMS

1. A horizontal force of 20 lb is required to pull a 100-lb trunk along a floor. What is the coefficient of kinetic friction?   *Ans. 0.2*

2. A weight of 8 lb hanging over the edge of a table on a cord is just sufficient to drag a 48-lb body along the horizontal surface of the table with unchanging velocity. What is the coefficient of kinetic friction?

3. A brake shoe is pressed against the rim of a wheel with a force of 50 newtons. If the coefficient of friction between the surfaces is 0.18, how much frictional force is developed?   *Ans. 9 newtons*

4. The angle of repose for a 10-lb block of metal on an incline is found to be 10°. How much force, parallel to the incline, is necessary to cause the body to begin to move up the incline?

5. A force of 100 lb exerted at an angle of 37° above the horizontal is needed to move a 500-lb box along a cement floor. Find the coefficient of kinetic friction. *Ans. 0.18*

6. A block slides down a plane that is inclined 40° with the horizontal. If the coefficient of friction between the block and the surface of the incline is 0.2, find the acceleration of the block.

7. A block rests on a plane that is inclined at an angle of 30° to the horizontal. The coefficient of kinetic friction between the block and the plane is 0.2. If the block has a mass of 30 kg, what is the force, parallel to the incline, necessary to cause it to slide up the plane?   *Ans. 198 newtons*

8. What force acting at an angle of 30° above the horizontal is necessary to move a mass of 10 kg with uniform velocity along a horizontal surface, the coefficient of friction being 0.2?

9. A 3,200-lb car begins to skid when traveling 90 ft/sec (61 mi/hr) around a level curve of 300 ft radius. Find the centripetal acceleration and the coefficient of friction between the tires and the road.   *Ans. 27 ft/sec²; 0.84*

10. What is the highest speed at which a 3,200-lb automobile can travel around a curve 100 ft in radius, on a level road, if the coefficient of friction between the road and the tires is 0.64?

11. A 25-kg block of ice is given a speed of 10 m/sec on the surface of a pond where the coefficient of friction is 0.015. How far will the ice go before coming to rest?   *Ans. 340 m*

12. A system of pulleys consists of a movable block with two pulleys and a fixed block with three pulleys. If one end of the rope is fastened to the movable block, what ideal mechanical advantage is obtained? How far must the free end of the rope be pulled in order to displace the movable block through 1 ft?

13. A water bucket weighing 80 lb is raised by a crank-and-axle arrangement. The axle has a radius of 6 in. and the crank has a radius of 2 ft. If a force of 30 lb is required on the crank, find the actual mechanical advantage, the ideal mechanical advantage, and the efficiency.   *Ans. 2.67; 4; 0.67*

14. The axle of a capstan is 8 in. in diameter. There are six bars, or levers, projecting from the capstan, and a man exerts a force of 25 lb at the end of each bar. How long must the bars be, in order that six men may raise a weight of 1.25 tons?

15. An inclined plane 13 ft long is used to slide a 390-lb box up to a loading platform 5 ft above ground level. A force of 250 lb is required. Find the efficiency of this inclined plane for this job. What force is required to overcome friction? What is the coefficient of friction between the plane and the box?

Ans. 60 per cent; 100 lb; 0.278

$AMA = \dfrac{w}{F}$

16. A jackscrew with a pitch of 0.25 in. has a handle 30 in. long.   A force of 20 lb must be applied when a load of 6,000 lb is being lifted.   Calculate the ideal mechanical advantage, the actual mechanical advantage, and the efficiency.

17. In the pulley system shown in Fig. 8.10 a force of 50 lb is required to lift a 150-lb weight.   Find the ideal mechanical advantage, the actual mechanical advantage, and the efficiency.   *Ans.* 4; 3; 75 per cent

18. Show that the ideal mechanical advantage of a differential pulley is given by $2R/(R - r)$, where R and r are the radii of the larger and smaller sheaves, respectively.

19. Find the ideal mechanical advantage of a differential pulley in which the radius of the larger pulley is 7 in. and that of the smaller pulley is 6 in.   *Ans.* 14

20. A man is pushing a 120-lb box along a level floor with a uniform velocity of 5 ft/sec by exerting a force on the box at an angle of 30° downward from horizontal. If the coefficient of friction between sliding surfaces is 0.2, what is the magnitude of the force?

21. A mass weighing 100 lb rests on an inclined plane that makes an angle of 30° with the horizontal.   If the coefficient of friction between the mass and the plane is 0.2, how much work is done in moving the mass up the plane a distance of 10 ft?
                                                                           Ans. 673 ft-lb

22. A mass of 6 kg rests on a plane that is inclined 15° to the horizontal.   It will just slide down the plane without acceleration.   Find its acceleration when the plane is inclined 30° to the horizontal.   What will be the kinetic energy when it has moved a distance of 2 m?

23. A mass of 16 kg rests on a horizontal table and is attached by means of a flexible cord passing over a weightless pulley to a mass of 8 kg.   The latter mass hangs vertically.   If the coefficient of friction between the mass and the table is 0.1, what is the acceleration of the system?   *Ans.* 2.6 m/sec²

24. A motor drives a hoist which lifts a 2-ton load a distance of 100 ft in 30 sec. The efficiency of the motor is 85 per cent and that of the hoist is 45 per cent.   What power in watts (1 hp equals 746 watts) is supplied to the load?   to the hoist?   to the motor?

25. Show that for a simple pulley system with two blocks, one fixed and one movable as in Fig. 8.10, the ideal mechanical advantage is the number of strands directly supporting the load.

CHAPTER 9

Liquids at Rest

9.1. Introduction. A liquid has no shape of its own, but takes the shape of the containing vessel. Liquids yield to a continued application of force that tends to deform them or change their shape. They do, however, manifest wide differences in their readiness to yield to distorting force. Water, alcohol, and ether are very mobile liquids which yield readily. Glycerin is less mobile and tar still less so. There is no sharp line of demarcation between liquids and solids. In warm weather paraffin candles yield under their own weight and bend double. Although shoemaker's wax will break readily when cold, it behaves like a very viscous liquid at higher temperatures. All liquids offer large resistance to efforts to change their volume.

9.2. Pressure in a Liquid. A liquid contained in a vessel exerts forces against the walls of the vessel. In order to discuss the interaction between the liquid and the walls, it is convenient to introduce the concept of pressure. *Pressure is defined as the ratio of force to area when the area is perpendicular to the force.*

$$p = \frac{F}{A} \qquad (9.1)$$

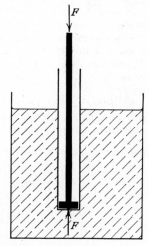

Fig. 9.1. A simple device for making crude measurements of pressure.

More precisely, the pressure at any point is the ratio of the normal force ΔF exerted on a small area ΔA surrounding the point to this area. Pressure may be expressed in pounds per square inch, pounds per square foot, newtons per square meter, and so forth—in general, as any unit of force divided by a unit of area.

If we explore a liquid confined in a vessel with a little device such as that of Fig. 9.1 for measuring the pressure, we find that at a given level in the liquid the magnitude of the force acting on the little area is the

103

same regardless of how the area is oriented. The force is always perpendicular to the area. Further, we find that the deeper we go, the greater the pressure becomes. If we adjust the device so that the pressure reads zero at the surface of the liquid (actually atmospheric pressure is acting here), we find that the pressure is directly proportional to the depth h to which we move. That this should be true is easy to understand if we consider the force on an area A at the bottom of a container (Fig. 9.2). This area supports the weight of a column of fluid above it.

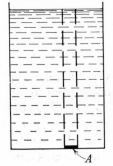

The weight is given by $hAdg$, where d is the density (mass/volume) of the liquid. The pressure is the ratio of the force to the area; $p = hAdg/A$. Hence,

$$p = hdg \qquad (9.2)$$

In many problems it is convenient to use weight density d_w (weight per unit volume) rather than density (mass per unit volume). The weight of a given volume of the fluid is equal to d_wV and the pressure becomes equal to hd_w. In the British engineering system we ordinarily use weight density, pounds per cubic foot (lb/ft³), rather than mass density, slugs per cubic foot (slugs/ft³). Hence the relation

$$p = hd_w \qquad (9.2a)$$

Fig. 9.2. The pressure at a depth h is proportional to depth and to the density of the liquid.

is frequently more convenient than $p = hdg$. (Note that, since $W = mg$, $d_w = W/V = mg/V = dg$.)

Although we have derived Eqs. (9.2) and (9.2a) only for the bottom of our container, they are applicable at any point in the liquid at rest. It should be observed that h is the *vertical* height from the point to the free surface.

Example. The hatch of a submarine is 100 ft under the surface of the ocean. If the weight density of sea water is 64 lb/ft³, find the pressure at the hatch and the total force on the hatch if it is a rectangle 2 ft wide and 3 ft long.

$$p = hd_w = 100 \text{ ft} \times 64 \text{ lb/ft}^3$$
$$= 6{,}400 \text{ lb/ft}^2$$
$$F = pA = 6{,}400 \text{ lb/ft}^2 \times 6 \text{ ft}^2$$
$$= 38{,}400 \text{ lb}$$

Example. Find the pressure at the bottom of a column of mercury 74 cm high if the density of mercury is 13,600 kg/m³.

$$p = hdg$$
$$= 0.74 \text{ m} \times 13{,}600 \text{ kg/m}^3 \times 9.8 \text{ m/sec}^2$$
$$= 99{,}000 \frac{\text{kg-m}}{\text{m}^2\text{-sec}^2}$$
$$= 99{,}000 \text{ newtons/m}^2$$

since 1 newton = 1 kg-m/sec².

Example. The pressure of water in the water mains is 35 lb/in.² How much work is required to pump 500,000 ft³ of water into the mains?

$$\text{Work} = \text{force} \times \text{distance} = (\text{force/area}) \times (\text{distance} \times \text{area})$$
$$= \text{pressure} \times \text{change of volume}$$
$$= 35 \text{ lb/in.}^2 \times 144 \text{ in.}^2/\text{ft}^2 \times 500,000 \text{ ft}^3$$
$$= 252 \times 10^7 \text{ ft-lb}$$

9.3. Pressure in Vessels of Different Shapes. Regardless of the shape of the vessel, the pressure at a given depth is given by Eq. (9.2). The question may be raised: If the pressure is due to the weight of the fluid above, why is the pressure not greater in vessel B of Fig. 9.3 in which the sides slope outward than in vessel

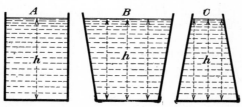

Fig. 9.3. The pressure at a given depth is independent of the shape of the vessel.

C where the sides slant inward? Certainly, vessel B contains a much greater weight of water. The answer is: In vessel B the slanting sides exert forces on the liquid which have an upward component. Thus, a portion of the weight of the fluid is actually held up by the sloping sides. On the other hand, in vessel C the force exerted by the slanting sides on the liquid is downward. When the force due to the slanting walls is added to the weight of the fluid, the pressure at the bottom is found to be exactly the same as in vessels A and B.

It is a matter of common experience that liquids seek their own level in interconnected vessels. If tubes of various sizes and shapes are connected, liquid poured into one of these tubes (Fig. 9.4) comes to the same level in all tubes (provided surface tension effects may be neglected). This result is to be expected from the fact that the pressure in the liquid depends on the depth below the free

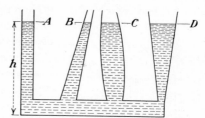

Fig. 9.4. A liquid stands at the same level in communicating tubes.

surface. For all points in the interior of the liquid at the same level the pressure must be the same. If it is not, the liquid flows from one point to the other until the pressure becomes equalized.

9.4. Liquids in Communicating Tubes. Let two liquids that do not react chemically be placed in a bent tube (Fig. 9.5). When the liquids are at rest, the pressure exerted by the column of lighter liquid is balanced by the pressure due to the column of heavier liquid above the junction level of the liquids. Let d_1 be the density of the lighter liquid, d_2 the density of the heavier liquid, h_1 the height of the lighter liquid, and h_2 the height of the heavier liquid above the junction. Then

$$p_1 = h_1 d_1 g = h_2 d_2 g = p_2 \tag{9.3}$$

from which $h_1/h_2 = d_2/d_1$.   *The heights of two liquids above their surface of separation are inversely proportional to the densities.*

In case the liquids react chemically, the bent tube may be inverted and the ends placed in cups containing the liquids (Fig. 9.6). The air from the upper part of the bent tube is partly removed and the stopcock closed. The pressure above both liquids inside the tube is the same and the atmospheric pressure on the liquids in the open vessels is the same. The difference between the pressure inside the tube and the atmospheric pressure is balanced in each case by the rise of the liquid in the tube. These differences in pressure are the same and again

$$h_1 d_1 g = h_2 d_2 g$$

Example. If one of the beakers in Fig. 9.6 contains sulfuric acid and the other contains water, and if the height of the column of water is 40 cm when the height of the column of acid is 30 cm, find the density of the sulfuric acid.

$$h_a d_a g = h_w d_w g \qquad d_w = 1,000 \text{ kg/m}^3$$
$$\frac{d_a}{d_w} = \frac{h_w}{h_a} = \frac{0.4 \text{ m}}{0.3 \text{ m}}$$
$$d_a = 1,330 \text{ kg/m}^3$$

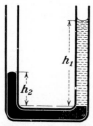

Fig. 9.5. The pressure at the bottom of column h_1 of the less dense liquid is the same as that at the bottom of column h_2 of the more dense liquid.

9.5. Pascal's Principle. If we have a liquid which is completely enclosed (Fig. 9.7) and increase the pressure at any one point in the fluid, the pressure increases by an equal amount at all other points. For example, if we add a weight of 1 lb to piston A of Fig. 9.7, it is found that a weight of 1 lb must be added to piston B in order to keep it from moving. This is a special case of a general principle known as Pascal's principle. *If the pressure at any point in an enclosed fluid at*

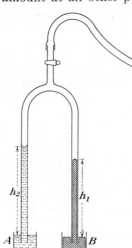

Fig. 9.6. The heights of the liquids are inversely proportional to the densities.

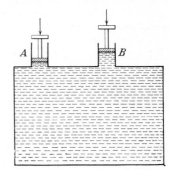

Fig. 9.7. If the pressure is changed at any point in an enclosed fluid, it changes by an equal amount at all points in the fluid.

rest is changed, the pressure changes by an equal amount at all points in the fluid. Here the term fluid is used to mean any thing which flows, i.e., either a liquid or a gas.   If the pressure is increased or decreased at one point in the fluid, it is increased or decreased uniformly throughout the liquid or gas.   Note that Pascal's principle does *not* say that the pressure is the same everywhere within the enclosed fluid.   The pressure continues to be greater at greater depth.   Pascal's principle deals with the change in pressure, not with the absolute pressure.

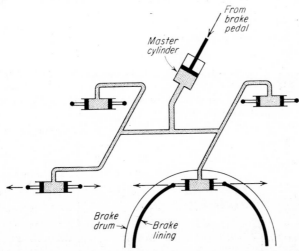

Fig. 9.8. Pascal's principle is applied in the brake system of an automobile.

9.6. Applications of Pascal's Principle.   An important application of Pascal's principle occurs in the hydraulic system of an automobile (Fig. 9.8).   If the pressure is increased in the master cylinder by pressing on the brake pedal, the pressure increases by an equal amount at each piston in the hydraulic system.

If all the pistons at the brake shoes have the same cross-sectional area, an equal force is applied at all the brake shoes.

Consider two cylinders which are connected together and filled with water (Fig. 9.9).   If each cylinder is fitted with a piston which moves without friction and if the two pistons are at the same level, the pressure at each will be the same.   If A is the area of the larger piston and a the area of the smaller one, the force f on the smaller piston is given by pa, while the force F on the larger piston is given by pA.

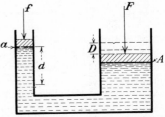

Fig. 9.9. Multiplication of force by transmitted pressure.

By applying a force of f lb on the small piston, it is possible to produce a force $F = Af/a$ on the larger piston.

If the larger and smaller pistons are not at the same level, the pressures on the two pistons are not the same; they differ by dgh, where h is the difference in the height of the two pistons.   If the pressure is increased 10 lb/in.² on the smaller piston, it also increases 10 lb/in.² at the larger piston, but the pressures are not equal.   A direct application of these ideas is found in the hydraulic press.

9.7. Archimedes' Principle.

It is a matter of common experience that bodies are apparently lighter under water than in air. A fresh egg sinks in pure water, but floats in salty water. A piece of iron sinks in water, but floats in mercury. If a diver picks up a stone under water and brings it to the surface, he finds that the stone is much heavier above the surface. The principle which explains these observations was discovered by the distinguished Greek mathematician and physicist Archimedes. Archimedes' principle states that:

A body immersed in a fluid is buoyed up by a force equal to the weight of the fluid displaced.

An experimental verification of Archimedes' principle can be obtained by use of the equipment of Fig. 9.10. A hollow cylindrical cup and a piece of brass turned so that it will just fill the cavity inside the cup are suspended from one arm of a balance and the necessary weights to restore equilibrium added to the

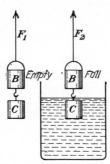

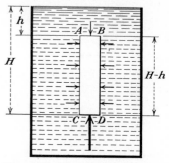

Fig. 9.10. Apparatus to show that the cylinder C is buoyed up by a force equal to the weight of the fluid it displaces.

Fig. 9.11. The net upward force on the cylinder $ABCD$ is equal to the weight of the displaced fluid.

other pan. When a vessel of water is brought up in such a way that the cylinder C is completely submerged, the side of the balance carrying the cylinder rises, showing that the water is pushing upward on the cylinder. If water is now poured into the cup until it is full, the original equilibrium of the balance is restored. The cylinder is buoyed up by a force equal to the weight of the water displaced.

Archimedes' principle follows directly from the laws of fluid pressure. If a cylindrical block (Fig. 9.11) is immersed in a vessel filled with liquid, the resultant of the forces on the vertical sides is zero. Upon the upper face of the cylinder there is a downward force equal to the pressure at the upper surface multiplied by the cross-sectional area A of the cylinder. On the lower face there is an upward force equal to the pressure at the bottom multiplied by the area. The upward force exceeds the downward force, because the pressure is greater at the greater depth. The net upward force is $HdgA - hdgA = (H - h)Adg = Vdg$, where V is the volume of the cylinder. The net buoyant force is equal to the weight of the fluid displaced. The same sort of reasoning holds for a body of any shape in any liquid. Hence, a body immersed in any fluid is lighter by the weight of fluid which it displaces.

Example.   An aluminum casting weighs 5.4 lb in air and 3.4 lb when submerged in water.   Find the volume of the casting and the weight density of Al.

Loss of weight = 5.4 − 3.4 = 2.0 lb, the weight of water displaced.   Since 1 ft³ of water weighs 62.5 lb, 2 lb occupy 2/62.5 = 0.032 ft³.

$$d_w = \frac{W}{V} = \frac{5.4 \text{ lb}}{0.032 \text{ ft}^3} = 169 \text{ lb/ft}^3$$

Fish are capable of moving toward the surface or into deep water by regulating the quantity of water which they displace and, therefore, the buoyant force. By a distension of the air bags in their bodies they can change their volumes and thus change the buoyancy of the water on them.   By a contraction of its air sacs the volume of a fish is diminished and it sinks.   Similarly, a submarine can submerge by letting water into tanks, thus making the submarine heavier than an equal volume of water.   It rises from below the surface by blowing or pumping this water out of the tanks.

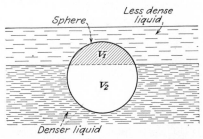

9.8. Floating Bodies.   When a body floats on a liquid, the buoyant force is equal to the weight of the body.   The body sinks until it displaces its own weight (Fig. 9.12) and then remains in equilibrium. This explains why a ship rides lower in the water when loaded than when empty and why it rides higher in salt

Fig. 9.12. A sphere floating at the interface between two liquids of different densities.   The sphere sinks until it displaces its own weight.

water than in fresh.   The upward force of the liquid on a wholly or partly immersed body is called *buoyancy*.

Example.   A barge is 30 ft long and 16 ft wide and has vertical sides.   When three horses are driven on board, the barge sinks 2 in. farther into the water.   How much do the horses weigh?

$$\text{Volume of displaced water} = 30 \text{ ft} \times 16 \text{ ft} \times \tfrac{1}{6} \text{ ft}$$
$$= 80 \text{ ft}^3$$
$$\text{Weight of water displaced} = 80 \text{ ft}^3 \times 62.5 \text{ lb/ft}^3$$
$$= 5,000 \text{ lb}$$
$$\text{Weight of horses} = \text{weight of displaced water} = 5,000 \text{ lb}$$

The point through which the force of buoyancy acts is the *center of buoyancy*. This point lies at the center of gravity of the displaced fluid.   The buoyant force of all the displaced fluid may be replaced by a single force acting through the center of buoyancy.   In order for a floating body, such as a ship, to be in stable equilibrium, it must return to its normal position when displaced.   The weight W of the body acts downward at G, the center of gravity, while the lifting force of the displaced water acts upward through the center of buoyancy.   If the body is to be in stable equilibrium, there must be a torque which restores the body to its normal position.   This condition for stability will be realized if the metacenter M lies above the center of gravity of the body.   The position of the metacenter is determined by the intersection of two lines, one drawn vertically through the center of buoyancy B and the other drawn vertically through the center of gravity G of the body *before displacement*.   If the metacenter lies above the center of gravity, there is a restoring torque and the body is in stable equilibrium (Fig. 9.13).   If, however, the metacenter lies below the center of gravity, the torque that comes into play when the body is displaced from its normal position increases the displacement further.   The body is in unstable equilibrium (Fig. 9.14) and turns over.

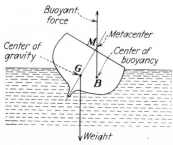

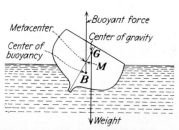

Fig. 9.13. When the center of gravity is below the metacenter, the boat is stable.

Fig. 9.14. When the center of gravity is above the metacenter, the boat is unstable.

9.9. Density and Specific Gravity.   The density of a body is the ratio of its mass to its volume, while the weight density is the ratio of weight to volume.   Table 1 lists the densities of a number of common liquids and solids.   It is often difficult to find the volume of a body, especially when it has an irregular shape.   In such cases the volume may be determined by the application of Archimedes' principle.   Since the

Table 1

DENSITIES OF SOLIDS AND LIQUIDS (20°C)

Substance	Density		Substance	Density	
	kg/m³	lb mass/ft³		kg/m³	lb mass/ft³
Alcohol.............	789	49.3	Iron (cast).........	7,200	450
Aluminum..........	2,650	164	Iron (wrought)......	7,800	480
Balsa wood.........	160	10	Kerosene...........	820	51.2
Brass..............	8,600	535	Lead..............	11,370	710
Brick..............	2,100	131	Mercury...........	13,600	840
Copper............	8,930	555	Oak..............	800	50
Cork..............	240	15	Pine..............	500	31.2
Diamond...........	3,520	220	Silver.............	10,500	655
Glass (crown).......	2,500	156	Turpentine.........	870	54.3
Glass (flint)........	3,700	230	Tin...............	7,290	455
Gasoline...........	790	49.4	Water (fresh).......	1,000	62.5
Gold..............	19,320	1,200	Water (sea)........	1,030	64.4
Glycerin...........	1,260	78.7	Zinc..............	7,150	446.2
Ice (0°C)...........	917	57.2			

˙ody displaces a volume of water equal to its own volume and since each cubic centimeter of water weighs 1 gram-force (g-wt), the loss of weight in water in gram-weights is numerically equal to the volume of the immersed body in cubic centimeters.   This fact makes it convenient to use the gram-weight as a measure of force and the cubic centimeter as a unit of volume in problems involving Archimedes' principle.

The specific gravity of a body is the ratio of its density to the density of water.   Thus, if the specific gravity of a body is equal to five, the body weighs five times as much as an equal volume of water.

When a body is heavier than an equal volume of water (and is insoluble in water), its volume can be determined by finding the loss of weight when weighed in water.   From this loss of weight we can compute the volume. From the mass and volume the density may be obtained.

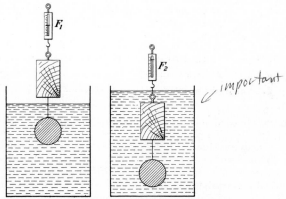

important

Fig. 9.15. The buoyant force on the block of wood, which would float if there were no sinker, is the difference between F_1 and F_2.

Example.   A piece of iron weighs 78 g-wt in air and 68 g-wt in water.   What volume of water is displaced?   What is the density of the iron?

Weight of water displaced = loss of weight of iron in water
= 78 g-wt − 68 g-wt = 10 g-wt
Volume of water displaced = volume of iron = 10 cm³
Density of iron = $\dfrac{\text{mass of iron}}{\text{volume}}$ = $\dfrac{78 \text{ g}}{10 \text{ cm}^3}$ = 7.8 g/cm³

If the object is lighter than water (and insoluble), its volume may still be determined by this method by fastening to the body a sinker large enough to pull it below the surface of the water.   In this case (Fig. 9.15) the combined weight of the body and the sinker is first determined when the sinker is immersed in water and the body is above the surface of the water.   The body is then also submerged and the combined weight redetermined.   The reduction in weight is equal to the weight of the water displaced by the body.

Example.   A piece of cork weighs 25 g-wt in air.   When it is fastened to a sinker and the sinker alone immersed in water, the combined weight of sinker and cork is

200 g-wt. When both sinker and cork are immersed, they weigh 75 g-wt. What is the density of the cork?

Loss of weight due to submerging body = 200 g-wt − 75 g-wt = 125 g-wt
Volume of water displaced by body = 125 cm³

$$\text{Density} = \frac{\text{mass of body}}{\text{volume}} = \frac{25 \text{ g}}{125 \text{ cm}^3} = 0.2 \text{ g/cm}^3$$
$$= 200 \text{ kg/m}^3$$

9.10. Specific-gravity Bottle. A specific-gravity bottle (Fig. 9.16) is used to determine the specific gravity of liquids. It consists of a glass bottle of convenient volume. This bottle is first weighed empty, then full of water, and then full of liquid of which the specific gravity is desired. From these data the specific gravity can be calculated by the method illustrated below.

Example. A specific-gravity bottle when empty weighs 240.30 g-wt. When filled with water, it weighs 390.30 g-wt; when filled with alcohol, it weighs 360.30 g-wt. Find the specific gravity of alcohol.

Weight of water = 390.30 − 240.30 = 150 g-wt
Weight of equal volume of alcohol = 360.30 − 240.30
$$= 120.00 \text{ g-wt}$$

$$\text{Specific gravity} = \frac{\text{weight of alcohol}}{\text{weight of equal volume of water}}$$
$$= \frac{120.00 \text{ g-wt}}{150.00 \text{ g-wt}} = 0.80$$

Fig. 9.16. A specific-gravity bottle.

9.11. Hydrometer. Another application of the principle of Archimedes is found in the hydrometer, which is extensively used for determining the specific gravity of liquids. It is usually made of a cylindrical glass tube (Fig. 9.17) which is provided with a narrow graduated glass stem. At the lower end of the hydrometer is placed a sufficient amount of mercury or shot to make the hydrometer sink to the desired level in the liquid. The depth to which it sinks is determined by the density of the liquid. When the buoyancy of the liquid is sufficient to balance the weight of the hydrometer, the hydrometer floats in the liquid. The point at which the surface of the liquid touches the stem can be read and the density found directly from the graduated stem. Since the weight of the hydrometer remains the same, it will sink farther in light liquids like alcohol or kerosene than in heavier liquids like brine. For this reason the larger numbers are near the bottom of the scale and the smaller numbers near the top. Hydrometers are commonly used in finding the density of the acid in storage batteries and in estimating the amount of antifreeze in automobile radiators.

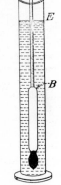

Fig. 9.17. A hydrometer for measuring the densities of liquids.

PROBLEMS

1. What is the average pressure due to the weight of a 150-lb person if the effective area of each foot is 20 in.² and the person is standing on both feet? on just one foot?   *Ans.* 3.75 lb/in.²; 7.5 lb/in.²

2. The pressure in an automobile tire is 28 lb/in.² greater than atmospheric pressure. If the wheel on which the tire is mounted supports 800 lb, what area of the tire is in contact with the ground? (Neglect the mechanical strength of the casing.)

3. What pressure due to the weight of the water does a swimmer experience at the bottom of a swimming pool 9 ft deep? *Ans.* 3.9 lb/in.²

4. A diver works at a depth of 20 m in sea water; density is 1.03 g/cm³. Find the pressure in excess of atmospheric pressure which he experiences at that depth.

5. The water level in a standpipe is 250 ft above the lowest part of a town. What is the maximum water pressure available in this town due to the "head" of water? *Ans.* 108.3 lb/in.²

6. A swimming pool 25 ft wide and 75 ft long has a depth of 3 ft at one end and 10 ft at the other. What is the total downward force of the water on the bottom of the pool? What is the average pressure on the bottom? Assume the bottom of the pool is plane.

7. Find the force on the glass side of an aquarium containing salt water with a density of 1.03 g/cm³, if the glass is 1.2 m wide and the water behind it is 50 cm deep. *Ans.* 1,514 newtons

8. A lock gate is 20 ft wide and 39 ft high. The depth of water on one side is 25 ft and on the other side is 12 ft. What is the net horizontal force on the gate due to water pressure?

9. A submarine is at a depth of 100 ft in sea water of weight density 65 lb/ft³. Find the pressure and the force on a rectangular hatch 3 ft long by 2 ft wide. *Ans.* 6,500 lb/ft²; 39,000 lb

10. A water tank is located in the tower of a building 500 ft above the level of the street. If the city water supply has a pressure of 60 lb/in.² at street level, how much additional pressure must be furnished by the pump used to fill the tank?

11. Water and oil are standing in opposite legs of a U tube open at both ends. Water fills the bottom and stands 38 cm above the oil-water interface. How high does the oil stand above the interface if its density is 0.8 g/cm³? *Ans.* 47.5 cm

12. The apparatus of Fig. 9.6 is used to determine the density of kerosene. The height of a kerosene column is 25 cm when a corresponding column of distilled water stands at 20 cm. Find the density of kerosene.

13. One hundred cubic centimeters of mercury is placed in an open U tube whose cross-sectional area is 1 cm². Then 100 cm³ of water is added to one leg. What is the difference in levels of the highest points in the water and the mercury? *Ans.* 92.65 cm

14. The lever of a hydraulic press gives a mechanical advantage of 6. The area of the small piston is 4 cm², and that of the large piston is 100 cm². A force of 20 kg-wt is applied to the handle. What force is exerted by the larger piston, if friction may be neglected and if both pistons are at the same level?

15. A liquid completely fills a reservoir which has two pistons in two cylinders as shown in Fig. 9.9. The two pistons are at the same level. One cylinder has a diameter of 1 in., the other has a diameter of 1 ft. A weight of 2 lb is placed on the smaller piston. What is the pressure at the smaller piston? What is the pressure at the larger piston? What weight on the larger piston will be balanced? Neglect all frictional effects. *Ans.* 2.55 lb/in.²; 2.55 lb/in²; 288 lb

16. A small hydraulic press has a pump piston ½ in. in diameter and a large piston 10 in. in diameter. If the efficiency of the machine is 85 per cent, find the actual mechanical advantage.

17. One end of a closed hydraulic system is 50 m above the other end. The system is filled with oil whose density is 0.8 g/cm³. On the higher end, a pressure of 500 g-wt/cm² is applied on an area of 10 cm². What is the total pressure at the lower end of the system? *Ans.* 4,500 g-wt/cm²

18. A truck loaded to a total weight of 8,000 lb drives on to a ferryboat, causing the

latter to sink ¼ in. deeper into the water.   What is the area of the horizontal section of the boat at the water line?

19. A liter of alcohol weighs 789 g.   Determine its density.   What is its specific gravity?   *Ans.* 0.789 g/cm³; 0.789

20. A body was weighed in water, in oil, and in alcohol.   Its loss of weight in water was 75 g, in oil 49 g, and in alcohol 60 g.   What is the specific gravity of the oil and of the alcohol?

21. A cube of nickel 2 in. on each side weighs 2.58 lb.   Determine its density. What is its specific gravity?   *Ans.* 556 lb/ft³; 8.9

22. Ice has a specific gravity of 0.917.   What is the weight of 1 ft³ of ice?

23. A piece of brass weighs 100 g.   When this is immersed in water, it "weighs" 88.4 g.   What is its density?   What is its specific gravity?   *Ans.* 8.6 g/cm³; 8.6

24. The density of aluminum is 2.65 g/cm³.   Find the volume and the mass of a specimen of aluminum that weighs 33 g under water.

25. A chunk of glass weighs 1,023 g in air, 746 g in water, and 675 g in glycerin. Find the density of the glass and of the glycerin.   *Ans.* 3.7 g/cm³; 1.26 g/cm³

26. A piece of wood with a weight of 82 g is immersed in water by using a sinker that weighs 42.5 g in water.   The combined weight of the wood and the sinker when both are immersed is 27.8 g.   Find the density of the wood.

27. A piece of cork weighs 3.2 lb.   A 12-lb sinker is attached to the cork.   With the sinker in water, the cork and sinker weigh 13.7 lb.   With the sinker and cork both in water, they weigh 0.4 lb.   What is the density of the cork?   What is its specific gravity?   *Ans.* 15 lb/ft³; 0.24

28. A piece of zinc weighs 42 g in air and 37.2 g when immersed in oil of sp gr 0.8. Find the specific gravity of the zinc.

29. A diver with his suit weighs 320 lb.   Blocks of lead with a volume totaling 60 in.³ attached to his shoes just cause him to sink.   How many cubic feet of water are displaced by the suit?   *Ans.* 5.5 ft³

30. Find the volume of cork, sp gr 0.25, that must be employed in a life preserver if it is designed to support one-fifth of a man's body out of water, assuming a mass of 75 kg and sp gr 1.00 for the body.

31. A piece of iron having a density of 7.8 g/cm³ floats on the surface of mercury. Water is poured into the vessel containing the block of iron and the mercury until the iron is completely submerged.   What fraction of the block is submerged in the mercury?   *Ans.* 0.54

32. A rectangular block of wood has a cross-sectional area of 150 cm² and a height of 25 cm.   It floats vertically in water and to its lower edge is fastened 600 g of silver. How much of the wood projects out of the water?   (Density of wood is 0.45 g/cm³ and that of silver is 10.5 g/cm³.)

Molecular Forces and Motions

10.1. Molecular Theory of Matter. In this chapter we turn to some of the special features of fluids for which we need some understanding of the *microscopic* nature of materials. Here we deal with particles too small to be seen in the most powerful microscope and of too little mass to be detected by the most sensitive analytical balance.

In the fifth century B.C. Greek philosophers, the most prominent of whom was Democritus, advanced the theory that all matter was composed of tiny particles called atoms (*atom* means "uncut," or "indivisible"). About 1800, the English chemist Dalton introduced experimental evidence for the existence of atoms and laid the groundwork for modern chemistry. Although we now know that the atom itself is composed of still smaller particles, we need not consider this fact in discussing the properties of interest here and we defer discussion of the structure of atoms to Chap. 48.

One or more atoms may be bound together to form a chemical compound. The smallest unit into which a substance can be divided without chemical decomposition is known as a *molecule*. In gases like helium and neon the molecule consists of a single atom. In other gases, such as hydrogen and oxygen, two atoms form a molecule. Molecules of carbon dioxide and of water vapor contain three atoms. In the gaseous state the molecules are usually separated by distances which are large compared with the molecular dimensions. The molecules at room temperature are moving with high velocities and have frequent collisions. The gas entirely fills the space of the containing vessel and exerts a pressure on it, which results from the change in momentum of the molecules in colliding with the walls (Chap. 21).

In general, the forces between molecules in a gas are small; for an "ideal" gas they are zero. When the forces between the molecules of a gas are sufficiently great and the molecular speeds are reduced by lowering the temperature, the molecules stick together to form a liquid. In the liquid, molecules cling together, but are free to move with respect to each other.   Liquids do not resist forces tending to change their shape, but they strongly resist forces tending to change their volume.   Because the molecules of the liquid can be easily displaced with respect to each other, layers flow relatively freely over each other and the liquid assumes the

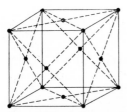

shape of the vessel in which it is placed.   In the liquid two or more molecules may stick to one another and move about as a unit.

In a solid, atoms cling strongly together and tend to keep the same relative positions.   Solids resist the tendency to change their shape or size.   They preserve their original form, unless acted upon by large external forces.   The true solid is crystalline in nature; the atoms of the crystal are arranged in a regular and repetitive way (Fig. 10.1).   The

Fig. 10.1. A face-centered cubic lattice.   In a crystal any one atom is bound to many others.

forces which hold the solid together are between atoms, and once a crystalline array is established, it is no longer meaningful to say that a particular atom belongs to a particular molecule.   In the crystalline solid the molecule is no longer a separate entity; rather, we have an array of atoms and any one atom is bound to many others.

Under suitable conditions it is possible to change a given material from the solid to the liquid state, and from the liquid to the gaseous state.   Water can be frozen to form ice and evaporated to form steam. The change from one phase to another is discussed in Chap. 22.

10.2. Diffusion.   One of the evidences for believing that a gas is made up of a large number of tiny molecules is found in the manner in which an odor penetrates to all parts of a room when a bottle of ammonia is opened.   The spread of the odor can be explained by the assumption that the ammonia molecules escape from the bottle and wander about among the air molecules.   They are buffeted back and forth, gradually spreading throughout the room.   This process by which the molecules of one kind penetrate and intermix with the molecules of another kind is called *diffusion*.   If a porous jar (Fig. 10.2) is surrounded by another vessel into which hydrogen is introduced, hydrogen diffuses through the porous jar and increases the gas pressure

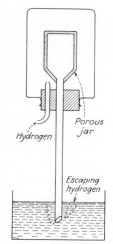

Fig. 10.2. Hydrogen diffuses through the porous walls of the jar and increases the pressure in the interior.

inside the jar, causing gas to bubble up from the water into which the end of the tube leading from the porous jar is dipping.   It is diffusion of this kind which keeps the air in such a state of uniform mixture and which accounts for the rapid disappearance of ether fumes when a bottle of ether is broken out of doors.

In liquids as well as in gases, the molecules are free to move about. If a little sulfuric acid is placed in a bottle of water, it diffuses to form a uniform concentration. When a lump of sugar is placed in a cup of coffee, the contents of the whole cup are sweetened by the distribution of the sugar molecules throughout the coffee; stirring promotes the rapid mixing of the molecules.

If stirring and convection currents are avoided, it can be shown that diffusion in liquids occurs very slowly. This may be demonstrated by taking a tall glass jar (Fig. 10.3) filled with water and, by means of a thistle tube extending to the bottom of the jar, carefully pouring a solution of copper sulfate until the bottom of the jar is filled to a height of a centimeter or two. If the jar is allowed to stand for some days without being disturbed, the upward diffusion of the copper sulfate can be observed. Gravity tends to keep the copper sulfate on the bottom, but diffusion occurs and the copper sulfate gradually rises in the jar. The action which takes place in this case is similar to that which takes place in the diffusion of gases, except that it occurs much more slowly.

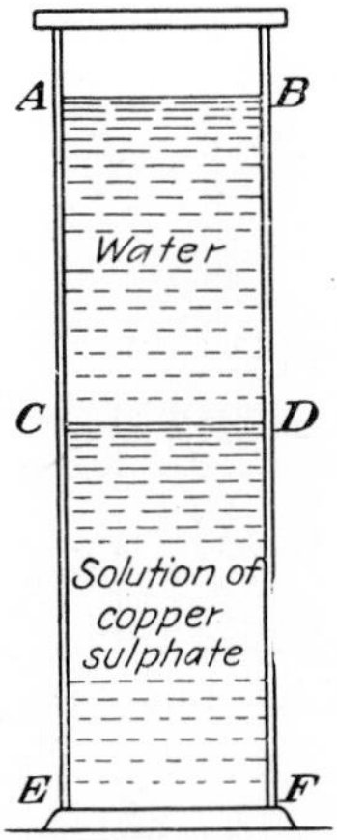

Fig. 10.3. Diffusion of copper sulfate.

If two metals, such as copper and nickel, are placed in contact, molecules of each gradually diffuse into the other. If the specimens are cut into sections after they have been in contact for some time, the concentrations of the two metals at different distances from the contact plane can be determined by chemical analysis. The rate of diffusion depends on the temperature, but in any case it is very slow for solids. Figure 10.4 shows the concentration of copper and nickel as a function of the distance from the inner face after an interval of 72 hr at a temperature of 1000°C. At room temperature the diffusion would be so slow that it would take many years to achieve this much intermixing.

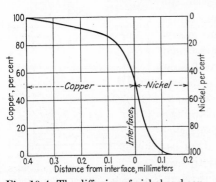

Fig. 10.4. The diffusion of nickel and copper across at interface at 1000°C after a period of 72 hr. The copper diffuses less rapidly into the nickel than the nickel diffuses into the copper.

10.3. Osmosis. The following experiment illustrates osmosis: Take a carrot (Fig. 10.5) and cut out its interior, filling the space with a thick sugar syrup. Insert in the mouth of the cavity a rubber stopper through which projects a long glass tube and immerse the carrot in a jar filled with water. There is a net flow of water into the carrot and the liquid slowly rises in the long glass tube. In a day or two it may rise to a height of several feet.

The explanation of this phenomenon is as follows: The carrot has a great number of very small holes in it through which water molecules may pass either into or out of the carrot.   Sugar molecules, on the other hand, are too large to pass through these tiny holes.   The fact that the water level rises in the tube means that more water flows in than flows out.   A qualitative explanation is that the large sugar molecules act somewhat as valves for many of the openings.   A water molecule moving inward may slightly displace the large sugar molecule at A in Fig. 10.6 and get into the carrot, but a water molecule coming from the other side would only push the sugar molecule more tightly against the hole. Of course, all of the time there are many holes through which water molecules pass in either direction.   However, there are more holes through which water molecules can enter than there are by which they can leave. When the liquid levels are the same inside and outside, water molecules enter more rapidly than they leave.

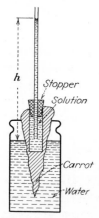

Fig. 10.5. Osmosis in a carrot.

As the water rises in the tube, the pressure becomes greater inside.   Eventually, the pressure becomes enough greater so that there is no longer a net inflow.   Because of the increased pressure, the water molecules now go out through the open holes more rapidly than they enter, while they still enter at the blocked holes more rapidly than they leave.   The pressure that just prevents further flow of the solvent is called the *osmotic pressure* of the solution.   In very dilute solutions in which the molecules are not disassociated, the osmotic pressure is proportional to the concentration of the dissolved substance.   In a solution of given concentration, the osmotic pressure increases as the temperature is increased, the rate of increase being the same for all solutions.   A membrane, or structure such as the carrot, which is useful for osmosis is said to be *semipermeable*.   By this we mean that smaller molecules can pass through while larger ones cannot.   *Osmosis is the process of diffusion through a semipermeable membrane.*

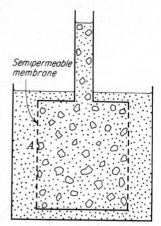

Fig. 10.6. Sugar molecules prevent water molecules from leaving through many of the submicroscopic holes, but they do not prevent water molecules from entering the solution.

When dried fruits, such as prunes and raisins, are cooked, they swell and burst if the pressure inside becomes sufficiently large.   The swelling is due to the fact that the vegetable sacs surrounding the fruit are semipermeable membranes through which there is a net diffusion of water from outside to inside.   If marine animals such as oysters are transferred from salt water to fresh water, more water flows into than out of the animal through the membrane that serves as its covering. A dilation of the animal results.

10.4. Cohesion and Adhesion. In liquids the molecules move freely with respect to each other, but are held together by attractive forces.   Not only do the molecules of a liquid cling to each other, but they also cling to the molecules of other substances, as may be seen when a piece of glass is dipped into a vessel of water.   The molecules of water adhere to the glass and form a thin film over its surface.   *The attraction of like molecules for one another is called cohesion; the attraction of unlike molecules for one another is called adhesion.*   It is *cohesive* forces which hold together so firmly the molecules of iron, copper, and other solid substances.

If the molecules of a liquid have less attraction for each other than for the molecules of the solid with which they are in contact, the liquid adheres to the solid and wets it.   Here *adhesive forces are greater than cohesive*.   When the cohesive forces are greater than the adhesive ones, the solid is not wet by the liquid.   Such is the case when mercury is in contact with glass.   If a drop of mercury and a drop of distilled water are placed on a clean glass surface, the water spreads over the glass in a thin layer while the mercury forms a distorted ball.

The attractive forces between molecules are large only when the molecules are very close together.   If molecules are much further apart than a few millionths of a centimeter, the attractive forces are not appreciably great.   Intermolecular forces have short ranges.   It takes a moderate force to break a piece of chalk, but after it is broken, the pieces do not adhere if they are pressed back together.   Because of the irregular surfaces, there are not enough molecules which are able to exert appreciable attractive forces.

Molecules of water adhere to glass, forming a thin layer over its surface.   If we place a little water between two sheets of glass and are careful to see that there is no air trapped between the plates, it requires a significantly greater force to separate the glass plates than it would if they were dry.   The water is acting as an adhesive.   Glues and cements act as much superior adhesives.   Once a glue has set, it may be stronger than materials which it is binding together.   If a thin layer of gold foil is placed over a layer of metal and carefully pressed into place, the molecular attraction between the gold and the base metal is strong enough to keep the gold foil in place without the use of a cement.   If a gold foil is pounded into a cavity in a tooth, the cohesive forces between gold molecules and adhesive forces between gold molecules and tooth material are sufficiently great so that a strong permanent filling is created.

10.5. Surface Energy and Surface Tension. If a needle is greased and gently placed on the surface of water, it floats although the density of the needle is greater than that of the water.   Some insects can walk on the surface of a lake or stream, which behaves as though it were covered with a thin elastic film.   It requires a force to break this film, the amount of force depending on the nature of the liquid.   The apparent surface film is due to molecular attraction in the liquid.

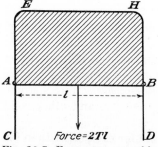

Fig. 10.7. Force on a movable wire due to surface tension.

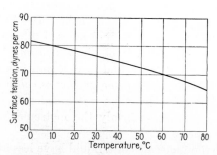

Fig. 10.8. Surface tension of water as a function of temperature (1 dyne = 10^{-5} newton).

A molecule inside a mass of liquid is attracted equally in all directions by neighboring molecules.   But a molecule on the top surface of the liquid is not attracted by molecules on the side away from the liquid, although it is attracted downward.   Because of this, a molecule at the surface is pulled toward the interior of the liquid.

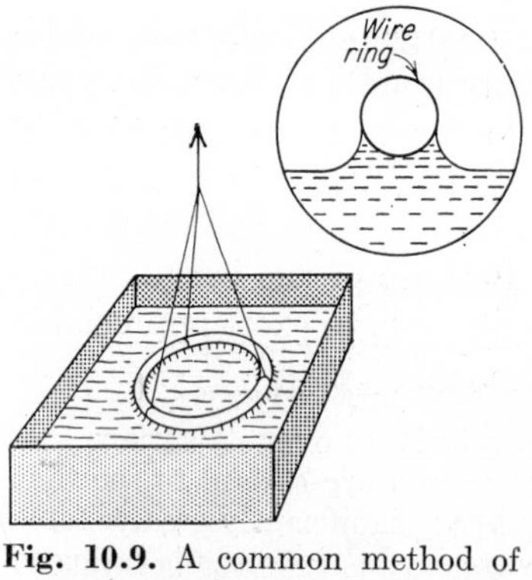

Consider Fig. 10.7 in which $CEHD$ is a bent wire and AB is a straight wire which may be moved in the direction of the arrow.   If we dip this system in a soap solution, we may have the area $AEHB$ covered by a soap film.   In order to prevent the soap film from contracting and pulling the side AB toward EH, a force F must be applied.   This force is given by $F = 2Tl$, where l is the length of the wire AB and T is the force per unit length.   The factor 2 is introduced because the film has two sides.   *The force per unit length which must be applied to overcome molecular forces is the surface tension.*

Fig. 10.9. A common method of measuring surface tension involves determining the force required to pull a ring from the surface. The insert shows why the length of surface broken is twice the circumference of the ring.

If the wire AB is drawn down a distance s, the work done is

$$Fs = T(2ls) = T \, \Delta A$$

where $\Delta A = 2ls$, the increase in area counting *both* sides of the film. Thus, T is the ratio of the work required to increase the area against the surface molecular forces to the change in area.

The surface tension of a liquid depends on the temperature as Fig. 10.8 shows for water. The values of the surface tension for several liquids are listed in Table 1.

One of the standard ways for measuring surface tension is to measure the force required to pull a platinum ring through the surface of a liquid (Fig. 10.9)   The

Table 1

SURFACE TENSION

Substance	Temperature, °C	Surface tension, newtons/m
Acetic acid.............	20	0.0234
Alcohol (ethyl).........	20	0.0216
Ether (ethyl)...........	20	0.0169
Glycerin...............	18	0.0632
Mercury...............	18	0.545
Turpentine.............	20	0.0289
Petroleum.............	20	0.0259
Water.................	20	0.0728

total length of liquid surface which must be broken is twice the circumference of the ring.   Thus the force required to break the surface is $T \times 4\pi r$, where r is the radius of the ring.

The splashes formed (Fig. 10.10) when drops of milk fall on a surface of milk give an illustration of effects produced by surface tension. If a drop of oil is placed in a mixture of water and alcohol of the same density, the oil droplet does not rise or fall. Under the action of molecular forces it assumes a spherical form. Lead pellets for a shotgun can be produced by allowing liquid lead to fall from an opening of suitable size. Because of surface forces the freely falling lead drops assume spherical shape in which they solidify before they strike a surface.

Fig. 10.10. Splashes on the surface of milk showing the effect of surface tension. (*Courtesy of Edgerton, Germhausen, and Grier, Massachusetts Institute of Technology.*)

The formation of bubbles is due to surface tension. The pressure inside of a soap bubble (Fig. 10.11) is greater than the external pressure. The forces across the equatorial plane $ABCD$ are in equilibrium. Hence,

$$\pi R^2 p = 4\pi R T$$

and
$$p = \frac{4T}{R} \qquad (10.1)$$

where p is the excess pressure.

10.6. Capillarity. If a piece of glass tube of very small bore is thoroughly cleaned and then dipped into water (Fig. 10.12), the water wets the inside of the tube and rises in it. If the liquid does not wet the tube (Fig. 10.13) as in the case of mercury in a glass tube, the liquid is depressed. The smaller the bore of the tube, the greater the height to which the liquid rises, or the greater the amount which it is depressed.

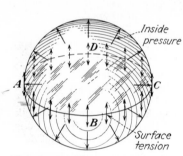

Fig. 10.11. The excess pressure inside the soap bubble is given by $p = 4T/R$.

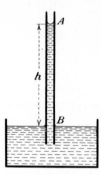

Fig. 10.12. Rise of water in a capillary tube.

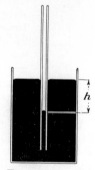

Fig. 10.13. Depression of mercury in a capillary tube.

This rise or depression of liquids in tubes of small bore is known as *capillarity*. It is caused by the molecular forces that are responsible for surface energy. The molecules of the liquid have an attraction for each other and also for the molecules on the surface of the wall of the tube. If the cohesive forces between molecules of the liquid are greater than the adhesive forces between liquid and wall, the liquid pulls away from the tube and is depressed. If the adhesive forces are greater, the liquid wets the capillary tube and rises.

When a glass tube is thrust into water, the molecules in the surface of the wall just above the water pull up on the molecules lying nearest to them and raise them above the level of the water in the vessel. This carries upward a column of water, which is supported by the surface forces. The net upward force available is the vertical component of the surface tension forces if we are dealing with a vertical cylindrical tube. The angle of contact (Fig. 10.14) between the surface of the liquid and the tube depends on the liquid, the gas above, and the kind of tube involved. Let us call this angle θ. The upward force per unit length is $T \cos \theta$ and the total upward force is $T \cos \theta$ multiplied by the length of liquid in contact with the tube, which is the circumference. Thus, the net upward force is $2\pi r T \cos \theta$. The liquid rises until the weight of liquid supported $\pi r^2 h d g$ is equal to this force. Hence, for equilibrium

$$2\pi r T \cos \theta = \pi r^2 h d g \qquad (10.2)$$

or
$$h = \frac{2T \cos \theta}{rdg}$$

For water in clean glass the angle θ is zero and $\cos \theta$ becomes unity. Whenever a liquid wets a tube thoroughly, θ is zero. When cohesive

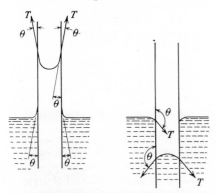

Fig. 10.14. Water wets glass and the angle of contact approaches zero; mercury does not wet glass and the angle of contact is 140°.

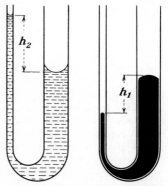

Fig. 10.15. Unequal heights of water and mercury in connecting glass tubes of different radii.

forces exceed adhesive, θ is greater than 90°, the liquid is depressed in the capillary, and h is negative. For water on paraffin θ is 107°. Water does not wet paraffin. For mercury the angle of contact is approximately 140°. Figure 10.15 shows how mercury and water behave when placed in glass containers with tubes of unequal radii.

Example. The liquid in a capillary tube rises to the height of 7 cm. The radius of the tube is 0.1 mm and the density of the liquid 800 kg/m³. If the angle between the liquid and the surface of the tube is zero, find the surface tension of the liquid.

$$2\pi r T \cos \theta = \pi r^2 h d g$$
$$2T \times 1 = 10^{-4} \text{ m} \times 0.07 \text{ m} \times 800 \text{ kg/m}^3 \times 9.8 \text{ newtons/kg}$$
$$T = 0.0274 \text{ newton/m}$$

In recent years the chemical industry has developed a number of *waterproofing* agents which prevent water from wetting a fabric. For these compounds θ is greater than 90°. Similarly, a number of *wetting agents*, or *detergents*, have been developed. These agents change θ to a smaller angle. The addition of a suitable detergent can make water wet paraffin.

There are many illustrations of capillary action in nature. The oil in a lamp rises in the wick by capillary action. Ink spreads in a blotter and water in a lump of sugar by this same action. If one end of a towel dips into a bucket of water and the other end hangs over the bucket, the towel soon becomes wet throughout.

PROBLEMS

1. The surface tension of water is 0.0728 newton/m. Express this in units of gram-weight per centimeter and in dynes per centimeter (1 dyne $= 10^{-5}$ newton).

Ans. 0.0744 g-wt/cm; 72.8 dynes/cm

2. The surface of the water in a glass capillary tube which is 0.22 mm in radius is at a height of 6.4 cm above the level of the water in the beaker in which the tube stands. What is the surface tension of the water?

3. A solid glass rod is immersed in water so that its axis is perpendicular to the surface of the water. The rod has a circular cross section and a diameter of 1 cm. Find the force exerted on the rod by surface tension.   *Ans.* 2.3×10^{-3} newton

4. How high will water rise in a glass tube with a diameter of 0.14 mm because of capillarity?

5. A thin sheet of metal is bent in the form of a hollow square and the open square end is dipped into soap solution whose surface tension is 0.025 newton/m.   The length of each side of the square is 5 cm. With what force does the surface tension pull the metal into the solution?   *Ans.* 0.01 newton

6. Find the surface tension of water, if the column supported by capillarity in a glass tube of 0.8 mm diameter is 3.5 cm high.

7. A capillary tube whose inside radius is 1 mm is dipped in water. What is the weight of the water raised by capillary action above the normal water level?   To what height is the water raised?   *Ans.* 4.6×10^{-4} newton; 0.0149 m

8. How much will the surface of mercury stand below the normal level of the mercury in a glass tube that is 1 mm in diameter? (Angle of contact is 140°.)

9. A capillary tube whose inside diameter is 1 mm is dipped in glycerin. The glycerin rises 20.4 mm in the tube. If the density of glycerin is 1.26 g/cm³, what is its surface tension? Assume the angle of contact is 0°.   *Ans.* 0.063 newton/m

10. A tube is bent in the form of a U (Fig. 10.15). The diameter of the larger arm is 1.5 cm and that of the smaller arm is 1.5 mm. Find the difference in levels when the U tube contains water.

11. One limb of a U tube is 2 cm in diameter and the other is 2 mm in diameter. What will be the difference in a level of the surface in the two tubes when mercury is poured into them? Take the angle of contact as 140° for mercury. *Ans.* 5.6 mm

12. What is the excess pressure inside of a soap bubble that is 1 cm in diameter, assuming 0.026 newton/m as the surface tension of the soap solution?

13. The pressure inside a soap bubble exceeds atmospheric pressure by 4 newtons/ m². If the radius of the bubble is 3 cm, find the surface tension of the soap solution.

Ans. 0.030 newton/m

14. What is the diameter of a soap bubble when the excess pressure inside is 6 newtons/m² and the surface tension of the soap solution is 0.025 newton/m?

15. Find the work which must be done to increase the outside surface area of a soap bubble by 200 cm² if the surface tension of soap film is 0.030 newton/m.

Ans. 0.0012 joule

16. Find the work that must be done to increase the surface of a soap film by 300 cm². Take the surface tension of soap solution as 0.025 newton/m.

CHAPTER 11

Gases

11.1. Composition of the Air. Just as water is the most widely distributed and most important of liquids, so air is the most important and intimate of gases. It consists for the most part of nitrogen and oxygen mixed together, but not chemically combined. In spite of the fact that there is no chemical union between them, the composition of the air is extraordinarily constant. Up to a height of 7 miles it always contains about 21 parts of oxygen to 78 parts of nitrogen by volume. Besides oxygen and nitrogen, the air contains small amounts of other gases, the most important of which are water vapor, argon, and carbon dioxide. A cubic yard of air weighs over 2 lb at sea level, although to an ordinary observer the air seems to have no weight and to offer little resistance to bodies moving through it.

That air has weight can be shown by the following experiment. A hollow glass sphere provided with a stopcock is weighed when the stopcock is open and then is connected to an air pump by which as much of the air as possible is removed from the sphere. The stopcock is closed and the sphere weighed a second time. The second weight is less than the first by the weight of the air removed from the sphere. If the volume of the sphere is known, a fair approximation to the density of the air can be obtained by this method. Table 1 lists the densities of several gases.

Example. A hollow glass flask weighs 25.556 g-wt when it is empty. When it is filled with dry air at atmospheric pressure, it weighs 26.849 g-wt. The volume of the flask is 1 liter. What is the density of air?

$$\text{Weight of air} = 26.849 \text{ g-wt} - 25.556 \text{ g-wt} = 1.293 \text{ g-wt}$$
$$\text{Density of air} = \frac{\text{mass of air}}{\text{volume of flask}} = \frac{1.293 \text{ g}}{1,000 \text{ cm}^3}$$
$$= 0.001293 \text{ g/cm}^3$$

11.2. Buoyant Effect of the Air. Since air has weight, it produces a buoyant effect on bodies immersed in it. Archimedes' principle applies to all fluids, gases as well as liquids. Since the density of air is so much less than that of liquids, its buoyant effect is also much less. That air exerts a lifting effect on bodies immersed in it may be shown by suspend-

125

ing a lead ball (Fig. 11.1) from one side of a small balance and a large hollow brass sphere from the other side. The hollow sphere is just heavy enough to balance the lead ball when both are in air. If the balance, together with the suspended spheres, is placed under a bell jar and nearly all the air removed by means of a pump, the lead ball no longer balances the hollow sphere. This is because the buoyancy of the air on the hollow

Table 1

DENSITIES OF GASES

Gas	Density at 0°C and 76 cm Hg pressure	
	kg/m³	lb mass/ft³
Air..........................	1.2930	0.0807
Acetylene...................	1.173	0.723
Ammonia....................	0.7708	0.0481
Carbon dioxide..............	0.9768	0.1234
Carbon monoxide............	1.25	0.0781
Chlorine....................	3.214	0.2011
Helium.....................	0.1785	0.01116
Hydrogen...................	0.0899	0.00561
Nitrogen....................	1.2507	0.0781
Oxygen.....................	1.4291	0.0892

brass sphere is greater than on the lead ball; when this lift has been removed, the true weights of the spheres become evident, and the hollow sphere weighs more than the lead sphere.

The gross lifting capacity of a balloon is equal to the weight of the air that it displaces. The pressure and density of the air become less at higher elevations. However, as the pressure outside the balloon decreases, the lighter gas inside the balloon expands, thus displacing a larger volume of the less dense air. In manned balloons ballast is carried along and thrown overboard when it is desired to make the balloon rise higher. By allowing some of the gas in the balloon to escape, the balloon can be made to descend.

Example. A balloon has a volume equal to that of a sphere 15 yd in radius. What is the gross weight which it will lift when the weight density of the air is 2 lb/yd³?

$$\text{Volume of balloon} = \tfrac{4}{3}\pi(15)^3 = 14,132 \text{ yd}^3$$
$$\text{Weight of air displaced by balloon} = \text{volume} \times \text{weight density}$$
$$= 14,132 \text{ yd}^3 \times 2 \text{ lb/yd}^3 = 28,264 \text{ lb}$$

11.3. Pressure of the Air. Since gas has weight, a column of it exerts a pressure just as a column of liquid does. Though a cubic foot of air weighs little, the height of the atmosphere is large, and the weight of all this air pressing on the earth is great.

About 1644 Torricelli, a pupil of Galileo, measured atmospheric pressure in the following way.   A glass tube 100 cm long was closed at one end and completely filled with mercury.   A finger was then placed over the open end of the tube, the tube inverted in a basin of mercury, and the finger was removed from the open end of the tube under the mercury. The mercury in the tube sank until its level was about 76 cm (Fig. 11.2) higher than the level in the basin.   The pressure of the atmosphere on the mercury in the basin supported the mercury in the tube.   Since each cubic centimeter of mercury weighs 13.56 g-wt, the weight of this column is 76 × 13.56 = 1,033 g-wt for each square centimeter of cross section.

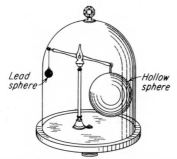

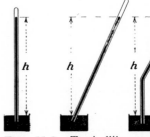

Fig. 11.1. A body immersed in air is buoyed up by a force equal to the weight of the air it displaces.

Fig.   11.2.   Torricelli's   experiment. The height of the mercury is independent of the shape of the tube.

This means that the atmospheric pressure is 1,033 g-wt/cm^2 or 10.1 newtons/cm^2 or 14.7 lb/in.^{2}.   Since mercury is 13.56 times as heavy as water, atmospheric pressure can support a column of water 13.56 times as high as this column of mercury, or 10.33 m (33.8 ft).

In 1647 Pascal showed that when a barometer tube is carried up a mountain, the level of the mercury in the tube drops because there is less air above the tube at the higher elevation.   The greater the height to which the tube is carried, the greater the drop.   At 1 mile elevation the column of mercury stands 15 cm lower than at sea level.

The breathing of animals is an application of atmospheric pressure.   A reduction of pressure is made by a movement of the diaphragm.   The greater pressure of the outside air causes a fresh supply to fill them.   Then air is forced out by making the internal pressure greater than atmospheric.   Sucking and drinking animals take advantage of atmospheric pressure to aid them in these operations. By reducing the pressure in the mouth they allow water to be forced into the mouth by the outside atmospheric pressure.

11.4. Barometers.   The work of Torricelli led to the development of the barometer, an instrument of great importance.   There are two forms of mercury barometers.   One (Fig. 11.3) is known as a cistern barometer and consists of a Torricellian tube.   The pressure of the air on the mercury in the cistern supports the mercury in the tube.   As the pressure of the atmosphere varies from hour to hour or from day to day, the height of this column varies.   These variations in the height of the barometer are important for weather predictions.

The other type of mercury barometer consists of a U tube partly filled with mercury, as indicated in Fig. 11.4. If both ends of the tube were open, the mercury would stand at the same height in both parts of the tube. One end of the tube is closed, however, and there is a vacuum above the mercury in this part of the tube. The weight of the column of mercury that stands between the level of the mercury in the closed tube and the level of the mercury in the open tube is supported by the atmospheric pressure on the mercury in the open tube. The length of this column then gives a measure of the atmospheric pressure. At sea level, the length is 76 cm on the average. Hence, it is customary to say that the atmosphere exerts a pressure which is equal to that at the bottom of a column of mercury 76 cm in height, or briefly 76 cm Hg.

The aneroid barometer consists of an airtight box (Fig. 11.5) from which most of the air has been removed so that the pressure inside the box is much less than atmospheric pressure. The top of the box is a flexible diaphragm which moves inward and outward as the external pressure changes. The movements of the diaphragm are slight, but they are magnified by a system of levers which are connected to a pointer which moves over a dial and thus indicates the change in pressure.

11.5. Compressibility of Gases; Boyle's Law. If an attempt is made to decrease the volume of a liquid by the application of pressure, enormous pressures are required to get appreciable changes in volume. The behavior of gases in this respect is quite different. It is easy to compress gas so that it occupies only one-third or one-tenth of its original volume. As soon as this pressure is removed, the gas returns to its original volume. The tires of automobiles are filled with air. As more air is forced into the tire, the volume of the tire increases very little, but the air from the outside is forced to occupy much less volume than it originally occupied.

Fig. 11.3. A cistern barometer. **Fig. 11.4.** A siphon barometer.

The relationship between the volume of any mass of gas and the pressure exerted by the gas upon the walls of the containing vessel was investigated by Robert Boyle. Boyle's law states that *the product of the pressure and the volume of a given mass of gas is constant if the temperature is not changed.* Thus, if V_0 and p_0 denote the original volume and pressure, while V and p are the final volume and pressure,

$$p_0 V_0 = pV = \text{constant} \qquad (11.1)$$

Figure 11.6 shows a plot of the pressure and volume of a gas at different temperatures.

By pouring mercury into the open end of the tube of Fig. 11.7, the pressure on the air in AC is increased and its volume decreased.   Since the density is inversely proportional to the volume, at constant temperature the density of a gas is proportional to the pressure.

$$\frac{p_1}{p_0} = \frac{d_1}{d_0} \qquad (11.2)$$

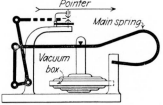

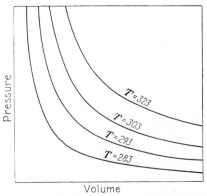

Fig. 11.6. Relation of pressure to volume at different absolute temperatures ($T = 273 + t°C$).

Fig. 11.5. An aneroid barometer.

Gases do not obey this law near the temperature and pressure at which they liquefy.   Under these circumstances we refer to them as vapors; laws governing vapor pressure are discussed in Chap. 22.

In applying Boyle's law, it is necessary to use *absolute pressures*.   Many types of pressure gauges tell how much the pressure exceeds atmospheric pressure—this is the so-called *gauge pressure*.   For example, when a tire gauge reads 24 lb/in.², the pressure is 24 lb/in.² greater than atmospheric pressure (14.7 lb/in.²).   The absolute pressure is then $(24 + 14.7) = 38.7$ lb/in.²

11.6. Applications of Boyle's Law.   There are many important applications of this law.   When the faucet of a kerosene can (Fig. 11.8) is turned on, only a small amount of kerosene will run out of the can if the cap A is screwed down so that the can is airtight.   As the kerosene runs out of the can, the volume of air above the kerosene increases and its pressure decreases.   On the kerosene flowing out at the faucet, there is, under normal conditions, a pressure of 1 atm.   When the sum of the pressure of the air in the can and the pressure due to the kerosene falls to a pressure of 1 atm or less, the flow becomes erratic.   If the cap A is open so that atmospheric pressure acts undiminished on the upper surface of the kerosene, the flow becomes regular again.

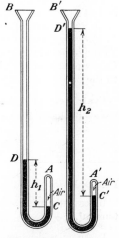

Fig. 11.7. Apparatus for showing that for a gas the product of pressure and volume is constant if the temperature is constant.

It is difficult to pour a liquid from a small-necked bottle without considerable gurgling.   While the flow is in progress, the air above the liquid expands and its pressure decreases.   Eventually the pressure at the neck becomes less than atmospheric pressure.   This occurs because the liquid, once in motion, keeps moving until forced to stop.   When the flow ceases, air rushes in through the mouth of the bottle.   The flow then begins again.   This action causes the familiar gurgling observed when liquids are poured from bottles.   To prevent gurgling and to obtain a steady flow, an auxiliary tube may be inserted in the stopper to permit air to enter the bottle continuously.

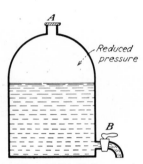

Fig. 11.8. Flow of liquid from a closed container in which the pressure over the liquid may become less than atmospheric.

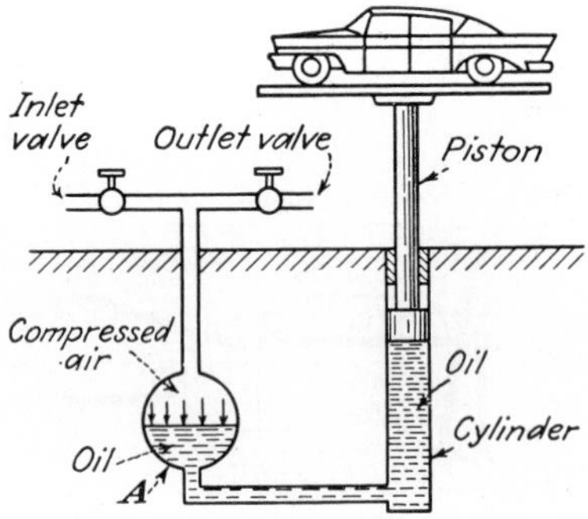

Fig. 11.9. An automobile lift pump illustrates Pascal's principle as applied to gases.

11.7. Pascal's Principle Applied to Gases.   Like Archimedes' principle, Pascal's principle applies to all fluids, gases as well as liquids.   A typical example of an application of Pascal's principle to gases is the automobile lift pump (Fig. 11.9).   Compressed air is admitted through the inlet valve.   It exerts a pressure on the oil in a reservoir which transmits it to a cylinder closed by a piston.   The force exerted on the piston, which lifts the automobile, is the pressure p applied to the oil by the compressed gas multiplied by the area A of the piston.

Example.   Find the minimum gauge pressure which must be supplied to an automobile lift pump with a piston of area 120 in.² to lift an automobile weighing 3,000 lb.

$$\text{Force} = \text{net pressure} \times \text{area}$$
$$3{,}000 \text{ lb} = p \times 120 \text{ in.}^2$$
$$p = 25 \text{ lb/in.}^2$$

PROBLEMS

Unless otherwise stated take atmospheric pressure to be 15 lb/in.² or 10^5 newtons/m².

1. An aneroid barometer used as an altimeter is sensitive enough to detect a difference of elevation of 1 m at sea level.   How small is the pressure change detected if the density of air is 1.29 kg/m³?   *Ans.* 12.6 newtons/m²

2. Assuming that the density of air at sea level is 1.29 kg/m³ and that the barometer reading is 760 mm Hg, what will be the barometer reading at an altitude of 50 m, neglecting the variation in the density of air?

3. How much lower does the barometer stand on the top of a building which is 150 m high when the barometer at the base of the building reads 76 cm Hg?   Take the density of air as 1.21 kg/m³.   *Ans.* 1.33 cm

4. A man carries a barometer from the bottom to the top of a building that is 108 m high. At the bottom of the building the barometer reads 76 cm Hg and at the top it reads 75.05 cm Hg. Find the average density of the air.

5. If the density of the atmosphere remained 1.29 kg/m³ regardless of the height (of course, the density of the atmosphere does depend on what is above it) and if the barometer reads 76 cm Hg at sea level, calculate the height of the atmosphere. Convert your answer to miles. *Ans.* 7.98 km; 4.97 miles

6. What is the reading of a barometer on the top of a building that is 150 m high when the barometer at the base of the building reads 74 cm Hg? Take the average density of air as 1.2 kg/m³.

7. What is the weight of the air in a living room that is 24 ft by 12 ft by 8 ft? The weight density of air is 0.081 lb/ft³. *Ans.* 187 lb

8. The tank of a water supply system contains 150 gal of air at atmospheric pressure; 120 gal of water are then forced in. How great is the pressure in the tank?

9. A gas occupies 2 ft³ under a pressure of 3 atm. If the pressure is reduced to 1 atm, the temperature remaining constant, what volume is occupied? *Ans.* 6 ft³

10. A cylinder 15 in. long is closed at one end. A gastight piston is introduced in the other end and pushed in a distance of 5 in. What is the ratio of the pressure in the cylinder to the external pressure of the air?

11. A tire pressure gauge reads 10 lb/in.² when a tube has been partially inflated. Weights are placed on the tube so that all of the air occupies one-third of its former volume. Neglecting any added forces caused by the tube, what does the gauge read? *Ans.* 60 lb/in.²

12. An air bubble released at the bottom of a pond expands to two times its original volume by the time it reaches the surface of the pond. How deep is the pond? (Barometer reading is 74 cm Hg.)

13. A balloon 100 ft in diameter is filled with helium whose density is 0.011 lb/ft³. The density of air is 0.081 lb/ft³. What is the net buoyant force of the balloon? *Ans.* 36,600 lb

14. The volume of the gas bags of an airship is 140,000 m³. The density of air at 0°C and at atmospheric pressure is 1.29 g/liter and that of the hydrogen with which the gas bags are filled is 0.092 g/liter. Find the maximum gross weight that the airship will lift.

15. A balloon has a spherical bag with a diameter of 14 m. What is the weight of the air displaced when the density of air is 1.25 g/liter? *Ans.* 1,800 kg-wt

16. A balloon has a volume of 1,250 m³ and weighs 4,000 newtons. It is filled with hydrogen, which has a density of 0.090 g/liter. What pull does it exert on the guy ropes when it is in air which has a density of 1.29 g/liter? What would the pull be if the balloon were filled with helium having a density of 0.178 g/liter?

17. A piece of cork has a density of 0.25 g/cm³. It is weighed by means of brass weights that are correct in air having a density of 0.00129 g/cm³ and is found to weigh 16.800 g. Find the weight in vacuum if the density of the brass is 8.4 g/cm³. *Ans.* 16.887 g

18. A block of wood having a density of 0.55 g/cm³ weighs 150 g in air when brass weights of density 8.4 g/cm³ are used. Find the correct weight of the block, taking the density of air as 0.00129 g/cm³.

19. A vessel having a capacity of 2 liters contains nitrogen under a pressure of 3 atm. It is connected to a vessel having a capacity of 1 liter containing oxygen at a pressure of 2 atm. What will be the pressure when the gases have mixed? *Ans.* 2.67 atm

20. A cylindrical diving bell, open at the bottom, has a volume of 210 ft³ and a diameter of 5 ft. How high will the water rise in the bell when it is immersed to a depth of 28 ft, if the pressure of the air originally was 29 in. Hg?

Fluids in Motion

12.1. Flow of Fluids; Viscosity. When liquids or gases are in motion, the shape as well as the position of a given mass of the fluid may be changing. Because different layers move with different speeds, the internal friction between the various layers must be considered. For example, the velocity of the water in a river is greater in midstream than it is near the bank, and the velocity of the wind increases as we go above the surface of the earth. Water flowing through a circular pipe moves with increasing velocity as we go from the pipe surface to its center. Each layer of water is pulled forward by the layer of water moving over it and backward by the layer of water over which it moves. The internal friction between fluid layers is known as *viscosity*.

If two beakers, one containing heavy oil and the other water, are tilted from side to side, it is seen that the mobility of the water is greater than that of the oil; oil is more viscous than water. Gases have lower viscosity than liquids, because of the increased distance between the molecules.

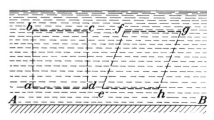

Fig. 12.1. Displacement of layers of a moving liquid with respect to a surface at rest.

Suppose that liquid flows over a horizontal surface AB (Fig. 12.1). The layer of liquid in contact with the surface remains stationary because of adhesion, but each successive layer of liquid moves with respect to the layer directly below it. The speed of each layer increases with the distance of the layer from the surface AB. A slowly moving layer retards the motion of an adjacent layer which is moving faster. Each horizontal layer is acted upon by the layer above with a tangential force in the direction of the motion and by the layer below with a retarding force. These forces arise from momentum transfer between the particles of the liquid. The dotted figures *abcd* and *efgh* (Fig. 12.1) show the distortion of the

132

liquid as it moves.   The upper layer *fg* travels faster than the lower layer *eh*.   Consider an imaginary cube represented by *abcd* which becomes *efgh* a short time later.   Let F be the tangential force on the plane which cuts the page in *bc* (and later in *fg*).   Let A be the area of this surface of the cube, l be the distance *ab*, and v represent the speed of *bc* relative to *ad*. When v is not too great, F/A is proportional to v/l, or

$$\frac{F}{A} = \eta \frac{v}{l} \tag{12.1}$$

where η is a constant called the *coefficient of viscosity*.   It is equal to the force per unit area necessary to maintain unit difference of velocity between two parallel planes, when the planes are unit distance apart. From Eq. (12.1) it is clear that η may have the dimensions newton-

Table 1

VISCOSITIES OF FLUIDS

Liquids	η, newton-sec/m^2	Gases	η, newton-sec/m^2
Ethyl alcohol at 20°C......	0.0012	Air at 20°C	18×10^{-6}
Glycerin at 20°C..........	1.48	Argon at 20°C	22×10^{-6}
Mercury at 20°C..........	0.0015	Hydrogen at 20°C	9×10^{-6}
Oil			
SAE 10 at 55°C..........	0.16–0.22	Oxygen at 20°C	20×10^{-6}
SAE 20 at 55°C..........	0.23–0.30		
Water at 20°C............	0.001		

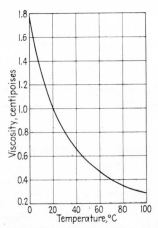

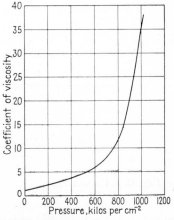

Fig. 12.2. The viscosity of water decreases rapidly with an increase of temperature.   (1 centipoise = 10^{-3} newton-sec/m^2).

Fig. 12.3. The viscosity of a typical oil increases rapidly as the pressure is increased.

seconds per square meter. In many handbooks viscosities are listed in poises; 1 poise = 0.1 newton-sec/m². The viscosities of several fluids are listed in Table 1.

The coefficient of viscosity of a liquid changes both with temperature and with pressure (Figs. 12.2 and 12.3).

12.2. Effect of Viscosity on Motions of Objects. If an object is dropped from a slow-moving airplane, the force of gravity at first exceeds the retarding force due to air friction. As the velocity of the body increases, these frictional forces also increase, while the force of gravity remains essentially constant. Eventually the frictional force becomes equal to the weight and there is no further increase in velocity. The terminal velocity depends on the shape and mass of the falling body as well as on the air density. A pilot who bails out of a plane at 20,000 ft may achieve a velocity of about 150

Fig. 12.4. Meteor trail showing sudden increase in brightness. The resistance of the air is large for high speeds. (*Astrophysical photograph from Yerkes Observatory. Reproduced by permission of University of Chicago Press.*)

mi/hr, which then decreases as the air becomes more dense. On the other hand, a streamlined bomb may have a terminal velocity at the earth well over 700 mi/hr.

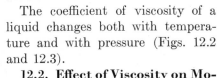

Stream lines

Fig. 12.5. Streamlining.

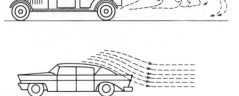

Fig. 12.6. Streamlining an automobile to reduce frictional losses.

The increase of air friction with the velocity of the moving body is one reason for the excessive cost of operation when automobiles or trains are run at high speeds. At moderate speeds fluid friction increases directly with the speed. At higher velocities it varies with the square or even a higher power of the speed.

Meteorites move through the air with such high velocities that they become incandescent and rapidly vaporize (Fig. 12.4).

"Streamlining" in airplanes and in automobiles (to some extent) is an attempt to reduce frictional drag by the air through which the body is moving.   The shape (Figs. 12.5 and 12.6) is so chosen that it reduces the eddies in the air to a minimum, since energy is wasted in producing these eddies.   By reducing eddy currents to a minimum, the power necessary to drive the airplane or automobile at a given speed is decreased.

Figures 12.7 to 12.11 show how the direction of flow is changed by inserting objects of different forms into the path of a fluid or by causing the fluid to flow through channels or orifices.   When the flow is steady and every particle passing a given point follows the same path as all preceding particles which passed the same point, we

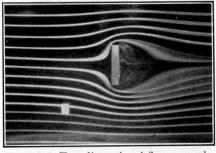

Fig. 12.7. Two-dimensional flow around a plane. Flow from left to right. (*Courtesy of R. C. Binder, Purdue University.*)

speak of *streamlined flow*.   Streamlines (or lines of flow) are clearly evident in the figures.   When the flow is erratic and swirling eddies are created, the flow is said to be *turbulent*.   Note how much more turbulence is evident behind the plane of Fig. 12.7 than behind the cylinder of Fig. 12.8.

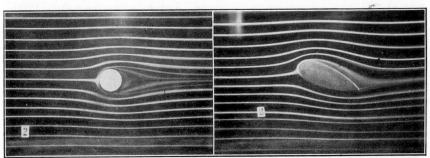

Fig. 12.8. Two-dimensional flow around a cylinder. Flow from left to right. (*Courtesy of R. C. Binder, Purdue University.*)

Fig. 12.9. Two-dimensional flow around a tapered section. Flow from left to right. (*Courtesy of R. C. Binder, Purdue University.*)

12.3. Pressure in a Moving Fluid—Bernoulli's Theorem. Consider a liquid flowing through a pipe of varying cross section (Fig. 12.12). Because the cross section of the pipe is smaller at B than it is at A, the velocity of the liquid must be greater at B than at A in order that the flow of the liquid through each cross section of the pipe may be the same. Consequently, the momentum of the liquid per unit volume increases in going from A to B.   According to Newton's second law, a force is necessary to produce a change of momentum. In this case, the force results from a difference in pressure between A and B. The pressure at A is greater than the pressure at B, thereby producing a positive acceleration of the liquid and an increase in its momentum per unit volume. *The pressure in the fluid is smaller where the velocity is greater.*

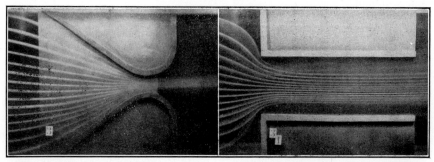

Fig. 12.10. Flow through a nozzle. Flow from left to right. (*Courtesy of R. C. Binder, Purdue University.*)

Fig. 12.11. Converging of streamlines in a jet. Flow from left to right. (*Courtesy of R. C. Binder, Purdue University.*)

The change in pressure can be measured by observing the heights of the liquid in transverse manometers at a, b, and c (Fig. 12.13). If the liquid is *incompressible*, the amount of liquid passing through every cross section of the tube per second is the same. Let v_a, v_b, and v_c represent the

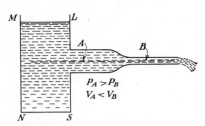

Fig. 12.12. Velocity of a liquid in a pipe of variable cross section.

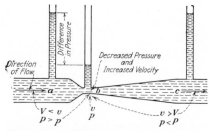

Fig. 12.13. The pressure is least where the speed is greatest.

velocities and A_a, A_b, and A_c represent the cross-sectional areas at a, b, and c, respectively. Then $v_aA_a = v_bA_b = v_cA_c$. *For steady flow the velocity is inversely proportional to the cross section of the tube.*

Example. The cross section of the tube at a is 10 in.² and at b is 2 in.² If the velocity of the stream at a is 12 ft/sec, what is it at b?

$$\text{Velocity at } b = \text{velocity at } a \times \frac{\text{area at } a}{\text{area at } b}$$

$$= 12 \text{ ft/sec} \times \frac{10 \text{ in.}^2}{2 \text{ in.}^2} = 60 \text{ ft/sec}$$

Consider the case in which all parts of a tube of varying cross section (Fig. 12.14) are not at the same height. Let us assume that (1) the liquid is incompressible, (2) the flow is streamlined, and (3) there is no fluid friction (no viscosity). Under these conditions we can use the conservation of energy to derive a relationship between the pressure, velocity, and height at any one point and pressure, velocity, and height at some other point. Let volume V of liquid be forced from a to c (Fig. 12.14). The work done *on* the system in forcing the

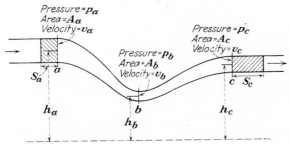

Fig. 12.14. Flow of a liquid through a tube of variable cross section at different heights.

liquid past a is $F_aS_a = (p_aA_a)(V/A_a) = p_aV$, where the subscript a represents the value at point a. The work done *by* the system when the volume V is forced past point c is $F_cS_c = (p_cA_c)(V/A_c) = p_cV$. The *net* work done *on* the system is $(p_a - p_c)V$. Since there are no energy losses, we have

Work done on system = energy of volume V at c − Energy of volume V at a
$$(p_a - p_c)V = [\tfrac{1}{2}(dV)v_c^2 + dVgh_c] - [\tfrac{1}{2}(dV)v_a^2 + dVgh_a] \qquad (12.2)$$

where d is the density of the liquid and dV the mass of the volume V. If we divide both sides of Eq. (12.2) by V and rearrange the terms, we obtain Bernoulli's theorem,

$$p_a + \tfrac{1}{2}dv_a^2 + dgh_a = p_c + \tfrac{1}{2}dv_c^2 + dgh_c = \text{constant} \qquad (12.2a)$$

The sum of the pressure, the kinetic energy per unit volume, and the potential energy per unit volume is the same at all points along the same streamline in the case of streamlined flow for a nonviscous, incompressible fluid.

If frictional forces are acting, some energy is lost and the sum of the three terms of Eq. (12.2a) decreases as we move in the direction of fluid velocity. When water flows through a horizontal tube of uniform cross section, the pressure drops along the tube (Fig. 12.15) if there is energy loss due to viscosity.

Fig. 12.15. When there is resistance to flow, the pressure decreases along a tube of constant area and height although the speed remains constant.

Although we have derived Bernoulli's theorem for an incompressible fluid, Eq. (12.2a) is approximately true for air so long as the speed is well below the speed of sound (about 330 m/sec or 740 mi/hr). In advanced treatises equations are developed which take into consideration the compressibility of the air.

12.4. Applications of Bernoulli's Theorem. Among the common applications of Bernoulli's theorem are the following:

1. *A Ball in an Air Jet.* A light ball can be held in position in an air jet, as shown in Fig. 12.16. In the space between the surface of the funnel and the surface of the ball the pressure is less than atmospheric pressure. This difference in pressure gives rise to a force which supports the ball.

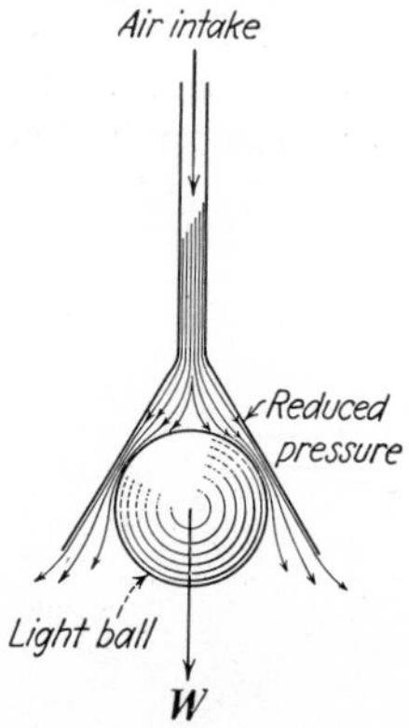

2. *The Sprayer.* The forward stroke of the piston (Fig. 12.17) produces a stream of air past the end of the tube D. The other end of this tube is immersed in the liquid to be sprayed. The stream of air flowing past the open end of the tube reduces the pressure on the liquid in the tube. Atmospheric pressure acting on the surface of the liquid in A forces liquid into the tube D from which it is carried away by the stream of air. A spray results from this mixture of air with the fine particles of liquid.

3. *Flow of Liquid through an Orifice.* In Fig. 12.18 liquid is flowing out of an orifice. Both at the top of the

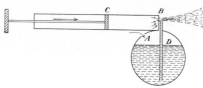

Fig. 12.16. The pressure is sufficiently reduced where the air speed is maximum so that a light ball is supported as shown above.

Fig. 12.17. A sprayer. Reduction of the pressure at B causes liquid to rise in the tube D.

liquid and at the orifice the pressure is atmospheric. At the top of the container the liquid has potential energy and no kinetic energy. If we pick the opening as our position of zero height, the escaping liquid has kinetic energy, but no potential

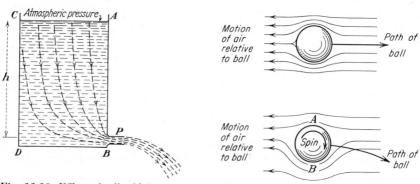

Fig. 12.18. Efflux of a liquid from an orifice.

Fig. 12.19. The motion of the air past a ball when it is not spinning (above) and when it is spinning (below).

energy. If we apply Bernoulli's theorem to points at the top of the fluid and at the orifice, we have

$$p_{atm} + 0 + dgh = p_{atm} + \tfrac{1}{2}dv^2 + 0$$

where p_{atm} represents atmospheric pressure, d the density of the fluid, and v the escape velocity.

$$dgh = \tfrac{1}{2}dv^2 \quad \text{or} \quad v = \sqrt{2gh}$$

4. *The Curving Ball.* It is well known that a ball follows a curved path if it is hit or thrown in such a way that it has both a high speed and a large amount of spin. This is readily understood in terms of Bernoulli's theorem. If we consider the center of the ball as the origin of a coordinate system, the air is rushing past the ball as shown in Fig. 12.19. Because of friction a thin layer of air is pulled around by the rotating ball. At B this layer is moving in the direction of the passing air and the resultant velocity is the sum of the velocities due to the rotation and to the linear motion. At A the velocity due to rotation is opposite to that due to translation and the net velocity is lower. Therefore, the pressure is greater at A and the ball curves in the direction shown.

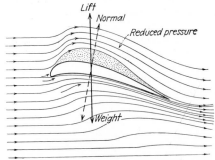

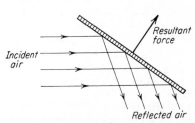

Fig. 12.20. Reduced pressure above the wing results in a net lifting force on the airfoil.

Fig. 12.21. There is a force on a surface inclined to fluid flow which is associated with the rate of change of momentum of the fluid.

5. *The Venturi Flowmeter.* A constriction in a pipeline similar to that of Fig. 12.13 can be used to measure flow through the line. When so used, it is called a *Venturi meter.* If the volume of liquid flowing through the pipeline each second is represented by Q, we have $Q = A_a v_a = A_b v_b$. By Bernoulli's theorem,

$$p_a + \tfrac{1}{2} d v_a^2 = p_b + \tfrac{1}{2} d v_b^2$$

or
$$p_a - p_b = \tfrac{1}{2} d (v_b^2 - v_a^2)$$

If we replace v_a by Q/A_a and v_b by Q/A_b, we obtain

$$p_a - p_b = \frac{1}{2} d Q^2 \frac{A_a^2 - A_b^2}{A_a^2 A_b^2} \quad \text{and} \quad Q = A_a A_b \sqrt{\frac{2(p_a - p_b)}{d(A_a^2 - A_b^2)}}$$

By measuring the pressure difference $(p_a - p_b)$ we can compute the volume of fluid flowing through the pipeline each second if we know the density and the areas A_a and A_b.

6. *Lift on an Airfoil.* In a well-designed aircraft wing the velocity of the air above the wing relative to the aircraft is greater than the velocity below the wing (Fig. 12.20). As a consequence, the pressure is less above the wing than below. This pressure difference gives rise to a net lift. Often the speed of the air below the wing is less than the speed of free air some distance from the plane so the pressure beneath the wing is greater than that in the free air.

When a stream of air strikes a surface inclined to the flow lines (Fig. 12.21), there is a net force directed upward and backward which arises from the rate of change of momentum of the air. The upward component contributes to the lift, the backward component to the drag. For many aircraft the lift due to the Bernoulli effect is enough to support the aircraft in normal flight so that no lift by impact is needed and the lower wing surfaces may be horizontal. When a plane is taking off, part of the lift is usually contributed by the impact of air on the lower wing surfaces. To enhance these forces, the angle of attack is increased and the wing flaps are lowered. This increases the drag as well as the lift. A very simple demonstration of the lift due to the Bernoulli effect may be made by blowing over a sheet of paper held at adjacent corners and lift due to impact can be shown by blowing under the sheet.

PROBLEMS

1. Find the velocity of efflux of water from a hole in the side of a tank when the water in the tank is 24 ft above the hole. If the area of the hole is 2 in.², how many cubic feet will be discharged each second? (Neglect contraction of the streamlines as they emerge from the hole.)   *Ans.* 39 ft/sec; 0.54 ft³

2. At what rate will water discharge from a tank which is 9 ft deep through an orifice which is 0.5 in. in diameter?

3. Water flows at the rate of 2 liters/sec from a hole at the bottom of a tank in which the water is 2 m deep. Find the rate at which the water would escape if an additional pressure of 10^6 newtons/m² were applied to the surface of the water.

Ans. 14.4 liters/sec

4. Find the velocity with which water in a tank will be forced through an orifice in the side of the tank if the orifice is 1 ft below the surface of the water in the tank and there is a pressure of 125 lb/in.² on the surface of the water in the tank. Take atmospheric pressure as 14.7 lb/in.².

5. Water is flowing through a horizontal pipe of varying cross section. The pressure is 60 lb/in.² where the diameter is 2.5 in. and 25 lb/in.² where the diameter is 1.5 in. What is the rate of flow of water in cubic feet per second? *Ans.* 0.95 ft³/sec

6. A reservoir is filled with mercury. In its side there is an opening 5 mm in diameter. If the opening is 2 m below the surface, how many grams of mercury will escape per second?

7. Compute the gauge pressure at a tank of water which will cause the water flowing from the orifice in the side of the tank at a height of 7.5 m from the ground to strike the ground at a distance of 22.5 m from the foot of the tank.

Ans. 1.65×10^5 newtons/m²

8. The level of the water in the manometer at A (Fig. 12.12) reads 30 cm and the cross section at A is 25 cm². The cross section of the constriction is 1.5 cm². Find the pressure in the constriction when the velocity in it is 25 cm/sec.

9. Air is streaming past a horizontal airplane wing such that the speed is 300 ft/sec over the upper surface and 250 ft/sec at the lower surface. If air density is 0.001 slug/ft³, find the difference in pressure between top and bottom of the wing. If the wing area is 100 ft², calculate the gross lift of the wing. *Ans.* 13.8 lb/ft²; 1,380 lb

10. Water is flowing through the pipe (Fig. 12.12), which has an area of 0.75 ft² at A and an area of 0.5 ft² at B. The pressure at the cross section A is 18 lb/in.² and that at B is 12 lb/in.². Find the velocity in each of the cross sections.

11. A viscosimeter consists of two concentric cylinders of large diameter with a thin annular space between them. The cylinders have a mean radius of 5 cm and a length of 15 cm. The thickness of the annular ring is 2 mm. If the outer cylinder is rotated 50 rev/min while the inner one is held fixed, find the torque on the inner cylinder when the viscosimeter contains oil of viscosity 0.2 newton-sec/m².

Ans. 0.062 newton-m

12. If the viscosimeter of Prob. 11 is filled with a different kind of oil and a torque of 0.05 newton-m is required to rotate the outer cylinder 30 rev/sec when the inner one is fixed, find the viscosity of the oil.

Rotary Motion

13.1. Rotational Velocity. Rotational motion is almost as common in our everyday life as translational motion. The flywheel of a stationary engine, the armature of an electric motor, and the spinning top all perform rotational motion. The wheel of a moving automobile describes rotational and translational motions simultaneously. In general, the motion of any moving body may be regarded as a translation of the center of mass and a simultaneous rotation about the center of mass.

Consider the flywheel shown in Fig. 13.1, which is rotating about the axis O. A straight line at OA on the flywheel rotates from A to B. The rate at which the line rotates is called its angular velocity. It is usually expressed in radians per second, although it might also be measured in revolutions per second, revolutions per minute, or degrees per second. If the rate of rotation is constant, the angular velocity is constant and is

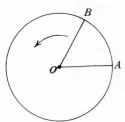

Fig. 13.1. A flywheel rotating about an axis through O.

equal to the angle turned through divided by the corresponding time. If we represent the angular velocity by ω, the angular displacement by θ, and the time by t, we have

$$\omega = \frac{\theta}{t} \tag{13.1}$$

If we consider the linear velocity of the point A on the flywheel, we observe that θ, the angle swept through in radians, is equal to the length of arc AB divided by the radius r. The distance s traveled by the point is just the arc length AB and

$$s = \theta r \tag{13.2}$$

The linear velocity v of the point is given by

$$v = \frac{s}{t} = \frac{\theta r}{t} = \omega r \tag{13.3}$$

141

If we are dealing with a rigid body (Fig. 13.1), the linear velocity of a point increases as the distance from the axis of rotation increases.   Note that Eqs. (13.2) and (13.3) are valid *only* if angles are measured in radians.

Example.   The spoke of a wheel makes 60 rev/min.   It is 18 in. in length.   Find the linear velocity of a point on its outer end and of a point halfway between the axis and the outer end.

$$v_e = \omega r_e = 2\pi \text{ rad/sec} \times 18 \text{ in.} = 113 \text{ in./sec}$$
$$v_m = \omega r_m = 2\pi \times 9 = 56.5 \text{ in./sec}$$

13.2. Angular Acceleration.   If we deal with situations in which rotating bodies are speeding up or slowing down, it is convenient to introduce the concept of angular acceleration.   The instantaneous angular acceleration α of a rotating object is defined as the rate of change of angular velocity.   If the angular acceleration is constant,

$$\alpha = \frac{\Delta\omega}{\Delta t} = \frac{\omega - \omega_0}{t} \tag{13.4}$$

where ω and ω_0 are the angular velocities of the body at the times t and 0.

If we consider any point in a rotationally accelerated body, this point has a linear acceleration a_t tangential to its path given by

$$a_t = \alpha r$$

if we measure α in radians per second per second.   This equation gives only the tangential component of the total linear acceleration of the point.   The point is moving in a circle and has also a centripetal acceleration a_c equal to v^2/r.

Example.   At a certain instant the angular velocity of a wheel is 10 rad/sec.   In 20 sec the angular velocity has become 50 rad/sec.   What is the angular acceleration?

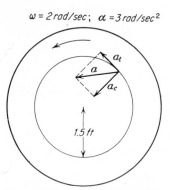

$\omega = 2\,rad/sec$; $\alpha = 3\,rad/sec^2$

1.5 ft

Fig. 13.2. The resultant linear acceleration a is the resultant of the tangential acceleration a_t and the centripetal acceleration $\mathbf{a}_c$.

Angular acceleration $= \dfrac{\text{change in angular velocity}}{\text{time}}$

$$= \frac{50 \text{ rad/sec} - 10 \text{ rad/sec}}{20 \text{ sec}}$$

$$= 2 \text{ rad/sec}^2$$

Example.   What are the tangential and the total linear accelerations of a particle that is 1.5 ft from the axis of a wheel (Fig. 13.2) when the angular acceleration of the wheel is 3 rad/sec² and ω is 2 rad/sec?

Tangential linear acceleration $= \alpha r$

$$a_t = 3 \text{ rad/sec}^2 \times 1.5 \text{ ft} = 4.5 \text{ ft/sec}^2$$

Centripetal linear acceleration $= \dfrac{v^2}{r} = \omega^2 r$

$$a_c = (2 \text{ rad/sec})^2 \times 1.5 \text{ ft} = 6.0 \text{ ft/sec}^2$$

Total linear acceleration $= \sqrt{a_t^2 + a_c^2}$

$$= 7.5 \text{ ft/sec}^2$$

13.3. The Equations of Angular Motion. The equations for angular motion have the same form as the corresponding equations for translational motion. This is true because the angular velocity and angular acceleration are defined analogously to linear velocity and linear acceleration. In the following paragraphs we treat several of the more common special cases.

1. If a body revolves with uniform velocity ω, the angle θ through which it turns in t sec is

$$\theta = \omega t \qquad (13.1a)$$

Example. An electric motor rotates at a constant angular velocity of 1,800 rev/min. Find the angle turned through in 10 sec.

$$\omega = 1{,}800 \text{ rev/min} \times \frac{1 \text{ min}}{60 \text{ sec}} = 30 \text{ rev/sec}$$
$$= 30 \text{ rev/sec} \times 2\pi \text{ rad/rev} = 60\pi \text{ rad/sec}$$
$$\theta = \omega t = 600\pi = 1{,}885 \text{ rad}$$

2. If a body begins to revolve from rest with a uniform angular acceleration α, the angular velocity ω at the end of t sec is αt by Eq. (13.4). During the acceleration the average angular velocity is given by

$$\omega_{\text{av}} = \frac{\omega_0 + \omega}{2} = \frac{0 + \alpha t}{2} = \frac{1}{2}\alpha t$$

The angle θ swept out in t sec is the average angular velocity times the time, so that

$$\theta = \tfrac{1}{2}\alpha t^2$$

Example. A flywheel starts from rest and has a uniform angular acceleration of 4 rad/sec² for a time of 10 sec. Find the final angular velocity, the average angular velocity during the 10 sec acceleration, and the angle turned through in the 10 sec.

$$\omega = \alpha t = 4 \text{ rad/sec}^2 \times 10 \text{ sec}$$
$$= 40 \text{ rad/sec}$$
$$\omega_{\text{av}} = \frac{(\omega_0 + \omega)}{2} = \frac{(0 + 40)}{2} = 20 \text{ rad/sec}$$
$$\theta = \tfrac{1}{2}\alpha t^2 = \tfrac{1}{2} \times 4 \text{ rad/sec}^2 \times 100 \text{ sec}^2$$
$$= 200 \text{ radians}$$

3. If a body has an initial angular velocity ω_0 and a uniform angular acceleration α, its velocity at the end of t sec is given by

$$\omega = \omega_0 + \alpha t \qquad (13.4a)$$

If the acceleration is uniform, the average angular velocity is

$$\omega_{\text{av}} = \frac{\omega_0 + \omega}{2} = \omega_0 + \frac{\alpha t}{2}$$

The angle θ swept out is given by

$$\theta = \omega_{\text{av}}t = \omega_0 t + \tfrac{1}{2}\alpha t^2 \qquad (13.5)$$

If we eliminate t between Eqs. (13.4) and (13.5), we obtain

$$\omega^2 = \omega_0^2 + 2\alpha\theta \qquad (13.6)$$

13.4. Kinetic Energy of Rotation. A rotating body has kinetic energy by virtue of the motion of its parts. To find the expression for

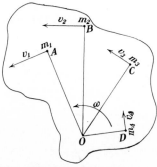

kinetic energy of rotation in terms of the angular velocity and the moment of inertia of the body, consider Fig. 13.3 which represents a body rotating with an angular velocity ω about an axis through O perpendicular to the plane of the paper. For the particle at A having a mass of m_1 and linear velocity v_1, the kinetic energy is $m_1 v_1^2/2$. Since $v_1 = \omega r_1$, the kinetic energy of the particle at A becomes

Fig. 13.3. The kinetic energy of rotation of a body is the sum of the kinetic energies of rotation of all the particles of which the body is composed.

$$\frac{m_1 r_1^2 \omega^2}{2} = m_1 r_1^2 \frac{\omega^2}{2}$$

For other particles m_2, m_3, m_4, . . . moving with velocities v_2, v_3, v_4, . . . similar expressions are found. The total kinetic energy is

$$\frac{m_1 r_1^2 \omega^2}{2} + \frac{m_2 r_2^2 \omega^2}{2} + \cdots = \frac{\omega^2}{2}(m_1 r_1^2 + m_2 r_2^2 + \cdots)$$

$$= \frac{1}{2}\omega^2 \sum_i m_i r_i^2$$

The quantity $\Sigma m_i r_i^2$ is called the *moment of inertia I* of the body about the axis through O. The kinetic energy of the rotating body is

$$\text{Kinetic energy} = \tfrac{1}{2} I \omega^2 \qquad (13.7)$$

This equation is the rotational analogue of $\frac{1}{2} mv^2$ for the kinetic energy of a mass m moving with a translational velocity v. Note that ω must be expressed in radians per second.

13.5. The Moment of Inertia. If we wish to obtain the moment of inertia of a rigid body about any axis, we regard the body as composed of a large number of small mass elements. If we multiply the mass of each element by the square of its distance from the axis and add the contributions of all the elements, we obtain the moment of inertia I.

$$I = m_1 r_1^2 + m_2 r_2^2 + m_3 r_3^2 + \cdots = \sum_i m_i r_i^2 \qquad (13.8)$$

Such a summing process for bodies of most shapes involves detailed numerical calculation or the application of integral calculus. However, we can compute the moment of inertia of a simple ring of mass m and radius r about its central axis by direct application of Eq. (13.8). Since all parts of the ring are essentially at the same distance R from the axis, the moment of inertia is $I = MR^2$. In Fig. 13.4 moments of inertia are given for bodies of several simple shapes—in every case for an axis through the center of mass as indicated. The moment of inertia may be expressed in kilogram-meters^2, slug-feet^2, or in terms of the product of any mass unit multiplied by the square of a unit of length.

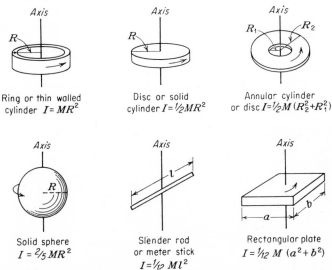

Fig. 13.4. Moments of inertia of several common shapes about the axis indicated through the center of mass.

If we know the moment of inertia about an axis through the center of mass, we may calculate the moment of inertia about any *parallel* axis by the relation

$$I = I_0 + MA^2 \tag{13.9}$$

where M is the mass, I_0 the moment of inertia about an axis through the center of mass, and A the distance from this axis to the *parallel* one about which the moment of inertia is I.

It is sometimes convenient to write the moment of inertia of an extended rigid object in the form $I = Mk^2$, where k is a constant called the *radius of gyration*. Clearly, k corresponds to the radius of a thin circular ring which has the same mass and the same rotational inertia as the rigid body in question.

Example. Find the moment of inertia of a thin rod of mass 2 kg and length 1.6 m about an axis through its center. Also find the moment of inertia about an axis at one end.

For an axis through the center of mass,

$$I_0 = \frac{Ml^2}{12} = \frac{2 \text{ kg} \times (1.6 \text{ m})^2}{12}$$
$$= 0.427 \text{ kg-m}^2$$

For an axis at one end,

$$I = I_0 + MA^2 = 0.427 \text{ kg-m}^2 + 2 \text{ kg} \times (0.8 \text{ m})^2$$
$$= 1.707 \text{ kg-m}^2$$

Example. Find the moment of inertia of a mass of 10 kg and another mass of 15 kg about an axis of rotation which is 0.3 m from the 10-kg mass and 0.4 m from the 15-kg mass. Find the radius of gyration for this sytem.

$$I = m_1 r_1^2 + m_2 r_2^2$$
$$= 10 \text{ kg} \times (0.3 \text{ m})^2 + 15 \text{ kg} \times (0.4 \text{ m})^2$$
$$= 3.30 \text{ kg-m}^2$$
$$I = mk^2$$
$$3.30 \text{ kg-m}^2 = (25 \text{ kg})k^2$$
$$k = 0.36 \text{ m}$$

13.6. Combination of Energy of Translation and Energy of Rotation.

Consider a solid wood disk and a brass ring which have identical radii R and masses M. If both are placed at the top of an inclined plane (Fig. 13.5), they have identical potential energies Mgh. If the disk and ring are allowed to roll down the plane starting from rest, which will reach the bottom first?

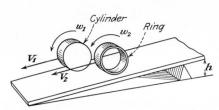

To answer this question, we apply the law of conservation of energy. At the bottom of the inclined plane both the solid cylinder and the ring will have kinetic energy equal to the original potential energy. For each, the kinetic energy is partly associated with the

Fig. 13.5. A solid cylinder and a ring of the same mass and radius roll down an inclined plane with different speeds; the cylinder has the greater speed.

translational velocity of the center of mass and partly with rotation about the center of mass. Let subscript c represent the cylinder and subscript r the ring. Then

$$Mgh = \tfrac{1}{2}Mv_c^2 + \tfrac{1}{2}I_c\omega_c^2$$

and

$$Mgh = \tfrac{1}{2}Mv_r^2 + \tfrac{1}{2}I_r\omega_r^2$$

For a uniform disk of mass M and radius R, $I = MR^2/2$, while for the ring $I = MR^2$. Further, $\omega^2 = v^2/R^2$. Therefore, for the cylinder

$$Mgh = \frac{Mv_c^2}{2} + \frac{Mv_c^2}{4}$$

or

$$v_c^2 = \frac{4gh}{3}$$

For the ring,

$$Mgh = \frac{Mv_r^2}{2} + \frac{Mv_r^2}{2}$$

or

$$v_r^2 = gh$$

Note that the object with the smaller moment of inertia has the greater linear velocity.

13.7. Newton's Laws for Rotational Motion.

Experiments show that the opposition of the body to being set in translation is proportional to the mass of the body and does not depend on the distribution of this mass.   We shall now show for one simple situation that the opposition which a body offers to being set in rotational motion about any axis depends on the moment of inertia about that axis.   Consider a small mass m fastened by a light rod to point O, about which the mass m is to be set in rotation, as indicated in Fig. 13.6.   Let us exert on this mass a force F tangential to the circle. The torque L exerted by force F about the axis through O is Fr and, since $F = ma$, $L = mar$.   The linear acceleration a is just equal to the angular acceleration α multiplied by the radius r, from which

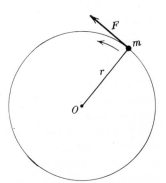

$$L = mr^2\alpha = I\alpha$$

In general, to change the angular velocity of a rigid rotating body, we must apply an unbalanced torque, just as we must apply an unbalanced force to change the linear velocity of a body.   The angular acceleration of a given rotating body is directly proportional to the torque applied.

Fig. 13.6. The angular acceleration is proportional to the unbalanced torque.

$$L = I\alpha \qquad\qquad (13.10)$$

where L is the unbalanced torque acting, α the angular acceleration, and I the *moment of inertia* (or the *rotary inertia*) of the body.   The moment of inertia is the measure of the opposition of the body to being set into rotation.   It is analogous to the mass of a body, which is a measure of the opposition of the body to being set into translational motion.

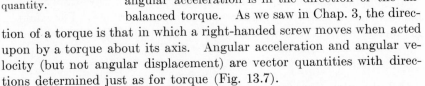

Equation (13.10) expresses Newton's second law for rotary motion, which we have developed from $F = ma$.   *If an unbalanced torque acts on a rigid body, an angular acceleration is produced which is proportional to the unbalanced torque and inversely proportional to the moment of inertia of the body.*   The angular acceleration is in the direction of the unbalanced torque.   As we saw in Chap. 3, the direction of a torque is that in which a right-handed screw moves when acted upon by a torque about its axis.   Angular acceleration and angular velocity (but not angular displacement) are vector quantities with directions determined just as for torque (Fig. 13.7).

Fig. 13.7. Representation of angular velocity or angular acceleration as a vector quantity.

Example.   A flywheel has a moment of inertia of 300 kg-m². Find the torque necessary to produce an angular acceleration of 3 rad/sec².

$$\text{Torque} = \text{moment of inertia} \times \text{angular acceleration}$$
$$L = 300 \text{ kg-m}^2 \times 3 \text{ rad/sec}^2$$
$$= 900 \text{ newton-m}$$

If we raise the front wheel of a bicycle off the ground and set it spinning, its angular velocity gradually decreases until finally the wheel comes to rest. We recognize that torques due to bearing friction and air friction produce the deceleration. If we reduce the friction, the wheel spins longer. If we could eliminate friction, the wheel would spin indefinitely with constant angular velocity. This is a direct analogue of Newton's first law for translational motion and is known as Newton's first law of rotational motion. *A rigid rotating body continues to revolve about an axis fixed in direction with constant angular velocity unless acted upon by some unbalanced external torque.* The rotation of the earth on its axis is a reasonable example, although the earth is not quite a rigid body and there are some unbalanced frictional torques introduced by tides and other considerations.

Newton's third law of rotational motion states: *For every torque acting on one body there is an equal and opposite torque about the same axis which acts upon some other body (or bodies).*

13.8. The Analogy between Linear and Angular Relationships. We have seen that for many of the equations which govern linear motion,

Table 1

LINEAR QUANTITIES AND THEIR ANGULAR ANALOGUES

Linear		Angular	
Displacement	s	Displacement	θ
Velocity	v	Angular velocity	ω
Acceleration	a	Angular acceleration	α
Force	F	Torque	L
Mass	m	Moment of inertia	I

there is an analogous equation in rotary motion. *These equations are valid when the angles are expressed in radians.* It is unnecessary to memorize many of the equations of angular motion, if one makes use of the analogy between linear and rotational motions. Table 1 lists quantities which correspond to one another in the two kinds of motion. If one knows the relationship between linear quantities, he can often write the corresponding relationship between angular quantities by simply replacing each linear quantity by the corresponding angular one. For example, in linear motion work = force $\times$ displacement. The corresponding expression for angular motion is work = torque $\times$ angular displacement. The angular analogue of $P = Fv$ is $P = L\omega$.

13.9. Angular Momentum. Earlier in this chapter, we considered Newton's laws of rotational motion for a rigid body. We now extend these laws to a situation in which moment of inertia may be varied by changing the distribution of mass. We begin by defining the angular momentum of a body as the product of the moment of inertia and the angular velocity. We may now state Newton's second law in the form: *The unbalanced torque acting on the object is equal to the time rate of change of angular momentum.* If there is no unbalanced torque, the angular momentum is constant.

In Fig. 13.8 a man stands on a platform mounted on ball bearings. In his hands he holds heavy weights. When his arms are outstretched, his moment of inertia is greater than when they are folded. If this man is set in rotation with his arms outstretched, he rotates with a constant angular velocity as long as he does not change the moment of inertia. If he folds his arms as indicated in the figure, the moment of inertia of the system (man plus weights) is decreased. Since the angular momentum remains constant, and since the angular moment is

Fig. 13.8. Conservation of angular momentum about a vertical axis requires that the angular velocity increase when the moment of inertia is decreased.

equal to $I\omega$, the angular velocity increases. If he stretches his arms out once again, his angular velocity is reduced. When a diver performs a somersault from the high board, he doubles up to make his moment of inertia small while he is making his turn and then he decreases his rotational velocity by increasing his moment of inertia through stretching out to his full length.

13.10. Gyroscopes. There are many different kinds of gyroscopes, but all include a body of high moment of inertia which is spinning rapidly about an axis. In the gyroscopic compass this gyro element is mounted in such a way that no significant torques are applied. Under these circumstances the law of conservation of angular momentum requires that the vector angular momentum remain constant. The axis of the gyro element points in the same direction, regardless of the maneuvers of the aircraft or ship. Thus, it can be made the key element of an automatic pilot.

If we have a gyroscope such as that of Fig. 13.9 which is supported at point O only, the gyroscope does not fall to the ground when the gyro wheel is in rapid rotation.   Rather, the entire frame rotates about a vertical axis through O at a constant speed.   This motion is called *precession.*

The behavior of the gyroscope can be understood in terms of the concept of angular momentum.   The initial angular velocity ω_0 of the rotating wheel may be represented by the vector OA (Fig. 13.9).   The torque due to the weight of the

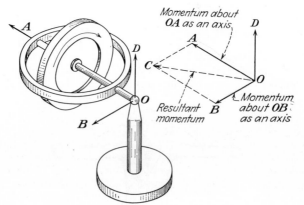

Fig. 13.9. Precession of a gyroscope.

gyro element produces an angular acceleration about the axis OB.   After a short time interval t the new vector angular velocity ω is given by Eq. (13.4).

$$\omega = \omega_0 + \alpha t$$

In Fig. 13.9 αt is represented by the vector OB.   If we add vector OA and vector OB, we obtain the vector OC, which is the new angular velocity vector.   Thus, the gyroscope precesses about the axis OD.

There is an alternative way of looking at the precession of a gyroscope.   Suppose that the rotating element of the gyroscope consists of a metal disk in which

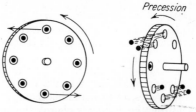

Fig. 13.10. If an effort is made to rotate the wheel about a vertical axis as shown, the loosely held balls fly off as shown and the metal disk tends to tilt.

eight balls are mounted in slots (Fig. 13.10).   When this disk is put into rapid rotation about an axis perpendicular to the plane of the paper, the balls move in the directions indicated in the figure.   Now, if a torque is suddenly exerted about a vertical axis, the upper balls continue to move to the left and the lower ones to the right.   Not only does the inertia of each ball keep it going in the same direction, but so also does the inertia of each particle comprising the disk. Hence, the entire wheel tilts and the axle precesses upward.

An aircraft moving eastward with a single propeller rotating clockwise tends to nose down when it turns south and to nose up when it turns north, since the rotating propeller acts like a gyroscope. If the airplane is traveling eastward and the propeller is rotating clockwise as viewed by the pilot, at any given instant the top blade of the propeller is traveling southward and the lower blade northward. If at this instant the airplane is suddenly turned toward the north, the upper blade continues to move southward and the lower one northward. As a result, the airplane noses upward.

PROBLEMS

1. An electric motor operates at 1,800 rev/min. Find its angular velocity in radians per second. What is the speed of a point 5 cm from the axis of rotation?
Ans. 189 rad/sec; 9.44 m/sec

2. Compute the angular speed about the axle of an automobile wheel 15 in. in radius when the car is moving 60 mi/hr (88 ft/sec).

3. A small motor starts from rest and attains its rated speed of 1,800 rev/min in 4 sec. Calculate the angular acceleration, assuming it to be uniform.
Ans. 47 rad/sec

4. A ball rolling down a slope increases its angular speed at the rate of 0.5 rev/sec². If it starts from rest, what will be its angular velocity at the end of 0.5 min?

5. A bicycle wheel initially at rest is accelerated uniformly until it attains an angular speed of 12 rad/sec in 4 sec. Find the angular acceleration and the angle turned through in this time. *Ans.* 3 rad/sec²; 24 radians

6. An electric generator turning at the rate of 3,000 rev/min is suddenly short-circuited. Its angular velocity drops 10 per cent within 0.25 revolution. Find the average angular velocity and the angular acceleration.

7. If a flywheel has a moment of inertia of 6 kg-m², what angular speed does the wheel attain if 30,000 joules of work are done in producing rotational kinetic energy?
Ans. 100 rad/sec

8. Calculate the moment of inertia of a wheel that has a kinetic energy of 14,000 ft-lb when it is making 600 rev/min.

9. A solid cylinder of steel is rotating around its axis. The cylinder is 10 ft long and 4 ft in diameter. Its weight density is 450 lb/ft³. Find the moment of inertia.
Ans. 3,540 slug-ft²

10. A circular hoop weighs 2 kg and has a radius of 75 cm. Find its moment of inertia about an axis through the center of the hoop and perpendicular to its plane and also about an axis through the hoop and parallel to the axis through the center.

11. A hollow cylinder weighs 80 lb and has a diameter of 3 ft. The mass is concentrated in the rim. It is rolling on a surface with a linear speed of 8 ft/sec. What is its kinetic energy of rotation? its total kinetic energy? *Ans.* 80 ft-lb; 160 ft-lb

12. A heavy flywheel has mass of 1,000 kg and a radius of 1.2 m. It is rotating with an angular velocity of 9 rad/sec. If all the mass may be considered as concentrated in the rim, how much work was necessary to give the flywheel this angular velocity?

13. Find the kinetic energy of a system consisting of two masses of 1 kg and 2 kg, respectively, connected by a rod of negligible mass 1 m long, when the center of gravity of the system has a velocity of 20 m/sec and the system rotates about its center of gravity with an angular velocity of 60 rad/sec. *Ans.* 1,800 joules

14. A cylinder having a diameter of 1.4 ft rolls down an inclined plane that is 120 ft in length. What is the angular velocity of the cylinder at the bottom of the plane if it requires 6 sec for it to reach the bottom? (The cylinder is solid.)

15. The rotary inertia of a body about its axis of rotation is 8 kg-m². A torque of 30 newton-m is applied to it. What is the angular velocity at the end of 40 sec?
Ans. 150 rad/sec

16. A body consists of a horizontal cylindrical shaft weighing 200 lb with a radius of 6 in. and a solid disk having a mass of 180 lb and a radius of 1.2 ft. The cylinder and the disk are mounted so that they have the same axis. What is the torque necessary to give the body an angular speed of 18 rad/sec at the end of 4 sec?

17. A turbogenerator with a moment of inertia of 300,000 slug-ft² rotates at the rate of 40 rev/sec. The power and load are shut off simultaneously, and friction stops the rotation in 3,000 sec. Find the torque friction due to friction. *Ans.* 25,200 ft-lb.

18. A flywheel has a mass of 4 tons and a radius of 5 ft. When it is turning at the rate of 90 rev/min, how many horsepower can be obtained from it during a quarter of a revolution if the velocity decreases 1 per cent in that time? Consider all the mass concentrated in the rim.

19. A 4-lb ring of radius 6 in. rolls down an inclined plane which has one end 2 ft above the other. If the ring starts from rest at the top, show that its kinetic energy of rotation is equal to its kinetic energy of translation at the bottom. Find the kinetic energy of rotation at the bottom. Find the speed of the center of mass at the bottom.   *Ans.* 4 ft-lb; 8 ft/sec

20. A hoop weighing 5 lb and having a radius of 1 ft rolls down an inclined plane that makes an angle of 30° with the horizontal. Assuming that there is no slipping, what is the linear speed of the hoop at the end of 5 sec?

21. A flywheel has a mass of 75 kg and a radius of gyration of 60 cm. It is making 30 rev/sec. It is stopped by means of a friction brake. What torque is needed to stop it in a time of 1 min? How much heat is generated in bringing it to rest?
                    Ans. 85 newton-m; 480,000 joules

22. What linear velocity is acquired by a solid iron disk that has a radius of 25 cm and a thickness of 10 cm when it rolls down an inclined plane which is 2 m long? The plane makes an angle of 5° with the horizontal.

23. What angular acceleration will be imparted to a solid wheel that has a radius of 1.5 ft and a weight of 80 lb by a weight of 64 lb hanging from a cord wound around the axle of the wheel? Neglect the weight of the axle, and assume that its radius is 3 in. Find the tension in the cord.   *Ans.* 5.44 rad/sec²; 61.3 lb

CHAPTER 14

Elasticity
and (Harmonic Motion)
very important

14.1. Elasticity. If we hang a weight from a spring, the spring stretches. If we increase the weight, the spring stretches still more. If we remove the weight, the spring returns to its original length. When a diver stands at the end of a diving board, the board is distorted, but when he leaves the board, it returns to its original position. When an archer prepares to shoot an arrow, he bends the bow, which springs back to its original form when the arrow is released. The spring, the diving board, and the bow are examples of elastic objects. *Elasticity is that property of a body by which it experiences a change in shape or volume when a deforming force acts upon it and by which it returns to its original size or shape when the deforming force is removed* (Fig. 14.1).

Materials which do not resume their original shape after being distorted are said to be *inelastic*. Mud, putty, and dough are inelastic materials. Lead and solder are relatively inelastic, since it is easy to distort them permanently.

Fig. 14.1. Elastic deformation of a golf ball struck with a club. Photograph taken with a high-speed motion-picture camera. (*Courtesy of Edgerton, Germhausen, and Grier, Massachusetts Institute of Technology.*)

14.2. Hooke's Law. Consider the spring of Fig. 14.2. Let its length when there is no load applied be l_0. If we add a load W_1, we find a new length l_1 for the spring. The change in length $(l_1 - l_0)$ we denote by y_1; in general, we shall represent the extension of the spring by y. If we now double the load on the spring, we find that y is twice as great. If we make the load $3W_1$, the extension is $3y_1$. The fact that the change in length is proportional to the applied force was first reported by the English physicist Robert Hooke about the middle of the seventeenth

153

century.   He wrote "Ut tensio, sic vis" (as the extension, so the force). We may extend Hooke's law to more general situations and state it as follows: *The deformation of an elastic body is directly proportional to the magnitude of the applied force.*

Before applying Hooke's law to other situations we shall calculate the amount of work required to stretch a spring a given distance.   When the extension is zero, the force is zero.   As we increase the displacement y, the force F required increases proportionally.   We may write Hooke's

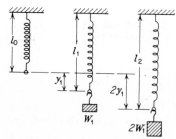

law

$$F = ky \qquad (14.1)$$

where k is known as the *force constant* of the spring.   The average force to produce the displacement y is just equal to $(0 + ky)/2 = ky/2$.   The work done is equal to the product of the average force and the displacement.

Fig. 14.2. When a spring is stretched, the elongation y is proportional to the applied force.

$$\text{Work} = \frac{ky}{2} y = \frac{1}{2} ky^2 \qquad (14.2)$$

The work required to stretch the spring is equal to the potential energy stored in the spring.

14.3. Stress and Strain; Young's Modulus.   In order to treat problems in elasticity in a convenient and consistent way, we introduce two new terms, *stress* and *strain*.   When we distort a body by applying a distorting force, the *stress is the ratio of the force to the area over which it is applied.*

$$\text{Stress} = \frac{\text{force}}{\text{area}}$$

As a result of the applied stress, some change in the shape or size of the elastic body is produced.   The term *strain* is applied to the relative change occurring in the dimensions or shape of a body when it is subjected to a stress.   We shall define three particular types of strain later in this chapter.   For all these types of strain Hooke's law states that *the stress applied is directly proportional to the strain produced.*

When a steel cable supports an elevator or a suspension bridge, it is stretched by the load.   How much its length changes depends on the load, on the cross-sectional area of the cable, on its original length, and on the material of which it is made.   The bigger the load, the larger the stretch expected; the greater the cross-sectional area of the cable, the smaller the stretch.   The stress in the cable is the force applied divided by this area.   *The stretching strain produced is the ratio of the change in length to the original length.*

Stretching (or longitudinal) strain $= \dfrac{\text{change in length}}{\text{original length}} = \dfrac{\Delta l}{l}$

For any elastic material the stretching stress is directly proportional to the longitudinal strain. *The ratio of the stretching stress to the longitudinal strain is known as Young's modulus* (or sometimes as the *longitudinal modulus* or *stretch* modulus) of elasticity. We denote it by Y.

$$\frac{F}{A} = Y \frac{\Delta l}{l} \tag{14.3}$$

Example. A wire 120 in. long with a cross section of 0.125 in.^{2} hangs vertically. When a load of 450 lb is applied to the wire, it stretches 0.015 in. Find Young's modulus of elasticity.

$$\text{Young's modulus} = \frac{\text{stress}}{\text{strain}} = \frac{F/A}{\Delta l/l} = \frac{450 \text{ lb}/0.125 \text{ in.}^2}{0.015 \text{ in.}/120 \text{ in.}}$$
$$= 2.88 \times 10^7 \text{ lb/in.}^2$$

14.4. Limit of Elasticity. A body that has been deformed and then released will return to its original size and shape unless the stress has exceeded a certain limit. In this case the body does not recover its original shape; it has acquired a *permanent set*. The maximum stress from which the substance will completely recover its original size and shape is called the *elastic limit.* It differs widely for different substances, being high for steel and low for lead. Figure 14.3 shows the typical relation between tension and elongation for a wire both above and below the elastic limit. The

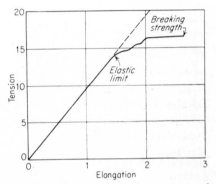

Fig. 14.3. Relation between tension and elongation for a wire. Near the elastic limit Hooke's law does not apply.

greatest stress which can be applied to the wire is the *ultimate tensile stress.* Table 1 lists some typical elastic constants.

When a metal rod is stretched beyond its elastic limit and the stress is increased still further, the stage is reached at which the rod begins to stretch rapidly even though the stress is somewhat decreased. The stress at which this begins is called the *yield point.* Even though the metal is cold, it behaves as if it were in a semifluid state. Once a metal is strained beyond the elastic limit, the strain becomes a function of the time which has elapsed after application of the load. Under such conditions there is a viscous flow which depends both on temperature and on the applied load. Figure 14.4 shows the rate of creep in tin wires as a function of temperature for three values of load.

Figure 14.5 shows the relation between the stress and strain in cork. This is an illustration of a case in which Hooke's law is not applicable because of the

Table 1

TYPICAL ELASTIC CONSTANTS

Material	Young's modulus		Bulk modulus, lb/in.²	Shear modulus, lb/in²	Elastic limit, lb/in.²	Ultimate tensile stress, lb/in.²
	lb/in.²	newtons/m²				
Aluminum...	10×10^6	6.9×10^{10}	10×10^6	3.8×10^6	19,000	21,000
Brass........	14	9.8	8.5	5.1	55,000	65,000
Copper......	17	12	17	6.0	22,000	49,000
Medium steel	30	21	24	12	37,000	70,000

cellular structure of the cork. At low stresses there is a small region where Hooke's law holds, but at higher stresses there are very rapid changes in strain with small changes in applied stress. At still higher stresses, when the cells of the cork have collapsed, there is again an approximate proportionality between stress and strain.

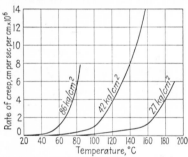

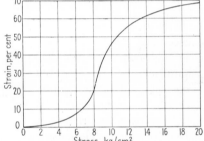

Fig. 14.4. Rate of extension of tin for different loads as a function of the temperature.

Fig. 14.5. Relation between stress and strain in cork.

14.5. Volume Elasticity. Liquids and gases have no fixed length and Young's modulus has no meaning for them. In dealing with fluids, stress (force/area) is change in pressure Δp. The corresponding strain is the change in volume ΔV divided by the original volume V.

$$\text{Volume (or bulk) strain} = \frac{\text{change in volume}}{\text{volume}} = \frac{\Delta V}{V}$$

The volume strain is proportional to applied stress. The ratio of the pressure change to the volume strain is called the bulk modulus (or volume modulus). We denote it by B.

$$\Delta p = B \frac{\Delta V}{V} \tag{14.4}$$

If a solid body, such as a piece of iron, is immersed in a liquid and a uniform pressure is applied to its surface, a change in volume of the solid occurs. The bulk modulus is applicable to solids as well as to fluids.

Example. A sphere of copper having a volume of 100 in.³ is subjected to a pressure of 1,000 lb/in.² Find the change in volume that takes place.

$$\Delta p = B \frac{\Delta V}{V}$$

$$1{,}000 \text{ lb/in.}^2 = 17 \times 10^6 \text{ lb/in.}^2 \frac{\Delta V}{100 \text{ in.}^3}$$

$$\Delta V = 0.0059 \text{ in.}^3$$

Table 2

COMPRESSIBILITY OF LIQUIDS

Substance	Tempera-ture, °C	Compressibility per atmosphere
Ethyl alcohol.............	14	0.0000987
Ethyl ether..............	0	0.000143
Kerosene................	20	0.0000543
Mercury................	20	0.0000039
Turpentine..............	20	0.000075
Water..................	20	0.000048

The reciprocal of the bulk modulus is called the *compressibility* k. Thus $k = 1/B$. It is customary to list compressibilities rather than bulk moduli for liquids (Table 2).

14.6. Shear Modulus. If one cover of a thick book is held firmly on the table and force parallel to the top of the table is applied to the other cover, the shape of the book is changed. Its thickness and volume

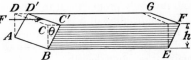

Fig. 14.6. Shearing stress and strain in a bar of rectangular cross section.

remain the same. This deformation in shape is called a *shear*. The *shearing stress* is defined as the tangential force per unit area of the surface and the shearing strain is the angle θ in Fig. 14.6 (θ is measured in radians).

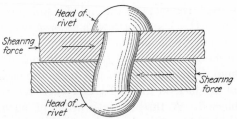

Fig. 14. 7. Shearing stress and resulting strain in a rivet.

Figure 14.7 shows a shearing strain occurring when a rivet is subjected to a shearing stress. The ratio of the shearing stress to shearing strain is called the *shear modulus S* of the material. (It is also known as the *torsion modulus* or *modulus of rigidity*.)

$$\frac{F}{A} = S\theta \qquad (14.5)$$

The shear modulus is the elastic constant involved when one twists a rod or a tube in an application such as that of the drive shaft of an automobile.

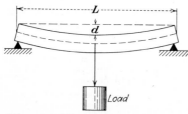

Fig. 14.8. The bending of a beam.

14.7. Stiffness and Strength of Beams. It is important in many engineering applications to be able to calculate the amount of bending that will be produced in a beam by a given load (Fig. 14.8). Experiments on beams of different sizes and shapes have shown that the deflection for a given load depends on the length of the beam, on its breadth, and on its depth.

$$\text{Deflection} = \frac{\text{load} \times (\text{length})^3}{4 \times \text{Young's modulus} \times \text{breadth} \times (\text{depth})^3}$$

The stiffer of two beams is not necessarily the stronger. The mere fact that the one beam bends more than the other does not mean that it will hold less. The strength depends on the same dimensions as the stiffness, but it depends on them in a different way; the strength is proportional to the breadth and to the square of the depth and inversely proportional to the length.

In the bending of a beam the top layer is shortened since it resists compression, while the lower layer is lengthened and must resist tension. A central layer of the beam remains the same length. Therefore, to make a beam as strong or as stiff as possible for a given amount of material, most of the material is put in the upper and lower layers and relatively little in the middle. For this reason steel beams are usually in shapes similar to that of Fig. 14.9. They are called I beams and give great strength and stiffness for a given amount of steel.

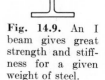

Fig. 14.9. An I beam gives great strength and stiffness for a given weight of steel.

14.8. Vibrations. If a mass on the end of a spring is pulled down and then released, it moves back and forth with a *vibratory* or *harmonic* motion (Fig. 14.10). Such periodic motions are very common. They occur in all sorts of mechanical structures (such as automobiles, bridges, and buildings), in sound sources, in waves, and in electric oscillations. When the pendulum of a clock is displaced and then released, a vibratory motion is established. A further illustration of harmonic motion is afforded by clamping one end of a strip of steel (Fig. 14.11) in a vise and displacing the other end. When released, the strip vibrates back and forth with a period which depends on the characteristic of the strip of steel Other examples of harmonic motion are those of a piston in a steam engine or an automobile and the vibration of a tree limb in a breeze.

Elastic forces lead to such periodic motions.   In the case of the mass on the end of a spring, the restoring force is upward when the mass is displaced downward.   The mass is pulled toward its equilibrium position, but when it reaches this position, it has a velocity and continues upward by virtue of Newton's first law.   Thus, it overshoots the equilibrium position until there is a displacement in the opposite direction. The mass on the end of the spring moves back and forth, until its energy is gradually dissipated in friction of various kinds.

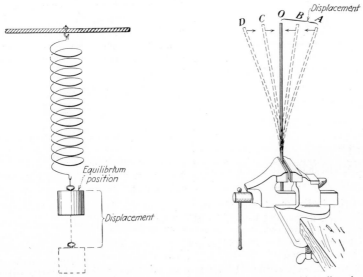

Fig. 14.10. Vibratory motion in a   Fig. 14.11. Harmonic vibrations of a
stretched spring.   strip of steel fastened at one end.

14.9. Simple Harmonic Motion.   Of the many kinds of vibratory motion, we shall consider quantitatively only the simplest type, which is called *simple harmonic motion.   Simple harmonic motion is motion in which the acceleration is proportional to the displacement from the equilibrium position and in the opposite direction.*

In discussing simple harmonic motion, there are several terms which must be defined.   They are as follows:

1. The displacement is the distance of a body from its equilibrium position.

2. The amplitude is the maximum value of the displacement, or the distance from the equilibrium position to the end of the vibrating path.

3. The period T is the time necessary for one complete vibration.

4. The frequency f is the number of complete vibrations made in unit time.   Clearly, the frequency is the reciprocal of the period; $f = 1/T$.

In order to develop equations relating the displacement, the amplitude, the frequency, and the acceleration in simple harmonic motion, we make use of the fact that the shadow of a body which is performing uniform circular motion describes simple harmonic motion. Consider an object moving around a circle (Fig. 14.12) with uniform speed. Imagine the shadow of this body being projected on the wall at the right by means of a beam of light coming from the left. The shadow moves up and down as the particle moves around the circle with constant speed. Let R be the radius of the circle, which we call the *circle of reference*, and θ be the angle

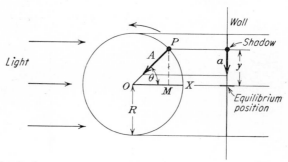

Fig. 14.12. The shadow of a body describing uniform circular motion performs simple harmonic motion.

between the radius vector to the particle and the reference line OX. The displacement of the shadow from the "equilibrium position" is

$$PM = y = R \sin \theta$$

Let A represent the acceleration of the particle P toward the center of the circle and a the acceleration of the shadow on the wall. A is given by V^2/R, where V is the speed of the particle and a is the vertical component of A.

$$a = A \sin \theta = -A \frac{y}{R} = -\frac{V^2}{R^2} y$$

Since neither V nor R changes in magnitude during the motion, V^2/R^2 is a constant. We observe that the acceleration of the shadow is proportional to the displacement and in the opposite direction. This establishes the fact that the shadow describes simple harmonic motion.

Of all the characteristics of a harmonic motion the period is one of the easiest to measure; therefore, let us rewrite our expression for the acceleration in terms of this quantity. To do so, we make use of the fact that the period T is the time for the body to make one revolution on the circle of reference. Hence, $T = 2\pi R/V$ and $V^2/R^2 = 4\pi^2/T^2$. Therefore

$$a = \left(-\frac{4\pi^2}{T^2} \right) y \tag{14.6}$$

If f represents the frequency, we may rewrite Eq. (14.6)

$$a = -4\pi^2 f^2 y \qquad (14.6a)$$

When Eq. (14.6) is solved for T, it yields

$$T = 2\pi \sqrt{\frac{-y}{a}} = 2\pi \sqrt{-\frac{\text{displacement}}{\text{acceleration}}} \qquad (14.6b)$$

The quantity under the square-root symbol is always positive since the displacement and acceleration are of opposite sign. The period of a simple harmonic motion is independent of the amplitude. If the amplitude is small, the body does not move far, but it moves slowly so that the time required to execute one complete vibration is the same as when the amplitude is larger. This interesting fact about simple harmonic motion was discovered by Galileo, who timed the swinging of a great chandelier in the cathedral at Pisa, using his own pulse as his clock.

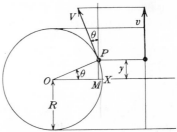

Fig. 14.13. The speed v of the shadow is $V \cos \theta$, where V is the speed of the body on the circle of reference.

Both the acceleration and the velocity of a body describing simple harmonic motion are constantly changing. The velocity of the shadow in our example varies between zero and the velocity V of the particle on the circle of reference. From Fig. 14.13 we see that the velocity v of the shadow describing simple harmonic motion is given by

$$v = V \cos \theta = V \frac{\sqrt{R^2 - y^2}}{R}$$

or

$$v = \frac{2\pi}{T} \sqrt{R^2 - y^2} = 2\pi f \sqrt{R^2 - y^2} \qquad (14.7)$$

When a shadow describes simple harmonic motion, of course no force need act on the shadow. However, if a mass such as the bob of a pendulum describes simple harmonic motion, there must be an unbalanced force to produce the acceleration. By Newton's second law,

$$F = ma = -4\pi^2 f^2 m y$$

where y is the displacement.

Example. A body describes simple harmonic motion with an amplitude of 5 cm and a period of 0.25 sec. Find the acceleration and speed of the body when the displacement is 5 cm, 3 cm, and 0 cm.

By Eq. (14.6), $\quad a = -\dfrac{4\pi^2}{T^2} y \quad$ and by Eq. (14.7) $\quad v = \dfrac{2\pi}{T} \sqrt{R^2 - y^2}$

The amplitude $R = 5$ cm.   When $y = 5$ cm,

$$a = -\frac{4\pi^2 \times 0.05 \text{ m}}{(0.25 \text{ sec})^2} = 31.6 \text{ m/sec}^2$$

and

$$v = \frac{2\pi}{(0.25 \text{ sec})} \sqrt{(0.05 \text{ m})^2 - (0.05\text{m})^2} = 0$$

When $y = 3$ cm,

$$a = -\frac{4\pi^2 \times 0.03 \text{ m}}{(0.25 \text{ sec})^2} = 19 \text{ m/sec}^2$$

and

$$v = \frac{2\pi}{(0.25 \text{ sec})} \sqrt{(0.05 \text{ m})^2 - (0.03 \text{ m})^2} = 1.0 \text{ m/sec}$$

When $y = 0$ cm,

$$a = 0 \quad \text{and} \quad v = \frac{2\pi}{(0.25 \text{ sec})} (0.05 \text{ m}) = 1.26 \text{ m/sec}$$

Example.   A mass of 0.5 kg stretches a spring 20 cm.   Find the force constant of the spring.   If the mass is pulled down an additional 5 cm and then released, find the amplitude and period of the resulting simple harmonic motion.

By Eq. (14.1), $F = ky$, so that $0.5 \text{ kg} \times 9.8 \text{ newtons/kg} = k(0.2 \text{ m})$.

$$k = 24.5 \text{ newtons/m}$$

The amplitude is the maximum displacement which is 5 cm or 0.05 m.   When the displacement is 0.05 m, the restoring force $F_r = ky = 24.5 \text{ newtons/m} \times 0.05 \text{ m} = 1.225 \text{ newtons}$.

By $F = ma$,

$$1.225 \text{ newtons} = (0.5 \text{ kg})a$$
$$a = 2.45 \text{ m/sec}^2$$

By Eq. (14.6b),

$$T = 2\pi \sqrt{\frac{0.05 \text{ m}}{2.45 \text{ m/sec}^2}} = 0.9 \text{ sec}$$

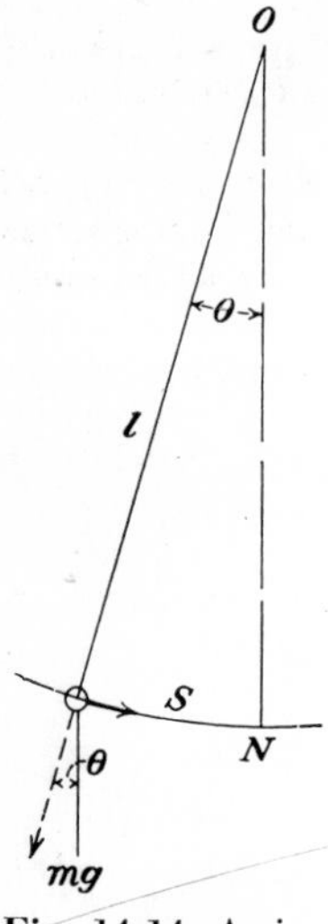

14.10. The Simple Pendulum.   A simple pendulum affords an illustration of simple harmonic motion.   When the pendulum is displaced from its position of equilibrium (Fig. 14.14), the restoring force is $F = -Mg \sin \theta$.   Since $F = ma$, the acceleration which this force produces is $a = -g \sin \theta$.   The displacement of the pendulum bob from its position of equilibrium N is $S = l\theta$.   Hence,

Fig. 14.14. A simple pendulum moves with approximately simple harmonic motion.

$$\frac{\text{Displacement}}{\text{Acceleration}} = \frac{S}{a} = \frac{l\theta}{-g \sin \theta}$$

For small angles $\sin \theta = \theta$ when the angle is measured in radians, and for small displacements of the pendulum

$$\frac{\text{Displacement}}{\text{Acceleration}} = -\frac{l}{g} = \text{constant}$$

Consequently, the pendulum moves with nearly simple harmonic motion for small angles of swing; it deviates from simple harmonic motion for large angular amplitudes.   Its period is, by Eq. (14.6b),

$$T = 2\pi \sqrt{\frac{l}{g}} \tag{14.8}$$

The longer the pendulum, the greater is its period; the greater the acceleration of gravity, the shorter the period of the pendulum.

14.11. Angular Harmonic Motion. When a heavy disk is suspended by a wire (Fig. 14.15) and rotated through an angle θ from its equilibrium position, there is a restoring torque L_r which is proportional to the angular displacement.

$$L_r = -K\theta \qquad (14.9)$$

where K is the *torsion constant* of the wire. By Eq. (13.10) $L = I\alpha$. Consequently, for this *torsion pendulum*

$$I\alpha = -K\theta$$

the angular acceleration is proportional to the angular displacement and angular simple harmonic motion is produced. It can be shown that Eqs. (14.6) and (14.7) are applicable to angular harmonic motion if angular displacement, angular velocity, and angular acceleration are substituted for the corresponding linear quantities.

Fig. 14.15. A torsion pendulum.

14.12. Damped Vibrations. If a particle is vibrating in a viscous medium, its amplitude of vibration decreases with the time. The vibrating particle does work on the surrounding medium and its energy of vibration decreases. For this reason the amplitude diminishes as the time increases. Such vibrations (Fig. 14.16) are known as *damped vibrations*.

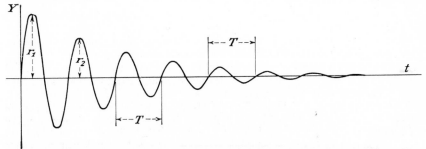

Fig. 14.16. In a damped vibration the amplitude decreases with time.

PROBLEMS

1. A wire made of medium steel is 10 ft long and has an area of 0.005 in.² What is the maximum load which this wire can support? What is the greatest load which can be supported without exceeding the elastic limit? If the wire is fastened at its upper end, how far can it be stretched without exceeding the elastic limit?

Ans. 350 lb; 185 lb; 0.148 in.

2. A brass wire with a cross section of 1.2 mm² is 1.8 m long when supporting a load of 3 kg. How much longer will it be when the load is increased to 5 kg?

3. A wire 2 m long, with a diameter of 0.8 mm, is elongated by 0.4 mm when a 2-kg weight is hung on it. What is Young's modulus for the material?

Ans. 1.95×10^{11} newtons/m²

4. A steel cable 200 ft long is to be thick enough so that an additional load of 200 lb on the cable will increase the length by no more than 0.1 in. What must be the cross-sectional area of the cable?

5. An elevator must carry a maximum load of 4,000 lb, and its maximum acceleration is to be 6 ft/sec². Find the cross section of a cable needed to operate this elevator, if the safe working stress of a steel cable is taken as 15,000 lb/in.²

Ans. 0.32 in.²

6. How much will a copper wire 15 m long stretch when a load of 1.8 kg is applied to it, if the cross section has an area of 0.025 sq cm?

7. The contraction per unit volume of water is 33×10^{-7} for a pressure increase of 1 lb/in.² Find the change in volume of the water in a tube 1 yd long and 2 in.² cross section, when a pressure of 600 lb/in.² is applied to the water. *Ans.* 0.14 in.³

8. A vertical steel column carries a load of 75 tons. The area of its cross section is 12.5 in.² and its length is 18 ft. Find the decrease in length produced by this load.

9. Find the depth in a lake at which the density of the water is 1 per cent greater than at the surface. Ignore temperature differences. *Ans.* 7,000 ft

10. When a pressure of 210 atm was applied to 2 liters of water, the volume changed to 1.98 liters. Find the compressibility of water.

11. A stone is swinging in a horizontal circle 3 ft in diameter, making 30 revolutions each minute. A distant light causes a shadow of the stone to be formed on a nearby wall. What is the amplitude of the motion of the shadow? What is the frequency? What is the period? *Ans.* 18 in.; 0.5 cycles/sec; 2 sec

12. A ball moves in a circular path of 30 cm diameter with a constant angular speed of 5 rev/sec. Its shadow performs simple harmonic motion on the wall behind it. Find the amplitude and period of this simple harmonic motion.

13. Find the acceleration and speed of the shadow in Prob. 12 (*a*) at the end of the motion, (*b*) at the equilibrium position, and (*c*) at a point 9 cm from the equilibrium position.

Ans. (*a*) 14,800 cm/sec², 0 cm/sec; (*b*) 0 cm/sec², 471 cm/sec; (*c*) 8,800 cm/sec², 377 cm/sec

14. A simple harmonic motion has a period of 0.005 sec and an amplitude of 0.06 cm. What is the acceleration when the body has its maximum displacement?

15. The mass on the end of a spring describes simple harmonic motion with a period of 1.5 sec. Find the acceleration when the displacement is 2 cm. *Ans.* 35 cm/sec²

16. A particle moves with simple harmonic motion along a line between two points that are 10 cm apart. If the frequency is 2 vib/sec, (*a*) what is the acceleration of the particle at maximum amplitude? (*b*) What is the speed of the particle as it passes the mid-point?

17. A 100-g mass is suspended from a spring. If the mass is pulled downward 4 cm by an additional force of 0.1 newton and then released, find the period of the motion. *Ans.* 1.26 sec

18. When a mass of 150 g is suspended from a spring, the spring stretches 10.8 cm. What is the period of oscillation of the weight when it is given a small displacement?

19. A pendulum has a length of 3.05 m and executes 20 complete vibrations in 70 sec. Find the acceleration of gravity at that place. *Ans.* 9.83 m/sec²

20. Find the length of a pendulum (in centimeters) which has a period of 1.5 sec.

21. In a gasoline engine the motion of a piston is approximately simple harmonic. If a piston has a mass of 0.5 kg and a stroke (twice the amplitude) of 10 cm, find the maximum acceleration and the maximum unbalanced force on the piston if it is making 50 complete vibrations each second. *Ans.* 4,940 m/sec²; 2,470 newtons

22. A mass of 10 g is moving with simple harmonic motion along a line 10 cm long with a period of 2 sec. (*a*) What will be the acceleration of the particle one-sixth of a period after it has passed the mid-point? (*b*) What will be the force acting on the particle at this instant?

23. A 0.2-kg mass is suspended from a spring. If the spring is pulled downward with a force of 0.25 newton, it stretches an additional 5 cm.   If the spring is released, the mass describes simple harmonic motion with an amplitude of 5 cm.   Find the period of the motion and the velocity and acceleration of the mass when the displacement is 3 cm.   *Ans.* 1.26 sec; 0.2 m/sec; 0.75 m/sec^2

24. Find the maximum values of the potential energy and of the kinetic energy of the vibrating mass of Prob. 23, taking the equilibrium position for the zero of potential energy.

25. To be acceptable, a 20-lb airplane radio receiver must pass a shake test in which it is forced to describe simple harmonic oscillations at 100 vib/sec with a maximum acceleration of 8 g's ($g = 32$ ft/sec^2).   Find the maximum displacement, unbalanced force, and velocity.   *Ans.* 0.0078 in.; 160 lb; 0.41 ft/sec

PART II

Wave Motion
and Sound

CHAPTER 15 $V = f\lambda$

Wave Motion

15.1. Waves. One of the most important phenomena in nature is the transmission of energy from one point to another by wave motion. This kind of motion may be illustrated in many ways. When a stone is dropped into a pool of still water, the surface of the water is covered with circular wavelets which widen out from the point where the stone fell. The water does not itself move outward from this central point; rather it rises and falls. That such is the case may be seen by observing a floating cork. It does not move forward, but moves up and down and back and forth in a roughly elliptical path. The water on which the cork rests has this same kind of motion.

In wave motion a disturbance of some kind propagates through a medium. An individual particle of the medium oscillates up and down or back and forth, but it returns eventually to its initial position. Energy is transferred through the medium, although the particles themselves are not transmitted. In a typical wave motion a vibrating center produces motions in particles of the medium immediately in contact; these particles in turn impart their motion to their neighbors.

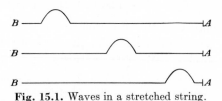

Fig. 15.1. Waves in a stretched string.

15.2. Transverse and Longitudinal Waves. It is convenient to classify waves in terms of the way in which the motion of the individual particles of the medium is related to the movement of the wave itself. In waves produced in a stretched rope (Fig. 15.1) the individual particles move up and down at right angles to the direction in which the wave itself propagates. A wave of this kind is known as a *transverse wave*, because the particles in the medium move perpendicular (*trans* = across) to the direction of the wave motion. In the simplest form of transverse wave each particle vibrates with simple harmonic motion with its displacement at right angles to the propagation direction. Light and other forms of

169

electromagnetic radiation, as well as waves in stretched strings, are illustrations of transverse waves. *A transverse wave is one in which the particles of the medium vibrate at right angles to the direction in which the wave travels.*

If a series of equal masses are joined together by springs (Fig. 15.2) and particle A is moved toward particle B, a wave is propagated down the system. The motion of A toward B compresses the spring between

A B   C   D   E   F

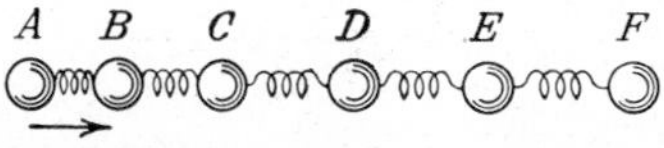

Fig. 15.2. Waves in compressed springs.

them. B is accelerated toward C, which in turn moves toward D. A compressional wave is produced. Similarly, when mass A is pulled away from B, the spring between them is stretched and B is accelerated toward A. If A is moved back and forth with simple harmonic motion, a wave motion is propagated along the system with each particle describing simple harmonic motion along the axis of the system. The various masses do not all vibrate in phase. *A wave motion in which the individual particles vibrate back and forth along the direction in which the wave travels is called a compressional or a longitudinal wave.* Sound waves are an important example.

15.3. Other Kinds of Waves. In many kinds of wave motion individual particles do not move back and forth along a single line. For example, in water waves water molecules move forward and back as well as up and down. When a particle is on a crest A (Fig. 15.3), it

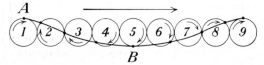

Fig. 15.3. Motions of particles in a water wave.

moves in the direction in which the wave is moving. In a trough B a particle is moving in the opposite direction. The paths are ellipses or circles. We have in this case a mixed wave, neither longitudinal nor transverse. We can, of course, resolve the motion of the particle into components perpendicular to and parallel to the propagation direction and treat the mixed wave as a combination of a longitudinal and a transverse wave.

There are many other kinds of waves besides those in material mediums in which the disturbances arise out of the displacement of particles. If the temperature of one end of a metal rod is first raised gradually, then lowered, raised again, etc., there is set up a succession of changes in the temperature of the rod. These changes travel forward in the rod as a wave of temperature. The daily heating and cooling of the surface of the earth, as it is turned toward and away from the sun, produce waves of temperature that go down into the earth for a short distance.

If one end of an ocean cable or telephone wire is suddenly joined to a battery, the change in potential thus produced in the wire is gradually felt along the conductor. If the potential is varied systematically, an electric wave is transmitted along the conductor.

Figure 15.5 shows the spread of a shatter wave in glass caused by the impact of a high-speed bullet.

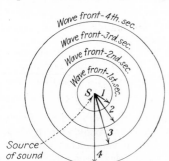

Fig. 15.4. An illustration of water waves on a large scale. (*Ewing Galloway.*)

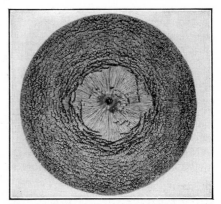

Fig. 15.5. Spread of a shatter wave in glass struck by a bullet. (*Courtesy of Edgerton, Germhausen, and Grier, Massachusetts Institute of Technology.*)

15.4. Wavelength, Frequency, and Velocity. When waves spread out from the center of a disturbance, a surface marking the points which the disturbance has reached is called a wave front (Fig. 15.6). When a drop of water falls on the surface of a pond, the wave front is a circle that expands continuously. When a small balloon bursts in the air, the wave front of the sound produced is a sphere with the balloon as the center. The waves of light from a distant star have spherical wave fronts of such large radius that small portions of them may be considered plane.

If we have waves passing across the sur-

Fig. 15.6. Wave fronts from a point source.

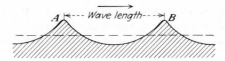

Fig. 15.7. Definition of a wavelength.

face of water, the distance from crest to crest (or trough to trough) is called the *wavelength* (Fig. 15.7). In general, *the wavelength is the distance in the propagation direction between two successive points which are in the same phase of vibration.* Let f be the frequency of the wave, or the number of complete vibrations made by each particle in 1 sec.   If each wave is of length λ, the total distance traversed by the disturbance in 1 sec is just the number of vibrations per second multiplied by the wavelength, or

$$V = f\lambda \qquad (15.1)$$

where V is the velocity of the wave motion.   This relation is applicable to all types of wave motion and is one of the most widely used relationships in physics.

Example.   If the velocity of a disturbance in a steel rod is 5,000 m/sec and the frequency of the vibrations is 2,500/sec, find the wavelength.

$$\lambda = \frac{V}{f} = \frac{5{,}000 \text{ m/sec}}{2{,}500 \text{ vib/sec}} = 2 \text{ m/vib} = 2 \text{ m}$$

15.5. Representation of Waves.   If each particle of a medium through which a wave is traveling describes simple harmonic motion, a simple way of representing the wave graphically is to choose two axes (Fig. 15.8) and to plot on the vertical axis the displacement of a particle at a given instant and on the horizontal axis the distance of that particle from the source of the disturbance.   Such a curve gives the displacement at any instant for all the particles in the medium along the direction in which the waves are traveling.   In Fig. 15.8a, the wave is constant in intensity as we go away from the source, since the amplitude of vibration remains constant.   In Fig. 15.8b the amplitude is decreasing as we go away from the source.

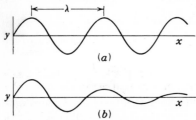

If the wave motion is complex and a number of frequencies are involved, it is always possible to consider the complex motion of any particle to be composed of a number of simple harmonic ones. Thus, a very complex motion may be treated as the sum of a number of simple ones.   Although many waves have a far more complicated picture than those of Fig. 15.8, Fourier has shown that all waves can be represented in terms of sine waves similar to those shown.   A Fourier analysis of a complex wave into simple harmonic (or sine) waves is beyond the scope of this book, but the fact that this can be done means that the arguments and developments which we base on simple sinusoidal curves can be extended to complex wave forms.

Fig. 15.8. Displacement of particles at a particular instant as a function of the distance from the source: (a) case in which amplitude is constant; (b) case in which amplitude decreases with distance.

When a wave passes through a medium, the individual particles describe simple harmonic motion.   The displacement of a particle moving with this type of motion can be represented by the equation

$$y = A \sin 2\pi f t \qquad (15.2)$$

where y is the displacement, A the amplitude, f the frequency, and t the time. The displacement of any particle in the medium through which a simple wave is passing in the x direction can be represented by the equation,

$$y = A \sin 2\pi f \left(t - \frac{x}{V} \right)$$

where x/V is introduced to take account of the fact that the vibrations are not all in the same phase. The displacement depends both on the time and on the distance of the particle from the origin. Each successive particle is a little later in phase than the adjacent particle nearer the source. The wave reaches point b, one-fourth wavelength from the origin (Fig. 15.9), one-fourth of a period

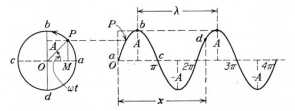

Fig. 15.9. The displacement depends on the time and on the distance from the origin.

later than it arrives at a. It reaches point c one-half period later. The wave reaches point d, which is the distance x from point a, in a time x/V sec later than it passes a. Let the displacement of a be given by Eq. (15.2). To obtain the displacement at d, we must deduct from t the time x/V. The displacement at a point which is any distance x from point a is given by

$$y = A \sin 2\pi f \left(t - \frac{x}{V} \right) \qquad (15.2a)$$

Although in our plot of displacement as a function of position we obtain a sine curve which suggests a traverse wave motion, this same curve represents equally well a longitudinal wave motion, since the displacement y obeys exactly the same equations. The only difference is that the displacement for longitudinal wave motion is in the direction of propagation, while for a traverse wave motion it is perpendicular to the propagation direction.

15.6. The Flow of Energy in a Medium.

When a wave passes, energy is propagated through the medium although the individual particles describe simple harmonic motion and have no net displacement. The energy transmitted in unit time through a unit area perpendicular to the direction of propagation is called the *intensity* of the wave motion. *The intensity is proportional to the square of the frequency and to the square of the amplitude of the vibrations of the oscillating particles*, as is shown below.

For a particle describing simple harmonic motion the energy is transformed from kinetic energy to potential and back to kinetic energy. Let m be the mass of a particle, A the amplitude of its harmonic oscillation, and f the frequency. The energy of a single particle is given by $\frac{1}{2} m v_{max}^2 = 2\pi^2 f^2 A^2 m$ since the maximum velocity v_{max} of the particle is $2\pi f A$. If we consider a steady wave propagated in the x direction (Fig. 15.10), the wave front sets in motion every particle which it passes. The intensity of the wave is then given by the total energy supplied to all the particles included in a cylinder having a base of unit area and of length equal to the distance traversed by the wave in unit time. The number of particles included in this tube is equal to nV, where n is the number of particles per unit volume and V is the velocity of the wave. Each particle receives energy $2\pi^2 f^2 A^2 m$ and the total power transmitted per unit area is the intensity, given by

$$I = 2\pi^2 f^2 A^2 mnV \tag{15.3}$$

If a disturbance produces waves which are sent out equally in all directions, the wave fronts are spheres with the source as the center (Fig. 15.11). If we assume that there is no transformation of the wave energy, the total energy per unit time which passes through any one sphere surrounding the source is exactly equal to the energy per unit time which passes through any other sphere. The energy per unit time passing

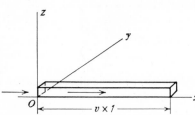

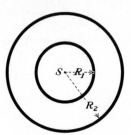

Fig. 15.10. The energy transmitted per unit area across the plane zOy in 1 sec occupies a volume of unit cross-sectional area and of length numerically equal to the speed of the wave motion.

Fig. 15.11. The intensity is inversely proportional to the distance from the source.

through a sphere is just the product of the area of the sphere and the intensity I. Therefore, $4\pi R_1^2 \times I_1 = 4\pi R_2^2 \times I_2$, where I_1 and I_2 are the intensities at the spheres of radii R_1 and R_2, respectively,

$$R_1^2 I_1 = R_2^2 I_2 \tag{15.4}$$

The intensity varies inversely as the square of the distance from the source.

When the energy cannot spread out freely in all directions, the intensity does not vary inversely as the square of the distance. A cheerleader's megaphone is designed to reflect sound waves toward his cheering section. In this case the intensity at equal distances from the source depends strongly on direction. If there is absorption between the source and a receiver, the intensity falls off more rapidly with distance than the inverse-square law suggests, even though the energy may be radiated equally in all directions.

15.7. Huygens' Principle. If we have a point source of waves radiating energy equally in all directions, the wave fronts are spherical.

If we place a series of obstacles in the medium through which the wave is traveling, we expect these obstacles to distort and change the wave fronts. How can we predict where the new wave front will be a time Δt after the wave front has struck an obstacle? The answer to this question was found by Huygens, who observed that in a typical wave motion each particle is set into vibration by a neighboring particle. This led him to postulate that *every point on a wave front acts as a new source sending out secondary wavelets.*

Consider a spherical wave front (Fig. 15.12). Let us, following Huygens, assume that each point on this wave front is a source of secondary spherical wavelets and ask where the wave front corresponding to AB will be a time Δt later. About each point 1, 2, 3, 4, . . . on the initial

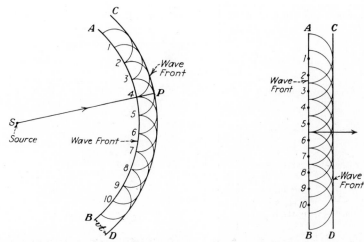

Fig. 15.12. Huygens' principle applied to a spherical wave front.

Fig. 15.13. Huygens' principle applied to a plane wave front.

wave front we draw little spheres of radius $V \Delta t$, where V is the velocity of the waves. To find the position of the new wave front, we find the surface which is tangent to all the secondary wavelets. This is the surface CD in Fig. 15.12. If we have a plane wave passing through a medium, we may find the new wave front by applying Huygens' method. The new wave front is again plane, as shown by Fig. 15.13.

Qualitatively, we may explain why Huygens' principle is valid as follows: Wavelets traveling to each side from any point source are canceled by those from neighboring sources, moving oppositely. Wavelets traveling back toward the original source are canceled by other forward moving wavelets. The only wavelets remaining uncanceled are those moving in the direction of propagation. Hence, the new wave fronts as in the figures. Although there is a surface which is tangent to the wavelets in the backward direction, it is rejected for the reason above.

Huygens' principle may be summarized as follows: *Every point on the wave front of any wave motion may be regarded as a secondary source of "Huygens" wavelets which spread out with the velocity of the primary wave. To find the wave front at any time Δt later, we find the forward surface which is tangent to all these secondary wave fronts. This surface gives the new position of the primary wave front.*

If the surface of a dish of mercury is agitated by means of the prong of a tuning fork to which is attached a piece of fine wire dipping into the surface of the mercury, a system of waves is set up. At a considerable distance from the source the waves are almost plane. If these waves fall on a small aperture in a partition (Fig. 15.14), the aperture acts as a small source which sends out almost circular waves in accordance with Huygens' principle.

Fig. 15.14. An aperture in a partition serves as a source of circular waves. (*From Webster, Drew, and Farwell, "Physics for College Students," Appleton-Century-Crofts, Inc.*)

Fig. 15.15. Reflection of a spherical sound wave by a plane mirror. (*Courtesy of Arthur L. Foley, University of Indiana.*)

15.8. The Reflection of Waves. One of the important applications of Huygens' principle is to the reflection of waves by an obstacle. Figures 15.15 and 15.16 show the reflection of a spherical sound wave by a plane mirror. In Chap. 16 we shall discuss how the wave front was photographed; at the moment we are concerned only with the fact that when the spherical wave strikes a mirror it is reflected and the curvature of the wave is reversed. That a spherical wave should be reflected in this way can be shown by direct application of Huygens' principle.

Consider a plane wave (Fig. 15.17) falling upon a plane reflecting surface. Let A_1B_1, A_2B_2, A_3B_3 be consecutive positions of the plane wave front.

Let us now use Huygens' construction applied to the wave front A_3B_3 to find the position of the new wave front. We choose the instant at which the end B_3 of the wave front reaches the plane surface as the time at which we wish to locate the new wave front. Let Δt be the interval required for the wave to move from B_3 to the surface. We observe from the figure that the new wave front is given by RS. Since $V\,\Delta t$ is perpendicular to the wave front and since the distance A_3S is the same for the triangles ASR and A_3B_3S, the two triangles are similar and equal. Therefore, the angle of reflection r is equal to the angle of incidence i.

In dealing with the reflection of waves, it is often more convenient to follow the path of a ray which moves in the direction of propagation of the wave than to observe the wave front. For isotropic mediums the ray is perpendicular to the wave front. If N represents a normal to the surface

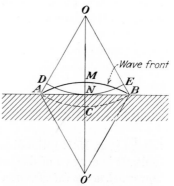

Fig. 15.16. Reflection of spherical sound waves. The curvature of the wave front is reversed by reflection.

(Fig. 15.18), the angle of incidence is the angle between the incident ray and N, while the angle of reflection is the angle between the reflected ray

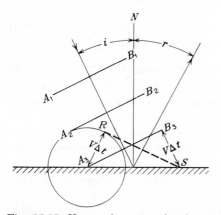

Fig. 15.17. Huygens' construction for a plane wave reflected from a plane surface.

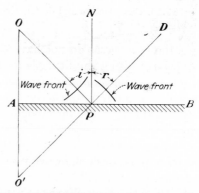

Fig. 15.18. Reflection of waves. The angle of incidence is equal to the angle of reflection.

and N. Also, the incident ray, the reflected ray, and the normal all lie in the same plane. This leads us to the two laws of reflection:

1. *The angle of incidence is equal to the angle of reflection.*
2. *The incident ray, the normal, and the reflected ray lie in the same plane.*

15.9. Superposition and Interference.   It is very common to have sound waves from two different sources moving through a room at the same time.   We may ask, "What happens when two or more wave motions pass a given point at the same time?"   *If two or more wave motions pass a given particle at the same instant, the displacement is the resultant of the displacements which would be produced by each of the waves if it acted separately.*   This is a statement of a very important law of nature, sometimes called the *principle of superposition.*

We shall at the moment apply this principle to the particular case in which we have two wave motions traveling in the same direction at the same time.   Let us suppose that these two wave motions have the same amplitude and the same frequency as well as the same direction.   If the two waves arrive in such a way that crests meet crests and troughs meet troughs (Fig. 15.19), the displacements due to the two waves add and the resultant is a wave of double the original amplitude.   These two waves show *constructive interference.*   On the other hand, if the two waves arrive at the same point in such a way that crest meets trough and trough meets crest, they cancel one another and we have *destructive interference.*

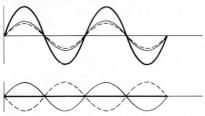

Fig. 15.19. Constructive and destructive interference.

Fig. 15.20. Waves in a stretched string reflected at a wall.

If the two waves do not have equal amplitudes, they may still interfere; the resulting amplitude is the resultant of the individual amplitudes. If the waves have different frequencies, they may interfere constructively at one moment and destructively at a later moment, as we shall see in the next chapter.   The phenomenon of interference is a fundamental property of wave motions.   Indeed, if there is a question as to whether some phenomenon is a wave motion or not, the test which resolves the question in favor of the wave position is one which produces interference between two "rays."

15.10. Standing Waves.   A particular type of interference which is of great importance in connection with musical instruments is interference between two waves which are traveling in opposite directions.   Consider a long elastic cord which is fixed at one end (Fig. 15.20) while the other end is held in the hand.   If the cord is stretched tight and the free end is moved up and down with simple harmonic motion, waves are set up in the cord which travel to the fixed end where they suffer reflection and travel back to the hand.   At any instant two trains of waves are traveling in the cord in opposite directions. If the frequency is chosen properly, the cord ceases to have the appearance of being traversed by trains of waves and vibrates transversely in one or more segments (Fig. 15.21). The behavior of the cord can be explained by consideration of Figs.

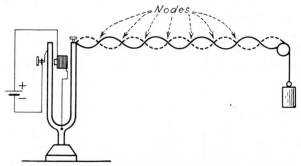

Fig. 15.21. Standing waves in a stretched string.

15.22 and 15.23. The dotted line represents a wave traveling from right to left, while the broken line represents a similar wave of the same frequency and amplitude traveling from left to right. The resultant disturbance which arises from the combination of these two trains of waves is represented by the continuous lines. The resultant at any instant has the form of a wave, but the wave pattern does not move. Each

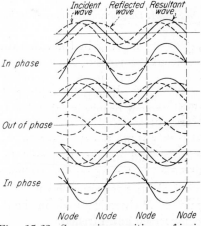

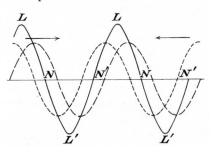

Fig. 15.22. Standing waves result when two wave trains of identical amplitude and frequency travel in opposite directions, interfering constructively at some points and destructively at others.

Fig. 15.23. Successive positions of incident and reflected waves producing standing waves.

particle vibrates, but the amplitude of vibration varies along the cord. When the frequency is high, all the eye sees is a characteristic blur that appears to remain motionless. This appearance has given rise to the name *standing waves*. At L (Fig. 15.22), the crests of two component waves are approaching each other. When the two crests coincide, the resulting displacement is maximum.   A quarter of a period later the two components exactly neutralize each other.   The crest of one wave meets the trough of the other.   At this instant the cord is straight.   As the waves travel farther in opposite directions, the portion of the string $N'LN$ is depressed below the horizontal and after another quarter of a period has its maximum displacement in the negative direction.   At the points N and N' there is never any displacement.   At these points, called *nodes*, the two waves traveling in opposite directions always interfere destructively.   All the particles of the cord between two adjacent

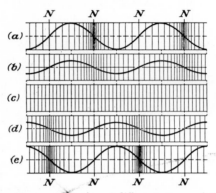

Fig. 15.24. Diagrammatic representation of different stages of standing sound waves.

nodes are moving in the same direction at any given instant, but two adjacent segments of the cord are always displaced in opposite directions. The length of the segment between two consecutive nodes is one-half wavelength.   The point midway between the nodes at which maximum displacement occurs is called an *antinode* (or *loop*).

Standing waves may result from any kind of wave motion.   The essential thing for their production is that two waves of the same frequency and amplitude travel in opposite directions in the medium. Figure 15.24 represents standing waves in a column of air.   The short vertical lines represent layers of air displaced as shown.   At the places marked N there is a node in the displacement; here the air is alternately compressed and rarefied.

PROBLEMS

1. Waves travel with a speed of 600 ft/sec through a medium.   If 50 waves pass a given point each second, find the wavelength.   *Ans.* 12 ft

2. It is 4 m from crest to crest in a system of waves.   If 20 waves pass a given point each second, find the speed of the waves.

3. Water waves are observed passing a certain point at a velocity of 20 mi/hr, with a distance of 22 ft between crests.   What is the frequency of the waves?

Ans. 1.33 sec^{-1}

4. A set of circular ripples is produced on the surface of a pond by throwing a stone into the water. At a certain instant, the first crest is 3 m from the point where the stone hit the water, and the third crest is 50 cm from the same point. What is the wavelength of the disturbance?

5. The displacement for a particle is given by $y = 10 \sin 2\pi ft$ cm. If $f = 20/\text{sec}$, find the displacement at times t of 0.01 sec, 0.03 sec, and 0.26 sec.

Ans. 9.51 cm; −5.88 cm; 9.51 cm

6. If a certain particle has a displacement given by $2 \sin 2\pi ft$, where $f = 0.1/\text{sec}$, find the displacement at times 1, 2, 3, . . . 9, and 10 sec. Plot the displacement as a function of time.

7. If the displacement along a wave is given by the relation $y = 6 \sin 4(t - 2x)$, what are the numerical values of the amplitude, frequency, wavelength, and the speed of the wave motion?   *Ans.* 6; $2/\pi$; $\pi/4$; 0.5

8. If the displacement along a wave is given by $y = 0.02 \sin (100t - 3x)$, where distances are in meters and times in seconds, what are the amplitude, frequency, wavelength, and speed of the wave motion?

9. If the frequency of a wave motion is doubled while the amplitude is kept constant, how does the intensity of the new wave motion compare with the old?

Ans. Increased by a factor of 4.

10. Two sources produce waves of identical frequency, but one produces waves of three times the amplitude of the other. Find the ratio of the two intensities.

11. Standing waves are produced in a stretched rope. If the distance between successive nodes is 0.7 m, what is the wavelength? If the waves travel with a speed of 84 m/sec, what is the frequency?   *Ans.* 1.4 m; 60 per second

12. Compressional waves with a frequency of 1,200 vib/sec are sent down a tube, the far end of which has a movable piston. Standing waves are produced. The reflected wave reinforces the source at two successive positions of the piston differing by 5.5 in. What is the velocity of the waves in the tube?

CHAPTER 16

Sound Waves

16.1. The Nature of Sound. Sound has its source in vibrating bodies. Consider the tuning fork of Fig. 16.1. As the tine A swings toward the right, it pushes air molecules to the right and produces a region

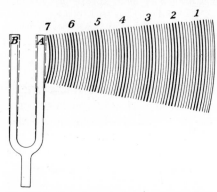

in which the molecules are crowded together. Such a region is called a *compression*. When the tine swings to the left, a region of reduced pressure called a *rarefaction* is produced. The next swing to the right produces another compression, and so forth. Thus, the sound wave consists of a series of alternate compressions and rarefactions. The molecules move back and forth along the line of propagation, which establishes the *longitudinal* nature of the waves. When the condensations and rare-

Fig. 16.1. Sound waves from a tuning fork showing alternate compressions and rarefactions.

factions reach the eardrum of a listener, they produce small inward and outward motions of the eardrum and this starts the physiological processes of hearing.

16.2. The Velocity of Sound. The velocity of sound in any medium depends upon the density of the medium and upon its elastic properties; the greater the elasticity and the less the density, the greater the velocity. In a wire or rod of a solid material the velocity of sound waves is given by

$$V = \sqrt{\frac{Y}{d}} \qquad (16.1)$$

where Y is Young's modulus for the rod and d the density. In fluids the velocity is given by

$$V = \sqrt{\frac{B}{d}} \qquad (16.2)$$

where B is the bulk modulus. We shall be particularly interested in the velocity of sound in gases. For a gas the appropriate elastic modulus is the *adiabatic bulk modulus* given by γp, where p is the pressure and γ is the ratio of two specific heats for the gas (Sec. 21.5). It is 1.67 for monatomic gases, 1.40 for diatomic gases, and 1.28 for triatomic gases. For air,

$$V = \sqrt{\frac{1.4p}{d}} \qquad (16.3)$$

The speed of sound in air at 0°C is 331.4 m/sec or 1,087 ft/sec. In hydrogen, which has a low molecular weight and therefore low density, the speed of sound at 0°C is about 1,270 m/sec.

According to Boyle's law, the ratio of the pressure to the density of a gas is constant if the temperature of the gas remains unchanged. Since the velocity depends only on the *ratio* of pressure to density, it is constant for a given gas so long as the temperature is constant. However, if the temperature is changed,

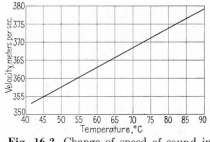

Fig. 16.2. Change of speed of sound in dry air with temperature.

the density varies with the temperature (Sec. 20.5) according to the relation $d_t = d_0/(1 + t/273)$, where d_t is the density at temperature t°C and d_0 the density at 0°C. Consequently, the velocity of sound in a gas increases with the temperature (Fig. 16.2) according to the equation

$$V_t = V_0 \sqrt{1 + \frac{t}{273}} \qquad (16.4)$$

If we introduce the absolute temperature $T = 273 + t$ (Sec. 19.6), we may rewrite this equation in the form

$$V_t = V_0 \sqrt{\frac{T}{273}} \qquad (16.4a)$$

Example. Find the velocity of sound in dry air at a 100°C.

$$V_{100} = V_0 \sqrt{1 + \frac{t}{273}} = 331 \sqrt{\frac{373}{273}}$$
$$= 386 \text{ m/sec}$$

The reason the speed of sound in a gas increases with temperature is that the velocity of the molecules increases. We have seen that in the sound wave the energy is transferred from one molecule to the next; in a gas the speed of the transfer cannot exceed the speed of the molecules. Indeed, we find that the speed of sound is somewhere in the vicinity of 70 per cent of the average speed of the gas molecules.

16.3. Frequencies and Wavelengths of Audible Sounds. A reasonably typical human ear can hear frequencies lying between 20 and 20,000 vib/sec. There is substantial difference in range between various individuals. Since the velocity of sound waves is given by the product of the frequency and the wavelength and since sounds of all different frequencies have the same velocity in air, the range of wavelengths we hear runs from about 55 ft to 0.6 in. The fact that all frequencies travel with essentially the same speed is clearly shown by the fact that the sounds from all instruments of an orchestra reach a listener at the same time. If the velocity depended on the frequency, the music would sound very different indeed to a person far from an orchestra than to one close by.

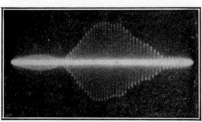

Fig. 16.3. High-frequency sound waves emitted by a bat. The frequency is too high to be audible to a human ear. (*Courtesy of Donald R. Griffin, Cornell University.*)

Sound waves of much higher frequency than the human ear can hear are readily produced. Dogs and birds can frequently hear these *ultrasonic* frequencies. Many animals and insects emit ultrasonic sounds. Indeed, the bat locates obstacles and finds its way about by emitting ultrasonic frequencies which it detects as they are reflected from various obstacles (Fig. 16.3).

16.4. Pitch, Loudness, and Quality. The word *sound* is used with two related but separate and distinct meanings. Sometimes we use the word to mean the *sensation due to the stimulation of the auditory nerve centers*, while other times we use it to mean the *longitudinal waves transmitted through elastic mediums*. To the psychologist "sound" is usually used in connection with hearing, whereas much of the time in physics we refer to "sound" as a type of wave motion, even though it may not be heard. For example, if we make a wire oscillate at a frequency of 30,000 vib/sec, human ears cannot hear the waves produced. In the sense that longitudinal waves exist in the air there is a sound, but from the point of view of hearing there is none.

To a listener sound is ordinarily characterized by the psychophysical properties *pitch, loudness*, and *quality*. These subjective characteristics are, of course, related to the physical properties of the waves; namely, the frequencies present, their amplitudes, and their phase relations.

In general, the pitch of a sound depends upon the frequency of the *fundamental*, or the lowest frequency present in the sound wave. As the fundamental frequency of a sound source is increased, the pitch is raised. A simple experiment which shows there is a direct relation between pitch and frequency can be performed with the aid of a siren (Fig. 16.4) which consists of a disk with a number of holes uniformly spaced on concentric circles. If a jet of air is directed against the holes while the disk is in rotation, a puff goes through each hole as it passes the jet and comes out the other side. When the number of puffs per second is increased, either by increasing the speed of the disk or by directing the stream of air to a radius where there are more holes, the pitch becomes higher. Although the pitch of a sound is determined primarily by the frequency, it depends to some extent on the loudness as well.

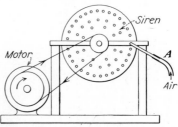

Fig. 16.4. A siren. The frequency is equal to the number of holes passing the air jet per unit time.

Loudness describes the magnitude of the auditory sensation produced by a sound. In addition to depending on the intensity and the physical composition of the sound, it also depends on the auditory acuity and experience of the individual listener. For a given frequency the loudness of a sound is closely related to the intensity; it increases roughly as the logarithm of the intensity. For a given intensity the loudness depends rather sensitively on the frequency. At a frequency of 200 vib/sec it takes many

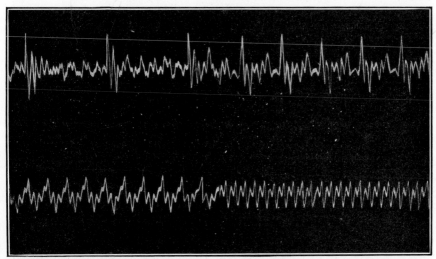

Fig. 16.5. Characteristics of sound emitted by a trumpet are changed by blowing it in different ways.

times as great an intensity to produce a given loudness as at 2,000 vib/sec. If a listener thinks a sound coming from a flute and the sound coming from a drum are equal in loudness, the sound from the drum has a far greater intensity. Special scales for loudness have been developed; they are discussed in Chap. 18.

Sounds which have the same loudness and pitch may have very different qualities. For example, if a piano and a trumpet play the same note at the same loudness, it is easy to distinguish between them. The reason is that neither sound source produces a single frequency; both send out a group of frequencies. As we have seen, the lowest frequency is called the *fundamental;* it is this frequency which primarily determines the pitch. In addition to the fundamental there are present many higher frequencies which are called *overtones.* When two notes differ in quality, they differ in the frequency and relative intensities of the various overtones. Figure 16.5 shows how the characteristics of the sound emitted by a trumpet change according to the way the musician blows it.

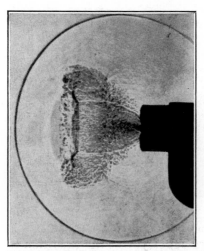

Fig. 16.6. Wave front from a revolver which has just been fired. (*After Quayle, National Bureau of Standards.*)

16.5. Photography of Sound Waves.

It is possible to obtain photographs of strong sound waves. One method depends essentially on properly timed illumination by an electric discharge which occurs when the sound wave is between

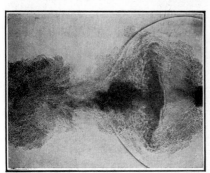

Fig. 16.7. Progress of wave front after shot has been fired. The muzzle wave has developed into much greater proportions. Some of the gases moving faster than the sound wave have blown through the spherical wave at the center. (*After Quayle, National Bureau of Standards.*)

Fig. 16.8. Spherical sound wave showing compression. (*Courtesy of Arthur L. Foley, University of Indiana.*)

the spark source and a photographic plate. The variations in the density of the air through which the sound waves travel cause the light to bend in such a way that shadows of compressions are produced on the photographic plate. Figures

16.6 and 16.7 show the sound wave produced when a revolver is fired.   Figure 16.8 shows the spherical sound wave expanding outward from a point sound source.

In the sections which follow we shall show examples of the reflection and transmission of sound waves with photographs taken by the method just described.

16.6. Reflection of Sound.

If an observer stands at some distance in front of a cliff and produces a sound, the sound is returned to him without having its characteristics essentially changed.   If the observer is 1,100 ft from the cliff, it takes about 2 sec for the sound to return to him.   In this case we call the reflected sound an *echo*.   The roll of thunder is due to the reflection of the original sound by clouds at different distances from the observer.   These reflections reach the observer at different times and produce the rolling continuation of the sound.

When an orchestra is to play out of doors, a large reflecting shell is often provided behind the orchestra so that sound waves are reflected toward the audience, thus greatly increasing the loudness.

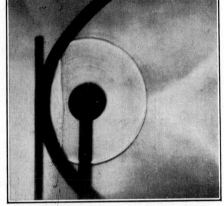

Fig. 16.9. Reflection of a spherical sound wave by a parabolic mirror. (*Courtesy of Arthur L. Foley, University of Indiana.*)

Whispering galleries are so constructed that they reflect sound to a particular point without much loss in intensity.

If a plane wave approaches along the axis, a parabolic reflector will focus all the energy of the wave at the focal point of the parabola.   Figure 16.9 shows the reverse process in which a sound wave produced at the focus is reflected by the parabolic mirror as a plane wave.   Both processes are indicated in Fig. 16.10.

Figure 16.11 shows the simultaneous reflection and transmission of waves.   The transmitted system of waves has passed through four rectangular apertures, while the reflected system has come from three rectangular bars and the solid surfaces above and below them.   The laws of reflection developed in Chap. 15 apply to sound waves as well as to other types.

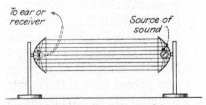

Fig. 16.10. Reflection of sound by parabolic mirrors.

In a speaking tube sound waves are reflected when they reach the walls of the tube, which thereby prevents them from spreading out. Consequently, the intensity of the sound does not decrease appreciably as the wave advances and the sound may be heard with only slightly diminished intensity at the other end of the tube many yards from the speaker. In an ear trumpet the waves entering the wide end are gradually diminished in area by reflections in the wall until at the small end the entire energy of the incident waves is concentrated over a small area. As a consequence, the intensity is greatly increased.

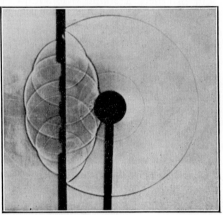

Fig. 16.11. Transmission of sound waves by rectangular apertures. (*Courtesy of Arthur L. Foley, University of Indiana.*)

16.7. Refraction of Sound.

When sound waves pass from one medium to another, there is usually a change in velocity. As a consequence, the direction of propagation of the wave in the second medium is changed, provided the incident waves meet the surface of separation obliquely. Let AC in Fig. 16.12 represent the advancing wave front. When it meets the surface AB and enters the second medium in which its velocity is less, the direction of propagation is bent toward the normal to the interface. While the end

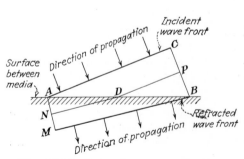

Fig. 16.12. Refraction of sound waves. Direction of propagation is changed because of change in speed.

of the wave front at C travels forward in the first medium with its normal velocity, the other end A is moving in the second medium where it traverses a smaller distance AM. As a consequence, the entire wave front is rotated as it enters the second medium. If the sound goes from the medium in which the velocity is less into a medium in which it is greater, the direction in which the wave is traveling is bent away from the normal.

Figure 16.13 shows how a spherical sound wave coming from a point source S is bent by a spherical gas-filled lens so that, instead of diverging, it is made to converge to point P. The lens here is a rubber bag filled with a gas such as carbon dioxide in which the velocity of sound is less than it is in air.

16.8. Interference of Sound Waves. When two trains of waves pass the same point, the displacement of a particle at this point is the resultant of the displacements which the two wave trains would produce if they acted alone. If the two trains have the same wavelength and direction, the resultant amplitude depends on the amplitude of the two waves and on the phases of the two component disturbances. If the two arrive at the same phase, they reinforce one another and we have constructive interference; if they arrive one-half wavelength out of phase, the

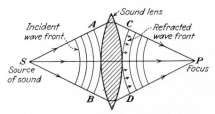

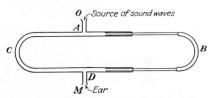

Fig. 16.13. Refraction and focusing of sound waves by a lens in which the sound travels more slowly than in air.

Fig. 16.14. Apparatus for showing interference of sound waves after traveling along paths of different lengths.

resultant amplitude is the difference in the individual amplitudes. If these amplitudes are equal, the waves cancel one another and we have total destructive interference.

The interference of sound waves can be demonstrated with the apparatus of Fig. 16.14. Sound waves from a source O travel to point D by two separate paths ACD and ABD. If the length of the two paths is exactly the same, the waves arrive at the ear in phase and we have constructive interference. If the path ABD is increased in length, the waves travel different distances and the resultant amplitude is less than when the interference was constructive. When the path ABD is one-half wavelength longer than path ACD, the waves are one-half wavelength out of phase and destructive interference results. As the path ABD is increased still more, the amplitude of the resultant disturbance increases and we have constructive interference once more when path ABD is one wavelength greater than ACD. In general, there is destructive interference when path ABD exceeds ACD by an odd number of half wavelengths and constructive interference when the paths differ by an integer number of whole wavelengths.

16.9. Beats. If two steady sound sources of the same frequency are sounded together, the intensity of the sound at a given place remains constant. If the frequencies are slightly different, however, the intensity of the sound fluctuates. There are bursts of louder sound with comparative silence between them. Each burst occurs when the disturbances from the two sources reinforce one another, while the periods of relative silence occur when the two waves interfere destructively. The fluctuations in intensity when two sound sources of slightly different frequency are activated simultaneously are called *beats*.

The origin of beats is as follows: Suppose at a certain instant compressions from both sound sources arrive simultaneously (*A*, Fig. 16.15). The amplitude of the resultant disturbance is large and the intensity relatively high. A short time later the more rapidly vibrating source is one-half vibration ahead of the other and a compression from one source arrives at the same time as a rarefaction from the other (*B*, Fig. 16.15). The two disturbances interfere destructively and a minimum intensity results. A little later the more rapidly vibrating source has picked up a full vibration and once again an intensity maximum is observed.

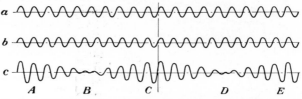

Fig. 16.15. Beats arising from the superposition of sounds differing slightly in frequency.

When two sound sources have almost identical frequencies, the number of beats observed each second is small. As the difference in frequencies increases, the number of beats increases. If the sounds differ in frequency by one vibration per second, they reinforce once each second and we observe one beat per second. In general, the number of beats observed per second is equal to the difference between the frequencies of the two sound sources.

$$\text{Number of beats per second} = N = f_1 - f_2 \qquad (16.5)$$

where f_1 and f_2 are the frequencies of the two sources.

Beats are of great service in tuning string instruments. As two strings are brought more and more nearly into unison, the number of beats per second becomes less; when no beats are observed, the strings have the same frequency. In organs two pipes having nearly the same frequency are sometimes used to produce a beating of the sounds to give a tremulous effect imitating the human voice.

PROBLEMS

Unless otherwise stated, take the speed of sound in air at room temperature to be 1,100 ft/sec, or 340 m/sec.

1. A violin string emits a sound having 440 vib/sec. What is the wavelength of the disturbance that passes through the air? What is the period of the vibration?

Ans. 77 cm; 0.0023 sec

2. A tuning fork with a frequency of 600 cycles/sec sends out waves which travel 1,080 ft/sec. How many vibrations does the fork make in the time required for the sound to travel 900 ft?

3. When a sound wave is transferred from one medium to another, its frequency does not change. If the wavelength of a disturbance is 20 cm in air, find its wavelength in water, steel, and brass if the speed of sound in water is 1,450 m/sec, in steel 5,000 m/sec, and in brass 3,500 m/sec. *Ans.* 0.85 m; 2.94 m; 2.06 m

4. A sounding source with a frequency of 500 cycles/sec sends out waves that travel from air into water. Find the wavelength in each medium if the velocity is 1,450 m/sec in water.

5. At what temperature would the speed of sound in air be 663 m/sec if it is 331.5 m/sec at 0°C? *Ans.* 819°C

6. A timer sets his watch by the report of a gun 100 yd away. What is the error due to the time required for the sound to travel from the gun to the ear?

7. A worker in pounding a spike strikes a steel railroad track. A person 1 mile along the track hears two reports due to the pounding. One travels through air and one through the rail. What time interval separates the reports if the speed of sound in steel is 16,300 ft/sec? *Ans.* 4.5 sec

8. A workman strikes the steel rail of a railroad track with a hammer. The sound thus produced reaches an observer through the rail and also through the surrounding air. The difference in time is 1 sec. If the speed of sound in steel is 16,300 ft/sec, how far is the observer away from the workman?

9. The vertical walls of a canyon are 8,800 ft apart. A man in the canyon fires a gun and hears the echo from the farther wall 6 sec after the echo from the nearer wall. How far is he from the nearer wall? *Ans.* 2,750 ft

10. One ship sends signals to a neighboring ship. The sound waves travel by two paths, one in air, and the other in sea water. The signals are heard on the neighboring ship at intervals that are 6 sec apart. How far is it from one ship to the other if the speed of sound in sea water is 1,450 m/sec?

11. What is the velocity of a compressional wave (sound) in a steel rod for which Young's modulus of elasticity is 21×10^{10} newtons/m²? Take the density of steel to be 7,800 kg/m³. *Ans.* 5,200 m/sec

12. Sound travels in water at the rate of 1,450 m/sec. What is the modulus of elasticity of water?

13. An oscillator emits a sound of 1,000 cycles/sec. The sound wave is divided into two parts which are subsequently combined. The two parts travel the same distances, so that constructive interference is experienced. In order to produce no sound, one path is lengthened. What is the shortest distance this path may be lengthened to satisfy this condition? If it is lengthened still further, the intensity increases and then decreases. What is the total change in path to obtain the second case of destructive interference? What is the total change in path to obtain the third case of destructive interference? *Ans.* 0.17 m; 0.51 m; 0.85 m

14. What is the speed of sound in helium at 0°C and 1 atm pressure? Four grams of helium under standard conditions occupy a volume of 22.4 liters.

15. A sound wave travels through two branches of a tube 4 ft long and 7 ft long, respectively. Name three frequencies which would suffer destructive interference on being recombined after traveling through the branches. *Ans.* 183, 550, and 917 cycles/sec

16. Two strings A and B originally had the same frequency. The tension of B is released slightly, thereby reducing the frequency, and the strings produce 5 beats per second when sounded together. If the frequency of A is 515 cycles/sec, what is the frequency of B?

Sound Sources

17.1. Sounding Bodies. Ordinary sound waves are set up by vibrating bodies. A typical source in vibration sends out a series of alternate compressions and rarefactions which are transmitted through the air. Most sound sources send out not a single frequency, but a combination of many frequencies. The lowest prominent frequency is the *fundamental;* the higher frequencies are called *overtones.* In vibrating strings and in organ pipes the overtones are usually integer multiples of the fundamental, and are called *harmonics. A harmonic is an overtone which has a frequency that is an integral multiple of the fundamental frequency.* Thus, the frequency of the third harmonic is three times that of the fundamental.

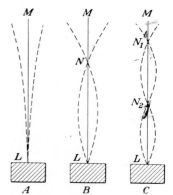

Fig. 17.2. Vibrations in a rod, showing fundamental A, first overtone (third harmonic) B, and second overtone (fifth harmonic) C.

Fig. 17.1. A tuning fork mounted on a resonator.

Some sound sources are especially designed to produce only a single frequency, or a *pure tone.* A tuning fork is an example of such a source. It is essentially a rod bent in the form of a U with the central region reinforced to suppress overtones (Fig. 17.1). A straight rod fixed at one end (Fig. 17.2) readily vibrates in such a way as to produce overtones which are odd harmonics. On the other hand, many of the overtones of bells, drums, and vibrating plates are not harmonically related to the fundamental.

In most musical sounds, the same frequency is emitted for an appreciable period of time during which the amplitude does not decrease rapidly. In a noise, on the other hand, we usually have a sudden burst of a wide range of frequencies with no regularity and a marked drop in intensity during the emission of a single vibration. Of course, the distinction between noises and musical sounds is not sharp and definite. What is music for one person may be noise to another.

17.2. Vibrations of Wires and Strings. Many musical instruments make use of stretched strings as sound sources. These strings may be set into vibration by striking, plucking, bowing, or strumming. When the string is displaced at some point and then released, the disturbance is passed from one element of the string to the next and transverse waves proceeding in both directions in the strings are produced. These waves are reflected at the fixed ends of the string, return in the opposite direction, and go on to the other ends where they are again reflected. Of the

many frequencies of which the initial wave is composed, only those frequencies which are suitable for establishing standing waves in the string are maintained for any length of time.

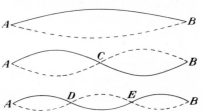

Fig. 17.3. Vibrations in a string fixed at both ends, showing fundamental and first two overtones.

Of the standing waves established in the stretched string the one with the longest wavelength is that for which the string vibrates as a single segment (Fig. 17.3). The longest wavelength corresponds to the lowest frequency and therefore to the *fundamental* of the string. The standing wave of next longest wavelength is that in which the string vibrates in two segments. In this case the length of the string is equal to the wavelength. The third longest standing wave which can exist in the stretched string occurs when the string vibrates in three segments, the next in four segments, etc.

The allowed modes of vibration for a stretched string are easy to recall if one remembers that both ends of the string are fastened. These ends cannot move and must therefore behave as nodes for any possible standing wave. We are dealing with a situation in which we impose a condition on the ends of the strings, namely, that they remain at rest. Such conditions are known as *boundary conditions* and they play a very important role in determining the types of vibrations which are allowed in various kinds of systems. Once we have established the boundary conditions that there be nodes at the ends of the stretched strings, we can readily find the fundamental by finding the longest wave that we can produce which has nodes at both ends. The first overtone corresponds to the next longest possibility, and so on.

If the string is plucked at random, it may vibrate in such a way that both the fundamental and overtones are present. For the string the overtones are all harmonics and the note from a string consists of the fundamental together with several harmonics. We shall calculate the frequency of the fundamental and of the various overtones.

The velocity of a transverse wave along a flexible stretched string depends on the tension and on the mass per unit length of the string. It can be shown (App. E.1) that the velocity is given by

$$V = \sqrt{\frac{T}{m_l}} \tag{17.1}$$

where V is the velocity of the disturbance, T the tension, and m_l the mass per unit length of the string.

Let L be the length of the string. Then for the fundamental the wavelength is $2L$ (Fig. 17.3). Since for any wave motion $V = f\lambda$, we have for the fundamental frequency f_1,

$$f_1 = \frac{1}{2L} \sqrt{\frac{T}{m_l}} \tag{17.2}$$

The frequency of the fundamental depends on the length, the tension, and the mass per unit length. A musical instrument, such as the piano, affords an illustration of how these factors apply. The strings which play the bass notes are ordinarily heavy, thus having large m_l, and they are also long. Strings for the high notes are short, light, and tightly stretched. In tuning a piano the tension is varied. In instruments such as the violin in which there are only four strings, the strings are of the same length, but they have different masses per unit length and different tensions. When the violinist wishes to play different frequencies on the same string, he varies the length of the string by placing his finger at the point at which he wishes to create a node.

The first overtone for the vibrating string occurs when $\lambda = L$ (Fig. 17.3) and therefore the frequency of the first overtone is given by

$$f_2 = \frac{1}{L} \sqrt{\frac{T}{m_l}} \tag{17.3}$$

The first overtone has a frequency twice that of the fundamental and is therefore the second harmonic. For the second overtone $\lambda = 2L/3$ and the frequency is

$$f_3 = \frac{3}{2L} \sqrt{\frac{T}{m_l}} \tag{17.3a}$$

Second overtone = third harmonic

In general, the allowed overtones of stretched strings consist of all harmonics.

Most harmonics blend well with the fundamental to produce pleasing tones. The seventh harmonic is an exception. In order to suppress the seventh harmonic, piano strings are struck at a point where the seventh harmonic would have a node. This assures that there cannot be a perfect node at this point. Violins are often bowed in the vicinity of a node for the seventh harmonic in order to suppress this relatively unpleasant overtone. The superior tonal quality of an expert violinist is associated with his ability to produce not only the desired fundamental, but also a combination of overtones which are pleasing. The relative intensities of the various overtones can be varied over substantial ranges by an expert.

17.3. Closed Organ Pipes. In an organ pipe the vibrating body is a column of air. At one end of a pipe the column of air is set into vibration by sending a narrow jet of air toward a thin edge or lip (Fig. 17.4). This end of the pipe is always open so that sound waves can be transmitted from the pipe into the surrounding air. In the case of a closed pipe the other end is blocked off. Thus, a closed organ pipe is closed at one end, open at the other. When air first strikes the lip, a condensation starts down the pipe, is reflected at the closed end, and returns to the lip as a condensation. When it reaches the lip, it pushes the air stream outside the lip and this starts a rarefaction down the tube. The rarefaction is reflected at the closed end, returns to the lip as a rarefaction, and draws the stream into the pipe again, thereby starting a new compression. Thus the air stream is made to move back and forth across the lip with its period determined by time required for a compression to travel up and back followed by a rarefaction traveling up and back. The period is four times the time required for sound to traverse the length of the tube.

An alternative approach to determining the fundamental frequency involves the application of boundary conditions. At the closed end of the pipe an air particle is unable to move forward when a compression comes down the tube. We have a *displacement node at the closed end of an organ pipe.* On the other hand, a particle at the open end is not

Fundamental tone ($L = \frac{1}{4}\lambda$)

Fig. 17.4. Closed organ pipe, showing fundamental.

restrained and the amplitude of the vibration of a particle is a maximum there. There is always an *antinode at the open end of a pipe;* the displacement there is maximum. The possible standing waves which can be set up in a closed organ pipe are those which have a node at the closed end and an antinode at the open end. The longest wavelength which can fit into the organ pipe is indicated in Fig. 17.4. In this case the wavelength is four times the length L of the pipe. The frequency f_1 of the fundamental is given by the ratio of the velocity V of the wave motion, which in this case is the velocity of sound in the gas in the organ pipe, to the wavelength λ. Therefore,

$$f_1 = \frac{V}{4L} \tag{17.4}$$

There are other possible modes of vibration for this column of air which make a node at the closed end and an antinode at the open end. The next longest frequency which can be emitted involves the vibration in which there is one additional node in the pipe (Fig. 17.5). For this case the wavelength is $4L/3$ and the *first overtone is the third harmonic* which has a frequency

$$f_3 = \frac{3V}{4L} \tag{17.5}$$

The second overtone is also shown in Fig. 17.5. Its frequency is $f_5 = 5V/4L$, which is that of the fifth harmonic. The closed pipe can emit any frequency which is an odd integer times the fundamental frequency. Harmonics which have a frequency 2, 4, 6, . . . times the fundamental frequency cannot be emitted by a closed organ pipe. *Closed organ pipes emit only odd harmonics.*

The fundamental frequency depends on the velocity of sound in the gas in the tube. If hydrogen is placed in the tube instead of air, the fundamental frequency is greatly increased. For any gas in the tube, the fundamental frequency depends upon the temperature, since the velocity of sound is a function of the temperature. As the temperature is raised, the frequencies emitted go up.

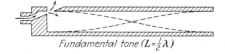

Fundamental tone $(L = \frac{1}{2}\lambda)$

First overtone $(L = \frac{3}{4}\lambda)$

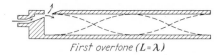

First overtone $(L = \lambda)$

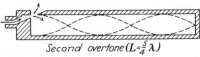

Second overtone $(L = \frac{5}{4}\lambda)$

Second overtone $(L = \frac{3}{2}\lambda)$

Fig. 17.5. First overtone (third harmonic) and second overtone (fifth harmonic) for a closed organ pipe.

Fig. 17.6. Fundamental, first overtone (second harmonic), and second overtone (third harmonic) of an open organ pipe.

17.4. Open Pipes. The boundary condition for an open end requires that the oscillation amplitude be maximum. Since both ends of an open pipe are open, there is an antinode at each end. The wavelength of the longest possible standing wave is twice the length of the pipe, as shown in Fig. 17.6. Since $V = f\lambda$, the frequency f_1 of the fundamental is

$$f_1 = \frac{V}{2L} \tag{17.6}$$

We observe that the fundamental of an open pipe has twice the frequency of a closed pipe of the same length. The next possible mode of vibration (Fig. 17.6) is that in which the pipe has a length equal to one wavelength. This gives rise to the first overtone (second harmonic) with a frequency

$$f_2 = \frac{V}{L} \qquad (17.7)$$

For the second overtone, $f_3 = 3V/2L$, which is the third harmonic. The frequencies of the harmonics of the open pipe are in the ratio of the integers 1, 2, 3, 4, ... In an open pipe it is possible to have all harmonics; in the closed pipe only the odd harmonics are present.

Clearly if one wishes to imitate a string section of an orchestra with a great organ, he must use open pipes, since closed pipes cannot produce the even harmonics. Since even harmonics are ordinarily prominent in the string music, it is impossible to produce a good imitation of string music by use of closed pipes.

Throughout this discussion we have assumed that an antinode occurs exactly at the open end of the pipe. Actually the antinode lies outside this open end by an amount which depends on the diameter of the pipe if round and on its shape and size if it is not round. The length must be corrected slightly for exact calculations of the frequencies.

17.5. The Human Voice and Other Sources. Vibrating air columns are important in the human voice and in the wind instruments of the orchestra. Flutes and piccolos are similar to open organ pipes in their action except that in these musical instruments a single pipe is made to produce many different tones by opening holes in the side and by the skillful blowing of overtones. The opening of a hole in the side of the tube creates an antinode at that point and has the effect of reducing the length of the tube. In the trumpet the air is blown past the vibrating lips of the player and standing waves are set up in the air column. Valves permit the use of air columns of different length. In the trombone the length of the vibrating air column is varied by movement of the slide. In the brass wind instruments the lips of the player are the key factor in setting up standing waves of the desired frequency.

In the human voice air is forced out of the lungs and the vocal cords, two tightly stretched membranes in the throat, are set into vibration. The frequency of the sound can be changed by varying the tension in these vocal cords. Vibrating bodies of air in the lungs, throat, and head cavities impress on the sound waves certain resonant characteristics which give the speech of each individual its particular quality. It is easy to observe how the quality of the sound is affected by changing the resonant columns in the head by holding the nose closed while talking. The resonant cavities in the head are now different in shape and there is a noticeable change in the quality of sound. Speech sounds are discussed in more detail in Chap. 18.

17.6. Resonance. If two identical tuning forks are placed a few feet apart and one of them is set into vibration, the second fork also begins to vibrate (Fig. 17.7). This can be shown by stopping the vibrations of the first fork by grasping the tines. Energy has been transferred through the air from the first fork to the second. Because the second fork has the same frequency as the first, the compressions set out by the first fork arrive at just the right time to build up the amplitude of vibration in the second fork. The two forks are said to be in *resonance*. When two bodies are in resonance, a substantial amount of energy can be transferred to one of the bodies from a series of very small, but perfectly timed, impulses from the other. The amplitude is built up just as the amplitude of a child's swing can be built up by small, well-timed pushes.

Fig. 17.7. Resonance. Vibration of one tuning fork produces sympathetic vibrations in another fork of the same frequency.

When marching men cross a bridge, they are often commanded to break step, because, if a bridge structure happened to be resonant to the frequency of the steps, large and perhaps destructive vibrations might be set up. In automobiles very annoying noises are sometimes produced at certain speeds when some loose object happens to be resonant to a small impulse which is received with the proper timing. The designers of aircraft must be careful to avoid flutters and oscillations which may build up to intolerable levels by virtue of resonance.

On the other hand, resonances are sometimes very desirable. If we want a tuning fork to produce a louder sound, we may hold it over a tube, which we gradually fill with water until the air column is resonant to the frequency emitted by the tuning fork.

17.7. The Doppler Effect. When an automobile, traveling at high speed and sounding its horn, passes a pedestrian, the pitch heard by the pedestrian drops sharply as the car passes. When a source of sound is moving toward an observer or an observer toward a sound source, the pitch of the sound heard is higher than the normal pitch. On the other hand, if the sound source moves away from the observer or the observer from the source, the pitch is lowered.

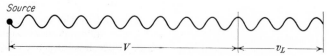

Fig. 17.8. An observer moving toward a sound source passes in 1 sec all the waves included in a distance $V + v_L$.

Let us consider first the case in which the observer approaches a sound source which is at rest relative to surrounding air. In this case the observer passes more waves each second than he would if he were at rest (Fig. 17.8). Let V represent the speed of sound and v_L the velocity of the listener toward the sound source. In 1 sec the source sends out f waves. In this same time the observer passes all the waves included in a distance $(V + v_L)$. The frequency f_L heard by the listener is the number of waves he passes each second; thus $f_L = (V + v_L)/\lambda$, where λ is the wavelength. Since $f = V/\lambda$,

$$\frac{f_L}{V + v_L} = \frac{f}{V} \tag{17.8}$$

If the observer is moving away from the source, v_L is negative and the observed frequency f_L is lower than f.

If the source is moving (relative to the surrounding air) toward a stationary listener (Fig. 17.9), the wavelength of the sound waves in the air is different in different directions. Let f be the frequency of the waves passing a point in the air and f_S the frequency emitted by the source. In 1 sec the sound waves moving to the right go a distance $V - v_S$ relative to the source, which has emitted f_S waves in this second. Therefore the wavelength in air is $(V - v_S)/f_S = V/f$, and

$$\frac{f_S}{V - v_S} = \frac{f}{V} = \frac{f_L}{V} \tag{17.9}$$

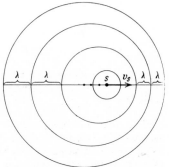

Fig. 17.9. When a sound source is moving, the wavelength is smaller in the direction of motion and longer in the opposite direction.

since the listener hears the frequency of the waves passing in the air. If the source is moving away from the listener, v_S is negative and the pitch heard is reduced. If both source and observer are moving relative to the air, we may write

$$\lambda_{\text{air}} = \frac{V}{f} = \frac{V - v_S}{f_S} = \frac{V + v_L}{f_L} \tag{17.10}$$

or

$$\frac{f_L}{V + v_L} = \frac{f_S}{V - v_S} \tag{17.10a}$$

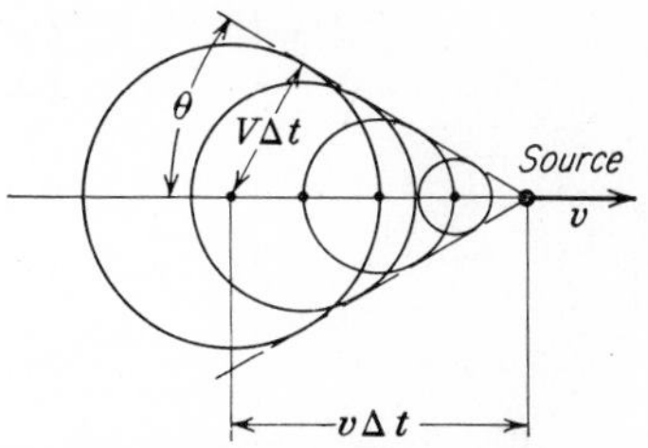

Fig. 17.10. Sound waves produced by a source moving faster than sound.

Note that both v_S and v_L are measured *relative to the air; both are positive when the source is moving toward the observer and the observer toward the source.*

17.8. Supersonic Velocities and Shock Waves. When a sound source travels with a speed greater than that of sound, it is said to be *supersonic*. Figure 17.10 shows a source moving faster than the speed of sound. We observe that the object is beyond the spherical sound waves which it sent out a short time before. However, there exists a surface tangent to all these sound waves which, by Huygens' principle, gives us the position of a compressional wave. Under these conditions this wave accompanying the source is called a *shock wave*. Figures 17.11 to 17.13 show shock waves accompanying bullets which are traveling at supersonic speeds. In Fig. 17.13 we observe how the wave front is modified when the bullet passes through a soap bubble filled with a mixture of hydrogen and air. The speed of sound in this mixture is greater than in ordinary air. Hence, the shock wave travels faster while the bullet is in the bubble and the wave front is ahead of the position it would have occupied if the bullet had remained in air.

We can see from Fig. 17.10 that the angle between the direction of the motion of the source and the shock wave permits us to compute the velocity of the bullet,

Fig. 17.11. Compressional wave traveling with a bullet moving 2,600 ft/sec. Note the formation of a base wave as well as one at the nose of the bullet. (*After Quayle, National Bureau of Standards.*)

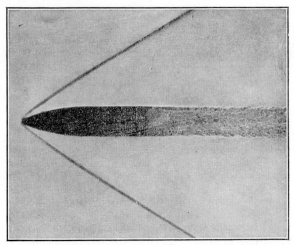

Fig. 17.12. Compressional wave front traveling with a tracer bullet. The gases generated by the tracing compound probably prevent the formation of the base wave, which is absent. (*After Quayle, National Bureau of Standards.*)

provided the velocity of sound in the medium is known. From the figure we see that $\sin \theta = V/v$, where v is velocity of the source and V the speed of the shock wave.

When a body is moving through the air at subsonic speeds, a compressional wave precedes it and some of the air particles are moved out of the way. At supersonic speeds the body is traveling faster than the compressional wave. Consequently, there is no preparation in the medium for the oncoming body and the region of sudden compression which we have called the *shock wave* is produced.

A great deal of energy may be associated with this shock wave—energy which comes from the object which is passing through the air. Sometimes when an aircraft dives at supersonic speeds, it builds up a substantial shock wave which continues on toward the ground after the plane has pulled out of its dive. When the shock wave reaches the earth, it may break windows and cause other damage.

Because of the build-up of a shock wave as an aircraft reaches the speed of sound, the drag on the aircraft increases markedly in this region. In discussing the drag under these conditions, it is customary to compare the speed of the aircraft with the local speed of sound. The latter depends, of course, on the temperature and is substantially lower at high altitudes where the temperature is low. The ratio of the velocity of the body to the local velocity of sound is called the *Mach number*. Mach 5 means five times the velocity of sound. The speeds of missiles and high-velocity aircraft are often quoted in Mach numbers.

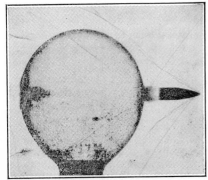

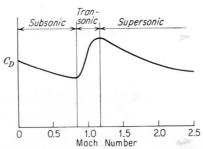

Fig. 17.13. Bullet fired through a soap bubble, which has not had time to collapse. Note change in shape of wave front. (*After Quayle, National Bureau of Standards.*)

Fig. 17.14. Drag coefficient of a particular missile as a function of missile speed in Mach numbers.

If a missile or aircraft is passing through the air, the frictional drag force D may be written

$$D = c_D S(\tfrac{1}{2}dv^2)$$

where S is the cross-sectional area normal to the air stream, d the density of the air, v the velocity of the object, and c_D is an empirical factor called the *drag coefficient*. A typical plot of drag coefficient as a function of Mach number for a missile is shown in Fig. 17.14. The drag coefficient depends on the velocity of the moving body and on its size, shape, and smoothness. At low Mach numbers c_D decreases as v increases because the actual drag is more nearly proportional to v than to v^2. However, as one approaches Mach 1, the drag increases rapidly and much faster than v^2. This region of rapid increase in drag coefficient is called the *transonic region* because it occurs where the speed passes from below to above sonic velocity. The drag coefficient decreases above Mach 1.5, which indicates that once again the drag force is increasing less rapidly than v^2.

When an atomic bomb is exploded in the air, a tremendously strong shock wave is set up. The shock front represents a moving wall of highly compressed air which may blow down buildings and produce other damage. It has been reported that at a distance of 1,500 ft from the detonation point of a nominal atomic bomb similar to that used as Nagasaki, the pressure of the shock wave is about 50 lb/in.² greater than atmospheric and the speed of the shock wave is about 2,000 ft/sec. The tremendous compressional shock wave is followed by a rarefaction or *suction phase*, which lasts much longer than the pressure phase.

PROBLEMS

Take the speed of sound in air to be 1,100 ft/sec or 340 m/sec.

1. What is the velocity of a transverse wave in a string 180 cm long with a mass of 10 g and subject to a tension of 20 newtons?   *Ans.* 60 m/sec

2. A steel wire weighs 0.5 g/cm and is 1 m long. It is stretched by a force of 98 newtons. What is the frequency when it emits its fundamental vibration?

3. The fundamental vibration of a wire is 800 cycles/sec when it is stretched with a force of 5 kg-wt. What is its frequency when it is stretched with a force of 2.5 kg-wt?

Ans. 566 cycles/sec

4. An air-driven turbine breaks up the stream of air into 16 pulses per revolution. What frequency of sound will be heard when the turbine is rotating at the rate of 7,200 rev/min?

5. A stretched string made from a certain batch of steel is vibrating with its fundamental frequency of 1,000 cycles/sec. What is the fundamental frequency of a second string made from the same batch of steel, but which has a diameter twice that of the original, a length twice that of the original, and which is stretched by twice the force of the original?   *Ans.* 354 cycles/sec

6. A string with a mass per unit length of 0.02 g/cm is stretched by the application of 320 newtons. What length of string will be required to produce a frequency of 625 cycles?

7. A stretched wire 11 ft long has a fundamental frequency of 200 cycles/sec. What is the velocity of the wave in the wire? What is the wavelength of the fundamental vibration? What is the frequency of the first overtone? What is the frequency of the third overtone? What is the frequency of the third harmonic?

Ans. 4,400 ft/sec; 22 ft; 400 cycles/sec; 800 cycles/sec; 600 cycles/sec

8. If the fundamental of a wire 96 cm long has a frequency of 212 vib/sec when the wire is stretched by a load of 12 kg, what will be its frequency when the load is decreased to 8 kg?

9. An open organ pipe is 11 ft long. What is the wavelength of the fundamental vibration? What is the frequency of its fundamental vibration? What is the frequency of the first overtone? What is the frequency of the third overtone? What is the frequency of the third harmonic?

Ans. 22 ft; 50 cycles/sec; 100 cycles/sec; 200 cycles/sec; 150 cycles/sec

10. The whistle of a streamer is in the form of a closed pipe 5½ ft long. Calculate the frequency of the fundamental produced.

11. A closed organ pipe is 11 ft long. Answer the questions of Prob. 9 for this pipe.

Ans. 44 ft; 25 cycles/sec; 75 cycles/sec; 175 cycles/sec; 75 cycles/sec

12. Calculate the lengths of open and closed pipes, respectively, for a fundamental frequency of 550 cycles/sec.

13. Find the frequencies of the fundamental and first two overtones for an open pipe 68 cm long.   *Ans.* 250 cycles/sec; 500 cycles/sec; 750 cycles/sec

14. Two open organ pipes of length 30 and 29 in. are sounded simultaneously. How many beats per second are produced?

15. Find the frequencies of the fundamental and first two overtones of a closed organ pipe 17 cm long.   *Ans.* 500 cycles/sec; 1,500 cycles/sec; 2,500 cycles/sec

16. A sounding tuning fork is held over a vertical glass tube into which water is poured slowly.   The remainder of the tube is filled with air.   What is the frequency of the tuning fork when the shortest column of air for resonance is 17 cm?

17. A glass tube open at both ends is so placed that one end is under water.   The tube is adjusted until there is resonance when a sounding tuning fork is held above the open end.   If the tuning fork makes 340 vib/sec, what is the shortest length of the tube for resonance?   *Ans.* 25 cm

18. Two closed organ pipes of lengths 40 and 41 in. are sounded together and produce 2 beats per second.   What is the velocity of sound in the medium with which the organ pipes are filled?

19. A passenger standing on the rear platform of a train notes that a warning bell at a grade crossing rings with an apparent frequency of 400 cycles/sec.   The observation is made after the train has passed the crossing and while it is moving at 45 mi/hr (66 ft/sec).   What is the true frequency of the bell?   *Ans.* 426 cycles/sec

20. A man on a train which is running 50 mi/hr listens to a siren which has a frequency of 360 vib/sec.   What is the apparent frequency of the sound when the train is approaching the siren?

21. Two automobile horns each emit a note having a frequency of 200 cycles/sec. If one of these horns is on a car approaching an observer at 15 mi/hr and the other is on a car moving away from the observer at 15 mi/hr, calculate the frequency heard by the observer in each case.   *Ans.* 204 cycles/sec; 196 cycles/sec

22. How rapidly must a train be moving away from a stationary observer so that the pitch of its whistle will seem to drop from 1,000 to 900 vib/sec?

23. At what rate must a source of sound approach an observer in order to have the pitch of each note raised by a half tone, i.e., to $^{16}\!/_{15}$ of the original frequency?
                                                                    Ans. 69 ft/sec

24. What speed of a source of sound away from an observer will cause the sound heard to have a frequency that is $^{15}\!/_{16}$ of the true frequency?

25. Estimate the angle θ in Fig. 17.12, and calculate the approximate speed of the bullet.

CHAPTER 18 Skip

Audition and Sound Spectra

18.1. The Ear. The human ear (Fig. 18.1) may be divided into three distinct parts: the external ear, the middle ear, and the inner ear. The external ear collects the sound waves and directs them along the auditory canal to the *eardrum*, which is caused to vibrate. These vibrations are carried across the middle ear by three small bones, called the *hammer*, the *anvil*, and the *stirrup* because of their shapes. Vibrations of the eardrum are passed from hammer to anvil to stirrup, which in turn is

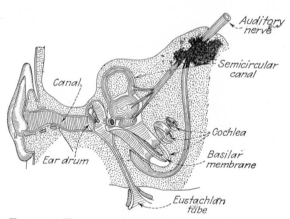

Fig. 18.1. The anatomical structure of the human ear.

attached to the "oval window" separating the middle ear from the inner ear. The principal parts of the inner ear are the *cochlea* and three semicircular canals. The cochlea, shaped somewhat like the shell of a snail, serves as a funnel leading to the nerve endings which are sensitive to sound. The cochlea is filled with fluid which is set into vibration by the movement of the oval window. Inside the cochlea are about 2.5 turns of the basilar membrane to which are connected the nerve endings which initiate signals to the brain. There are roughly 30,000 of these nerve endings in a human ear. Figure 18.2 indicates the part of the cochlea

204

which shows maximum response for a pure tone of 700 cycles/sec and moderate loudness.   The semicircular canals are not part of the hearing mechanism, but are vital in keeping one's balance.

18.2. Limitations of Hearing.   The ear responds only to a limited band of frequencies, which varies from person to person with a range from about 20 to 20,000 vib/sec.   The existence of vibrations too rapid to be detected by the ear has long been known.   Sounds that have frequencies above the range of audibility are known as *ultrasonic* sounds.   *Infrasonic* sounds have frequencies too low to be audible.

The human ear is a remarkably sensitive detector of sound waves.   At 3,000 vib/sec the faintest sound the ear can hear has pressure variations of about 2×10^{-5} newton/m², which corresponds to a displacement amplitude less than 10^{-11} m, or about 0.1 the diameter of a molecule! Yet it can also hear sounds with pressure variations a million times this great.   Through a moderate range, the loudness of a sound, as judged by the ear, is proportional to the logarithm of the intensity.   The intensity level n of a sound wave is defined by the equation

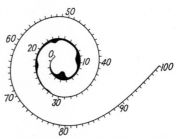

$$n = 10 \log \frac{I}{I_0} \qquad (18.1)$$

where I_0 is a reference level taken arbitrarily as 10^{-12} watt/m² which is roughly the weakest sound which can be heard. Intensity levels are measured in *decibels* (db).   A sound which has an intensity level of 60 db is one million times as in-

Fig. 18.2. The parts of the cochlea which show maximum response for a pure tone of frequency 700 cycles/sec. (*Courtesy of Harvey Fletcher.*)

tense as a sound of the reference intensity level.   Sound levels above 120 db are so loud that they may cause pain.   For ordinary speech, n ranges from 30 to 70 db, while for loud music it may reach 100.   Sound level meters (Fig. 18.3) provide a means of measuring sound levels.

The lowest sound level which can produce an audible sound depends on the frequency.   The range of intensity levels and frequencies which can be heard by a typical ear is shown in Fig. 18.4.   A sound more intense than that corresponding to the upper curve produces pain rather than hearing.

The least perceptible difference in frequency that can be detected by the ear depends on the frequency of the sound.   The way in which the fractional change in frequency that can be detected varies with the frequency is shown in Fig. 18.5.

18.3. Speech Sounds.   Speech sounds produced in ordinary conversation are transmitted through the air by means of pressure waves, which are exceedingly complicated.   The amplitudes and frequencies of the various components that are present in speech sounds vary from one voice to another, but average speech may be represented by a curve such as that of Fig. 18.6 which indicates the pressure of the waves in relation to the frequency of the different components. Speech energy extends from a frequency of about 60 per second to more than 6,000 per second. The energy is a maximum at a frequency somewhat less than

Fig. 18.3. A sound level meter. (*General Radio Corp. of America.*)

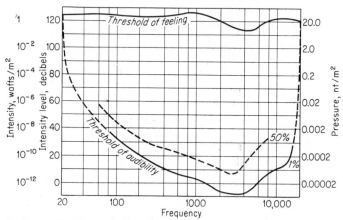

Fig. 18.4. Intensity levels showing threshold of audibility and threshold of feeling.

200 per second. The vowel sounds carry most of this speech energy. The consonants are weak in energy and rather high in frequency. The speech output of the normal human voice is about 10^{-5} watt, a very small amount of power.

Figure 18.7 shows the results of the analysis of some simple vowel sounds by Fletcher. In these figures, the frequencies present are plotted on the horizontal axis, and the amplitude of the sound of a given frequency is plotted on the vertical axis. These figures show that a simple vowel sound is composed of a number of frequencies and that the amplitudes corresponding to these frequencies vary over a wide range.

When we speak, the lungs by their bellows action supply streams of air which pass through the vocal passages. The vibrations of the vocal cords start a train of sound waves through the vocal passages. The tongue, the lips, and the cavities of the chest, nose, and throat impress on this train of waves certain resonant characteristics, and the vibrations finally emerge from the mouth as speech

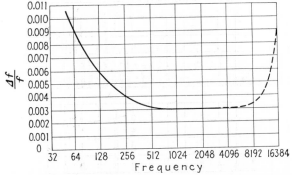

Fig. 18.5. Minimum perceptible difference in frequency.   (*Western Electric Company.*)

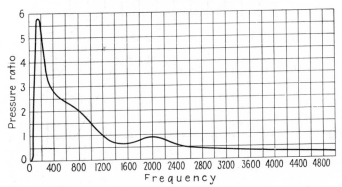

Fig. 18.6. Pressure-frequency distribution for ordinary speech.   (*Western Electric Company.*)

sounds. The differentiation of speech sounds is nearly all accomplished by the mouth and positions of the lips. Figure 18.8 shows the shape of the mouth in sounding the vowels *a*, *u*, and *i*. The *voiced sounds* include all the vowel and consonant sounds except *p*, *t*, *ch*, *k*, *f*, *s*, *th* (thin), and *sh*. The vocal cords do not enter into the production of these latter speech sounds, which arise from vibrations set up in the mouth itself.

18.4. Influence of Atmospheric Conditions on Audibility. Since the speed of sound in warm air is greater than it is in cold air, the direction of propagation of the sound changes as it passes from a layer of air at one temperature to a layer at a different temperature. If the air is at rest and the temperature and density are uniform, a wave front from a point source on the surface of the earth is spherical and the sound travels

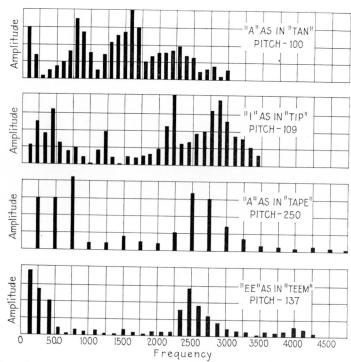

Fig. 18.7. Amplitude associated with various frequencies in vowel sounds. (*Bell Laboratories.*)

in straight lines.   If the air at the ground is warmer than it is at higher altitudes, the speed of the sound is greater at the surface.   A wave front is no longer spherical (Fig. 18.9).   Since the direction of propagation is perpendicular to the wave front, the sound is deflected upward and it cannot be heard for as great distances as it could if this distortion did not take place.   When air at the ground is colder than it is at the higher altitudes, the sound travels more slowly near the ground.   The sound is deflected downward (Fig.

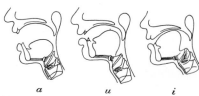

Fig. 18.8. Position of the vocal organs in uttering the vowels *a*, *u*, and *i*.

18.10) and the distance at which the sound can be heard is increased. This condition is sometimes noticed over a lake at the end of a hot day. Figure 18.11 shows how these effects influence the region in which a fog-horn may be heard.

When the wind is blowing, the speed of the sound with respect to the earth is decreased in the direction from which the wind comes and increased in the direction toward which the wind is blowing. Near the earth the higher the altitude,

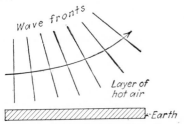

Fig. 18.9. Upward deflection of wave front when air at ground is warmer than that higher above the surface.

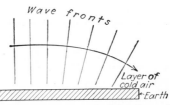

Fig. 18.10. Downward deflection of a sound wave when air at surface is colder than air above.

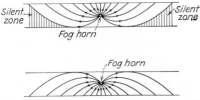

Fig. 18.11. Changes in audibility with atmospheric conditions. Above, surface air warmer; below, surface air colder.

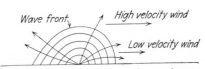

Fig. 18.12. Change in the shape of wave front and of propagation direction by a high wind.

the greater the velocity of the wind and the greater the change in the speed of the sound with respect to the earth. This unequal change in the speed of the sound waves causes a distortion in the wave front. On the windward side of the source the speed of the sound is greater at the ground than at points above the ground (Fig. 18.12). This inequality of speed causes the wave front near the ground to be inclined to the vertical and the line of propagation to be directed upward from the earth. On the side of the source of sound toward which the wind is blowing the speed near the ground is less than at higher altitudes. In this case, the direction of propagation is bent toward the ground, making it possible for the sound to be heard at greater distances.

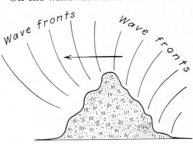

Fig. 18.13. Change in shape of a wave front by a hill.

If the wind blows against a hill, the wave fronts are distorted (Fig. 18.13) so that there is a space behind the hill which the sound does not reach. Beyond this point, the sound is heard again.

18.5. Architectural Acoustics. When sound waves are produced in a room, they spread out until they strike the walls, ceiling, or floor of the room. Here they are partly reflected, partly absorbed, and partly transmitted. A hard smooth wall reflects most of the sound; it transmits and absorbs little.   On the other hand, a porous, soft material absorbs most of the sound energy and reflects little.

If a steady sound source is maintained for some time in a room, the sound level in the room builds up, as shown in Fig. 18.14.   After a short time a state of equilibrium is reached in which the energy lost each second through absorption is equal to the sound power provided by the source. When the source is shut off, the intensity of the sound dies down, as indicated in the second half of the curve in Fig. 18.14.

The echoing and reechoing of sounds in a room because of repeated reflections is known as *reverberation*.   *The reverberation time of a room is defined as the time required for the sound level to fall 60 db after the sound source is shut off.*   A drop of 60 db means that the intensity falls to one millionth of its original value.   If the reverberation time of a room is too long, the sound waves bounce back and forth many times; a speaker's words become blurred because of the presence of these reflected waves which blend with the new sound waves.   Such a blending effect is familiar to anyone who has sung in a hard-walled shower room that has a long reverberation time.   On the other hand, if the reverberation time is too short, sounds are thin and weak; we say the room is "dead."   In general, a somewhat longer reverberation time is desirable for music than for speech.   A reverberation time of about 1 sec for a small room and 1.5 to 2 sec for a larger one is desirable for ordinary uses.   For making phonograph recordings a very dead room with virtually no reverberation is used because the desired reverberation properties are supplied by the room in which the listener sits.

Fig. 18.14. Rise and decay of sound in a room.

The reverberation time of a classroom or auditorium may be estimated by the use of a formula due to Sabine, who was a pioneer in the field of architectural acoustics.   He found that the reverberation time t_R in seconds for a typical room was given by

$$t_R = 0.16 \frac{V}{A} \qquad (18.2)$$

where V is the volume of the room in cubic meters and A is the total absorbing power of the room and its contents.   The total absorbing power of the room is found by adding the contributions of all sound-absorbing surfaces, the contribution of each surface being the product of the exposed area in square meters and the appropriate absorption coefficient.   The absorption coefficient, in turn, is the fraction of the incident sound wave energy which is removed either by absorption or transmission. It is 1.00 for an open window because all the incident energy goes on through and is thus removed from the room. The absorption coefficients of a number of typical materials is listed in Table 1.

Table 1

SOUND-ABSORPTION COEFFICIENTS

Open window*...............	1.00	Hair felt....................	0.40
Brick wall..................	0.02	Heavy curtains..............	0.50
Clay tile...................	0.03	Perforated acoustic ceiling........	0.60
Concrete....................	0.02	Plaster.....................	0.03
Glass.......................	0.03	Wood.......................	0.05

* Absorbing power of typical person is 0.5 m² of open window.

Example. A shower room has the dimensions 5 by 4 by 3 m. All the walls are of tile and the door has the same absorption coefficient as tile. Find the approximate reverberation time if a single man is showering and singing in this room.
A = (20 + 20 + 12 + 12 + 15 + 15) × 0.03 + the absorbing power of the naked man which we shall take to be equivalent to 0.25 m² of open window (at least half the absorption of a person is associated with his clothing).

$$A = 2.82 + 0.25 = 3.07$$
$$t_R = 0.16 \frac{V}{A} = 0.16 \times \frac{60}{3.07} = 3.1 \text{ sec}$$

Example. A classroom has a volume of 400 m³. There are exposed 600 m² of tile and 500 m² of wood in chairs, doors, and woodwork. There are 30 persons occupying the room. Estimate the reverberation time.

$$A = (600 \times 0.03) + (500 \times 0.05) + (30 \times 0.5 \times 1)$$
$$= 18 + 25 + 15 = 58$$
$$t_R = 0.16 \times \frac{400}{58} = 1.1 \text{ sec}$$

18.6. Musical Scales. Some combinations of sounds are pleasing to the ear; others are not. What is pleasing depends in no small measure on the training of the listener. As long ago as 530 B.C. Pythagoras experimented with stretched strings and found that simultaneous notes from strings were harmonious when the ratios of the frequencies were the ratios of two small whole numbers. When one frequency is double another, we say they differ by one *octave;* this ratio of 2 to 1 is a pleasing one. On the other hand, ratios such as 100 to 81 are ordinarily displeasing, at least in part because of the existence of unpleasant beat notes. Modern occidental music is written with scales which consist of notes with frequencies related by fairly simple ratios. We call the ratio of the frequencies of two sounds the *musical interval* of the two notes. The diatonic C major scale is an example of a typical scale which is rather commonly used. The relationships between the notes in this scale are shown in Table 2.

A piano can be tuned to play a diatonic scale in any one key, but then the frequencies would not be satisfactory for other keys. In order that a piano be able to play in a number of different keys it is customary to make certain compromises so that the piano is not tuned perfectly for any key. The compromise usually adopted is known as the *equal-tempered scale*. In one octave of this scale there are 13 notes and 12 intervals; there is a constant ratio between the frequencies of adjacent notes.

Table 2

DIATONIC C MAJOR SCALE
(Based on $A = 440$/sec)

Major scale note	C	D	E	F	G	A	B	C'
Name	Do	Re	Mi	Fa	Sol	La	Ti	Do
Frequency	264	297	330	352	396	440	495	528
Interval relative to C	1	$\frac{9}{8}$	$\frac{5}{4}$	$\frac{4}{3}$	$\frac{3}{2}$	$\frac{5}{3}$	$1\frac{5}{8}$	2
Musical interval		$\frac{9}{8}$	$1\frac{0}{9}$	$\frac{16}{15}$	$\frac{9}{8}$	$1\frac{0}{9}$	$\frac{9}{8}$	$\frac{16}{15}$
Musician's interval		Major tone	Minor tone	Semi tone	Major tone	Minor tone	Major tone	Semi tone

This ratio is the twelfth root of 2, or 1.05946. The standard frequency of this scale is A = 440 per second so that this note agrees with that on the diatonic C major scale shown in Table 2. No other note in the octave has exactly the same frequency on the two scales.

PROBLEMS

1. What is the intensity level for a sound of intensity of 10^{-8} watt/m² relative to the reference level of 10^{-12} watt/m²?   *Ans.* 40 db

2. The threshold of pain involves an intensity level of roughly 120 db. What is the corresponding intensity in watts per square meter?

3. If the intensity due to five violins is five times that of a single violin, how many decibels is the sound level raised by having five violins playing rather than a single one?   *Ans.* 10 log 5 or 6.99 db

4. If a loudspeaker is regarded as a point source radiating equally in all directions, what acoustic power must it develop to produce a sound level of 60 db at a distance of 100 m?

5. A lecture room has a volume of 10,000 m³. If it has 800 m² of acoustic ceiling, 2,000 m² of plaster, 800 m² of concrete, and 4,000 m² of wood, find the reverberation time when the room is empty and when it holds 300 people.   *Ans.* 2.1 sec; 1.8 sec

6. An auditorium is essentially a rectangle 40 m by 25 m by 10 m in height. It has a perforated acoustic ceiling, cement floor, and tile walls. It contains 800 seats each of which is equivalent to 4 ft² of felt. Find the approximate reverberation time of the auditorium when empty and when full.

7. A major diatonic scale is built upon a first note of 360 cycles/sec. Find the frequencies of the other seven notes.   *Ans.* 405, 450, 480, 540, 600, 675, 720

8. Find the notes of a major diatonic scale based on C = 256 cycles/sec.

9. The major diatonic scale of Prob. 7 is based on F = 360 cycles/sec. Show that for this scale the intervals D/C = $1\frac{0}{9}$ and E/D = $\frac{9}{8}$. How do these intervals compare with those for the C major scale of Table 2? In view of the fact that the intervals for the key of C and for the key of F are different, how does one make a piano which can play reasonably well in both keys?

PART III

Heat

CHAPTER 19

Temperature and Heat

19.1. Temperature. Our first ideas about temperature come from our physiological senses. By touching a body we may decide whether it is hot or cold. For some purposes our senses give us an adequate description of temperature, but often sensory impressions are unreliable. For example, a room may feel hot to a person who has been outdoors in snow, while it may feel cold to a person entering it from a steam bath. Indeed, sensory impressions of temperature depend greatly on the environment during the recent past.

There is a second situation in which the senses give an unreliable comparison of temperature. If one removes a cardboard container and a metal ice tray from the freezing compartment of a refrigerator, both objects are at the same temperature. Nevertheless, the tray feels much colder to the hand than does the cardboard container. The sense of touch is not always able to distinguish between a very hot object and a very cold one. In view of the uncertainties associated with our sensations of temperature it is not surprising that scientists have developed objective and reproducible methods for measuring the relative "hotness" of bodies under various conditions.

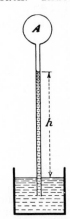

Fig. 19.1. Galilean thermometer utilizing the expansion of air with a rise in temperature.

The first recorded effort to make an instrument for measuring temperature was that of Galileo about 1593. He took a glass bulb with a long stem and submerged the end of the stem in water (Fig. 19.1). By heating the bulb some of the air was driven out; as the bulb cooled, water rose in the stem. A change in the temperature of the bulb gave rise to a change in the water level in the stem. Such thermometers were used for many years by physicians and others. The Galilean thermometer has several serious handicaps, the most serious of which is that changes in atmospheric pressure also affect the height of the water in the stem.

215

In the seventeenth century thermometers using water or alcohol sealed in glass tubes were developed. Alcohol is still widely used in cheap thermometers. Early in the eighteenth century Fahrenheit introduced thermometers which used mercury as the thermometric substance. These thermometers rapidly won wide acceptance among scientific workers because they were consistent with each other over the whole length of scale and they were convenient, reliable, and reasonably cheap.

19.2. The Fahrenheit and Centigrade Temperature Scales. Fahrenheit elected to call zero on his thermometer "the most intense cold obtained artificially in a mixture of water, of ice, and of sal ammoniac." The temperature of the human armpit he called 96°. The choice of these two "fixed points" established the Fahrenheit temperature scale.

The centigrade temperature scale, proposed by the Swedish astronomer Celsius about 1742, takes as its zero the temperature of a mixture of ice and water under standard pressure. The temperature at which water boils under standard atmospheric pressure is 100°C.

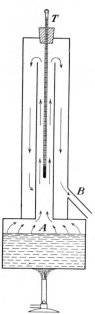

Fig. 19.2. Apparatus for determining the steam point for a thermometer.

To determine the first of the Celsius fixed points for a thermometer, the bulb is surrounded with finely divided ice and water. The melting ice keeps the temperature constant. When the mercury in the bulb reaches the temperature of the ice, the height of the mercury in the stem of the thermometer does not change. The point at which the mercury stands is marked 0°C. Then the bulb, and as much as possible of the stem of the thermometer, are placed in steam rising from water boiling at standard atmospheric pressure (Fig. 19.2). The mercury expands and assumes a new position in the stem. This position, which does not change after the temperature of the thermometer has reached the temperature of the steam, is marked 100° on the scale.

It was soon found that the fixed points of the Celsius (or centigrade) scale could be reproduced easily and with far greater accuracy than could the original fixed points of the Fahrenheit scale. The melting point of ice was approximately 32° on the Fahrenheit scale and the boiling point of water 212°F. Eventually it became standard practice to use the ice point and the boiling point as the fixed points for the Fahrenheit scale.

It is frequently desirable to convert a centigrade temperature to a Fahrenheit one, and vice versa. This can be done readily if one recalls the fixed points of the two temperature scales. Let F be the temperature on the Fahrenheit scale and C the temperature on the Celsius (or centigrade) scale (Fig. 19.3). The number of Fahrenheit degrees above the freezing point is related to the total temperature difference between the boiling point and the freezing point on the Fahrenheit scale (180°) as the number of centigrade degrees above the freezing point is to 100°C. This proportion may be written

$$\frac{F - 32}{180} = \frac{C}{100} \tag{19.1}$$

19.3. Maximum and Minimum Thermometers. In making observations on the temperature of the atmosphere, it is convenient to use a maximum and minimum thermometer, which registers the highest and lowest temperatures reached since the last setting. One common form is shown in Fig. 19.4. It consists of a bulb A filled with benzol. A mercury column fills the lower part of the tube, while the tube

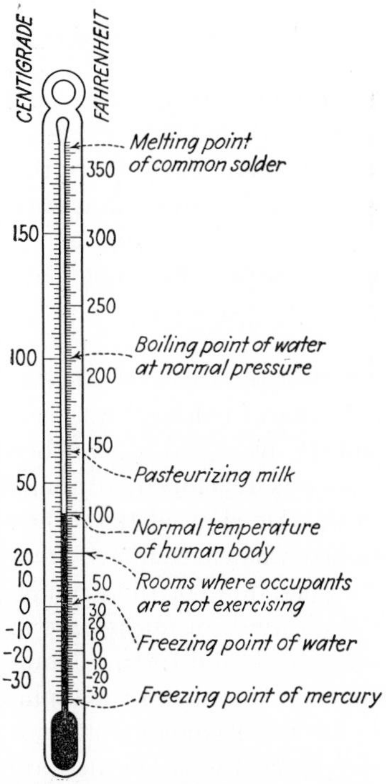

Fig. 19.3. Comparison of centigrade and Fahrenheit temperature scales.

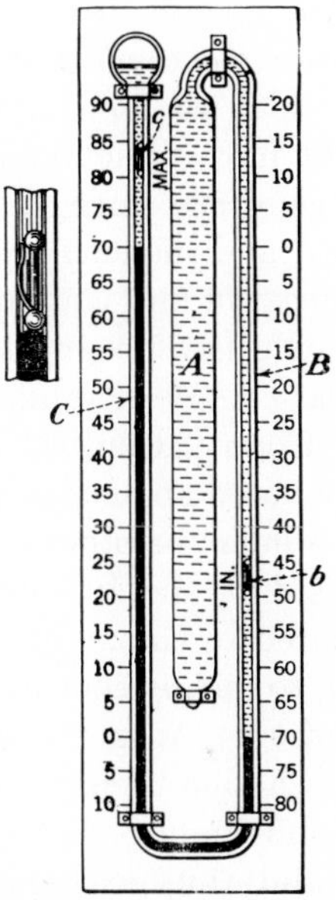

Fig. 19.4. Maximum and minimum thermometer.

above C is also partly filled with benzol. When the temperature rises, the expansion of the liquid in the bulb A causes the mercury column to sink at B and to rise at C, pushing upward a little index of iron in the tube above C, which in consequence of friction remains where pushed and marks the maximum temperature. On cooling, the contraction of the liquid in A causes the mercury to rise at B, pushing upward another index of iron which marks the minimum temperature. To set the instrument, the indices are drawn downward against the mercury by means of a small magnet.

19.4. The Clinical Thermometer. The thermometers commonly used by physicians are maximum thermometers, having a short scale ranging from about 95 to 105°F. The tube is made very flat and narrow just above the bulb. The mercury passes readily through this constriction in rising; but as it contracts, capillarity causes the column to separate at that point, leaving the upper end of the mercury column to mark the highest temperature.

19.5. Heat as a Form of Energy.   If we wish to raise the temperature of some water, we know we must "heat" the water.   What is the nature of the process?   This question was speculated upon and argued over for more than twenty centuries before the answer became clear at the end of the eighteenth century.   One idea which had held wide support for many years was that a fluid called *caloric* entered a body when it was heated and leaked away as the body cooled.   When measurements of the mass of a body showed no increase when the body was heated, the proponents of the caloric theory argued that the fluid was massless.   As a rival for the caloric theory, the idea was advanced that *heat is energy associated with the random motions of atoms and molecules.*   It is this latter view which we now hold.   It is not surprising, however, that such a view might have difficulty in gaining supporters in the middle of the eighteenth century, since the very existence of atoms had not been demonstrated and modern ideas of the structure of matter had not yet been introduced in any convincing form.

One of the decisive experiments which supported the theory that heat is mechanical energy of random motion rather than "caloric" was performed by Count Rumford in 1798.   Rumford observed that when cannon were bored an enormous amount of heat was developed, although there was no flame or other source of "caloric."   He showed that when the drill was dull, the amount of heat developed was exceedingly great and was related to the amount of mechanical work done in the drilling.

According to our present ideas, the atoms of all kinds of matter are in constant motion.   Atoms in solids are vibrating back and forth in complex motions about their equilibrium positions.   Molecules in a liquid wander around among the other molecules, having frequent collisions with them and thus exchanging energy.   In gases the molecules are traveling about at high speeds and have frequent elastic collisions with their neighbors.   When we heat a substance, the random motions and the energy associated with them are increased.

We know that if we pound a nail with a hammer, the nail becomes hot. When the hammer hits, it has kinetic energy associated with the movement of all its particles toward the nail.   As the hammer is stopped, the atoms in the nail are given energy which shows up in the form of heat. After the hammer has struck, the atoms are vibrating with greater amplitudes about their equilibrium positions.   When we add heat to any substance, we transfer to its atoms and molecules more energy of random motion.

When we put a thermometer in a beaker of water, the random motions of water molecules produce collisions with the molecules of the glass in the thermometer.   In turn, the glass molecules exchange energy with the mercury molecules until eventually the "level" of this random motion is the same for the water molecules, the glass molecules, and the mercury molecules.   When this occurs, the position of the mercury in the thermometer becomes stationary and we say the thermometer has come to the same temperature as the water.   *Temperature is a measure of the heat level.*

If we put any kind of thermometer in water which is at a higher temperature, heat flows from the water to the thermometer until the temperatures are equal.   If the thermometer is at the higher temperature, the molecules of the thermometer lose some of their heat energy to the water molecules.   In general, whenever two bodies are placed in contact, heat is transferred from the one at higher temperature to the one at lower temperature, just as when two bodies of water are connected, water flows through the connection from the higher surface to the lower one.   When two bodies are placed in contact and neither gains heat from the other, the two bodies are at the same temperature by definition.

19.6. The Absolute Temperature Scales.   If heat is the energy associated with the random motions of atoms and molecules, there must be a lower limit or an *absolute zero* of temperature.   If we took away from the atoms and molecules all their available energy of random motion, we could properly assign a temperature of absolute zero, since temperature measures the level of the energy of random motion.   We shall see in Chap. 20 that there is substantial evidence for the existence of such an absolute zero of temperature, which turns out to be at $-273.16°$C.

Lord Kelvin established an absolute temperature scale based on thermodynamic reasoning (Chap. 24) which uses degrees identical in size with the Celsius degree.   On this scale the ice point is $273.16°$K and the steam point $373.16°$K.   We shall henceforth use T to indicate absolute temperatures, t to represent centigrade or Fahrenheit temperatures, and the approximation

$$T(°K) = t(°C) + 273 \tag{19.2}$$

The Scotch engineer Rankine devised an absolute scale based on the Fahrenheit degree.   Absolute zero on the Rankine scale ($0°$R) corresponds to $-460°$F and $T(°R) = t(°F) + 460$.

19.7. Heat Units.   Although heat is a form of energy and can be measured in the units of mechanics (e.g., joules), heat units were established before it was known that heat is a form of energy.   In dealing with heat it is convenient to use a unit based on raising the temperature of a unit amount of water.   In the metric system the unit of heat energy is defined as follows: *The calorie is the quantity of heat which is required to* *raise the temperature of one gram of water one centigrade degree.* In terms of mechanical units 1 cal = 4.186 joules.

The heat required to raise the temperature of 1 g of water 1° depends slightly on the temperature, as is shown in Fig. 19.5. In view of this variation an exact definition of the calorie requires specification of the particular centigrade degree over which the temperature is to be raised. The temperature range chosen is 14.5 to 15.5°C. It can be seen from Fig. 19.5 that this particular choice has the result that it takes almost exactly 100 cal to raise 1 g of water from 0 to 100°C.

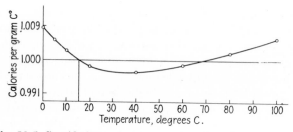

Fig. 19.5. Specific heat of water as a function of temperature.

The kilocalorie, as its name implies, is one thousand calories. In the biological sciences, the kilocalorie is referred to as a *Calorie* (sometimes not capitalized). Thus, if a book on diet suggests that an apple has 100 "calories" of food value, the calories referred to are kilocalories.

In the English system heat is measured in British thermal units (Btu). *One British thermal unit is the quantity of heat needed to raise the temperature of one pound of water from 58.5 to 59.5°F.* Since 1 lb is equal to 453.6 g and 1 F° is $\frac{5}{9}$ C°, it is clear that 1 Btu is equal to 453.6 × $\frac{5}{9}$ = 252 cal. In mechanical units 1 Btu = 778 ft-lb.

19.8. Specific Heat. If we add equal amounts of heat to a kilogram of water and to a kilogram of copper, the temperature of the copper goes up far more than the temperature of the water. It takes 0.093 calorie to raise the temperature of a gram of copper one centigrade degree. *The heat required to change the temperature of a unit mass of a substance one degree is the specific heat of the substance.* This definition is worded in such a way that it is applicable to both the metric and the British system of units.

Let Q denote the quantity of heat added to a mass m and let t_1 and t_2 be the initial and final temperatures, respectively. If c is the specific heat of the material,

$$Q = mc(t_2 - t_1) = mc\,\Delta t \tag{19.3}$$

Example. Find the number of calories required to raise the temperature of 100 g of brass from 25 to 75°C.

Specific heat of brass is 0.09 cal/(g)(C°).

Heat = mass × sp ht × change of temperature
  = $m \times c \times (t_2 - t_1)$
  = 100 × 0.09 × (75 − 25) = 450 cal

The specific heats of a number of solids and liquids are listed in the tables of heat constants in Appendix D, Tables D.1 and D.2.   The specific heats of a few elements are shown in Table 1.   The lightest element listed, aluminum, has the largest specific heat, while the heaviest element has the lowest specific heat.   If we multiply the specific heat of each element by its atomic weight, we obtain the number in the last column of the table.   *The product of the specific heat of an element and its atomic*

Table 1

SPECIFIC HEATS OF SOLID ELEMENTS

Element	Atomic weight	Specific heat, cal/(g)(C°)	Specific heat × atomic weight
Aluminum............	27	0.22	5.9
Titanium.............	47.9	0.14	6.7
Iron.................	55.8	0.11	6.1
Copper..............	63.6	0.093	5.9
Tin.................	118.7	0.054	6.4
Lead................	207.2	0.031	6.4

weight is approximately 6 cal/C° *g-atomic wt for most solid elements.*   This is known as the *law of Dulong and Petit.*   The physical meaning of the law of Dulong and Petit is readily seen if we remember that one atomic weight of any element contains 6×10^{23} atoms.   It requires an average of about 10^{-23} cal per atom to raise the temperature of most solid elements one centigrade degree.

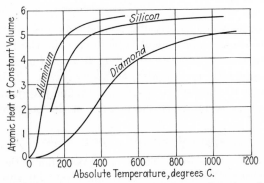

Fig. 19.6. Product of specific heat and atomic weight as a function of temperature for carbon, silicon, and aluminum.

There are a few solid elements which are notable exceptions to the law of Dulong and Petit.   For example, carbon in the form of diamond has a specific heat of only 1.46 cal/C° g atomic wt at room temperature.   However, the value approaches six as the temperature is raised (Fig. 19.6).   For all elements the specific heat is small at low temperature, approaching zero as the temperature approaches 0°K.   Modern quantum theory gives us an understanding of the reasons for the discrepancies between observed specific heats and the law of Dulong and Petit.

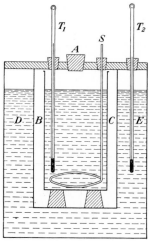

19.9. Calorimetry.   One of the most familiar methods of measuring a quantity of heat is by imparting this heat to a known mass of water and observing the change that it produces in the temperature of the water. Experiments of this kind are carried on with the aid of a vessel known as a *calorimeter* (Fig. 19.7) which is carefully insulated so that it neither gains nor loses heat from its surroundings during the experiment.   The basic principle underlying all calorimetry experiments is the law of conservation of energy, which for calorimetry takes the form: *Heat gained by those bodies which gain heat equals heat lost by those bodies which lose heat.*

Fig. 19.7.   Calorimeter for measuring the heat transferred from one body to another.

Example.   A 450-g cylinder of lead is heated to 100°C and then dropped into a 50-g copper calorimeter containing 100 g of water at 10°C. After stirring until equilibrium is established, the temperature of the whole system is 21.1°C. Find the specific heat of lead.

$$\text{Heat gained} = \text{heat lost}$$
$$100 \times 1 \times (21.1 - 10) + 50 \times 0.093 \times (21.1 - 10) = 450c(100 - 21.9)$$
$$1{,}162 = 35{,}500c$$
$$c = 0.033 \text{ cal}/(\text{g})(\text{C}°)$$

When a body such as a calorimeter is used over and over again in heat experiments, it is often convenient to compute the thermal capacity of the body.   *The thermal capacity of a body is defined as the heat required to raise the temperature of the entire body one degree.*   This quantity is sometimes known as the *water equivalent.*   To find the thermal capacity, it is necessary only to multiply the mass m of the body by the specific heat c.

$$\text{Thermal capacity of body} = mc \qquad (19.4)$$

19.10. Heat of Combustion.   The heat of combustion is the heat liberated by burning unit mass or unit volume of a fuel, such as coal or gas.   One method of finding it for a solid or liquid fuel is to place a measured quantity in a crucible C (Fig. 19.8) inside a bell jar, which is closed so that the products of combustion can escape only through the openings at the base of the jar.   The bell jar is placed inside a calorimeter, the mass of which is known, and this vessel is then filled with a known weight of water.   The temperature of the water is determined, and then the fuel is oxidized.   A supply of oxygen is admitted through the opening at the top of the bell jar until all the fuel has been burned.   The products of combustion bubble up through the water.   When the combustion is complete, the temperature of the water is again determined. The heat energy gained by the water and the calorimeter is equal to the chemical energy released in the oxidation.

Example. A sample of coal weighing 0.15 lb was burned in the crucible in Fig. 19.8. The water weighed 100 lb, and its temperature at the beginning was 60°F; the temperature at the end was 80°F. Find the heat of combustion of the coal. The vessel forming the calorimeter has a water equivalent of 5 lb.

$$\text{Energy released} = \text{heat gained}$$
$$(0.15 \text{ lb})(\text{heat of combustion}) = 100 \times (80 - 60) \times 1 + 5 \times (80 - 60) \times 1$$
$$= 2100 \text{ Btu}$$
$$\text{Heat of combustion} = \frac{2100 \text{ Btu}}{0.15 \text{ lb}} = 14,000 \text{ Btu/lb}$$

A method of measuring the heat of combustion of a fuel that can be burned as a gas is shown in Fig. 19.9. The gas to be studied is burned in a burner which is inside the calorimeter. The products of combustion pass out through a series of pipes. Around these pipes there is a continuous flow of water. This water enters the calorimeter at a constant temperature that is measured by the thermometer T_2. The water leaves by an outlet, its temperature being determined

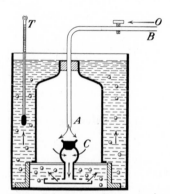

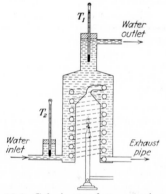

Fig. 19.8. Calorimeter for measuring the heat of combustion of fuels.

Fig. 19.9. Calorimeter for measuring the heat of combustion of gases.

just before it leaves the calorimeter. The temperature of the water as it leaves is, of course, higher than when it enters. By weighing the water and measuring the quantity of gas that has been burned, it is possible to calculate the quantity of heat generated per unit volume of gas. If the rate of generation of heat is constant, the difference between the temperature of the ingoing and outgoing water remains constant.

Example. In determining the heat of combustion of natural gas, it was found that 2,400 g of water flowed through the calorimeter while 3 liters of gas were being burned. The temperature of the ingoing water was 20.0°C and that of the outgoing water was 30.0°C. Find the number of calories generated by the combustion of 1 liter of gas.

$$\text{Heat of combustion} = \frac{\text{mass of water} \times \text{temperature change} \times \text{sp ht}}{\text{volume of gas}}$$
$$= \frac{2,400(30 - 20) \times 1}{3} = 8000 \text{ cal/liter}$$

PROBLEMS

1. What is the temperature (98.6°F) of the normal human body on the centigrade scale?   *Ans.* 37°C

2. A Fahrenheit thermometer shaded from the sun on a hot day reads 95°. What is the temperature on the centigrade scale?

3. The boiling point of pure methyl alcohol, widely used as an antifreeze, is 66°C. Find the corresponding temperature on the Fahrenheit scale and on the Kelvin scale.
                                                               Ans. 150.8°F; 339°K

4. A thermostat is set to maintain the temperature at 30°C. What is the corresponding temperature on the Fahrenheit scale?

5. Solid carbon dioxide (dry ice) turns to the gaseous phase at −112°F. Find the corresponding temperature on the centigrade scale.   *Ans.* −80°C

6. What is the temperature on the centigrade scale when a Fahrenheit thermometer indicates 0°?

7. The Reaumur temperature scale is widely used in France. On this scale the ice point is 0°R and the steam point 80°R. Extend the relationship

$$\frac{C}{100} = \frac{F-32}{180} = \frac{R}{80}$$

to include a term for the Reaumur scale. Find the centigrade and Fahrenheit temperatures corresponding to 20°R.   *Ans.* 25°C; 77°F

8. The temperature at which mercury boils is 357°C and that at which it freezes is −40°C. Find the corresponding temperatures on the Fahrenheit scale.

9. A man of mass 70 kg daily consumes food with a fuel value of about 3,500,000 cal. If this heat were used to heat a mass of water of 70 kg, how many degrees would the temperature be raised?   *Ans.* 50C°

10. How many Btu are required to raise the temperature of 4 ft³ of water from 40 to 190°F?

11. A 200-g piece of lead heated to 100°C is dropped into 100 cm³ of water at 4.5°C. The final temperature is 10°C. Compute the specific heat of lead.
                                                        Ans. 0.031 cal/(g)(C°)

12. A piece of sheet aluminum rolled into a spiral with a mass of 62 g is heated in a steam jacket to a temperature of 98°C and then plunged into 120 g of water at 9°C, causing the temperature to rise to 18°C. What is the specific heat of aluminum, assuming that no heat was lost or gained during the experiment?

13. If 400 g of aluminum at 220°C are dropped into 300 g of water at 10°C, contained in a 100-g copper calorimeter, find the resulting equilibrium temperature.
                                                               Ans. 56.5°C

14. A piece of iron weighing 150 g was taken out of an oil bath and immediately immersed in a beaker containing 160 g of water at 14°C. The temperature of the water rose to 26°C. What was the temperature of the oil bath?

15. To find the temperature of a furnace, a 150-g piece of platinum was placed inside until temperature equilibrium was reached. The platinum was then dropped into a 200-g copper calorimeter containing 500 g of water at 5°C. If the final temperature of the water was 15°C, find the temperature of the furnace.   *Ans.* 1095°C

16. A copper calorimeter contains 200 g of water at 0°C and 216 g of silver. The calorimeter has a mass of 150 g. How much will the temperature be increased by adding 750 cal?

17. The atomic weight of germanium is 72.6. Estimate the specific heat of *Ge* by use of the law of Dulong and Petit.   *Ans.* 0.083 cal/(g)(C°)

18. Estimate the specific heat of columbium which has an atomic weight of 93.

19. The heat of combustion of natural gas is 1500 Btu/ft³. Find how many cubic feet of gas is needed to heat 10 ft³ of water from 40 to 180°F in a hot-water heater, assuming that 80 per cent of the energy released is absorbed by the water.   *Ans.* 73 ft³

20. Natural gas from the mains with a heat of combustion of 1500 Btu/ft³ is used to heat water. Assuming that half of the available heat is wasted, how much gas will be required to heat 5 lb of water from 50°F to the boiling point?

21. A sample of methyl alcohol weighing 15 g was burned in a fuel calorimeter containing 9 kg of water. The water equivalent of the calorimeter was 600 cal. The initial temperature was 12.2°C, and the final temperature was 20.5°C. Calculate the heat of combustion of the methyl alcohol.   *Ans.* 5300 cal/g

22. A sample of coal weighing 2 oz with a heat of combustion of 12,500 Btu/lb was burned in a crucible of a calorimeter (Fig. 19.8). The calorimeter contained 12 lb of water, and it had an initial temperature of 50°F. The glass parts of the calorimeter weighed 6.2 lb and had a specific heat of 0.19. To what temperature was the water raised?

23. A specimen of coal with a mass of 2.5 g was burned in a copper calorimeter having a mass of 1.2 kg. The mass of the water in the calorimeter was 1.8 kg and the initial temperature was 14°C. The final temperature of the water was 21°C. Find the heat of combustion.   *Ans.* 5360 cal/g

24. Into a copper calorimeter weighing 120 g and containing 250 g of water at 12°C there are dropped simultaneously 55 g of silver at 110°C, 40 g of iron at 60°C, and 20 g of platinum at 72°C. What is the resulting temperature?

CHAPTER 20

Thermal Expansion

20.1. Expansion of Solids. Most substances expand when heated (Fig. 20.1). This is not surprising when we remember that heating a solid increases the amplitude of vibration of the atoms and has the effect of moving the atoms somewhat farther apart. The change of length of a typical solid is small—only a few parts in ten thousand for an ordinary daily range in outside temperature—but the forces associated with such expansion can be tremendously great and must be allowed for in all sorts of structures. The amount of expansion depends on the nature of the substance and on the change in temperature. On railroads small distances are usually left between rails to permit expansion without having the tracks bow. In laying cement roads and sidewalks, expansion joints filled with tar are provided. Care is taken in selecting types of glass and of metal when one wishes to bring conductors through glass walls into vacuum tubes and light bulbs.

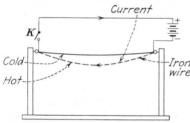

Fig. 20.1. Increase in the length of an iron wire when the temperature is raised.

When we heat a solid, the change in length ΔL depends on the material, on the original length L, and on the change in temperature Δt. For most materials we may write the approximate equality:

$$\Delta L = \alpha L \, \Delta t \qquad (20.1)$$

where α is known as the *coefficient of linear expansion* of the material. From Eq. (20.1) we see that the *coefficient of linear expansion α is the change in length per unit length for a one degree rise in temperature.* Clearly, α is independent of the units in which the length is measured, but it does depend on the temperature unit. A change of one Fahrenheit degree corresponds to a change of only $\frac{5}{9}$ centigrade degree. Therefore, α per F° is only $\frac{5}{9}$ of α per C°. The coefficient of linear expansion varies with

226

the temperature (Fig. 20.2), usually slowly for room temperatures but rapidly at very low temperatures (Fig. 20.3). The coefficients of linear expansion of many solids are listed in Appendix D, Table D.1.

Example. The main cable of a suspension bridge is 5,000 ft in length at 0°C. If the cable is made of steel, find its length on a hot summer day when the

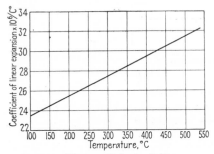

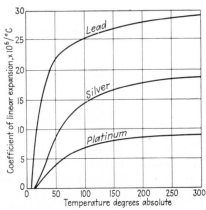

Fig. 20.2. The coefficient of linear expansion of aluminum as a function of temperature.

Fig. 20.3. The coefficient of linear expansion of lead, silver, and platinum at low temperatures.

temperature is 35°C.

$$\Delta L = \alpha L \, \Delta t$$
$$= 13 \times 10^{-6} \times 5{,}000 \times 35$$
$$= 2.3 \text{ ft}$$

Thus the length is 5,002.3 ft at 35°C.

In the construction of an iron bridge (Fig. 20.4) provision is made for the expansion of the iron. To make it possible for the bridge to expand, one end of the bridge is mounted on a roller. As the length of the bridge increases or decreases, the end of the bridge moves forward or back without injuring the piers.

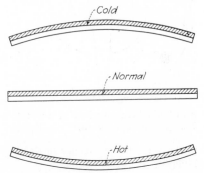

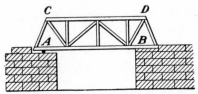

Fig. 20.4. To allow for the expansion of the bridge, one end may be supported on a large roller.

Fig. 20.5. Unequal expansions of metals. At higher temperatures the metal with the larger coefficient of linear expansion is on the outside.

20.2. Differential Expansion. Consider a strip of brass and a strip of iron welded together (Fig. 20.5) to form a composite bar. If this bar is heated, it bends because of the unequal expansion of the metals. The brass expands more rapidly than the iron so that the brass is on the outside of the curve when it is heated. A device of this kind is called a *bimetallic strip* and it has found many uses. One of the most familiar is in the thermostat, which may be made to open and close electric circuits as the movable end of the bimetallic strip changes its position (Fig. 20.6). Bimetallic strips are used in a common type of thermometer.

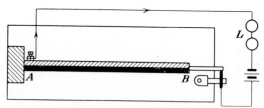

Fig. 20.6. The temperature regulator for a thermostat. A change in temperature produces a bending of the bimetallic strip *AB* to open or close an electric circuit.

In a watch, the balance wheel (Fig. 20.7) is made of bimetallic strips. As the temperature increases, the ends *A* and *B* are carried inward, making the moment of inertia of the wheel less; at the same time the expansion of the radius carries the rim of the wheel farther from the center, thereby producing an increase in

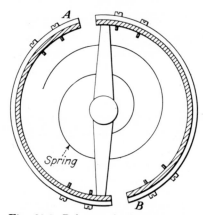

Fig. 20.7. Balance wheel of a watch. Change in temperature results in change of moment of inertia just adequate to correct for change in elastic properties of the hairspring.

the moment of inertia. Meantime, the elasticity of the hair spring is reduced by the higher temperature. This would make the balance wheel move more slowly if the moment of inertia of the wheel were not reduced to compensate. By proper design the balance wheel can be made to change its moment of inertia just enough so that the period of vibration remains the same at all temperatures.

20.3. Expansion in Area. Consider a square of material with sides of length L. The area is L^2. If we raise the temperature by Δt, each side becomes of length $L + \Delta L$ and the area becomes

$$(L + \Delta L)^2 = L^2 + 2L\,\Delta L + (\Delta L)^2$$

Since ΔL is very small compared with L, we may neglect $(\Delta L)^2$ in comparison with the other terms and write the new area as $L^2 + 2L\,\Delta L$. The change in area ΔA is then given by

$$\Delta A = 2L\,\Delta L = 2\alpha L^2\,\Delta t = 2\alpha A\,\Delta t \qquad (20.2)$$

From this equation we see that *the coefficient of area expansion is twice the coefficient of linear expansion.*

If we have a hole in a sheet of material, the area of this hole expands exactly as though it were filled with the material in question, regardless of the shape of the hole or of the sheet.   The pioneers made use of this fact in putting iron tires on the wooden wheels of their wagons.   The iron tire was made slightly smaller than the wooden wheel upon which it was to be placed.   Then the tire was heated red hot and, thanks to its expansion, it could be slipped over the wood.   As the iron cooled, it shrank around the wood.   In modern manufacturing, whenever one cylinder is to fit inside and be fastened to another cylinder, the two are often "sweated" together.   In this process the inner cylinder is made slightly larger than the hole in the outer cylinder.   Then the outer cylinder is heated and the inner one cooled.   Because of the expansion of the outer cylinder and the contraction of the inner one, the outer cylinder may be slipped over the inner.   When the two come to the same temperature, they are held together by tremendously strong frictional forces.

20.4. Volume Expansion.   Fluids do not have a fixed length. When they are heated, their volumes usually increase.   The change in volume ΔV depends on the fluid, the change in temperature Δt, and the original volume V.

$$\Delta V = \beta V \, \Delta t \tag{20.3}$$

where β is the *coefficient of volume expansion* of the fluid.   *The coefficient of volume expansion is the change in volume divided by the product of the original volume and the change in temperature.*   The coefficients of volume expansion for several liquids are listed in Appendix D, Table D.2.

The volume of a solid also increases when the temperature is raised. Consider a cube of length L on each side.   If the temperature is raised by an amount Δt, each side becomes of length $L + \Delta L$.   The volume is then $(L + \Delta L)^3 = L^3 + 3L^2 \, \Delta L + 3L(\Delta L)^2 + (\Delta L)^3$.   Since ΔL is very small compared with L, we may neglect the last two terms in comparison with the first two.   The initial volume was L^3 and the change in volume is then

$$\Delta V = 3L^2 \, \Delta L = 3\alpha L^3 \, \Delta t = 3\alpha V \, \Delta t \tag{20.3a}$$

If we compare this equation with Eq. (20.3), we see that *the coefficient of volume expansion is three times the coefficient of linear expansion* for a solid.

Liquids like alcohol and kerosene expand when heated, but the most familiar liquid, water, does not behave in so simple a fashion.   When water is warmed from 0 to 4°C, it contracts.   As the temperature is raised above 4°, the water expands (Fig. 20.8).   Thus a given mass of water has its minimum volume and its maximum density at 4°C.   For this reason the water at the bottom of a deep northern lake is 4°C the year around.   In the winter the surface may freeze over, but the water at great depths remains at 4°C. In the summer the upper layers of the lake are warmed, but very deep layers ordinarily do not increase appreciably in temperature.

20.5. The Expansion of Gases. Gases as well as liquids and solids expand when heated and contract when cooled. If we keep the pressure on the gas constant (Fig. 20.9), we find that a plot of the volume as a function of temperature gives a straight line (Fig. 20.10). The coefficient of volume expansion for the gas is given by $\beta = \Delta V/V \Delta t$. Let us agree to use 0°C as our reference temperature. Let V_0 be the volume of the gas at 0°C and V_t the volume at some temperature t. For 0°C,

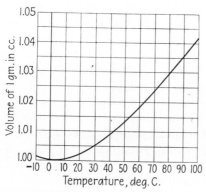

Fig. 20.8. The volume of 1 g of water in cubic centimeters. The specific volume is minimum at 3.98°C.

$$\beta_0 = \frac{\Delta V}{V_0 \Delta t} = \frac{(V - V_0)}{V_0 \Delta t}$$

or $$V = V_0(1 + \beta_0 t) \quad (20.4)$$

This relation is known as Charles' law. By careful experiments Charles found that the coefficient of volume expansion of all noncondensing gases at constant pressure and 0°C is equal to 0.00367, or $\frac{1}{273}$. *The coefficient of volume expansion is the same at a given temperature for all gases.* If we extrapolate (Fig. 20.10) a plot of the volume as a function of temperature of any gas to the x axis, the intercept is −273°C, regardless of the original volume of gas taken, of the gas chosen, and of the particular pressure

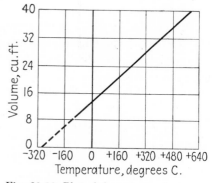

Fig. 20.10. Plot of the volume of a gas as a function of temperature.

Fig. 20.9. Expansion of a gas at constant pressure.

which was used. The fact that this intercept of −273°C is the same for different gases, different original volumes, and different pressures suggests this temperature has a very special significance. It was the first indication of an absolute zero for temperature. Of course, it should not be concluded that if the temperature of the gas were actually lowered to −273°C, it would follow the extrapolated line of Fig. 20.10 and occupy zero volume.   Before any such low temperature is reached, the gas would liquefy.   On the basis of our absolute temperature scale we may rewrite Eq. (20.4) as

$$V = V_0\left(1 + \frac{t}{273}\right) = V_0\left(\frac{273 + t}{273}\right) = V_0\frac{T}{273} \qquad (20.4a)$$

The volume of a gas at constant pressure is proportional to the absolute temperature.   In general $V_1/V_2 = T_1/T_2$, where V_1 and V_2 are the volumes occupied by the gas at temperatures T_1 and T_2, respectively, when the pressure is kept constant.   From this relation it follows immediately that *the coefficient of volume expansion of a gas is given by the reciprocal of the absolute temperature,* as can be shown by letting T_2 be $T_1 + \Delta T$ and V_2 be $V_1 + \Delta V$.

20.6.   Heating a Gas at Constant Volume.   If a gas is heated and its volume is kept constant (Fig. 20.11), the pressure varies, increasing

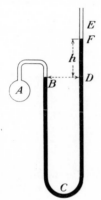

Fig. 20.11. Apparatus for keeping the volume of a gas constant as the temperature is raised.

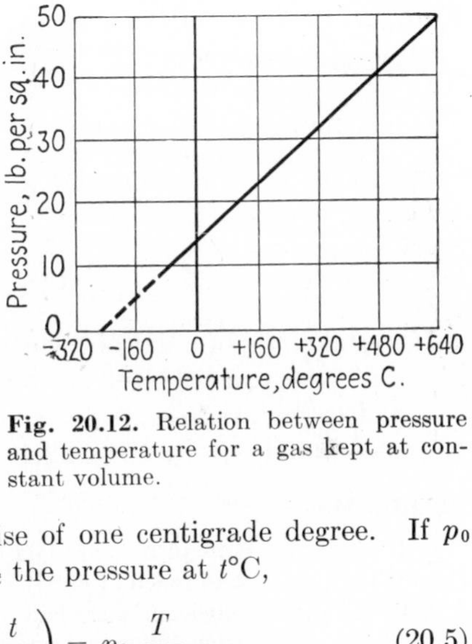

Fig. 20.12. Relation between pressure and temperature for a gas kept at constant volume.

$\frac{1}{273}$ of its value at 0°C for every rise of one centigrade degree.   If p_0 represents the pressure at 0°C and p_t the pressure at t°C,

$$p_t = p_0\left(1 + \frac{t}{273}\right) = p_0\frac{T}{273} \qquad (20.5)$$

Figure 20.12 shows the relation between the pressure and temperature of a gas at constant volume.   Note that once again the intercept on the temperature axis is −273°C (or more exactly −273.16°C).

20.7.   The General Gas Law.   From Boyle's law we know that the product of the pressure and the volume of a gas remains constant if the temperature is held fixed.   From Charles' law we know that the volume of a gas is proportional to the absolute temperature if the pressure is constant. If the volume is kept constant, the pressure is proportional to the absolute temperature. If we combine these relations, we may write that for any given mass of gas

$$pV = bT \tag{20.6}$$

where b is a constant for the particular mass of gas in question. If subscript 1 represents one particular set of conditions for the gas and subscript 2 another set of conditions, we may write

$$\frac{p_1 V_1}{T_1} = \frac{p_2 V_2}{T_2} \tag{20.7}$$

It is well known that one gram-molecular weight of any gas occupies the same volume as a gram-molecular weight of any other gas at the same temperature and pressure. At 0°C and one standard atmosphere (76 cm Hg) pressure a gram-molecular weight of any gas occupies 22,421 cm³. If we are dealing with one mole of a gas, the constant b in Eq. (20.6) is exactly the same for all gases; let us represent this constant by R. Then, if we have n moles of any gas, we may write

$$pV = nRT \tag{20.8}$$

The constant R is called the *universal gas constant*. It has the value

$$R = \frac{1.01 \times 10^5 \text{ newtons/m}^2 \times 22.4 \times 10^{-3} \text{ m}^3}{273°\text{K}} = 8.317 \frac{\text{joule}}{(\text{mole})(\text{K}°)}$$

or

$$1.987 \frac{\text{cal}}{(\text{mole})(\text{K}°)}$$

If we take m g of a gas of molecular weight M, the number of moles n is m/M. For example, the molecular weight of oxygen is 32 and hence 480 g of oxygen represents 15 moles. Under standard conditions these 15 moles would occupy $15 \times 22.4 = 336$ liters.

PROBLEMS

1. If 60-ft steel railroad rails are laid at 10°C, what space should be left between them if they are just to touch at 40°C?   *Ans.* 0.28 in.

2. Steel rails in 40-ft lengths are laid in winter at 0°C. How much space between consecutive rails must be allowed to permit expansion to a summer temperature of 45°C?

3. The channel span of the steel Ohio River bridge in Cincinnati is 1,057 ft in length. Calculate the maximum change in its length if it is subject to extreme temperatures of 0°F and 100°F.   *Ans.* 9.3 in.

4. A bar of copper is measured at 15°C and found to be 65 cm long. At what temperature will it be 1 mm shorter?

5. A brass cap is to be "sweated" on a brass cylinder. If the inner diameter of the cap is machined to 1.000 in. while the cylinder has an outer diameter of 1.002 in., how hot must the cap be heated before it can be slipped over the cylinder, if the cylinder is at 20°C?   *Ans.* 125°C

6. An iron ring which is 1 ft in diameter is to be shrunk on a pulley which is 1.003 ft in diameter. If the temperature of the ring is 10°C, find the temperature to which it must be raised so that it will just slip on the circumference of the pulley.

7. A glass flask holds exactly 1,000 cm³ of mercury at 0°C. If it is heated to 100°C, how many grams of mercury will run out? *Ans.* 213 g

8. A glass flask holds exactly 1 liter. It is filled with ethyl alcohol at 0°C and then heated to 80°C. How much ethyl alcohol runs out?

9. A sheet of brass has an area of 110 cm² at 10°C. What will be the area at a temperature of 100°C? *Ans.* 110.4 cm²

10. What volume would be occupied by a sample of gas that occupies 400 cm³ at 0°C and 76 cm pressure if it were cooled to −30°C and the pressure reduced to 73.5 cm?

11. The bag of a partially inflated balloon contains 5,000 ft³ of hydrogen at 75 cm Hg pressure and 27°C. The balloon rises to a height of 3 miles where the temperature is −13°C and the pressure is 40 cm Hg. Find the volume of the hydrogen under these circumstances. *Ans.* 8,125 ft³

12. A flask contains air at room temperature (17°C) and a pressure of 74 cm Hg. Find the pressure in the flask after it is sealed and cooled to −80°C.

13. Illuminating gas is stored in a tank designed so that the volume may change but the pressure remains constant. If the tank contains 30,000 ft³ under standard pressure, how much does the volume change when the temperature rises from 7 to 35°C? *Ans.* 3,000 ft³

14. Air pumped into a tank has a temperature of 90°F, and the pump stops when a pressure of 150 lb/in² in excess of atmospheric pressure is reached. What will be the pressure in the tank after the air has cooled down to 68°F?

15. An air bubble has a volume of 10 cm³ at the surface of a lake where the temperature is 27°C. What is its volume at a depth of 300 m where the temperature is 5°C? *Ans.* 0.3 cm³

16. A long U tube is filled with alcohol. One arm of the tube is kept at 10°C and the other arm at 30°C. Find the length of the column in the tube at the higher temperature, if the length of the column in the tube at the lower temperature is 60 cm.

17. At the beginning of the compression stroke of an automobile engine, the gas occupies a volume of 12 in.³ at atmospheric pressure. At the end of the compression the pressure is 8.6 atm and the volume 2.1 in.³ What is the temperature according to the general gas law, if the original temperature was 27°C? *Ans.* 178°C

18. Instruments for the study of the upper atmosphere are sent up in a free balloon. What volume would be assumed by 120 m³ of gas admitted at 2°C, and 75 cm pressure in a region where the pressure is 40 cm and the temperature −33°C?

19. A stratosphere balloon has a gas bag that has a volume of 500,000 ft³ when the barometer reads 75 cm Hg and the temperature is 20°C. Find its volume when the balloon has risen to such a height that the atmospheric pressure is 12 cm Hg and the temperature −33°C. *Ans.* 2.56 × 10⁶ ft³

20. A rod of steel and one of brass have exactly the same length, 120 cm, at 0°C. The rods are heated until they differ in length by 0.08 mm. What is the temperature?

21. A clock which has a brass pendulum beats seconds correctly when the temperature of the room is 22°C. How many seconds per day will it gain or lose when the temperature of the room is 16°C? *Ans.* Gains 5 sec

22. A brass pendulum is adjusted to beat seconds at 15°C. What will be the gain or loss per day if the temperature of the clock drops to 0°C?

23. A steel rod 25 cm long has a cross section of 0.8 cm². What force would be required to extend the bar by the same amount as the expansion produced by heating it through 10°C? *Ans.* 2,200 newtons

CHAPTER 21

Kinetic Theory of Gases

21.1. Brownian Motion. The molecular nature of matter is well established by chemical and physical evidence. For developing a theory of gases we shall assume that the gas is composed of a large number of molecules which are in constant motion and we shall attribute the pressure exerted by the gas to the transfer of momentum to the wall by the molecules which are bouncing off. Although we have previously advanced the idea that molecules are in constant motion, we have not yet discussed experimental evidence for this point of view.

Perhaps the simplest and the most direct evidence for the motion of molecules was noted by an English botanist, Robert Brown. With a microscope he observed that very fine particles held in suspension in water were constantly in motion. The smaller the particles, the more freely they moved. The motion is caused by the incessant bombardment of the particles by the molecules of the liquid in which they are suspended. Because of the minute size of the particles, the bombardment on one side is not always equal to the bombardment on the other. Hence, the particles are driven hither and thither. An approximate picture of the behavior of such small particles is obtained by projecting on a screen (Fig. 21.1) the shadows of finely divided glass particles that are set in motion by rapidly boiling mercury.

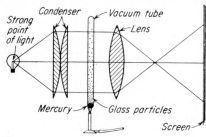

Fig. 21.1. Motions of glass particles illustrate the behavior of molecules.

21.2. Kinetic Theory of Gas Pressure. In many respects the behavior of gases is simpler than that of liquids or solids. To explain the physical properties of gases, we shall make the following assumptions:

1. A gas consists of very large numbers of molecules which are so small that the volume of the molecules themselves is negligibly small compared with the volume of the gas. One justification for this assumption is the

fact that the gas can be compressed so that it occupies a small fraction of its normal volume at atmospheric pressure. When a cubic centimeter of water at 100°C is converted to steam at 100°C, it occupies a volume of about 1,670 cm³. The distance between molecules in the steam is $\sqrt[3]{1,670}$ (roughly 12) times the distance between molecules in the liquid.

2. When the rapidly moving molecules collide with one another or with the walls of the container, the collisions are elastic.

3. For an *ideal* gas the attractive forces between molecules are negligible.

Let us now calculate the pressure exerted by a gas on the walls of a container due to the bombardment of the walls as the molecules strike against them. We begin with a single molecule of mass m moving with a velocity v_x parallel to the x axis in a cubical box of length L (Fig. 21.2) and compute the average force which this molecule exerts against one of the faces parallel to the YZ plane. As the molecule approaches the wall in question, the x component of its momentum is mv_x. After the collision the x component of the velocity is reversed, since we have postulated that the collision is elastic. The change of momentum is $2mv_x$. After the collision the molecule strikes the other parallel wall and eventually returns to the first wall. Between two successive collisions at this wall the molecule travels a distance $2L$. Therefore, the time between collisions at the same place is $2L/v_x$. The number of collisions per second is $v_x/2L$. Since at each collision the change of momentum is $2mv_x$, the change in momentum per second at one wall for one molecule is

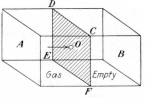

$$(2mv_x)\left(\frac{v_x}{2L}\right) = \frac{mv_x^2}{L}$$

Let there be n moles of identical molecules in the box. To find the total change in momentum per second at the wall in question, we must add the contributions of all these molecules of which there are $6.02 \times 10^{23}\, n$. (One mole contains 6.02×10^{23} molecules.) The number 6.02×10^{23} is known as Avogadro's number and is represented by N. The number of molecules in the box is therefore nN and the total change in momentum per second at the wall is given by

Fig. 21.2. A single molecule moving parallel to the x axis in a cubical box.

$$\text{Change in momentum per sec} = \frac{m}{L}\left(v_{x1}^2 + v_{x2}^2 + \cdots + v_{xNn}^2\right)$$
$$= \frac{nNm}{L}\frac{\left(v_{x1}^2 + v_{x2}^2 + \cdots + v_{xNn}^2\right)}{Nn}$$
$$= \frac{nNm}{L}\overline{v_x^2}$$

where $\overline{v_x^2}$ represents the average value of the square of v_x for all the molecules in the box.

By Newton's second law of motion the change in momentum per second is equal to the average force. Therefore

$$F = \frac{nNm\overline{v_x^2}}{L} = pL^2$$

since the pressure p is the ratio of the force to the area. Hence,

$$pL^3 = nNm\overline{v_x^2}$$

Now L^3 is just the volume V of the box, so that

$$pV = nNm\overline{v_x^2}$$

For a wall of the box parallel to the XZ plane, $pV = nNm\overline{v_y^2}$ and for a wall parallel to the XY plane, $pV = nNm\overline{v_z^2}$. We know from experience that the pressure due to the molecular bombardment is the same on all walls (we assume pressure due to the weight of the gas is negligible); thus we expect that $\overline{v_x^2} = \overline{v_y^2} = \overline{v_z^2}$. By the extension of the Pythagorean theorem to three dimensions, $\overline{v_x^2} + \overline{v_y^2} + \overline{v_z^2} = \overline{v^2}$, so that $\overline{v_x^2} = \overline{v^2}/3$ and we write

$$pV = \frac{nNm\overline{v^2}}{3} = \frac{2nN}{3}\left(\frac{1}{2}m\overline{v^2}\right) \tag{21.1}$$

The product of the pressure and the volume is given by two-thirds of the number of molecules multiplied by the average kinetic energy of translation of the molecules.

By the general gas law [Eq. (20.8)] $pV = nRT$. Consequently, $nRT = (2nN/3) \times (m\overline{v^2}/2)$ or

$$\frac{1}{2}m\overline{v^2} = \frac{3}{2}\frac{R}{N}T \tag{21.2}$$

R is the universal gas constant [8.317 joules/(mole) (K°)] and N is Avogadro's number. The expression on the left of Eq. (21.2) is the average kinetic energy of translation for the gas molecules and we see it is directly proportional to the absolute temperature. Thus, *the absolute temperature is a measure of the average translational kinetic energy of the molecules in a gas.* If we double the absolute temperature, we double this kinetic energy. If we wish to double the average velocity of the molecules in a gas sample, we must increase the absolute temperature by a factor of 4.

If we put into Eq. (21.2) the known values of R and N, we can compute the velocity of the molecules of a gas. As a particular example, let us choose nitrogen molecules and calculate the *effective velocity* of nitrogen molecules at 27°C. By the effective velocity we mean the velocity of a molecule which has the average energy. Hence,

$$\frac{1}{2} m v_{\text{eff}}^2 = \frac{1}{2} m \overline{v^2} = \frac{3}{2} \frac{R}{N} T \qquad (21.2a)$$

For nitrogen molecules at 27°C, one mole has a mass of 0.028 kg and one molecule a mass of $0.028/N$ kg.

$$\frac{1}{2} \frac{(0.028)}{N} v_{\text{eff}}^2 = \frac{3}{2} \times \frac{8.317}{N} \times 300$$

$$v_{\text{eff}}^2 = 26.7 \times 10^4 \text{ m}^2/\text{sec}^2$$

$$v_{\text{eff}} = 517 \text{ m/sec}$$

21.3. Dalton's Law of Partial Pressures. We have derived the equations for the pressure exerted by a gas for the case in which the gas contains only molecules of one kind. If the gas contains several different kinds of molecules, each kind rebounds from the walls and contributes to the pressure. The total pressure is the sum of the pressures which each of the various kinds would exert if that kind occupied the volume alone. We may write

$$p_t = p_1 + p_2 + p_3 + \cdots \qquad (21.3)$$

where p_t is the total pressure exerted by all the molecules and $p_1, p_2, p_3 \ldots$ are the pressures which molecules of type 1, 2, 3, . . . would exert if they filled the volume alone. This law is known as *Dalton's law of partial pressures.*

In the air we have a mixture of gases with nitrogen, oxygen, water vapor, carbon dioxide, argon, hydrogen, and many other kinds of molecules present. The atmospheric pressure is the pressure exerted by the nitrogen plus that due to oxygen, plus that due to each of the other atmospheric constituents. Equation (21.2) shows that the average kinetic energy is the same for each kind of molecule. If we apply this fact to compare the effective velocities of hydrogen and oxygen molecules at a given temperature, we have

$$\frac{3}{2} \frac{R}{N} T = \frac{1}{2} m_h v_h^2 = \frac{1}{2} m_0 v_0^2$$

where m_h and v_h are the mass and effective velocity of hydrogen molecules and m_0 and v_0 the corresponding quantities for oxygen molecules. Since $m_0 = 16 m_h$, $v_h = 4 v_0$. Thus, the effective speed of hydrogen molecules in the atmosphere is four times that of oxygen molecules.

21.4. Distribution of Molecular Velocities in Gases. In writing the expression for the pressure exerted by the ideal gas, we have assumed that a given molecule travels back and forth striking the walls without taking into account the effects of col-

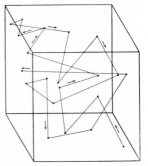

Fig. 21.3. Collisions of a molecule with other molecules and with the walls of the container.

lisions with other molecules. Although molecules collide frequently with other molecules (Fig. 21.3), these collisions are *elastic.* Therefore, the kinetic energies and momenta of two molecules after collisions add to the same value as before the collision. Although the velocity of any individual molecule undergoes sharp changes and is different one time from another, the average kinetic energy of the molecules is the same at a given temperature. Some molecules are moving rapidly and some slowly.   Figure 21.4 shows the distribution of velocities for gas molecules.

The distance a given molecule travels between collisions differs considerably from collision to collision but its average value is again well defined.   The average length of the path over a large number of collisions is called the *mean free path*.   For molecules of the air it is of the order of ten millionths of a centimeter.   Table 1 lists some of the important molecular quantities for oxygen and hydrogen molecules.

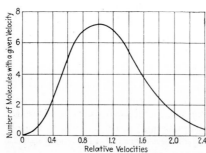

Fig. 21.4. Maxwellian distribution of speeds for gas molecules. The abscissa is the ratio of the speed to the most probable speed. The effective speed is 1.225 times the most probable speed, while the average speed is 1.13 times the most probable speed.

21.5. Specific Heats of Gases. The specific heat of any substance is defined as the amount of heat required to change the temperature of a unit mass of the substance one degree.   For gases the specific heat depends on how the heating is carried out.   It takes more heat to raise the temperature of a unit mass of gas 1° if we keep the pressure constant than it does if we keep the volume constant.

1. *The Specific Heat at Constant Volume.*   From Eq. (21.2) we know that $m\overline{v^2}/2 = 3RT/2N$.   Since N is the number of molecules in one mole and m the mass of an individual molecule, the product Nm is equal to M,

Table 1

MOLECULAR QUANTITIES AT 0°C AND PRESSURE OF 76 CM HG

	Hydrogen	Oxygen
Number of particles per cubic centimeter.....	2.69×10^{19}	2.69×10^{19}
Diameter of each molecule.................	$2.4 \ \times 10^{-10}$ m	$3.2 \ \times 10^{-10}$ m
Mass of each molecule....................	3.34×10^{-27} kg	$5.3 \ \times 10^{-26}$ kg
Mean free path..........................	$1.8 \ \times 10^{-7}$ m	$1.0 \ \times 10^{-7}$ m
Number of collisions per second.............	1.00×10^{10}	$4.6 \ \times 10^{9}$
Effective speed..........................	1,840 m/sec	461 m/sec
Average speed...........................	1,700 m/sec	425 m/sec
Most probable speed......................	1,500 m/sec	376 m/sec
Mass per cubic meter......................	0.0899 kg	1.43 kg
Volume per gram.........................	$1.11 \ \times 10^4$ cm³	699 cm³
Number of molecules in 1 g-mole............	6.025×10^{23}	6.025×10^{23}

the gram-molecular weight of the gas.   If we keep the gas at constant volume and if all the energy goes into additional kinetic energy of translation of the molecules, to raise the temperature of one mole 1° we must increase its kinetic energy by $3R/2$.   Hence, for any gas for which all the thermal energy is associated with the translational motion, the specific heat is given by $3R/2M$. This is the case for monatomic gases. Since $R = 1.987$ cal/mol (K°), we have the specific heat of the following monatomic gases: for helium

$$c_V = \frac{(3 \times 1.987)}{(2 \times 4)} = 0.745 \text{ cal/(g)(C°)}$$

for argon $c_V = (3 \times 1.987)/(2 \times 39.93) = 0.075$ cal/(g)(C°), etc. For any *monatomic* gas

$$c_V = \frac{3R}{2M} \tag{21.4}$$

For diatomic and triatomic gases the value $3R/2M$ gives a value for the specific heat which is too low. A diatomic molecule has not only its kinetic energy of translation increased when the temperature is raised,

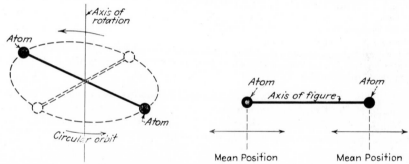

Fig. 21.5. A diatomic molecule may have kinetic energy of rotation as well as kinetic energy of translation.

Fig. 21.6. At a high temperature a diatomic molecule may have kinetic energy of vibration.

but also the kinetic energy of rotation. We may think of a diatomic molecule as a dumbbell which is rotating as it moves about (Fig. 21.5). When we raise the temperature, the kinetic energy of rotation increases as well as the kinetic energy of translation. This is the reason that the specific heat at constant volume for diatomic gases is greater than predicted by Eq. (21.4). At room temperature the specific heat at constant volume for most diatomic gases is given by $5R/2M$. At a high temperature it becomes still greater; the additional energy goes into exciting vibrations of the two atoms along the axis of the dumbbell (Fig. 21.6). For triatomic gases around room temperature the specific heat is $3R/M$ or more, depending on how much energy is associated with vibration.

2. *Specific Heat at Constant Pressure.* When a gas is kept at constant pressure, the heat required to increase the internal energy of the molecules is the same as when the gas is heated at constant volume. In addition, however, it is necessary to supply heat energy *to do the external work*

required to expand the gas. For example, if the gas is expanding in a cylinder closed by a moving piston, additional energy must be supplied to make up for the external work done against the piston. If the pressure remains constant, the additional work done is $p \Delta V$, where p is the pressure and ΔV the change in volume. This may be seen as follows:

$$\text{Work} = Fs = pAs$$

where F is the force, s the distance through which the piston moves, p the pressure, and A the area of the piston. The product As is the increase in volume ΔV of the gas during expansion. Therefore

$$\text{Work} = p \Delta V \tag{21.5}$$

Consider the work done when one mole of gas is heated one degree centigrade under constant pressure. By the general gas law $pV = RT$. If we raise the temperature $1°$ at constant pressure, we have

$$p(V + \Delta V) = R(T + 1)$$

Therefore, $p \Delta V = R$. Thus, the energy which must be supplied to one mole of gas at constant pressure to perform external work is R and the energy which must be added per unit mass of gas is R/M. Therefore, the specific heat of the gas at constant pressure is R/M greater than the specific heat at constant volume.

$$c_p = c_V + \frac{R}{M} \tag{21.6}$$

The ratio of the specific heat of the gas at constant pressure to the specific heat at constant volume is ordinarily represented by γ. For a monatomic gas c_p is $3R/2M$ and $c_p = 5R/2M$. Therefore

$$\gamma = \frac{c_p}{c_V} = \frac{5R/2M}{3R/2M} = \frac{5}{3}$$

for a *monatomic* gas.

For diatomic gases at room temperature,

$$c_V = \frac{5R}{2M} \quad \text{and} \quad \gamma = \frac{7R/2M}{5R/2M} = 1.4$$

21.6. Deviations from the General Gas Law. In our discussions of gases we have made two important assumptions which are not always justified. We have assumed (1) that the volume of the molecules themselves is negligible in comparison with the total space occupied by the gas and (2) that the attractive forces between gas molecules are negligible. For experiments with gases like oxygen and hydrogen at room temperature and ordinary pressures, these assumptions are justified. However, if they were true under all circumstances, we would never have molecules sticking together to form liquids or solids. Indeed, for those molecules or atoms for which the attractive forces are great, at room temperatures we find materials already in the form of solids or liquids.

Let us keep the temperature of a given mass of gas constant and study how the pressure and volume behave for a real gas. If Boyle's law held rigorously, the product pV would be constant for all pressures and volumes so long as the temperature was kept constant. But accurate observations show that the product is not constant (Fig. 21.7) when the pressure is varied over a large range. At exceedingly high pressures, the molecules are close together and the space occupied by the molecules themselves is no longer negligible. Therefore an increase

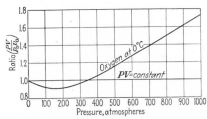

Fig. 21.7. Over a very broad range of pressures pV is not constant at a fixed temperature because the molecules occupy some volume themselves and because there are attractive forces between molecules.

in the pressure of the gas results in too small a decrease in volume, so that pV increases with p instead of remaining constant according to Boyle's law. At exceedingly low pressure the product pV decreases somewhat as p is increased.

Van der Waals has shown that the intermolecular attraction and the space occupied by the molecules themselves can be simply taken into account by a modification of the general gas law. According to Van der Waals, for one mole of gas

$$\left(p + \frac{a}{V^2}\right)(V - b) = RT \tag{21.7}$$

where a and b are constants characteristic of a given gas, but independent of temperature, pressure, and volume. The constant b is a correction to take account of the fact that the molecules themselves occupy a finite amount of space. A detailed analysis shows that b is four times the actual volume of the molecules in the mole of gas. The term a/V^2 takes account of the attractive forces between the molecules which have the effect of reducing the volume just as does the pressure.

PROBLEMS

1. If the average speed of a hydrogen molecule is 1 mi/sec at 27°C and 76 cm Hg pressure, find (a) the average speed of an oxygen molecule under the same conditions and (b) the average speed of a hydrogen molecule at 27°C and 100 cm Hg pressure.

Ans. (a) 0.25 mi/sec; (b) 1 mi/sec

2. Find the number of gas particles, each with a mass of 3.3×10^{-26} kg and an effective speed of 560 m/sec, that would maintain normal atmospheric pressure against the walls of a containing vessel with a volume of 5 cm³.

3. If the average speed of a hydrogen molecule is 1 mi/sec at 27°C, at what temperature is the average speed of 2 mi/sec?   *Ans.* 927°C

4. How long would it take for a toy balloon to deflate to half its original volume at atmospheric pressure, if it were losing hydrogen molecules at the rate of a million per second?   (Assume an original volume of 1 liter, 100 cm Hg pressure, and a constant temperature of 27°C.)

5. Compute the effective speed of a nitrogen molecule under standard conditions from the general gas law plus the fact that one gram-molecular weight occupies 22.4 liters under these conditions.   *Ans.* 490 m/sec

6. Calculate the effective speed of molecules of carbon monoxide under standard conditions if the density of the gas is 1.25 g/liter.

7. How many molecules of air remain in each cubic centimeter of a radio tube at 27°C in which the pressure has been reduced to 10^{-7} mm Hg?   *Ans.* 3.2×10^9

8. A vessel containing hydrogen is attached to a pump, and the pressure is reduced to 10^{-5} mm Hg at a temperature of 17°C.   How many molecules per cubic centimeter remain in the vessel?

9. The specific heats of air at constant pressure and at constant volume are 0.24 and 0.17 cal/(g)(C°), respectively.   If 1 kg of air is heated from 0 to 30°C at constant pressure, find (a) how much external work is done and (b) how much the kinetic energy of the air molecules is increased.   *Ans.* (a) 2100 cal; (b) 5100 cal

10. Pure oxygen at 0°C is enclosed in a cylinder having a volume of 15 liters.   If the pressure in the cylinder is 250 cm Hg, what is the mass of the enclosed gas?   How much pressure would it exert if the temperature were increased to 750°C?

11. A McLeod gauge can indicate pressures as low as 0.000001 mm Hg.   How many molecules per cubic centimeter of nitrogen would be required to produce this pressure at 0°C?   *Ans.* 3.54×10^{10}/cm³

12. How many molecules per cubic centimeter are there in a vessel in which the temperature is 27°C and the pressure 10^{-6} mm Hg?

13. A carefully evacuated vessel has a volume of 2 liters.   It develops a small leak through which 2 million molecules of air pass each second.   How long before the pressure of the air in the vessel will be 0.25 atm?   *Ans.* 6.7×10^{15} sec = 2.1 billion years

CHAPTER 22

Change of Phase

22.1. Change of Phase. The kinetic theory of matter leads naturally to an understanding of many properties of liquids and solids as well as of gases. When we reduce the temperature of a gas, we reduce the average kinetic energy of translation of the molecules. As the molecules move more and more slowly, attractive forces between molecules, which played a negligible role at high temperatures, become important. Eventually, groups of molecules stick together and fall to the bottom of the container. The gas is beginning to liquefy.

In the liquid phase molecules wander about freely but they find difficulty in leaving the surface (Chap. 10). If the temperature of the liquid is reduced, the energy of the molecules decreases still more. Eventually, the translational kinetic energy becomes so small that the molecule is trapped by the attractive forces exerted by its neighbors. Once the molecule is able only to vibrate about some equilibrium position, the material loses its fluid properties and retains its shape. We then speak of it as a *solid*. If each atom of the material is located in a particular place in a regular array, we have a *crystalline solid* of which diamond, quartz, and calcite are examples. In some cases each atom is confined to a small region about an equilibrium point by the attractive forces of neighboring particles, but no perfectly repetitive structure is formed. This is the case when glass cools and when butter solidifies. The structure is not crystalline.

As a solid is cooled, the energy associated with random motions of the particles is reduced to lower and lower values. If one attained the temperature of 0°K, the motions of all atoms would be reduced to their lowest possible value. At one time it was believed that this would correspond to a state of absolutely no motion, but modern quantum mechanics has shown there is necessarily some zero-point energy.

22.2. The Melting Point. If ice is heated, the temperature rises until it reaches 0°C and then remains stationary until all the ice is melted. Once the ice is all melted, the temperature of the water begins to rise.

The temperature at which the solid changes into liquid is called the melting point.   At the melting point more heat serves to hasten the melting process without any change of temperature.

The temperature at which the liquid changes into the solid state is its freezing point.   This temperature is ordinarily the same as the temperature at which the solid melts.   For crystalline substances, such as ice or copper, the freezing point and the melting point coincide and are sharply defined.   For substances that are not crystalline, such as wax or glass, the substance gradually softens in passing from the solid to the liquid state.   Such substances do not have a definite melting point.   In the cases of certain fats, the melting point is not the same as the freezing point.   For example, butter melts between 28 and 32°C and solidifies between 20 and 23°C.

22.3. Supercooling.   If a pure liquid is carefully protected from mechanical disturbances, it may be cooled below the temperature at which it normally solidifies.   Thus water has been cooled to about −40°C without becoming ice. The liquid at such a temperature is in a state of unstable equilibrium and immediately solidifies if it is disturbed or if a crystal of the solid is dropped into it.

22.4. Heat of Fusion.   To melt a solid like ice it is necessary to supply a given quantity of heat to each unit mass.   This is true even though the temperature of the ice at the beginning is the same as the temperature of the water at the end of the process.   The ice has a crystalline structure, and the heat that is supplied is necessary to tear down this structure.   Water in changing back to ice (in general, a liquid in changing back to a solid) gives up the heat that it absorbed in melting.   *The heat of fusion of a substance is the heat necessary to convert a unit mass of solid into liquid at the same temperature and pressure.*   To change 1 g of ice to water at 0°C requires 80 cal; to convert 1 lb of ice to water at 32°F requires 144 Btu.   Heats of fusion of several solids are listed in Appendix D, Table D.1.

Example.   In an experiment designed to measure the heat of fusion of ice 25 g of ice at 0°C were dropped into 195 g of water at 30°C contained in a copper calorimeter of mass 100 g.   The final temperature was 18°C.   Find the heat of fusion of ice.

$$\text{Heat gained} = \text{heat lost}$$
$$25L + 25 \times 1 \times (18 - 0) = 195 \times 1 \times (30 - 18) + 100 \times 0.093 \times (30 - 18)$$

where L is the latent heat of fusion and $25L$ is the heat needed to melt the ice

$$25L + 450 = 2{,}452$$
$$L = 80 \text{ cal/g}$$

22.5. Change of Volume during Freezing.   It is a familiar fact that ice floats (Fig. 22.1) and that pipes or bottles filled with water burst when frozen. One cubic foot of water makes about 1.09 ft³ of ice.   Cast iron and type metal behave like water in this respect.   They expand when they solidify, and for this reason they are suitable for making castings in which it is desired to reproduce the detail of a mold.   Most metals and other substances contract on solidification. This is one reason why gold and silver coins are stamped rather than cast.

That the forces exerted by freezing water are very large may be seen from the fact that they are sufficient to burst the strongest water pipes on a cold night. These forces are of importance in the formation of soils from rocks.   The water penetrates into the crevices in the rocks and freezes.   The expansion breaks off

Fig. 22.1. An iceberg, about nine-tenths of which is submerged. (*Underwood and Underwood.*)

fragments, which after a time are made into soil by this process.   The alternate freezing and thawing of soils tend to pulverize them.   Ice forming in the interstices of the soil serves to loosen compact land and give it better tilth.

The fact that water expands when it freezes is responsible for the fact that ice forms on top of a lake or stream rather than the bottom.   A layer of ice is an excellent insulation which protects all but the shallowest water from freezing to the bottom.   Fish and other water life can carry on in the water below the ice layer.

22.6. Effect of Pressure on the Melting Point.   Since an increase of pressure causes a body to contract, such an increase favors the liquid phase for any substance which contracts on melting and results in a lower melting point.   Ice contracts when it melts; therefore the melting point is lowered by application of pressure.   Careful experiments show that this lowering is 0.0075°C for an increase of 1 atm of pressure (Fig. 22.2).   If a substance expands upon melting (Fig. 22.3), its melting point is raised by the application of pressure.

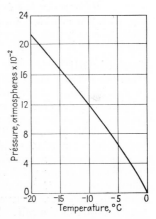

Fig. 22.2. The melting point of ice as a function of pressure.

The effect of pressure on the melting point of ice may be shown by taking a piece of ice (Fig. 22.4) and hanging over it a loop of wire from which a heavy weight is supported.   The pressure of the wire on the ice lowers the melting point of the ice, so that it is in a condition to melt as soon as the necessary heat is supplied. In order to melt each gram, it is necessary to supply 80 cal. This heat is taken from the water above the wire, causing it to freeze again. This process continues until the wire cuts its way through the block of ice, leaving the block as solid as it was at the beginning of the experiment. The process is called *regulation*.

22.7. Freezing Point of Solutions. When any material is dissolved in water, the freezing point of the solution is lower than the freezing point of water. This is also true for other liquids. The freezing point of the solution is always lower than that of the pure solvent. This fact is used to prevent the water in the cooling system of automobiles from freezing.

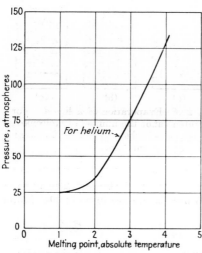

For solutions that are not too concentrated, the lowering of the freezing point is proportional to the number of

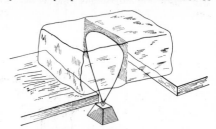

Fig. 22.3. The melting point of any substance which expands as it melts is raised by an increase in pressure.

Fig. 22.4. A regelation experiment in which ice melts under pressure and refreezes above the wire.

dissolved particles per unit volume. A given number of salt (NaCl) molecules lower the freezing point more than an equal number of sugar molecules, because the salt ionizes, thus producing two particles per dissolved molecule.

When a dilute solution begins to freeze, only solvent freezes out. This makes the remainder of the solution more concentrated and lowers its freezing point still further. This process continues until the solution becomes saturated. Then both dissolved substance and solvent freeze out in such a way that the concentration of the solution remains unchanged. Figure 22.5 represents the relation between the freezing point and the percentage of salt in a solution. The freezing point decreases as the pure solvent freezes out, and the concentration of the solution thus increases. Curve *AB* shows the relation between temperature and concentration of the salt. The temperature at which the solvent and the dissolved substance crystallize out as a mixture is called the *eutectic temperature*. If the temperature of the solution is higher than the eutectic temperature and the solution is saturated, the dissolved substance crystallizes out as the temperature is lowered. The line *BC* represents the relation between the temperature and the concentration.

22.8. Evaporation. The molecules of a liquid are in constant motion with varying velocities. When the liquid is heated, the velocities are increased and the spaces between the molecules are increased. Sooner or later some of the molecules near the surface attain sufficient velocity to escape (Fig. 22.6). Only the more rapidly moving molecules can escape, as the forces of attraction due to the other molecules are sufficient to hold

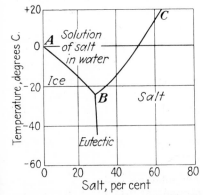

Fig. 22.5. Freezing point of NaCl solution as a function of salt concentration.

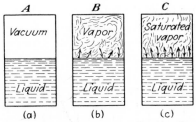

Fig. 22.6. Evaporation of a liquid. For a saturated vapor the number of molecules escaping per unit time is equal to the number returning per unit time.

the more slowly moving molecules in the liquid. Since only the more rapidly moving molecules escape from the surface, the average speed of the molecules in the liquid decreases, and the temperature of the liquid is lowered during rapid evaporation.

22.9. Saturated Vapor. If the space above the surface of the liquid is enclosed, some molecules of vapor return to the surface of the liquid and are captured. As more and more molecules escape, the number returning to the surface increases also. When the number of molecules returning to the surface is equal to the number escaping from it, the space above the liquid is said to be *saturated*. The vapor then above the liquid is called a *saturated vapor*. The pressure of the vapor for a given temperature depends on the nature of the liquid (Fig. 22.7). If the temperature of a saturated vapor remains unchanged, the vapor condenses and changes into liquid when an attempt is made to increase the pressure. *The saturated vapor pressure of any given liquid depends only on the temperature.*

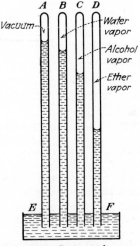

Fig. 22.7. Saturated vapor pressures of different liquids at same temperature are different.

Curves showing the saturated vapor pressures of several liquids as a function of temperature are presented in Figs. 22.8 and 22.9. As the temperature of the liquid increases, the pressure of the saturated vapor also increases. In the case of water, when the temperature becomes 100°C, the vapor pressure is 76 cm Hg. A vapor-pressure curve may be obtained by measuring the difference in level between the surfaces of mercury in the apparatus of Fig. 22.10 as the temperature is increased.

22.10. Heat of Vaporization.   Just as a certain amount of heat is required to convert a unit mass of ice into water without changing its temperature, so a certain amount of heat is required to change a unit mass of water into steam without changing its temperature. When the steam condenses, this heat is liberated.

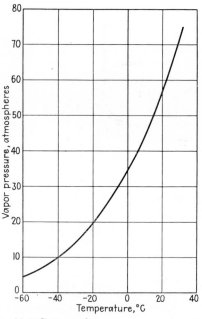

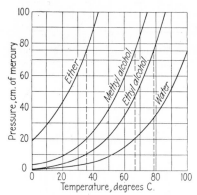

Fig. 22.8. Saturated vapor-pressure curves for water, ethyl alcohol, methyl alcohol, and ether. Under 1 atm (76 cm Hg) pressure each liquid boils at the temperature indicated by the appropriate dotted line.

Fig. 22.9. Saturated vapor pressure of carbon dioxide as a function of the temperature.

The heat of vaporization of a substance is the heat necessary to change a unit mass of the liquid to the vapor state without any change in the temperature and pressure.   For water at 100°C and 1 atm pressure it is found to be 540 cal/g or 970 Btu/lb.   It takes more than five times as much heat to change 1 g of water at 100°C into steam at 100°C as it takes to heat that same gram of water from 0 to 100°C.   The heats of vaporization of several other liquids are listed in Appendix D, Table D.2.

The heat of vaporization depends on the temperature (and pressure) at which the change takes place.   The higher the temperature, the easier it is to evaporate the liquid; i.e., the higher the temperature, the less the heat of vaporization (Figs. 22.11 and 22.12).

The following experiment may be used to determine the heat of vaporization of water.   Take a calorimeter C (Fig. 22.13) filled with a known weight of water and a boiler B.   Pass dry steam from the boiler into the calorimeter.   To prevent water from being carried over, the steam passes through the trap D, which

atches the condensed droplets.   Note the temperature of the water in the calo-
imeter at the beginning and its temperature after steam has been condensed in
⸬.   The mass of condensed steam is found by weighing the calorimeter after the
team has been condensing in it for a sufficient time to produce the desired rise

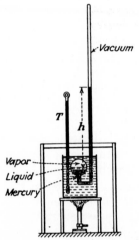

Fig. 22.10. Apparatus for measuring the
aturated vapor pressure of a liquid.

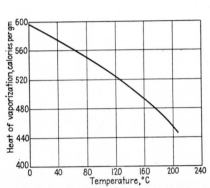

Fig. 22.11. The heat of vaporization of
water as a function of temperature.

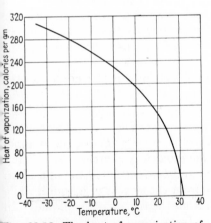

Fig. 22.12. The heat of vaporization of
carbon dioxide as a function of temperature.

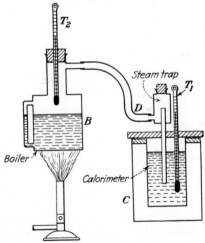

Fig. 22.13. Apparatus for measuring the
heat of vaporization.

in temperature.   The latent heat of vaporization of water can now be calculated
as illustrated below.

Example.   Dry steam at 212°F is condensed in a large calorimeter of water
equivalent 0.6 lb, which contains 6.2 lb of water at 42°F.   The final temperature of

82°F is reached after 0.25 lb of steam, has been condensed.   Find the latent heat of vaporization V as given by these data.

$$\text{Heat gained} = \text{heat lost}$$
$$6.2 \times 1 \times (82 - 42) + 0.6 \times (82 - 42) = 0.25V + 0.25 \times 1 \times (212 - 82)$$
$$248 + 24 = 0.25V + 32.5$$
$$V = 958 \text{ Btu/lb}$$

The correct value is 970 Btu/lb.

When a liquid is evaporating, heat is taken from the remaining liquid and the surrounding bodies.   The withdrawal of this heat causes their temperatures to decrease.   For this reason the evaporation of the water sprinkled on the sidewalk causes the air to become cooler.   The evaporation of perspiration from the skin lowers the temperature of the body.

22.11. Boiling Point of Water.

If water is heated in a flask, air bubbles may escape, but no boiling occurs until the temperature reaches 100°C if the ambient pressure is 76 cm Hg.   Eventually bubbles forming at the bottom of the flask rise to the surface.   That temperature at which vapor bubbles reach the surface is the *boiling point* or *boiling temperature*.

The boiling point can be defined in another way.   Let p be the pressure on the surface of the liquid. This pressure is, according to Pascal's principle, transmitted throughout the liquid.   Hence, the pressure that a bubble of vapor inside the liquid must sustain is p plus the hydrostatic pressure due to the liquid above it.   Until the pressure of the vapor in the bubble becomes as great as p, the bubble collapses before it reaches the surface of the liquid.   *The boiling point can then be defined as the temperature at which the pressure of the saturated vapor of the liquid is equal to the applied pressure.*

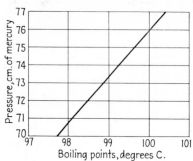

Fig. 22.14. Change of boiling point of water with pressure.

The distinction between *evaporation* and *boiling* should now be clear. *Evaporation* is the escape of molecules from the *surface* of a liquid, while *boiling* is the escape of vapor bubbles from the *volume* of the liquid.   In both cases we have a change of phase from liquid to gas.   This phase change is called *vaporization*.

Since the boiling point of a liquid is the temperature at which the vapor pressure of the liquid is the same as the applied pressure, it follows at once that when the applied pressure is changed, the boiling point also changes.   Figure 22.14 shows how the boiling point of water depends on pressure.   The boiling point is given as a function of pressure in Appendix

D, Tables D.3 and D.4.   On the top of a mountain atmospheric pressure
is less than at the base; thus the temperature at which water boils is lower.

The influence of pressure on the boiling point can be shown by filling a flask
(Fig. 22.15) half full of water and boiling it vigorously for some time to remove the
air from above the water.   Insert a rubber stopper in the flask, rendering the
flask airtight.   Remove the flask immediately from the flame.   Invert the flask,
and pour cold water on the bottom.   This cold water causes some of the vapor in
the flask to condense, and the pressure on the hot water in the flask is reduced
sufficiently to allow the water to begin boiling again.

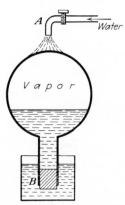

Fig. 22.15. The boiling point is lowered
by reducing the pressure above the
liquid.

Fig. 22.16. Union Geyser, in the Shoshone
Basin, erupts from three sinter cones simultaneously.   The highest jet reaches
an altitude of 114 ft.   (*Courtesy of Carnegie Institution of Washington.*)

The effect of pressure on the boiling point of water is well illustrated in the
action of geysers (Fig. 22.16).   If it is 100 ft down from the surface of a narrow
column of water to a cavity surrounded by hot rocks, the pressure at these rocks
is about 4 atm, three of the four being due to the column of water.   At this pressure water boils between 140 and 150°C.   Once water in the cavity begins to
boil, bubbles rush up the column carrying quantities of water with them, thus
reducing the pressure at the cavity and encouraging more rapid boiling until the
temperature of the water in the cavity is lowered to the point where boiling ceases.

In the pressure cooker the increased pressure results in a higher boiling point
for water and a higher cooking temperature.   On the other hand, when sirups or
milk are to be evaporated, they may be placed in "vacuum pans" so that boiling
can be carried out at a reduced temperature, thereby eliminating undesirable
changes which would occur at the normal boiling temperature.

22.12. Boiling Point of Solutions.   When water has some substance like sugar dissolved in it, the temperature at which it boils is
raised.   The amount the boiling point is raised is proportional to the
amount of the substance dissolved in the water.   In making candies or
sirups, the temperature is taken as a means of determining the concen-

tration of the solution. By observing the temperature at which the
solution is boiling, it is possible to know when the candy or sirup has been
boiled sufficiently long. When vegetables, fruits, meats, etc., are boiled
in water, some of their contents dissolve in the water. This raises the
boiling point slightly, so that the water boils above 212°F. The effect of
a dissolved substance on the vapor pressure and the boiling point is
shown in Fig. 22.17. The continuous curve gives the relation between
the temperature and the vapor pressure of the pure solvent, and the
dotted curve the same relation for the solution.

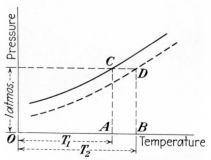

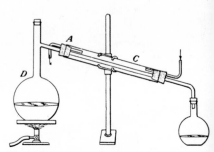

Fig. 22.17. The boiling point of a solution. The addition of a salt or other
solute raises the boiling point.

Fig. 22.18. Fractional distillation of liquids. The more volatile components
evaporate first.

22.13. Distillation. When solids, like salt or sugar, are dissolved in liquids,
the vapor that rises above the liquid does not contain the dissolved substance.
To obtain pure water from water containing solids in solution, it is only necessary
to evaporate the water and condense the vapor. The solids are left behind.
The way in which this is ordinarily done is represented in Fig. 22.18.

22.14. Sublimation. If a substance, such as solid camphor or solid
iodine, is left for some time in a closed vessel, the sides of the vessel
become covered with small crystals of the substance. This is due to
the fact that vapor which is given off by the solid is afterward condensed
on the sides of the vessel. This escape of molecules directly from a solid
without passing through the liquid phase is called *sublimation*. In like
manner, the vapor may go directly to the solid state. For most solids,
the vapor pressure is nearly zero at ordinary temperatures, but in many
cases the sense of smell tells us that some vapor is being given off. For
ice at 0°C, the vapor pressure is 4.6 mm Hg; as the temperature decreases,
the vapor pressure becomes smaller.

*The heat of sublimation is the heat necessary to change a unit mass of a
substance from the solid to the vapor state without change of temperature.*
Vapor-pressure curves (Figs. 22.19 and 22.20) showing the vapor pressure
when a solid is in equilibrium with its vapor may be plotted for solids
just as for liquids. Such a curve is called a *sublimation curve*.

22.15. Triple Point. Under certain conditions of temperature and pressure a liquid may be in equilibrium with its vapor. On a temperature-pressure diagram these conditions are represented by the vapor-tension curve. Similarly, a solid may be in equilibrium with its vapor; the conditions are represented by the sublimation curve. In like manner, a curve may be drawn showing the relation between the

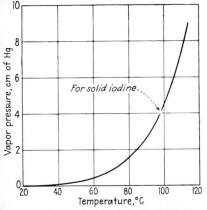

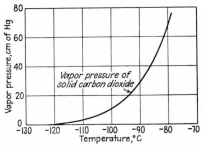

Fig. 22.19. Vapor pressure of solid iodine as a function of temperature.

Fig. 22.20. The vapor pressure of solid carbon dioxide ("dry ice") increases rapidly with the temperature.

temperature and pressure when a solid is in equilibrium with the liquid. If all these curves are drawn for a substance like water (Fig. 22.21), they intersect at a point called the *triple point*. It indicates the temperature and pressure at which the solid, vapor, and liquid can exist together with-

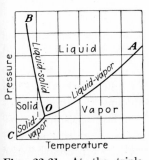

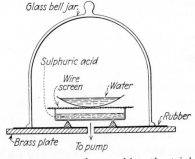

Fig. 22.21. At the triple point O solid, liquid, and vapor are all in equilibrium.

Fig. 22.22. Apparatus for reaching the triple point. Evacuation of the bell jar causes the water to boil at room temperature.

out one of them gaining in mass at the expense of the others. At this temperature and pressure, the solid, liquid, and vapor are in equilibrium. There is only one such point for a simple substance like water.

The triple point for water can be reached by the following experiment. Some water is placed on a watch glass under a bell jar (Fig. 22.22). Evacuation of the bell jar produces boiling, the heat for which is removed from the water which is cooled. Eventually the temperature falls to the point at which water is simultaneously boiling and freezing. With care one can reach the triple point for water which is at a temperature of 0.0076°C and a pressure of 4.6 mm Hg. If evacuation is continued and the pressure is reduced below 4.6 mm Hg, only the solid and vapor phases can exist in equilibrium. A wafer of ice remains on the watch glass.

22.16. The Critical Point. If an *unsaturated* vapor is enclosed in a cylinder *HFEG* (Fig. 22.23) and piston *M* is moved in while the *temperature of the vapor remains constant*, the pressure at first increases as the volume is decreased as represented by the curve *AB*. Near *A* Boyle's law is almost followed, but deviations increase as *B* is approached. At *B* the vapor is *saturated* and liquefaction begins. Along *BC* the volume

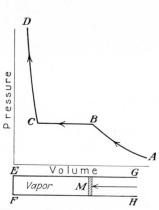

Fig. 22.23. Isothermal (constant temperature) curve for a vapor.

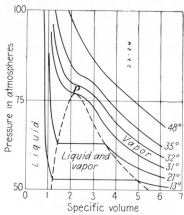

Fig. 22.24. Isothermal curves for carbon dioxide. Only the gaseous phase can exist above the critical temperature.

decreases while the pressure remains constant (showing that Boyle's law does not apply to saturated vapors). Meantime, the quantity of vapor decreases and that of liquid increases. At *C* liquefaction is complete. A further application of pressure to the piston causes a small decrease in the volume of the liquid, and the curve *CD* representing the relation between the pressure and the volume of the liquid becomes very steep. The curve *ABCD* shows the relation between the volume and the pressure when the *temperature is kept constant;* it is called an *isothermal* curve.

If this process be carried out at higher and higher temperatures (Fig. 22.24), the horizontal part of the curve becomes shorter until a temperature is reached at which the horizontal portion disappears and is replaced by a slight bend in the curve. At a temperature just below this, it is possible to liquefy the vapor by the application of pressure alone; at temperatures above this, it is impossible to liquefy the vapor, however great the pressure.   The highest temperature at which it is possible to liquefy a vapor is called the *critical temperature*.   The point *P* (Fig. 22.24) at which the horizontal part of the isothermal just disappears is known as the *critical point*.   The pressure and specific volume (volume per unit mass) of the vapor at the point *P* are known as the *critical pressure* and *critical volume*, respectively.

   The isothermals of Fig. 22.24 refer to carbon dioxide.   Its critical temperature is 31.1°C and its critical pressure 77 atm.   If a heavy-walled glass tube (Fig. 22.25) closed at both ends is partly filled with liquid carbon dioxide, the remainder of the tube being filled with the saturated vapor of carbon dioxide, at room

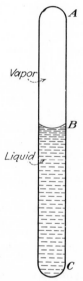

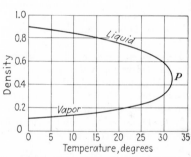

Fig. 22.25. As the temperature approaches the critical temperature, the surface of separation between liquid and vapor disappears.

Fig. 22.26. Densities of vapor and liquid near the critical point.   At the critical point liquid and vapor have the same density.

temperature there is equilibrium between the liquid and its vapor.   As the temperature of the tube and its contents is increased, the meniscus marking the boundary between the liquid and the vapor becomes less distinct until it finally disappears.   The temperature at which the meniscus disappears is the critical temperature.   The densities of liquid and vapor carbon dioxide are shown in Fig. 22.26 as functions of temperature.

   To liquefy a gas, it is necessary to cool it below its critical temperature and then apply sufficient pressure to produce liquefaction.   Most of the so-called "permanent" gases have low critical temperatures and require the application of large pressures (Table 1).

Table 1

CRITICAL TEMPERATURE, BOILING POINT, AND FREEZING POINT OF COMMON GASES

Name of gas	Freezing point, °C	Boiling point, °C	Critical temperature, °C
Helium..............	−272	−268.8	−267.9
Hydrogen............	−259	−252.7	−239.9
Argon...............	−189	−186.0	−122.0
Nitrogen............	−210	−195.7	−147.1
Oxygen..............	−219	−182.9	−118.8

PROBLEMS

1. If the specific heat of snow is 0.5 cal/(g)(C°), how much heat energy is required to turn 100 kg of snow at −10°C into water at the melting point?   *Ans.* 8500 kcal

2. A specimen of copper with a mass of 500 g is heated to 200°C and placed on a mass of ice. If 115 g of ice is melted, what is the specific heat of copper?

3. Four ice cubes at 0°C, each of 25 cm³ volume and 0.9 specific gravity, are dropped in a glass and 200 cm³ of water at 20°C are added. If the effects of the glass and of the losses are negligible, how many grams of ice are left when the water has cooled to 0°C?   *Ans.* 40 g

4. A sphere of iron weighing 180 g is heated in an oil bath and then placed on a block of ice, causing 50 g of ice to be melted. What was the temperature of the iron?

5. One hundred grams of ice at 0°C are dropped into 380 g of water at 30°C contained in a 200-g copper calorimeter. The final temperature is 8°C. Find the heat of fusion of ice.   *Ans.* 79.6 cal/g

6. An experiment on the heat of fusion of ice is to be performed in a room at 18°C. The mass of water in the calorimeter is 250 g and the quantity of ice to be melted is 40 g. It is desired to have the initial temperature of the water as much above room temperature as the final temperature will be below. What must be the initial temperature? (Neglect the heat capacity of the calorimeter.)

7. What power is required to melt 50 kg of ice at 0°C and to raise the temperature of the water to 100°C in 300 sec?   *Ans.* 126 kw

8. Find the number of Btu required to heat 6 lb of ice from a temperature of 12°F to the melting point, to melt it, and then to heat the water to the boiling point. Specific heat of ice = 0.5 Btu/(lb)(F°).

9. If 100 cm³ of saturated pure ether vapor at 25°C exert a pressure of 53 cm of Hg, find the pressure if the volume is reduced at 50 cm³ without changing the temperature.   *Ans.* 53 cm Hg

10. Water produced by melting ice comes from a refrigerator at a temperature of 45°F and the quantity obtained in 2 hr is 7 lb. How many Btu of heat penetrate the walls of the refrigerator per hour?

11. Steam at 100°C is received by a radiator and water at 80°C leaves. (*a*) How many grams of steam are required per hour if the radiator delivers 10⁶ cal/hr? (*b*) What fraction of the heat is associated with the cooling of the water?
                                                        Ans. (*a*) 1.79 kg; (*b*) 3.6 per cent

12. A condenser receives steam at 100°C and changes it to water at 45°C. The cooling is done by water which enters at 15°C and leaves at 40°C. How much cooling water is required for each kilogram of steam condensed?

13. A 200-g copper calorimeter contains 300 g of water at 15°C. How many grams of steam at 100°C would have to be added to raise the temperature to 75°C?

Ans. 33.9 g

14. How much steam at 150°C will be needed to turn 120 g of ice at −15°C to water at 40°C? Specific heat of ice = 0.5; specific heat of steam = 0.48 cal/(g)(C°).

15. How many pounds of coal must be burned to produce 100 lb of steam at 290°F if one starts with water at 50°F and 80 per cent of the heat of combustion goes into the water? Take the heat of combustion of coal to be 11,000 Btu/lb and the specific heat of steam to be 0.5 Btu/(lb)(F°). *Ans.* 13.3 lb

16. A steel sphere with a mass of 162.82 g is placed in an atmosphere of steam at 100°C and after reaching equilibrium is weighed with the water condensed on it. The observed weight is 164.04 g. What was the original temperature of the sphere?

17. How many calories are required to heat 100 g of mercury from 20 to 357°C and to vaporize it at that temperature? *Ans.* 7.92 kcal

18. How much heat is required to change 25 lb of ice at 10°F to steam at 340°F? The specific heat of ice is 0.50 Btu/(lb)(F°) and that of steam is 0.48 Btu/(lb)(F°).

19. If 500 g of ice at 0°C and 20 g of steam at 100°C are mixed with 480 g of water at 30°C in a calorimeter with a water equivalent of 20 g, find the final temperature. How much ice remains? *Ans.* 0°C; 153 g

20. Into a copper calorimeter that weighs 200 g there was passed 18 g of steam at 150°C. The calorimeter contained 200 g of water and a certain amount of ice. The ice and water were at 0°C. The final temperature was 35°C. How much ice was in the calorimeter?

21. A calorimeter contains 400 g of water at 0°C and 40 g of ice. The mass of the calorimeter is 150 g and its specific heat is 0.12 cal/(g)(C°). How many grams of steam at 100°C must be introduced into the water to make the final temperature 50°C?

Ans. 44 g

22. Ten grams of steam at a temperature of 100°C were passed into a copper calorimeter containing a given amount of water. The initial temperature of the water was 12°C, its final temperature 38°C, and the mass of the calorimeter was 250 g. Find the mass of the water in the calorimeter.

23. If the specific heat of water vapor is 0.5 cal/(g)(C°) and the heat of vaporization at 100°C is 540 cal/g, calculate the approximate heat of vaporization of water at 90°C. (*Hint:* By conservation of energy it should take same amount of energy to change 1 g of water at 90° to 1 g of water vapor at 100°C whether the evaporation is done first or last.) *Ans.* 545 cal/g

CHAPTER 23

Transfer of Heat

23.1. Heat-transfer Processes. There are three natural processes by which heat energy is transferred from one point to another.

1. *Conduction is the process by which heat energy is transferred from molecule to molecule in a substance by collisions.*

Heat is transferred by conduction from the bowl to the handle of a spoon when the bowl is placed in a hot liquid. Conduction occurs in solids, liquids, and gases. It is the only method by which heat is transferred through opaque solids. The molecules in the hotter part of the material vibrate with greater amplitude than those of the colder part. The molecules with greater thermal energy pass part of this energy to their neighbors, which in turn pass energy to their own neighbors. In most materials this transfer occurs because of intermolecular collisions, but in metals free electrons are responsible for most of the transfer of thermal energy between molecules. These same electrons are responsible for electric conductivity and it is for this reason that the best thermal conductors are also the best electric conductors.

2. *Convection is the process of heat transfer by the actual movement of the heated material itself.*

Steam produced in a boiler may be transported to radiators throughout a building. The transfer of heat by moving the hot steam is a convective process. Convection is ordinarily the most important heat-transfer process for liquids and gases. The distribution of heat in practically all houses and buildings is achieved by means of convection currents of heated air, hot water, or steam.

3. *Radiation is the transmission of energy through electromagnetic waves.*

The earth's primary source of energy is the radiation from the sun. Part of this energy is in the form of visible light, but much more of it comes in the form of infrared rays which have wavelengths too long for the eye to see. Radiation traverses a vacuum as well as transparent media.

In the radiation process the molecules of a body at a higher temperature

258

emit energy as radiation, which passes to the cooler body where it is absorbed and reconverted to thermal energy. Radiation is of primary importance for bodies at high temperatures and for transmission across regions where there is no material medium. For temperatures only 100°C or so above or below room temperature, radiation is relatively unimportant compared to conduction and convection for most material mediums.

If one has a steam radiator to provide heat in a room, all three processes play a role in transferring the heat. Conduction brings the heat from the steam to the outside of the radiator. From here the primary heat transfer is by convection, although radiation does play a role in distributing the heat. The first evidence that convection is of principal importance is the fact that a person several feet from the radiator feels equally warm on both sides. It is characteristic of radiation transfer that the energy moves in straight lines from the heat source to the point where it is absorbed. The familiar roast-one-side, freeze-the-other situation, which arises when one has an outdoor bonfire on a cold night, is typical of radiative transfer.

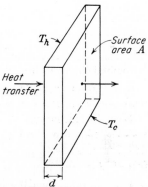

23.2. Conduction. If heat is to be conducted through a material, there must be a difference in temperature between two regions. If we have a slab of material (Fig. 23.1) and a constant temperature difference is maintained between the two faces, the heat Q conducted through this slab is proportional to the area A of the slab, to the temperature difference

Fig. 23.1. The heat transferred per unit time through a slab of material depends on the thickness, area, and material of the slab and on the temperature difference between its surfaces.

$(t_h - t_c)$ between the two faces, and to the time the temperature difference is maintained. It is inversely proportional to the thickness d of the slab.

$$Q = \frac{kA(t_h - t_c)\ \text{time}}{d} \qquad (23.1)$$

The proportionality constant k for a given material is called the *coefficient of thermal conductivity*. The coefficients of thermal conductivity of a number of common materials are listed in Table 1. In the metric system k is usually given as *the quantity of heat in calories which flows through one square centimeter of area in one second when a temperature difference of one centigrade degree is maintained across a thickness of one centimeter.* In the British system of units k is numerically equal to the number of Btu conducted per hour through an area of one square foot when a temperature difference of one Fahrenheit degree is maintained across a thickness of one inch.

Table 1
THERMAL CONDUCTIVITIES

Substance	Thermal conductivity, cal/(sec)(cm)(C°)	Substance	Thermal conductivity, cal/(sec)(cm)(C°)
Aluminum..........	0.50	Sand (white dry).....	0.00093
Air..............	0.000055	Sawdust............	0.00012
Brass.............	0.24	Silver...............	0.99
Copper............	0.918	Soil (dry)...........	0.00033
Cork.............	0.00011	Water..............	0.00143
Glass.............	0.0015	Wood (across grain)..	0.0003
Ice...............	0.00396	Zinc...............	0.265
Rock or glass wool..	0.00009		

To obtain value in Btu-in./(hr)(ft²)(F°), multiply by 2,900.

In problems of thermal conductivity it is imperative that one use the actual temperatures of the slab faces in Eq. (23.1). For example, if one calculates the heat conducted through a glass window when the indoor temperature is 70°F and the outdoor temperature is 0°F, he obtains a heat loss which is far too great if he puts 70°F as t_h and 0°F as t_c. Actually, the temperature of the inner surface of the glass under conditions of this sort might well be 20° lower than the 70°F of the air in the room while the outer face of the glass may similarly be some 20F° or more warmer than the outside air. There are major temperature drops in the thin air layers adjacent to each side of the glass. Equation (23.1) gives acceptable values of Q only when the actual surface temperatures are used.

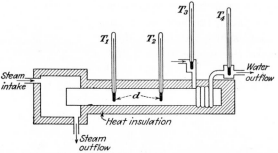

Fig. 23.2. Apparatus for measuring the thermal conductivity of a solid rod.

An apparatus for measuring the coefficient of thermal conductivity of a good conductor such as copper is represented in Fig. 23.2. It consists of a rod, the coefficient of thermal conductivity of which is to be determined. This rod is typically about 30 cm long and has a diameter of about 3 cm. On one end is soldered a copper box through which steam may be passed to make the temperature of that end of the rod about 100°C. Around the other end is soldered a coil of copper tubing through which cold water is circulated. The temperature of this water as it enters is found by means of the thermometer T_3, and its temperature as it leaves is read on the thermometer T_4. The difference in temperature between ingoing and outgoing water multiplied by the mass of water gives numerically the quantity of heat that has flowed down the rod. The coil and the rod are carefully lagged with felt to prevent heat losses. Two small holes drilled at right angles to the axis of the rod contain thermometers T_1 and T_2 by which the fall of temperature across the thickness d is measured.

Example. In measuring the thermal conductivity of a rod (Fig. 23.2), the following data were obtained. Temperature of ingoing water = 20.0°C; temperature of outgoing water = 30.0°C. Temperature t_h read by thermometer T_1 = 80.0°C; t_c = 60.0°C. Distance between thermometers = 10 cm; area of rod = 20 cm². Mass of water flowing through box = 650 g in a time of 180 sec. Find the coefficient of thermal conductivity.

Heat gained by water = mass of water $\times$ temp. change $\times$ sp ht
$$= (650 \times 10) \times 1 = 6500 \text{ cal}$$

$$Q = \frac{kA(t_h - t_c)}{d} \text{ (time)}$$

$$6,500 = k \times 20 \times {}^{20}\!/_{10} \times 180 = k \times 20 \times 2 \times 180$$

$$k = \frac{6,500}{20 \times 2 \times 180} = \frac{6,500}{7,200} = 0.90 \text{ cal/(sec)(cm)(C°)}$$

The ratio of the temperature change Δt to the thickness over which it occurs is called the *temperature gradient*. In the example above it is given by $\Delta t/d = (t_h - t_c)/d = (80 - 60)\text{C°}/10 \text{ cm} = 2 \text{ C°/cm}$.

The thermal conductivity of carbon (Fig. 23.3) increases with the temperature. On the other hand, the thermal conductivity of metals decreases with an increase of the temperature. The thermal

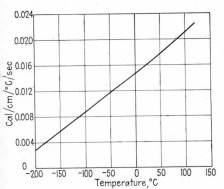

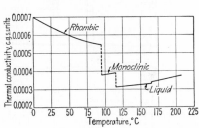

Fig. 23.3. The thermal conductivity of carbon increases with a rise in temperature.

Fig. 23.4. The thermal conductivity of sulfur changes when the crystalline form changes.

conductivity changes abruptly when a substance like sulfur (Fig. 23.4) changes from one crystalline state to another.

Very often the walls of a house or of a refrigerator consist of two or three layers of different materials. To compute the heat conducted through such a system of layers, we make use of the fact that the only heat which can be conducted through the second layer is that which has already passed through the first layer, and so forth. When equilibrium is established, the heat conducted per unit area per second through each of the layers is the same.

Example. The wall of a shed in which ice is stored consists of an outer layer of wood 2 cm thick and an inner layer of rock wool 3 cm thick. Find the heat conducted through 50 m² of the wall in 1 hr when the outer wood surface is at 20°C and the inner rock-wool surface is at 5°C. Also find the temperature of the wood–rock-wool interface.

Let t be the temperature of the interface. The heat conducted through both layers is the same, so that

$$Q = \left[\frac{ka\ \Delta t(\text{time})}{d}\right]_{\text{wood}} = \left[\frac{ka\ \Delta t(\text{time})}{d}\right]_{\text{rock wool}}$$

$$Q = \frac{3 \times 10^{-4} \times 50 \times 10^4(20 - t) \times 3{,}600}{2} = \frac{9 \times 10^{-5} \times 50 \times 10^4(t - 5) \times 3{,}600}{3}$$

Solving for t yields $t = 17.5°C$, the temperature of the interface. If we put this value into the equation for Q, we have

$$Q = \left[\frac{3 \times 10^{-4} \times 50 \times 10^4(20 - 17.5) \times 3{,}600}{2}\right]_{\text{wood}}$$

$$= 6.75 \times 10^5 \text{ cal}$$

It may be of interest to check this answer by showing that the same heat is conducted through the rock wool.

23.3. Convection. The transfer of heat from one place to another by the motion of the heated substance is known as convection. The convection is said to be *forced* if the heated material is moved by means of fans or pumps, as is the case in a forced-air heating system in a home where fans blow the hot air from the furnace throughout the rooms. *Natural* convection arises from the change in density that takes place when a fluid is heated.

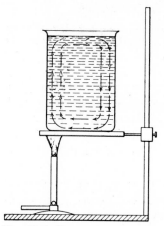

Fig. 23.5. Convection currents in a beaker. The heated liquid is less dense and rises.

For example, when a gas or a liquid is heated, it expands and becomes lighter than the cold gas or liquid. When water is heated in a vessel on a stove, the liquid in the bottom of the vessel becomes hotter than that on the top. The density at the bottom is less than that near the top. The cool liquid sinks and forces the warmer liquid to a higher level. The currents thus set up in the liquid are known as convection currents (Figs. 23.5 and 23.6). In case a block of ice is placed on the top of a vessel of warm water, the convection currents are reversed from what they were in the preceding case.

23.4. Radiation. Sunlight falling on an object warms it above the temperature of the surrounding air. In like manner, radiation from a roaring fire in a fireplace warms the objects on which it falls. Radiation passes through the air without producing appreciable heating. Radiation from the sun passes through millions of miles of empty space until eventually it falls upon absorbing matter where it is transformed into the mechanical energy of random motion which we know as heat.

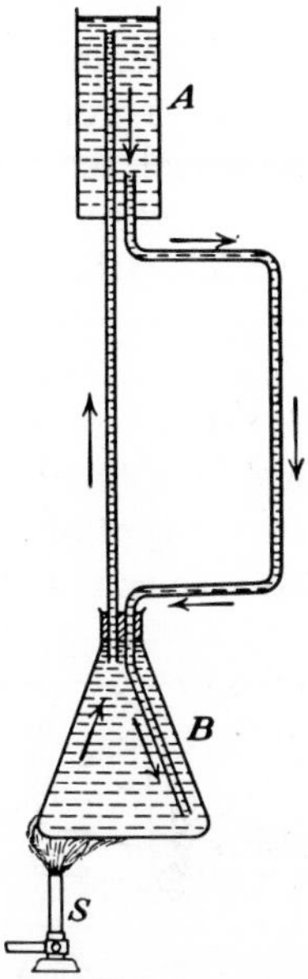

All bodies, whether cold or hot, radiate. If two bodies are exactly alike in every way, except that one is at a higher temperature, the hotter body radiates more heat than the colder one. When a body is at a higher temperature than its surroundings, it radiates more heat than it receives; when it is at a temperature lower than that of its surroundings, it receives more energy than it radiates. The energy radiated by a body increases rapidly as its temperature is raised; it is proportional to the fourth power of the absolute temperature.

The rate at which heat is radiated depends not only on the temperature of the body, but also on the character and area of the radiating surfaces. Some surfaces are good radiators, others poor. Generally, polished surfaces are poor radiators; rough, blackened ones are good radiators.

There is an intimate relationship between the rate at which a surface radiates energy and the rate at which the same surface under the same conditions absorbs heat. Good radiators are also good absorbers of heat. That this must be true can be seen easily. Consider a polished reflecting sphere and a rough black sphere which are put in an enclosure and eventually reach the same temperature as the enclosure (Fig. 23.7). Radiation from the enclosure falls upon each at the same rate, but the polished surface reflects most of the energy which falls upon it while the blackened surface absorbs the energy which falls upon its surface. Therefore, the blackened surface is receiving energy at a more rapid rate than the polished one. However, if the bodies and the enclosure are all at the same temperature, they remain at the same temperature. Therefore, the blackened body which is receiving energy at a greater rate is also radiating at a greater rate.

Under equilibrium conditions both bodies are absorbing energy at the same rate at which they are radiating.

The arguments of the preceding paragraph apply to the situation in

Fig. 23.6. Convection currents in connected vessels caused by the difference in density of the liquid at different temperatures.

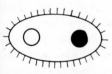

Fig. 23.7. A reflecting sphere and a blackened one remain at the same temperature as the enclosure, once thermal equilibrium is established.

which equilibrium has been reached and all bodies are at the same temperature. If the blackened sphere and the polished one are placed in the sunlight on a bright day, the blackened sphere attains a substantially higher temperature than the polished one. In this case the bodies and their surroundings, which in this case must include the sun, never attain identical temperatures. However, it is still true that *a good absorber is a good radiator and a poor absorber a poor radiator*.

23.5. Black-body Radiation. The best emitter of radiation is necessarily the best absorber. A perfect absorber of radiation is known as *an ideal black body*. A *black body is one which absorbs all the radiation incident upon it.* Although no body with a perfect absorbing surface exists, a body covered with a thick coating of lampblack absorbs about 99 per cent of the radiation which falls upon it. An almost perfect black surface can be achieved by making a small opening in the wall of a cavity

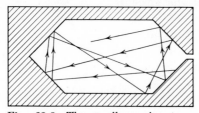

(Fig. 23.8). Any radiant energy which enters this small hole is completely absorbed. Radiant energy is emitted from each point on the surface of the cavity. This energy falls on other points of the cavity where part is reflected and part absorbed. Radiation of all wavelengths is reflected back and forth in this cavity until there is a uniform density of radiation

Fig. 23.8. The small opening to a cavity of rough internal surface is essentially an ideal black body.

throughout it. If the temperature of the wall is increased, the radiation level is also increased.

If some of the radiation is allowed to emerge from an opening in the cavity and is examined by means of suitable instruments, it is found that a wide range of wavelengths is present. The amount of energy associated with each wavelength can be measured. The distribution of the energy in this spectrum changes with temperature. The radiation emitted from such a cavity is called *black-body radiation*. The total radiation emitted by a black body increases rapidly with the temperature. If R is the energy radiated per unit area per second, Stefan has shown that

$$R = \sigma T^4 \tag{23.2}$$

where σ is a constant equal to 5.67×10^{-8} watt/$(m^2)(K°)^4$ and T is the absolute temperature. This is known as *Stefan's law* (or the Stefan-Boltzmann law). If the temperature of a black body is doubled, the rate of energy emitted is increased by a factor of 16.

If the radiating body is not a black body, it radiates less than a black body of identical size and temperature. If the *absorption factor* α represents the fraction of incident radiation absorbed by the surface of the radiator, the energy radiated per unit area per second is

$$R = \alpha \sigma T^4 \tag{23.2a}$$

Thus a body which absorbs only half the radiation incident upon it has $\alpha = 0.5$ and it emits only half as rapidly as a black body of the same size and shape.   For copper α is roughly 0.3; thus a copper radiator radiates only 0.3 the power per unit area as a black body at the same temperature. This follows directly from the argument of Sec. 23.4.

As the temperature of a black body is increased, the power emitted at every wavelength increases, but not in the same proportion.   The curves of Fig. 23.9 show the relation between intensity emitted and wavelength.

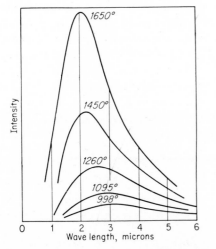
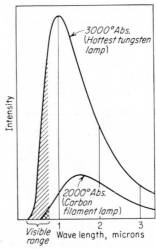

Fig. 23.9. Energy emitted per unit time in a narrow wavelength region by a black body as a function of wavelength for several temperatures.

As the temperature is increased, the wavelength at which the maximum intensity is radiated moves toward smaller values. If λ_m is the wavelength at which the radiation is maximum for a particular absolute temperature T,

$$T\lambda_m = 2890°\text{K}\mu \tag{23.3}$$

This relation is known as *Wien's displacement law.*

For temperatures up to 600°C or about 900°K, essentially all the radiation is in wavelengths too long for the human eye to see.   However, by the time the temperature reaches 1000°K, the black body emits some of the longer waves which the eye can detect (Fig. 23.9) and the body appears dull red.   As the temperature is increased further, energy is emitted in the blue and violet regions of the visible spectrum and the color of the body appears to change from red to orange to yellow and eventually to white-hot.

23.6. The Surface Temperature of the Sun.   If we assume that the sun is roughly a black body, we can estimate its surface temperature by applying either Stefan's radiation law or the Wien displacement law.   Let us consider first the use of Stefan's law.   Measurements at the earth reveal that a surface perpendicular to the sun's rays when the sun is directly overhead receives roughly 1,400 watts/m². The energy received per unit area per unit time on a surface perpendicular to the sun's rays is called the *solar constant*.   The solar constant of 1,400 watts/m² is equivalent to about 2 cal/cm²-min.   If we assume that the sun's energy is emitted equally in all directions, the total power in watts emitted is given by 1,400 times the area in square meters of a sphere of radius r equal to the distance from the sun to the earth.   The power radiated by the sun is therefore

$$P = 1,400 \text{ watts/m}^2 \times 4\pi \times (1.5 \times 10^{11} \text{ m})^2$$
$$= 4 \times 10^{26} \text{ watts}$$

If we divide this by the area of the sun's surface, we obtain as the energy emitted

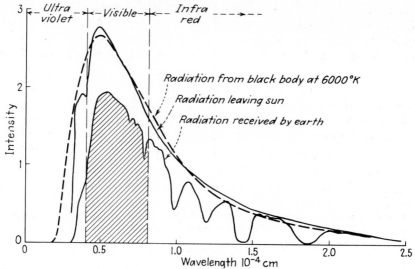

Fig. 23.10. Comparison of radiation received by earth with that which leaves the sun and with that which would be emitted by a black body at a temperature of 6000°K.

per square meter per second the value

$$R = \frac{4 \times 10^{26} \text{ watts}}{4\pi \times (7 \times 10^8 \text{ m})^2} = 6.5 \times 10^7 \text{ watts/m}^2$$

If we insert this in Stefan's law, assuming the sun is a black body, we obtain

$$R = \sigma T^4 \qquad \text{or} \qquad 6.5 \times 10^7 = 5.67 \times 10^{-8} T^4$$
$$T^4 = 1.14 \times 10^{15}$$
$$T = 5800°\text{K}$$

If the spectral distribution of the radiation from the sun is studied and a curve of intensity at a given wavelength is plotted as a function of wavelength (Fig. 23.10), it is found that maximum energy is radiated at approximately 0.49

micron (μ).   If we put this value in Wien's displacement law, we obtain

$$\lambda_m T = 2890 \ \mu°K$$
$$0.49T = 2890$$
$$T = 5900°K$$

Both these values have been obtained on the assumption that the sun is a black body.   Actually, this is not the case.   The curves of the sun's radiation fall substantially below the black-body curves for 5900°K in the short-wavelength region and are substantially above in the far infrared region.

Our best methods for measuring very high temperatures involve the use of the radiation laws.   Instruments called *optical pyrometers* are used to compare the radiation from the body whose temperature is to be measured with the radiation from a calibrated source.

23.7. Newton's Law of Cooling.

Whenever a body is at a somewhat higher temperature than its surroundings, the rates at which energy is lost due to conduction, convection, and radiation are all roughly proportional to Δt, the temperature difference between the body and its surroundings.   Therefore, the rate at which the body loses temperature is proportional to the difference between its temperature and that of the surroundings.   This is known as *Newton's law of cooling*.   Thus, a cup of coffee loses temperature twice as rapidly when it is 80 C° above its surroundings as when it is 40 C° above.

If the body is somewhat cooler than its surroundings, Newton's law is still applicable.   In this case both the "rate of cooling" and Δt are negative since the body gets warmer and its temperature is lower than that of the surroundings.

Example.   A pan filled with hot food cools from 92°C to 88°C in 2 min when the room is at 20°C.   How long will it take to cool from 71°C to 69°C.

The average of 92°C and 88°C is 90°C, which is 70 C° above room temperature. Under these conditions the pan cools 4 C° in 2 min or 2 C°/min.

$$\frac{\text{Change of temperature}}{\text{time}} = k \ \Delta t$$

$$\frac{4 \ C°}{2 \ \text{min}} = k \ (70 \ C°) \tag{A}$$

The average of 69°C and 71°C is 70°C, which is 50 C° above room temperature. k is the same for this situation as for the original.

$$\frac{2 \ C°}{\text{Time}} = k \ (50 \ C°) \tag{B}$$

If we divide (A) by (B), we have

$$\frac{4 \ C°/2 \ \text{min}}{2 \ C°/\text{Time}} = \frac{k \ (70 \ C°)}{k \ (50 \ C°)}$$

or
$$\text{Time} = 1.4 \ \text{min.}$$

PROBLEMS

1. A brass rod 20 cm long and 13 cm² in cross-sectional area is thermally insulated. One end is kept at 100°C in a steam bath and the other end is cooled by circulating

water, as shown in Fig. 23.2. In 5 min 400 g of water enter at 20°C and leave at 25°C. Two thermometers 10 cm apart along the rod read 80°C and 55°C, respectively. Compute the coefficient of thermal conductivity for brass.

Ans. 0.205 cal/(C°)(cm)(sec)

2. Find the coefficient of thermal conductivity for asbestos paper if it is found that 116 cal flow per minute through a slab 4 mm thick and 20 cm² in area when the temperature of one face is maintained at 100°C and that of the other 36°C.

3. How many calories will be lost each hour through a glass window 100 cm by 80 cm by 4 mm thick if the inner surface is at 56°F and the outer surface is at 11°F?

Ans. 2700 kcal

4. A refrigerator has a window with an area of 1.5 m². If the window is 1.2 cm thick and the inside temperature is 8°C, how many calories per day are lost when the outside temperature is 30°C?

5. How many grams of boiling water are evaporated each minute from an aluminum pan 3 mm thick if the area of the bottom is 600 cm² and the temperature is 100°C inside and 150°C at the outer surface? Neglect the heat transferred through the side.

Ans. 5.6 kg

6. Steam at 240°C is flowing through an iron pipe that has a length of 4 m. The internal diameter of the pipe is 5 cm and its external diameter is 5.5 cm. If the outside surface of the pipe has a temperature of 50°C, how much heat escapes in 5 min? [Assume the wall of the pipe is approximately a thin slab and take the thermal conductivity of iron to be 0.11 cal/(cm)(C°)(sec).]

7. A glass window is 0.5 cm thick, 180 cm wide, and 150 cm high. The temperature of the inner surface is 15°C and that of the outer is 10°C. How much heat is lost per hour through the window?

Ans. 1460 kcal

8. A glass window has an area of 4 m² and is 0.4 cm in thickness. The outer surface is at 10°C and the inner surface at 12°C. How much heat flows through the window each hour?

9. How much water would be evaporated per hour per square foot by the heat which flows through a boiler plate which is made of iron ¼ in. thick when there is a difference in temperature of 175 F° between the faces of the plate? For iron, $k = 160$ Btu-in./(hr)(ft²)(F°).

Ans. 115 lb/hr-ft²

10. Heat sufficient to evaporate 1.8 kg of boiling water per hour passes through the aluminum bottom of a pan, 2 mm thick and 250 cm² in area with a certain flame under the pan. What is the temperature of the bottom of the pan on the side next to the flame?

11. A brass bar has a length of 60 cm and a cross section of 5 cm². One end is kept in steam at 100°C and the other in ice at 0°C. Neglecting losses due to radiation, find the number of grams of ice melted in 15 min.

Ans. 22.5 g

12. A boiler with a copper bottom that is 1.5 mm thick rests on a hot stove. The area of the bottom of the boiler is 1,500 cm². The water inside the boiler is at temperature 100°C, and 0.75 kg is evaporated every 25 min. Find the temperature of the lower surface of the copper bottom, i.e., the surface in contact with the stove.

13. If the temperature of the sun were 5500°K, what would be the wavelength of the radiation maximum emitted by the sun? What is the wavelength of the radiation maximum emitted by a body at room temperature of 27°C?   *Ans.* 0.525 μ; 9.63 μ

14. If a furnace is closed in such a way that it can be considered a black body and its temperature is 1500°C, what is the wavelength at which the intensity of the radiation is maximum according to Wien's displacement law?

15. A black body whose temperature is initially 27°C is heated to 127°C. The radiation emitted at the higher temperature is how many times that emitted at the lower temperature?

Ans. 3.16

16. To what temperature must a black body be raised in order to double the total radiation given out by it if the present temperature is 927°C?

17. The filament in a tungsten lamp radiates energy at the rate of 120 watts when operating at a temperature of 2400°K. A second lamp operating at a temperature of 3200°K radiates the same amount of energy. What is the ratio of the areas of the two filaments?   *Ans.* 3.16

18. What is the temperature of a black body which gives out radiation which has 5.5×10^{-5} cm for the wavelength at which the radiation is maximum?

19. If it takes 10 min for a glass of water to warm from 49 to 51°F in a room at 70°F, how long will it take for the temperature to rise from 59 to 61°F? *Ans.* 20 min

20. The surface of a radiation pyrometer receives 0.1 cal/sec from a furnace whose temperature is 727°C. How many calories per second will it receive when the temperature of the furnace is 1227°C?

21. A copper-clad, stainless-steel pan has a conducting area of 500 cm². It has a 0.2-mm layer of copper on 2 mm of stainless steel. If the coefficient of thermal conductivity of stainless steel is 0.05 cal/(°C)(cm)(sec), find (*a*) the temperature at the copper–stainless-steel interface when the outer surface is at 200°C and the inner surface is at 100°C; (*b*) how many calories are conducted through the pan each second.

Ans. (*a*) 199.46°C; (*b*) 12,400 cal/sec

CHAPTER 24

Heat and Work

24.1. Mechanical Equivalent of Heat. If two sticks are rubbed vigorously together, they become hot. Drills or augers become too hot to hold in the hand when used to bore hard wood or metal. Heat is generated (Fig. 24.1) when a chisel is ground on an emery wheel. When a hole is drilled in a brass block, most of the mechanical work done in the drilling appears as heat. When a moving automobile is stopped, its kinetic energy is dissipated as heat in the brake drums and on the road. In all such cases, work is done on some body, and heat is developed in consequence of this work. According to the law of conservation of energy, it is not possible to create or to destroy energy. A definite

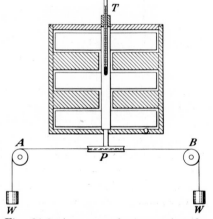

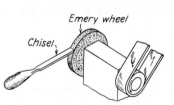

Fig. 24.1. Heat is generated by work done against friction.

Fig. 24.2. Apparatus for measuring the mechanical equivalent of heat.

quantity of work is required to produce a given amount of heat. Experiments have shown that this amount of work is the same under all conditions.

The following experiment first performed by Joule shows one method of determining the amount of mechanical work necessary to generate one unit of heat. The apparatus used is shown in Fig. 24.2. It consists of a calorimeter in which a series of paddle wheels revolves. The calorimeter is fitted with baffle plates that have spaces cut in them to allow the paddle wheels to pass. By this means, the water in the calorimeter is thoroughly churned. The paddle wheels are driven by weights which are hung over pulleys. When the weights are allowed to descend through a given distance, the paddle wheels revolve and do work on the water in the calorimeter. This work causes the water to increase in temperature. By measuring the weights and the distance through which they descend, the work done on the water can be calculated. From the mass of the water, the mass of the calorimeter, and the change in temperature, the heat resulting from this work can be computed. It is found that it requires 778 ft-lb to generate 1 Btu or 4.186 joules to generate 1 cal.

The number of units of mechanical energy necessary to generate one unit of heat energy is called *the mechanical equivalent of heat*. It is represented by J in honor of Joule, who was a pioneer in studying the relationship between work and heat.

$$J = 4.186 \text{ joules/cal} = 778 \text{ ft-lb/Btu}$$

Example. How much heat is generated each second by an electric mixer that makes 15 rev/sec and generates a torque equal to 3 newton-m?

$$\text{Work per sec} = \text{torque in newton-m} \times \text{angular velocity in rad/sec}$$
$$\text{Heat per sec in cal} = \frac{\text{work per sec in joules}}{4.186 \text{ joules/cal}}$$
$$= \frac{3 \times 2\pi \times 15}{4.186}$$
$$= 67 \text{ cal}$$

The heat engines that play such a large part in modern life depend on the reverse of the operation described in Joule's experiment, i.e., on the transformation of heat into work. The heated steam in the cylinder of a steam engine does work in pushing the piston back. This work is available for driving the machinery connected to the engine. A gasoline engine drives an automobile only when it is supplied constantly with heat from the exploding gasoline in the cylinders.

24.2. First Law of Thermodynamics. The first law of thermodynamics is a special case of the law of conservation of energy with particular emphasis on heat. It may be stated in the general form: *In any transformation between heat and other forms of energy, any increase in heat energy is accompanied by an equal decrease in some other form of energy, and vice versa.*

We shall be interested in the application of thermodynamics to heat engines. In this case we are concerned with transformations between thermal energy and mechanical energy. If only these two forms of energy are involved, the first law of thermodynamics can be stated in the form: *When mechanical energy disappears, an equal quantity of thermal energy appears; any disappearance of thermal energy results in the appearance of an equal quantity of mechanical energy.* When fuel is burned in a cylinder of a gasoline engine, chemical energy is transformed into thermal energy. The hot gases do work on the piston in shoving it downward.

In this latter case we have thermal energy being transformed into mechanical energy.   When we deal with an ideal gas, we may write the first law of thermodynamics:

| Heat added to the gas in the cylinder | $=$ | Increase in the internal energy of the gas as evidenced by its increase in temperature | $+$ | Mechanical work done on the piston |

We may write this in the form

$$\Delta Q = mc_V \, \Delta t + p \, \Delta V \qquad (24.1)$$

where ΔQ is a small amount of heat added in the system, $mc_V \, \Delta t$ is the increase in the internal energy, and $p \, \Delta V$ is the external mechanical work done by the gas (Sec. 21.5).

Before developing the theory of transformation of thermal energy into mechanical energy further, it is instructive to look qualitatively into the way in which various practical engines convert heat energy to mechanical energy.

24.3. The Steam Engine.   The first heat engine to be widely used in transportation and industry was the steam engine.   In a steam engine (Fig. 24.3) a

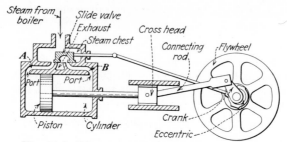

Fig. 24.3. Schematic diagram of a steam engine.

closely fitting piston moves in a cylinder that is connected to the steam chest by means of two pipes, A and B.   These pipes, which are provided with valves, serve alternately as inlet and exhaust for the steam.   As the piston moves to the right, steam enters through A and the used steam is forced out through B. When the piston moves in the opposite direction, steam enters the cylinder at B and used steam is forced out at A.

With this simple arrangement, the steam would leave the cylinder on exhaust at a temperature nearly as high as that at which it entered.   A considerable quantity of heat would thus be exhausted and lost so far as useful work is concerned.   In order to reduce this waste, an automatic cutoff is provided.   When the piston has moved through about one-fourth of its stroke, the slide valve automatically cuts off the supply of steam.   After this cutoff, the steam already in the cylinder expands and pushes the piston forward through the remainder of the stroke.   During this expansion, the piston does work, the pressure of the

Fig. 24.4. A gasoline engine.   (*General Motors Corp.*)

steam is reduced, and the temperature of the steam is lowered.   Thermal energy contained in the steam is thus converted into useful work.

24.4. The Gasoline Engine.   The gasoline engine (Fig. 24.4) is perhaps the most common type of engine.   A diagram of the common four-stroke-cycle gasoline engine is shown in Fig. 24.5.   This engine makes four *strokes* or two revolutions of the flywheel for each power stroke.   During the *intake stroke*, the flywheel pulls the piston forward, and a mixture of gasoline vapor and air enters through the intake valve *A*.   When the cylinder has been filled, the valve closes, and the piston moves back, compressing the mixture of air and gasoline vapor in the cylinder.   When the *compression stroke* is near its end, a spark ignites the mixture.   The oxidation of the fuel releases much heat energy, resulting in a great increase in the temperature and pressure of the gas in the chamber.   The large force on the piston during the *power stroke* moves it forward with considerable velocity.   In the *exhaust stroke* the valve *B* is opened and the gases are pushed out.   The cycle is then repeated.   Out of four strokes

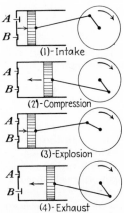

Fig. 24.5. Schematic diagram of the operation of a four-stroke-cycle gasoline engine.

such an engine gives only one working stroke.   The working strokes of other cylinders or a flywheel provide the energy to carry the piston through the other three strokes.

24.5. The Two-stroke-cycle Engine.   The principle of the two-stroke-cycle internal-combustion engine is shown in Fig. 24.6.   On the upward stroke of the piston P the pressure is reduced in the crankcase C, and the explosive mixture of air and gasoline vapor is drawn in through the valve at A.   At the same time, a quantity of this mixture previously taken into the space above the piston P is compressed.   Near the end of this compression, the explosive mixture is fired by means of a spark from the spark plug shown at S.   This explosion produces an increase of pressure in the cylinder behind the piston P.   The pressure drives the piston down, and this is the working stroke of the piston.   As the piston descends, it compresses the mixture in the crankcase.   During this downward stroke the admission valve A is closed and the exhaust valve E is also closed.   Near the end of the downward stroke, the exhaust valve E is opened, and the burned gases are allowed to escape to the atmosphere.   The piston continues its downward stroke

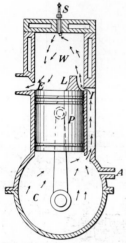

and soon opens the port I through which the slightly compressed gases in the crankcase are forced into the space W above the piston.   The port I and the exhaust port E are opened and closed by the piston.   The inlet valve in the crankcase is operated like the valves in the other type of gasoline engine.

24.6. Diesel Engine.   On the compression stroke of a gasoline engine, the temperature of the air and gasoline vapor increases rapidly because external work is done in compressing the gas.   If the gas is compressed to the point at which its final volume is less than about an eighth of its original volume, the gasoline ignites spontaneously because of the high temperature.   If such ignition occurs before the cylinder is at the top of its stroke, *knocking* results with serious loss of efficiency.   The ratio of the initial volume of gas to the final volume in the cylinder is called the *compression ratio*.   The greater the compression ratio, the greater the efficiency of the engine, but the greater the difficulty in bringing the explosive mixture safely to the point at which the spark is desired.   Modern

Fig. 24.6. A two-stroke-cycle gasoline engine.

developments in high-octane fuel have permitted substantial increases in the compression ratios of modern automobiles, but there remains a serious practical limitation.

In the diesel engine preignition is avoided by compressing air without any fuel vapor.   In this way compression ratios of 16 to 1 or more may be obtained; this results in compressed air temperatures of 500 to 600°C.   When the desired compression ratio has been reached, fuel is injected into the system where it ignites spontaneously because of the high temperature.   Thus, no electric ignition is required.   The diesel engine can use ordinary fuel oil and can operate on powdered coal.   Because the diesel engine is more efficient than an ordinary gasoline engine and because it can burn lower-grade fuel, large internal-combustion engines are usually diesels.

24.7. The Steam Turbine.   Modern electric generators are driven by turbines, which obtain their energy from water stored behind a dam or from steam. The steam turbine has a much higher efficiency than the reciprocating steam engine.   It produces rotational motion directly.   Steam impinges (Fig. 24.7) upon a set of rotating blades.   The steam is deflected from the rotating blades to a set of fixed blades, where its direction is reversed once more and the steam impinges upon a second set of rotating blades fastened to the same axle as the first set.   In a modern steam generator a substantial number of sets of rotating and fixed blades may be used (Fig. 24.8). As the steam transfers energy to the blades, its temperature drops, the pressure falls, and the volume of the steam increases.   To take care of this, the wheels upon which the blades are assembled increase in diameter as one goes from the high-pressure end to the exhaust end.

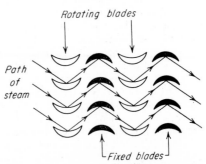

Fig. 24.7. Steam recoiling from the moving blades is directed against the next set of rotating blades by fixed blades.

24.8. Jet Engines.   If a firecracker is set off in a tube closed at one end (Fig. 24.9), the tube is driven forward by the increased pressure on the closed end.   At the open end the hot gases escape.   The momentum transferred to the pipe is equal to the momentum in the opposite direction of the escaping gases.   In jet propulsion it is the reaction from the escaping gases themselves and not the inter-

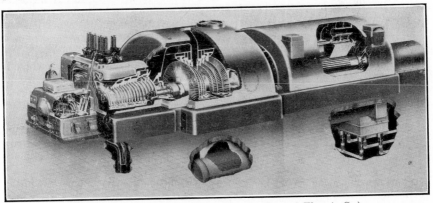

Fig. 24.8. A modern steam turbine.   (*General Electric Co.*)

action of the escaping gases with the air which provides the thrust.   This is the reason that jet motors are sometimes called *reaction motors*.   For many years jet motors have been used in fireworks for rockets, pinwheels, and other displays.   Only in recent years have they been adapted for propelling aircraft and large missiles.

Fig. 24.9. The increased pressure on the closed end of the tube drives it forward when the firecracker is exploded.

A number of different types of jet engines have been developed.

1. *Rocket Engines.*   Rocket engines carry all their own fuel and oxidizer.   They can operate in a vacuum, since they carry with them all the materials which are needed.   Figure 24.10 shows a typical rocket arrangement.   A common fuel for a rocket motor is a mixture of kerosene and other hydrocarbons, while the oxi-

dizer may well be liquid oxygen (*lox*). Of course, other fuels and oxidizing agents may be used.

2. *Ram Jets.* Of the jet engines which use oxygen from the atmosphere the simplest is the ram jet (Fig. 24.11). When such an engine is moving through the

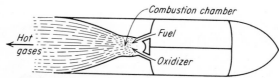

Fig. 24.10. Schematic diagram of a rocket engine.

air at high speed, air enters the nose and passes into the combustion chamber where it is mixed with fuel and the mixture is burned. The expanding combus-

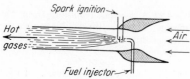

Fig. 24.11. Schematic diagram of a ram-jet engine.

tion products exert a forward thrust on the ram as they escape through the exhaust. Such a ram-jet motor develops high thrust when moving at high speed; it develops low thrust at low speeds because insufficient air is supplied to burn the fuel efficiently. Planes and missiles which use ram-jet motors are launched by means of catapults, additional rockets, or from another aircraft so that their speed is high enough for reasonable operation. A ram jet acts much as an open organ pipe and operates with a roar.

The German V-1 buzz bomb utilized a modified ram-jet engine indicated in Fig. 24.12. The bomb was launched and air entered through the nose where it

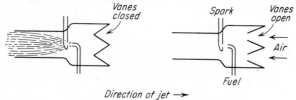

Fig. 24.12. Modified ram-jet engine used in the German V-1 buzz bombs of World War II.

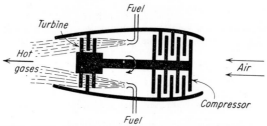

Fig. 24.13. Schematic diagram of a turbojet engine.

passed the vanes *V*. The incoming air opened a valve which admitted fuel and the mixture was ignited by a spark. The explosion drove the air vanes closed and the ram forward as the hot gases exhausted. When the fuel had been burned and the pressure fell low enough, the vanes opened and the cycle was repeated.

3. *The Turbojet.* The turbojet engine (Fig. 24.13) passes the escaping gases through a turbine to provide power for a compressor, which in turn provides air necessary to burn fuel. The compressor and the turbine are operated from a common shaft which runs through the combustion chamber. Many modern aircraft use turbojet engines. They are particularly good for aircraft flying at high speeds and high altitudes where air resistance is low. It is precisely in this region that propellers are not able to exert substantial thrust against the rare air. At low speeds and low altitudes, propeller aircraft are more efficient and have a number of superior features. A combination of the desirable (and undesirable) features of the propeller and jet engine can be achieved by operating a propeller from the shaft of the turbojet engine. When this done, we have a *turboprop engine*.

24.9. Work Done by an Expanding Gas. All the heat engines described are essentially dependent upon the work done by expanding gases to achieve mechanical work output. We now consider quantitatively the behavior of an ideal gas when it is used in a heat engine, treating special situations in which one or more variables are kept constant. In actual engines all variables are changing simultaneously; therefore, the reactions are more complex than those which we discuss.

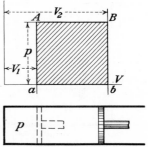

Fig. 24.14. Work done by a gas expanding at constant pressure is equal to the product of pressure and change in volume.

When a gas expands *at constant pressure,* the work done by the gas is the product of the pressure p and the change in volume ΔV (Sec. 21.5).

$$\text{Work} = p\,\Delta V \qquad (24.2)$$

It is convenient to represent the work done by the gas by plotting the pressure on the vertical axis and the volume on the horizontal axis (Fig. 24.14). If V_1 denotes the original volume and V_2 the final volume, the length of the line AB represents the change in volume during expansion. The product of the change in volume and the pressure is represented by the rectangle $ABba$. This area stands for the work done by the gas during its expansion. Since this work is equal to the heat supplied to the gas during expansion, this area also represents the heat taken in by the gas during its expansion.

If the gas expands under a variable pressure, the work which it performs may be represented by a similar diagram (Fig. 24.15). In this case the line AB, instead of being horizontal as in the preceding case, slopes toward the horizontal axis. Nevertheless, the area under AB represents the work done by the gas as it expands. It is possible to construct a rectangle having the same base as $ABba$ and the same area.

The height of this rectangle is the *average pressure* of the gas during its expansion.

In the preceding cases the work done *by the expanding gas* was discussed. Such work is considered *positive*. In order to force the dead steam or the burned gases out of the cylinder, the piston exerts a force and therefore does work *on the gas* in returning to its initial position ready for a new stroke. This process represents a loss of energy that must take place in order to make the next working stroke of the piston possible. This work done *on the gases by the piston* must be subtracted from the work done *on the piston by the gases* in order to obtain the useful work done by the piston in one complete cycle. *The work done on the gas by*

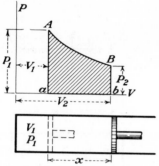

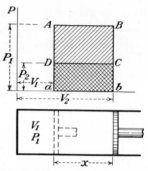

Fig. 24.15. Work done by expanding gas at variable pressure is measured by area under the curve on a *pV* diagram.

Fig. 24.16. The work done *by a gas* in expanding from *A* to *B* is taken as positive, while the work done *on the gas* in compressing it from *C* to *D* is negative.

the piston is taken to be negative, since we call work done on the piston by the gas positive.

Consider a situation in which gases push a piston back at a high pressure p_1 (Fig. 24.16) and the piston is then returned to its initial position against a lower pressure p_2. The work done *on the gases by the piston* may be represented by the area *DCba*, while the work done by the gases on the piston is given by the area *ABba*. The net work is the difference between these areas, which is the area *ABCD*.

24.10. Thermal Efficiency. Since heat and work are convertible, an important thing to know about any heat engine is its *efficiency*, which gives a measure of the fraction of the heat energy supplied which is transformed into useful work. *The ratio of the work obtained from the engine to the heat energy supplied is the thermal efficiency.* In any heat engine the operation of transforming heat into work is inefficient; only a small fraction of the heat developed by the combustion of fuel is converted into work. In a steam engine much of the heat passes out with the exhaust steam. Gasoline engines are more efficient, but even so provision must be made for removing the excess heat not converted to mechanical work.

Example. If 1 lb of coal which has a heating value of 8000 Btu was burned in a machine which raised 500 gal of water 100 ft, what percentage of the heat from the coal was converted into useful work?

$$\text{Heat supplied} = 8000 \text{ Btu}$$
$$\text{Work done} = \text{weight} \times \text{height}$$
$$= 500 \times \text{weight of water per gal} \times 100$$
$$= 500 \times 8.3 \times 100 = 415,000 \text{ ft-lb} = 533 \text{ Btu}$$
$$\text{Efficiency} = \frac{\text{mechanical work performed}}{\text{heat supplied}}$$
$$= \frac{533}{8,000} = 6.7 \text{ per cent}$$

24.11. Isothermal and Adiabatic Processes. A gas may be expanded or compressed and at the same time the temperature of the gas may be kept constant. In order that such a change be made, heat must be removed from the gas if it is being compressed, and heat must be added if the gas is expanding. When a gas is compressed without removing heat from it, the temperature increases. If, on the other hand, the gas is expanded without heat being supplied to it, the temperature decreases.

A process which is carried out in such a way that the temperature of the substance—gas, liquid, or solid—remains constant is called an *isothermal process.* If the walls of a cylinder are good conductors of heat and if the compression (or expansion) of a gas is carried out slowly so that there is a chance for the heat to flow out of the gas during the compression (or into the gas during the expansion), the process will be nearly isothermal. The relation between the pressure and volume of a gas during isothermal expansion or compression is shown in Fig. 24.17 by the line *ST.* The equation of this curve is $pV = constant$, where p is the pressure of the gas and V its volume.

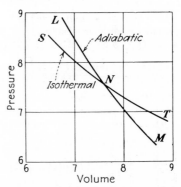

Fig. 24.17. A comparison of the curves followed by an ideal gas if it expands isothermally (*ST*) and adiabatically (*LM*). The slope of the adiabatic has a greater magnitude than that of the isothermal.

If a gas is compressed in such a way that no heat is allowed to enter it or to escape from it, the temperature increases during the compression. On the other hand, the temperature falls during expansion. An expansion or compression during which no heat enters or escapes may be realized experimentally by enclosing the gas in a cylinder which is surrounded by nonconducting materials. *A process in which there is no exchange of heat between the substance and its surroundings is called an adiabatic process.*

The relation between the volume and the pressure of a gas during an adiabatic expansion is shown by the curve LM in Fig. 24.17. The curve for the adiabatic process is steeper than the corresponding curve for the isothermal process. Consider two identical gas samples, one of which undergoes an adiabatic expansion and the other an isothermal one. If the pressure, temperature, and volume of two samples are the same at the beginning and if they expand to the same final volume, the temperature and pressure of the sample expanded adiabatically are less than the corresponding temperature and pressure of the gas expanded isothermally. When a gas expands adiabatically, the product pV^γ is constant, where γ is the ratio of the specific heat of the gas at constant pressure to the specific heat at constant volume.

Let us consider isothermal and adiabatic processes from the point of view of the first law of thermodynamics. If we add a small quantity of heat ΔQ to a mass m, by the first law of thermodynamics [Eq. (24.1)]

$$\Delta Q = mc_V\,\Delta t + p\,\Delta V$$

where $mc_V\,\Delta t$ is the increase in internal energy and $p\,\Delta V$ is the work done by the gas in expanding. In terms of this equation, for an isothermal process $\Delta t = 0$ and $\Delta Q = p\,\Delta V$. For an adiabatic process $\Delta Q = 0$ and $p\,\Delta V = -mc_V\,\Delta t$.

24.12. Carnot Cycle. An ideal engine was devised by Carnot to analyze the fundamental principles involved in heat engines. This engine was imagined to consist of a cylinder filled with gas and closed by a movable piston. By allowing the gas in the cylinder to expand isothermally and then adiabatically, and later compressing the gas isothermally and then adiabatically, the gas in the cylinder is carried through a cycle and made to yield work.

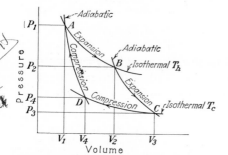

Fig. 24.18. A Carnot cycle for an ideal gas. The cycle is bounded by two isothermals and by two adiabatics.

Suppose that the gas in the cylinder has a volume and pressure represented by point A in Fig. 24.18. If the gas is expanded isothermally in contact with a hot source which supplies heat to keep the temperature at T_h (h for hot), the volume increases and the pressure decreases. After the isothermal expansion let the volume and pressure be represented by point B on the curve. The area under the curve AB represents the work done by the gas during this expansion. From point B the gas expands adiabatically until the pressure and volume have the values indicated by point C. During this adiabatic change, in which the cylinder must be insulated so that no heat is added or removed, the temperature of the gas falls so that the temperature is now T_c (c for cool) instead of T_h. The area under the curve BC represents the work done by the gas during this adiabatic expansion.

Now conditions are again changed, and the gas is compressed iso-thermally at the temperature T_c until it has the pressure and volume indicated by point D.   To do this, we must remove heat from the cylinder during the expansion.   The point D is so chosen that the cycle can be closed by an adiabatic compression along the curve DA.   The area under CD represents the *work done on the gas* during the isothermal compression. This work is negative.

Again we insulate the cylinder so that the gas may be compressed adiabatically until it has once again the volume and pressure represented by point A.   The gas has been returned to its original condition.   The area under the curve DA represents work done *on the gas* during the adiabatic compression.   Again this work is negative.

The net work output of the cycle is represented by the area enclosed in $ABCD$.   It is the difference between the work done *by the gas* during the isothermal expansion AB and the adiabatic expansion BC and the work done *on the gas* during the isothermal compression CD and the adiabatic compression DA.

During the isothermal expansion along the line AB at the temperature T_h, Q_h units of heat flowed into the gas.   During the adiabatic expansion along the line BC, no heat flowed into the gas or out of it.   During the isothermal compression along the line CD, Q_c units of heat were rejected from the gas at a temperature T_c.   During the adiabatic compression along the line DA, no heat flowed into the gas or out of it.   During the cycle $(Q_h - Q_c)$ units of heat have been transformed into mechanical energy.   If W denotes the work done by the engine during this cycle,

$$W = Q_h - Q_c \qquad (24.3)$$

24.13. The Efficiency of a Carnot Engine.   The efficiency of a Carnot engine depends only on the temperatures between which it works. By definition, for a Carnot engine

$$\text{Eff} = \frac{Q_h - Q_c}{Q_h} \qquad (24.4)$$

In establishing his absolute thermodynamic temperature scale, Lord Kelvin showed that

$$\frac{Q_h}{T_h} = \frac{Q_c}{T_c} \qquad (24.5)$$

where Q_h and Q_c are the heats transferred in a Carnot cycle at absolute temperatures T_h and T_c, respectively.   Hence, the efficiency of a Carnot engine becomes

$$\text{Eff} = \frac{T_h - T_c}{T_h} \tag{24.6}$$

where T_h is the temperature of the hot source from which heat is taken and T_c the temperature of the cold body to which the heat not transformed into useful work is delivered.

No real engine can have an efficiency greater than that of a Carnot engine working between the same two temperatures.   If a real engine could have a greater efficiency than a Carnot engine working between the same temperatures, we could use it to drive a Carnot engine in reverse and transfer net energy from the cold to the hot body with no other change. This would violate the second law of thermodynamics (Sec. 24.14).

Example.   Find the efficiency of an ideal engine working between temperatures of 127°C and 77°C.

$$\text{Eff} = \frac{T_h - T_c}{T_h} = \frac{400 - 350}{400} = 12.5 \text{ per cent}$$

To obtain high efficiencies, we want heat engines to have T_h as high and T_c as low as is practical.   Modern electrical generating plants using steam turbines usually use lakes or rivers to condense the steam.   This gives them the lowest practical T_c.   Steam locomotives exhaust live steam into the atmosphere; therefore T_c is high and the efficiency correspondingly low.   Internal-combustion engines and jet engines are more efficient than steam engines, primarily because T_h is much greater.

24.14. Second Law of Thermodynamics.   We see that in the Carnot engine, the most efficient conceivable engine, we take a quantity of heat Q_h from the hot reservoir at a temperature T_h.   Some of this heat is rejected to a cold reservoir at temperature T_c and the rest of the energy is converted into work.   Only if we have a heat source which is at a temperature T_h greater than that of its surroundings can we get useful work from thermal energy.   This idea was formalized by Kelvin in a statement of what he called the second law of thermodynamics: *There is no natural process the only result of which is to cool a heat reservoir and do external work.*   Ultimately, this law follows directly from the fact that *heat by itself flows only from bodies at higher temperature to bodies at lower temperature.*   Indeed, we may state the second law in the form: *Heat can be made to go from a body at lower temperature to one at higher temperature only if external work is done.*   Every electric refrigerator is evidence that we can make heat go from a colder to a warmer body, but the second law of thermodynamics tells us that work must be done to produce this unnatural heat flow.

There is a vast store of thermal energy in the ocean.   However, we cannot simply take this thermal energy and convert it into work to operate a submarine.   Only if we have some body at a lower temperature than the ocean to which we can transfer part of the energy can we make an engine operate from the ocean's heat energy.   Even then we can convert into work only the *difference* between the heat energy provided at the source and the heat energy rejected to the cold reservoir.

On the other hand, we can always convert mechanical energy into heat energy completely.   Thus, the second law of thermodynamics indicates a certain *irreversibility* of natural processes.   For example, we can always convert the kinetic energy of an automobile into heat in the brake drums and tires, but we cannot reconvert all this energy to kinetic energy.

If we have 50 g of water at 0°C and 50 g at 100°C, we can always mix them to obtain 100 g at 50°C.   But, if we have 100 g of water at 50°C, we cannot pour half of it into one vessel and have it at 0°C and the other half into a second vessel and have it at 100°C.   This would be in violation of the second law of thermodynamics, which tells us that many natural processes occur only in one direction.   The world is filled with irreversible processes.   For example, people age, eggs rot, and zinc dissolves in acid.

If the second law of thermodynamics is applicable throughout the universe and if heat always flows from bodies at higher temperatures to those at lower temperatures, eventually the entire universe will come to the same temperature.   Then, although the total energy in the universe will be the same as before, none of the energy will be available for doing mechanical work.   Thus, the second law of thermodynamics tells us that although the total energy is constant, the available energy becomes always less.   This implication of the second law of thermodynamics has aroused wide philosophical interest and leads to what philosophers of the nineteenth century called the *wärmetod* or *heat death*.

24.15. The Refrigerator and the Heat Pump. The process of reducing the temperature of a body below that of its surroundings is essentially the reverse of the process employed in a heat engine.   One may imagine a Carnot cycle operated in reverse so that the gas is expanded isothermally at a lower temperature T_c and then compressed isothermally at the higher temperature T_h.

In a typical electric refrigerator (Fig. 24.19) liquid Freon is pumped into the cooling coils where the pressure is reduced.   As a consequence, the liquid vaporizes and the gas expands.   Both processes remove heat from the surroundings which are cooled.   The gas is pumped out of the cooling chamber, and in an external set of coils it is compressed and liquefied.   In both of these processes large amounts of heat are given up.   This heat is removed by water cooling in large systems or by air cooling in small systems.   The liquid is then ready to pass through the same cycle.   In the refrigerator heat is transferred from a lower to a higher temperature, but the work necessary to do this must be supplied by the "pump." This pump is usually operated by an electric motor, although a gas flame can also be used.

Some modern homes are heated by means of *heat pumps* which take heat from ground water or some other heat reservoir and transfer it into the house by means of processes similar to those in the refrigerator. Let us consider a system using water in a well. The heat pump takes heat from the water which may be at a lower temperature than the house and transfers or "pumps" it into the house. Just as in the refrigerator the cycle may involve the vaporization and expansion of a liquid in coils in the water. In the house a compression and liquefaction of the vapor is accomplished with the release of heat there. One of the major

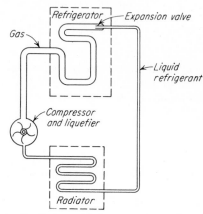

Fig. 24.19. Schematic diagram of the operation of an electric refrigerator.

advantages of the heat pump is that in the summer it may be used to reduce the temperature inside the house by transferring heat to the water in the well. In this case the vaporization and expansion occur in the house, thereby removing heat, and the compression and liquefaction occur in the well where the heat is transferred to the water.

PROBLEMS

1. Upper Yosemite Falls is 1,430 ft high. If all the potential energy lost in this fall is converted into heat, how much is the temperature of the water raised?
Ans. 1.8 F°

2. One cubic foot of water falls from the top to the bottom of Niagara Falls, a distance of 160 ft. If all the potential energy lost in the fall is transformed into heat, how much is the temperature of the water raised?

3. A man consumes food with a total fuel value of 3,000,000 cal in one day. If all this energy were converted into mechanical energy, how high would it lift a 1-kg mass?
Ans. 1,280 km

4. A truck and its load together weigh 6 tons. The brakes are used to bring it to rest from a speed of 60 mi/hr. How much heat is developed?

5. A hiker with his equipment weighs 100 kg. If he climbs 1,000 m up a mountain in 6 hr and 20 per cent of the food energy consumed goes into potential energy, find how many eggs at 80,000 cal each he would have to eat to supply him with food energy for the climb.
Ans. 15

6. How much heat is generated in stopping a flywheel that is making 90 rev/min about an axis through its center? The flywheel has a moment of inertia of 2 slug-ft².

7. A steel bullet that has a velocity of 1,500 ft/sec strikes a target. If one-half the kinetic energy of the bullet is absorbed by the target and the other half is retained by the bullet as heat, how much is the increase in the temperature of the bullet?

Ans. 206 F°

8. Suppose that a steam engine develops 3,000 hp. How many Btu of heat must be supplied per minute if the over-all efficiency is 8 per cent?

9. Compute the efficiency of an ideal heat engine operating between 127°C and 27°C.

Ans. 25 per cent

10. Find the efficiency of an ideal heat engine operating between temperatures of 177°C and 127°C.

11. Steam is injected into a turbine at 277°C and exhausted at 127°C. If the turbine is 60 per cent as efficient as an ideal heat engine, find its efficiency.

Ans. 16.3 per cent

12. The efficiency of an engine that is working between 40°C and 300°C is 20 per cent. What would be the efficiency of a Carnot engine working between the same limits of temperature?

13. A kilogram of water occupies a volume of 1 liter at 100°C and 76 cm Hg pressure, while a kilogram of steam under the same conditions occupies a volume of 1.67 m³. How much external work is done in evaporating 1 kg of water at 100°C and 76 cm Hg pressure? What fraction of the heat of vaporization goes into external work?

Ans. 1.69×10^5 joules; 7.6 per cent

14. If a meteor of 2 g mass reaches the earth's atmosphere with a velocity of 50 km/sec, how much heat would be generated if it were brought to rest by the frictional resistance of the air?

15. A Carnot engine takes 500,000 cal from a heat source at 227°C, does some external work, and delivers the balance of the energy to a heat sink at 127°C. Find how much work is done and how many calories are delivered to the sink.

Ans. 418,600 joules; 400,000 cal

16. A brake is applied to the driving shaft of an engine that develops 4 hp. The brake and the shaft are immersed in a calorimeter so that all the work done against friction is transformed into heat and goes to increase the temperature of the water in the calorimeter. If the mass of the water in the calorimeter is 140 lb, how much will its temperature rise per minute?

17. A Carnot refrigerator takes 50,000 cal from a freezing chamber at −23°C and rejects heat at 27°C. How much work must be done? How many calories are rejected?

Ans. 41,860 joules; 60,000 cal

18. Ice is used to cool a Prony brake that is absorbing 8 hp. If the water escapes at a temperature of 10°C, how long will a 40-kg piece of ice last?

19. An eight-cylinder gasoline engine makes 1,800 rev/min. Each piston has an area of 60 cm² and a length of stroke of 10 cm. If the average pressure during a power stroke is 4×10^5 newtons/m², find the power developed.

Ans. 28,800 watts = 38.6 hp

20. A gasoline engine makes 1,800 rev/min. It has eight cylinders and develops 55 hp. The cylinder has a bore that is 3½ in. in diameter, and the length of the stroke is 5.5 in. Find the average pressure that is developed during each working stroke.

21. How much heat must be added to 10 g of nitrogen gas in a cylinder originally at 0°C to double the volume if the pressure is kept at 1 atm? How much external work is done? What happens to the difference between the energy supplied and the work done?

Ans. 683 cal = 2,860 joules; 810 joules

Physics of the Weather

25.1. Weather and the Atmosphere. Nowhere in our daily lives do we meet heat phenomena on a more grandiose scale than in our contacts with the weather. The weather and its patterns can be explained in terms of the mechanical and heat principles which we have been studying. Meteorology is a major facet of physical science devoted to the study of weather patterns, to predicting the weather to come, and to explaining weather phenomena.

In our everyday life we meet the sun's radiation which is the prime source of all our energy. We observe giant convection currents we call *winds*. We see the changes of phase of water to vapor, and sometimes to snow and ice. The weather at any one point is determined by a myriad of conditions, some general and readily understood, others local and of very special nature. In the sections which follow we shall try to outline some of the principal considerations which are of importance. Before we can discuss the weather patterns in any great detail we must become somewhat familiar with the atmosphere of the earth, with how the sun's radiation produces daily and seasonal variations in temperature, and with how the amount of water vapor in the air influences the situation.

Our atmosphere is a great ocean of air, which becomes steadily less dense as we go upward in it. At an altitude of 18,000 ft the pressure is half that at sea level. The variation in pressure with altitude is shown roughly in Fig. 25.1. At a height of 7 miles, less than a quarter of the atmosphere remains above. As one goes higher, the air thins out into nothingness. Above about 60 miles, most of the oxygen is dissociated by ultraviolet light from the sun and exists as atomic rather than molecular oxygen. Man has never been to such heights, although aircraft have flown to above 25 miles and manned balloons have attained a height of almost 20 miles. Rockets have been sent over 250 miles into the atmosphere.

It is only in the lower few miles of the earth's atmosphere that weather phenomena occur. This portion in which winds, clouds, and weather occur is called the *troposphere*. It extends to a height of about 7 miles over the United States, about 5 miles above the North Pole, and roughly 11 miles at the equator. The greater height at the equator is due to the higher average temperature there and to the rotation of the earth. Above the troposphere is a region called the *stratosphere* which extends to a height of approximately 50 miles. The stratosphere is particularly well suited for long-distance flying since the meteorological conditions are roughly constant there and there are no clouds or storms. The stratosphere gets its name from the idea that the region is stratified in layers with roughly constant properties. Above the stratosphere is the *ionosphere*, a region where many molecules are ionized and at which radio waves are strongly reflected.

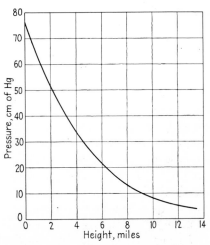

Fig. 25.1. Variation of atmospheric pressure with height above sea level.

25.2. The Sun's Radiation. On a clear day a surface placed normal to the sun's rays receives approximately 330 cal/m²-sec from the sun. If the rays from the sun strike the surface of the earth at an angle other than 90°, the energy in a given bundle of rays is spread out over a larger area (Fig. 25.2). Specifically, the amount of power received is proportional to the intensity of the beam and to the cosine of the angle between the rays and the perpendicular to the surface.

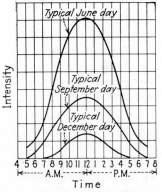

Fig. 25.3. Variation in the intensity of solar radiation at the earth's surface with time of day. The intensity also varies with season of the year and with latitude.

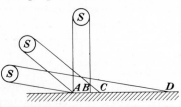

Fig. 25.2. Position of the sun affects the energy received per unit area of the earth's surface each second.

Figure 25.3 shows the importance of the angle at which the sun's rays reach the earth. A glance shows how much more energy reaches a unit area in a day during a summer month than during the winter. This is the primary factor which establishes our seasons. In addition to the importance of the change in the area over which a given bundle of rays is spread, there is another factor which helps to diminish the amount of heat from the sun's rays as the sun approaches the horizon. This is the fact that at the horizon the rays must travel through a greater layer of the earth's atmosphere (Fig. 25.4). Consequently, there is somewhat greater absorption.

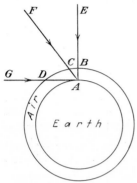

Fig. 25.4. Radiation from directly overhead suffers least absorption in earth's atmosphere. The greater the thickness traversed, the greater the absorption.

25.3. General Circulation of the Air. The inequalities of solar radiation received in different regions of the earth's surface are in part responsible for the general circulation of the atmosphere. If the earth were not in rotation, one might expect a relatively simple circulation pattern in which air in equatorial regions would be heated and rise. The more dense air at greater latitudes would then push underneath and we would have a pattern with air at the surface of the earth flowing toward the equator. The warmed air would rise and flow at high altitudes toward the polar regions where it would cool and descend. This oversimplified picture is complicated by the rotation of the earth.

The earth revolves on its axis once each day. A point at the equator is carried eastward with a speed of roughly $2\pi \times 4,000/24$, or $1,050$ mi/hr. A point at latitude 40° is carried eastward at a speed of about 800 mi/hr, while at the poles there is no eastward velocity. If a mass of air in the Northern Hemisphere starts moving toward the south, its eastward velocity component is less than that of points on the earth's surface farther south. As it approaches these points, it appears to come from the north *and east.* Similarly, a mass of air moving northward has a greater eastward velocity component than points on the earth's surface farther north. When this air reaches these northern points, it is traveling eastward faster than the ground; therefore, the wind comes from the south *and west.*

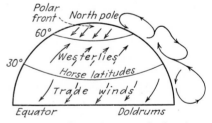

Fig. 25.5. General atmospheric circulation.

The combination of unequal heating in equatorial and polar regions and the rotation of the earth lead to a general atmospheric circulation indicated in Fig. 25.5. At any given point on the earth's surface there may be local factors which may profoundly influence the wind distribution.

25.4. Humidity. The next important factor governing the weather is the humidity, which is a measure of the amount of water vapor in the air. *The absolute humidity is the mass of water vapor per unit volume in the atmosphere.*

One method of determining the absolute humidity is the chemical hygrometer. In this instrument (Fig. 25.6) a measured volume of air is passed through a series of U tubes which are filled with a substance that absorbs water vapor. These tubes are weighed before and after passing the known volume of air through them. The increase is the mass of water vapor absorbed. The absolute humidity is obtained by dividing the mass of water absorbed in the tubes by the volume of air passed through.

Fig. 25.6. In a chemical hygrometer the water vapor is absorbed by calcium chloride or some other drying agent.

From the point of view of weather the actual mass of water vapor per unit volume is considerably less important than how nearly saturated the air is. At a high temperature the air can hold vastly larger quantities of water vapor per unit volume than at a low temperature. We can expect water to condense out of the atmosphere only when the air is saturated or supersaturated in some region. The ratio of the actual mass of water vapor per unit volume to the mass per unit volume which the air could hold at the same temperature if saturated is the relative humidity.

$$\text{Relative humidity} = \frac{\text{mass of water vapor per unit volume}}{\substack{\text{mass of water vapor per unit volume if air were} \\ \text{saturated at the same temperature}}}$$

Since the pressure exerted by the water vapor is proportional to the mass per unit volume, the relative humidity is also given as the ratio of the vapor pressure of the water to the saturated vapor pressure at the same temperature (Appendix D, Table D.4).

The relative humidity of the air may be measured with a number of different types of instruments. Some of these depend on the hygroscopic properties of hair or of a thin strip of an appropriate material. When the moisture content of hair changes, its length also changes. Instruments based on this property are convenient, but are ordinarily not very accurate.

The wet- and dry-bulb hygrometer (Fig. 25.7) is the simplest of the reliable instruments. It consists of two thermometers, one of which reads the true temperature of the air. The other thermometer is covered with a wet cloth and reads a temperature that depends on the rate of evaporation of the water into the air.

If the air is saturated, the rate of evaporation is no greater than the rate of condensation and the wet bulb has the same temperature as the dry one.   The drier the air, the greater the evaporation from the wet bulb and the lower the temperature which is indicated by that thermometer.   Charts showing the relative humidity in terms of the readings of the two thermometers have been prepared and may be found in many handbooks.

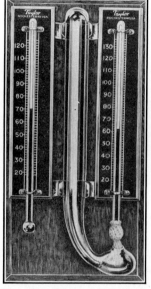

Fig. 25.7. Wet- and dry-bulb hygrometer for determining the relative humidity.   (*Taylor Instrument Co.*)

25.5. Importance of Atmospheric Humidity.   The moisture of the air plays a major part in the health and comfort of everyone.   When the relative humidity is high in hot weather, perspiration evaporates very slowly from the skin and we have hot "sticky" weather.   If the relative humidity is low at the same high temperature, water evaporates rapidly from the surface of the skin and the body is cooled because it supplies the heat of vaporization.   Extremes of heat and cold are felt less when the humidity is relatively low.   The relative humidity has a marked effect on the physical conditions and behaviors of many materials, such as wood, wool, and other textiles.   Lack of moisture often causes woodwork and furniture to shrink and become unglued.   An excess of moisture results in swelling and in some cases deterioration.   In many forms of manufacture it is necessary to control the humidity.   For example, in the production of bread or cigars it is important that the humidity remain constant and that it be neither too high nor too low.   One of the important functions of any good air-conditioning system is to maintain a desirable relative humidity as well as a desired temperature.

25.6. Clouds, Fog, and Dew.   On a humid summer day water condenses on the outside of a glass filled with ice water.   The temperature of the outside glass surface is lowered and the air in close proximity is also cooled.   As the temperature of air is lowered, the amount of water vapor it can hold is reduced.   Eventually air in contact with the glass becomes saturated.   If the temperature is lowered still more, water vapor condenses on the cold surface.   *The temperature at which the air is saturated is called the dew point.*

Any surface which has a temperature lower than the dew point has water condense upon it.   One simple way of determining the dew point is to lower the temperature of a polished metal container by evaporating ether from it.   When the dew point is reached, a thin film of water is formed on the polished surface.

When the sun goes down at night and the surface of the earth begins to cool, some objects lose heat more rapidly than others.   When warm, moist air comes in contact with these objects, some of the moisture from the air is deposited in the form of *dew*.   If the temperature happens to be below the freezing point, water vapor is deposited as *frost*.   On a typical clear night exposed objects usually cool off faster than the air. As soon as their temperatures fall below the dew point, moisture condenses on them.

If the air cools until it reaches the dew point, moisture condenses out on minute particles in the air.   Such a collection of water particles is called a *fog* if the particles are sufficiently small so that they do not fall to the earth as rain.   Fog often forms in low areas during the night.   As the temperature rises during the morning, the water particles reevaporate as the air warms.   If fog is formed in a region above us, we speak of it as a *cloud*.   Whether we use the term fog or cloud to describe the formation depends on whether we are in it or observing it from some distance.   Not all clouds, of course, are formed of water droplets.   The high fleecy-white cirrus clouds are composed of ice crystals; they exist where the temperature is below freezing.

A cloud is often found above an island.   During the day the sunlight produces greater warming of the island than of the surrounding ocean.   The warm air above the island rises.   As it moves upward, its temperature falls because the pressure becomes less and the gas expands.   The expansion is essentially adiabatic.   In a standard atmosphere this expansion results in a drop of temperature of 1°C for every 340 ft increase in altitude.   Eventually the air above the island is cooled to the point at which it becomes saturated; here a cloud begins to form. A cloud of this type is usually characterized by a flat bottom which suggests that the temperature at that particular height is uniform over a wide area.

25.7. Local Temperature Differences.   Along shores and coastal areas there are movements of air known as land and sea breezes, which are

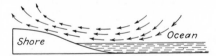

Fig. 25.8. Sea breezes from ocean to the shore due to higher temperatures on land during the day.

Fig. 25.9. Land breezes from shore to ocean caused by lower temperatures on land at nighttime.

caused by diurnal variations in the temperature.   As the sun shines on land adjacent to the sea, differences of temperature are developed.   In the daytime the land becomes warmer than the water.   Convection currents are set up in the air over the land.   As the air rises, the pressure over the land is decreased and there is a movement of air from water to land (Fig. 25.8).   At night the land cools more rapidly than the water. Convection currents are again set up but they are now from shore to water (Fig. 25.9).

25.8. The Weather Map.   As a consequence of unequal heating of various parts of the earth's surface and of the rotation of the earth, huge

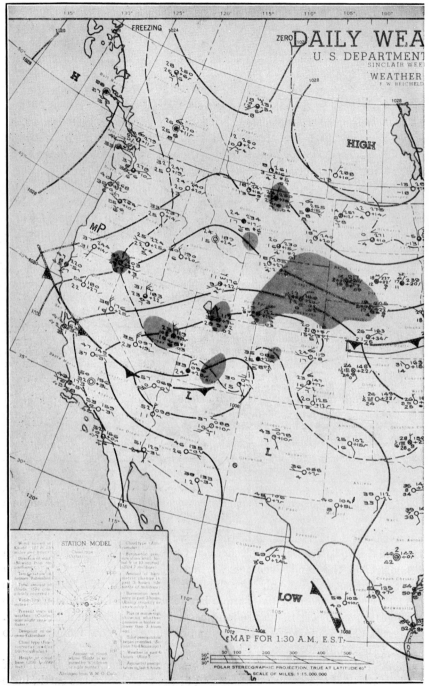

Fig. 25.10. A weather map with a well defined low in the Tennessee region.   Associ-
southwest, and an extensive rain area.

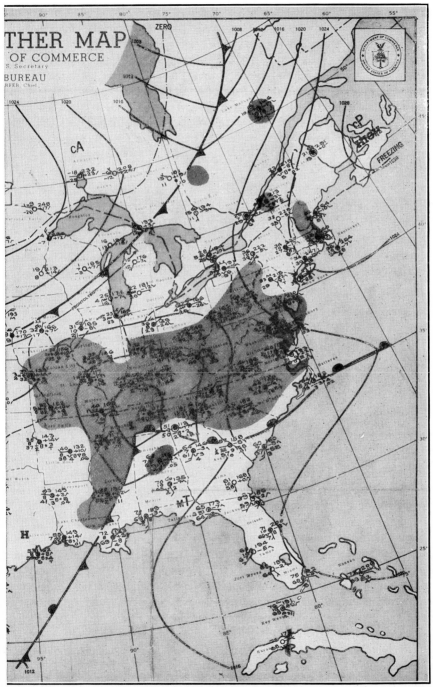

ated with this low are a warm front extending toward the east, a cold front to the

convection currents which we call winds are established. In regions where excessive heating has occurred there are updrafts and reduced pressure, while in cold regions one expects increased density and pressure. Regions of high pressure are known as *highs* and regions of low pressure as *lows*. These regions are shown on typical weather maps by drawing lines known as *isobars*. An isobaric line connects all neighboring places at which the atmospheric pressure is the same. Such lines are shown in Fig. 25.10. The characteristic pattern of highs and lows in the United States moves from west to east with a speed of roughly 500 mi/day.

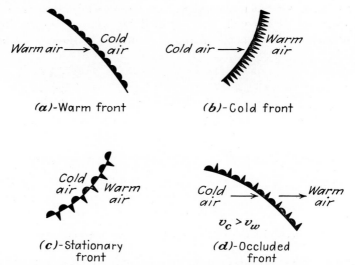

Fig. 25.11. Symbols for various kinds of fronts: (*a*) warm; (*b*) cold; (*c*) stationary; (*d*) occluded.

Over fairly extended regions we have large bodies of air which are nearly homogeneous in the horizontal plane with respect to both temperature and pressure. Such a body is called an *air mass*. It is, of course, never homogeneous in the vertical plane; even in the horizontal plane there are gradual variations. An air mass may cover thousands of square miles and extend to heights of many thousand feet. An air mass acquires its characteristics by moving for some time over an area where conditions are reasonably uniform. One which has developed over northern Canada is called a *polar continental* or *polar Canadian* air mass, while one which has originated in the northern regions of the Pacific Ocean is called a *polar Pacific* or *polar maritime* air mass. One which has originated over a tropical land mass is described as *tropical continental* and one over tropical water as *tropical maritime*.

As an air mass moves, it is modified by heating or cooling, by the addition or removal of moisture, and by mixing with other air.   Weather conditions are determined to a great extent by the characteristics of the air masses, by the direction of their movements, and by the resulting changes in their characteristics.

When air masses at different temperature and pressure meet, the surface of separation is called a *front*.   Across a front there is a sharp transition in weather conditions, which may include temperature, pressure, humidity, and wind velocity.   Several different types of fronts are recognized (Fig. 25.11).

A *warm front* is a surface on which the direction of motion of the air is such that warm air replaces cold air.   On the weather map, warm fronts are represented by drawing black semicircles pointing in the direction toward which the warm air is moving.   Figure 25.12 shows a warm front

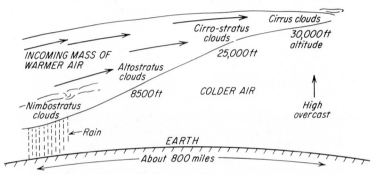

Fig. 25.12. Schematic diagram of an advancing warm front.

advancing.   Because the warm air is less dense, it rides over the colder air and in the early stages of the warm front, high clouds are formed by the condensation of moisture in this invading mass of warmer air.   As the warm front moves in, lower clouds are formed and, if the warm front involves air of high relative humidity, rain is produced.   It ordinarily takes roughly half a day from the first signs of approaching warm air before the warm front passes on the earth's surface.

A *cold front*, in contrast to a warm front, is defined as the surface along which cold air is replacing warm.   It is represented by drawing small black wedges along the front and pointing them in the direction in which the cold air is moving.   If the cold air which moves in under the warmer air is at a much lower temperature and if the warm air is reasonably humid, the cold air pushes the warm air upward into violent thunderheads.   Ordinarily, a cold front moves more rapidly than a warm front and there is not a great deal of warning before it arrives.   As the cold front passes, there is often a hard shower which removes much water vapor from the air and leaves crisp bright weather in its wake.   Cold fronts move about 25 mi/hr and are steeper and faster than warm fronts. When a cold front overtakes a warm front, the result is known as an occluded front, represented by a combination of cold-front and warm-front symbols pointing the direction of motion of the front.

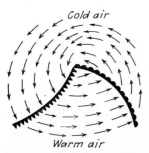

Fig. 25.13. Cyclonic circulation about a low, showing typical warm and cold fronts.

A stationary front is a surface separating cold and warm air when the surface is not moving.

25.9. Cyclones and Anticyclones. A low-pressure region surrounded by closed isobars is called a cyclone. As air from the south moves northward (Fig. 25.13), it is deflected to the east in the Northern Hemisphere, while colder air from the north is deflected toward the west. Thus the circulation about a cyclone is counterclockwise in the Northern Hemisphere. Often warmer air moving from the south forms a warm front and the colder air from the north a cold front, as indicated in the figure.

A high-pressure region on the weather map is known as an anticyclone. About this high-pressure region winds circulate clockwise in the Northern Hemisphere. A high-pressure area is ordinarily characterized by bright, clear weather. The pattern of cyclones and anticyclones which migrates across the country is largely responsible for exchange of heat between high and low altitudes.

Fig. 25.14. A tornado. (*Wright and Gale.*)

25.10. Tornadoes. Tornadoes (Fig. 25.14) are gigantic whirling funnels of air. The motion of the air is characterized by a cyclonic upward spiral that causes rapid expansion, cooling, and condensation. This condensation forms the dark cloud of the tornado funnel. The width of the storm may vary from 30 yd to a mile, and the forward velocity may vary from 20 to 40 mi/hr. The tapering end of the funnel may skip over one area and descend on another. It often has a whirling and serpentine appearance. The whirling velocity of the air causes a decrease in pressure at the center of the funnel. The wind velocity is excessive, both in horizontal and vertical directions. Vertical wind speeds may be as much as 200 mi/hr, and horizontal speeds may exceed vertical ones.

25.11. Upper-air Movements. Movements of the air above the surface of the earth are important in meteorology. To obtain data at high altitudes, various devices are in use. Observations from the tops of mountains give information on meteorological elements. Balloons, either free or captive (Fig. 25.15), are used for this purpose. Balloons carrying recording instruments, called *sondes* (Fig. 25.16), are used for very high altitudes. The balloon finally bursts and allows the instruments to return to the earth with the records on temperature, pressure, humidity, etc. Figure 25.17 gives data on the relation between the height and the temperature of the atmosphere.

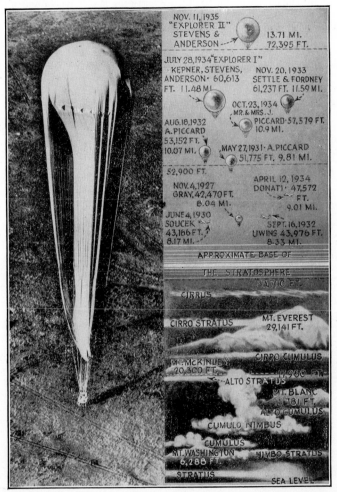

Fig. 25.15. Exploring the stratosphere with manned balloons. (*a*) Landing of *Explorer II*. (*b*) Altitudes of clouds of various kinds and heights reached in the 1930s. Manned balloons now explore to heights of about 20 miles. (*Reproduced by special permission of the National Geographic Society.*)

25.12. Meteorological Instruments. In order to describe and predict the weather at a given time and place, there are a number of physical properties of the atmosphere which must be observed and measured at many places. The more important are (1) temperature, (2) pressure, (3) speed and direction of wind, (4) humidity, (5) precipitation, (6) visibility, and (7) electrical conditions. Typical instruments for measuring some of these quantities are the following.

1. *Thermograph.*   A recording thermometer, or thermograph, is used to get continuous records of the temperature.   A simple form consists of a flattened metal tube filled with liquid and sealed.   One end is fastened rigidly and the other is free to move.   As the temperature changes, the expansion or contraction of the liquid changes the curvature of the tube containing it.   This change of curvature

Fig. 25.16. A radiosonde.   (*Friez Instrument Division, Bendix Aviation Corp.*)

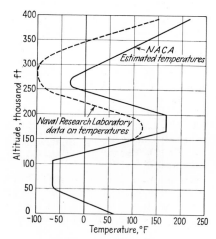

Fig. 25.17. Variations in the temperature of the atmosphere at high altitudes.

Fig. 25.18. Hygrothermograph.   (*Friez Instrument Division, Bendix Aviation Corp.*)

Fig. 25.19. A cup anemometer.   (*Taylor Instrument Co.*)

causes the free end of the tube to move.   This movement is transmitted to a pen which makes a record on a moving drum.   With suitable calibration this record can be made to give the temperature of the air surrounding the instrument.   It can be combined with an instrument to record humidity and it is then known as a *hygrothermograph* (Fig. 25.18).

2. *Barograph.*   A barograph is a form of aneroid barometer designed to give a continuous record of the pressure.   The combined motion of several metallic cylinders, one on top of the other, is transmitted to a lever which actuates a pen which records the pressure on a moving drum.

3. *Cup Anemometer.* The force exerted by moving air on an object in its path is roughly proportional to the square of the speed of the air. This force can be utilized to measure the velocity of the moving air. An instrument designed for this purpose is called an *anemometer.* In one form of instrument (Fig. 25.19), a set of cups mounted on a vertical axis rotates. The number of revolutions per second is a measure of air speed.

PROBLEMS

1. The solar constant is 330 cal/m²-sec and the latitude of Columbus is 40°. How much energy falls each minute on a square meter of a lake on a clear day at high noon, in June when the sun is 23°N of the equatorial plane? in December when the sun is 23°S of the equatorial plane?   *Ans.* 18.9 kcal; 9.0 kcal

2. At a time when the solar constant is 2 cal/min-cm² find the area that receives energy at the rate of 1 hp.

3. Find the relative humidity on a day when the temperature is 30°C and the dew point is 20°C.   *Ans.* 55 per cent

4. A chemical hygrometer gains 0.14 g in weight by having 5 liters of air at 18°C passed through it. Calculate the absolute humidity of the air.

5. If the density of saturated water vapor at 10°C is 9.3 g/m³, find the total mass of water in an auditorium with a volume of 10,000 m³ when the dew point is 10°C.
Ans. 93 kg

6. Taking the density of saturated water vapor at 12°C as 11 g/m³, find the amount of water vapor which will be contained in a room which is saturated at 12°C if the room has a volume of 1,000 m³.

7. A room has a temperature of 30°C. When a surface is cooled to 10°C, moisture just begins to condense on it. Find the dew point, the relative humidity, and the absolute humidity.   *Ans.* 10°C; 29 per cent; 9.3 g/m³

8. How great is the vapor pressure of water in a room at 20°C if the humidity is 25 per cent?

9. An air-conditioning system delivers 1,000 m³ of air each hour at 20°C with a relative humidity of 40 per cent. How much water must be removed each hour if the incoming air is saturated at 20°C?   *Ans.* 10.3 kg

10. A room is 8 m long, 6 m wide, and 3 m high. The temperature is 20°C. How much water must be evaporated in the room to raise the relative humidity from 15 to 30 per cent?

11. Air that is saturated at 20°C rises vertically until its volume is doubled. At the same time, its temperature decreases until it is 0°C. Find the number of grams of water that will condense out of each cubic meter of the air, measured at the original temperature and pressure.   *Ans.* 7.4 g

12. The relative humidity of an auditorium that has a volume of 600 m³ is 20 per cent at the beginning of a concert and 65 per cent at the end of the concert. If the temperature of the room is assumed to remain 24°C throughout the concert, how many grams of water have been added to the room?

PART IV

Light

important

Illumination and the Propagation of Light

26.1. The Nature of Light. One of our principal contacts with the world around us is through light. Most of what we know about the stars and the solar system has come to us through light waves and our picture of the structure of atoms comes largely from observing the radiations which they emit. We have many instruments which make use of light in their operation. Important among them are the microscope, the telescope, and many kinds of spectrometers.

Much of the early knowledge of light dealt with its general behavior when it strikes materials: how it is reflected, how it is bent when it goes from one medium to another, and similar phenomena. Fortunately, the fundamental nature of light is not important in studying these phenomena, and the great science which we know as geometrical optics developed largely before an adequate understanding of the basic nature of light developed in the nineteenth century. One of the early theories of light was that it consisted of a series of light particles which were shot out of bodies in some mysterious way. These corpuscles struck other objects and bounced into our eyes. $m\mu$ = millimicrons

Early in the nineteenth century evidence that light has wave properties became plentiful. In Chap. 32 we present evidence of the wave nature of light; for the moment we assert without proof that visible light involves transverse electromagnetic waves with wavelengths between roughly 400 and 700 millimicrons (1 mμ = 10^{-9} m). Light has not only wave properties, but also some which we may describe as particle properties. In some reactions the particle characteristics dominate, in others the wave characteristics. This "wave-particle duality" was a source of great confusion until the development of modern quantum mechanics.

In addition to visible light there are radiations characterized by longer and shorter wavelengths than the eye can see, but still with physical properties identical with those of visible light in other respects. This leads us to a situation

303

much like that which we found in connection with sound in that we sometimes use the term *light* to describe only those radiations which we see, while other times we use light in a broader sense to describe radiations of the same basic nature, regardless of visibility. From the psychophysical point of view we may define light as radiant energy that is capable of producing a standard response in the human eye. In the broader physical sense we may define light as visible light plus those radiations characterized by longer and shorter wavelengths which have the same fundamental properties.

Most objects emit no visible light; rather they are visible by light which is reflected from them. Relatively few objects are *self-luminous;* that is, emit light themselves. Bodies which emit visible light are called light sources. The sun is our chief source of light and heat, but there are many artificial sources. Any body which is heated to a sufficiently high temperature becomes self-luminous. In addition to producing light by raising the temperature of a body to a high value, we may produce light by passing an electric discharge through a gas. A few chemical reactions result in the emission of visible light even though the chemicals themselves are at a low temperature.

26.2. Rectilinear Propagation of Light. Under ordinary circumstances light travels in straight lines and does not bend around objects

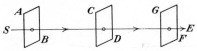

Fig. 26.1. Rectilinear (straight-line) propagation of light.

appreciably. That light travels in straight lines may be shown in placing a candle or other source of light behind a screen having in it a small hole (Fig. 26.1). In front of this screen AB are placed two screens CD and GF, each with a small hole at the center. When these screens are so adjusted that the eye E can see the source of light S distinctly, it is found that the straight line as determined by a taut string joining S and E passes through the center of the holes in the screens. This shows that light from S to E travels in a straight line. Indeed, we depend on light to tell us when a meter stick is straight.

The rectilinear (straight-line) propagation of light is also shown by the fact that a small source of light casts a sharp shadow of an object. Thus a small source of light S (Fig. 26.2) illuminates all points on a screen above A and below B. No light arrives at the screen between A and B because it is stopped by the opaque body M.

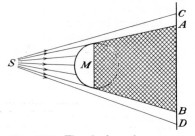

Fig. 26.2. The shadow of an opaque body. Light from a point source gives sharp shadows.

The fact that the boundary of the shadow appears to be sharp shows that light from S does not bend appreciably into the shadow of the opaque body.

When the source of light is not small, the boundary of the shadow is not sharp

(Fig. 26.3).   Points on the screen above A and below D are fully illuminated by S.   The part of the screen between B and C receives almost no light.   The screen between A and B and between C and D is partly illuminated and is in a less dense shadow than the part between B and C.   This outer shadow gradually shades off from complete shadow at B to complete illumination at A.   This gradual shading off gives the shadow the blurred appearance that characterizes most shadows. The region of total shadow is called the *umbra*, while the partially shadowed region is the *penumbra*.

When the source of illumination is larger than the object casting the shadow (Fig. 26.4), the only region of complete shadow is the cone ENF having the object as a base.   If the screen is placed near the object, there is a small umbra surrounded by a large penumbra.

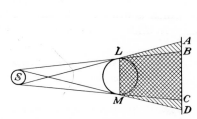

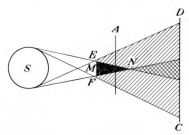

Fig. 26.3. The shadow from source of significant size has both umbra and penumbra.

Fig. 26.4. The shadow cast by an object smaller than the source.

The best illustration of shadows on a large scale is found in the eclipses of the sun or moon.   When the moon is interposed between the sun and the earth in such a way that its shadow falls wholly or partly on the earth, the sun is wholly or partly obscured by the moon and there is a total or partial eclipse of the sun. If the earth is sufficiently near the moon and passes through the complete shadow represented by the cone FNE (Fig. 26.4), the eclipse is *total*.   If, however, the earth is farther away from the moon and passes through only the partial shadow, the eclipse is said to be *annular*.   When the earth, moon, and sun are not in exactly the same straight line, there may be a partial eclipse.   Sometimes the moon, when it is full, passes through the shadow of the earth.   There is then an eclipse of the moon.

The pinhole camera (Fig. 26.5) illustrates the rectilinear propagation of light.   If the pinhole is circular, the light from each point on the object strikes the photographic plate in the form of a small circle.   If the pinhole

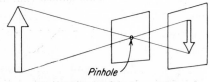

Fig. 26.5. A pinhole camera.

is large, these circles overlap badly and the image is blurred.   The smaller the hole, the sharper the image (unless the hole is so small that diffraction becomes important), but the longer it takes to expose the picture.   Note that the image is upside down or *inverted*. in a pinhole camera.

26.3. The Inverse-square Law.   If we have a point source of radiation, it emits energy equally in all directions.   It turns out that an ideal

point source is not something that we can make, but we can discuss its properties. Consider the light waves proceeding from a small point source L (Fig. 26.6). As the light advances, it is distributed over a larger and larger area (Fig. 26.7). If we assume that the medium through which the light travels does not absorb any of the energy, the total light distributed over any spherical surface concentric with L is the same.

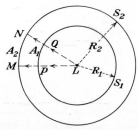

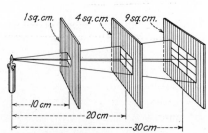

Fig. 26.6. The amount of light from a point source L falling on a unit area of a sphere is inversely proportional to the square of the distance from the source.

Fig. 26.7. Variation of light intensity with distance from the source.

Since the area of a sphere is given by $4\pi R^2$, the light falling on a unit area of a sphere of radius R is given by

$$\text{Light per unit area} = \frac{\text{light emitted}}{4\pi R^2} \qquad (26.1)$$

The light emitted is measured in lumens (Sec. 26.4) and is represented by F (for *luminous flux*). The light incident per unit area is called the *illumination* or *illuminance*; it is represented by E.

In terms of these symbols

$$E = \frac{F}{4\pi R^2} \qquad (26.1a)$$

If we have two concentric spheres (Fig. 26.6), the luminous flux F is the same for both; thus

$$E_1 = \frac{F}{4\pi R_1^2} \qquad \text{and} \qquad E_2 = \frac{F}{4\pi R_2^2}$$

The amount of light per unit area arriving from a point source varies inversely as the square of the distance from the source.

If the eye were equally sensitive to radiant energy of all wavelengths, we could measure the illuminance E of a surface in terms of the amount of energy falling on a unit area of the surface in unit time. However, the eye does not recognize some radiations as light at all and is more sensitive to some wavelengths than to others (see Sec. 30.5). Therefore, if we are interested in light from the point of view of seeing, we must compare illuminances on surfaces by use of the eye or of an instrument which is deliberately constructed to respond like the eye.

26.4. Standards of Illumination. To compare light sources and illumination it is convenient to make measurements in terms of some arbitrary standard. In the early days the standard light source was the *British standard candle*, which was made of spermaceti and burned at the rate of 120 grains/hr. This standard is not of current scientific value, but modern standards have been chosen in such a way that we still measure source intensities in *candles*. At one time, the *lumen*, which is the unit of light flux, was the light emerging through an opening made by cutting an area of one square foot out of a spherical surface of radius one foot when

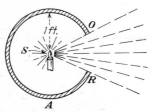

Fig. 26.8. A standard candle at the center of a sphere sends out 4π lumens, of which 1 lumen emerges from the opening OR made by removing 1 ft^2 of area from the sphere.

a standard candle emitted light at the center of the sphere (Fig. 26.8).

The present standard is based on the following arbitrary, but highly reproducible operation. The standard source, developed by the United States National Bureau of Standards and adopted by the International Commission of Weights and Measures in 1948, consists of a glowing cavity with its temperature that of melting platinum. A schematic diagram of the standard source is shown in Fig. 26.9. A cylindrical tube of thorium oxide is surrounded by pure platinum at its melting point. The thorium oxide tube with powdered thorium oxide in the bottom acts as an ideal black-body radiator. The tube is closed at the top except for a small hole, the area of which is known. The light, or luminous flux, emitted depends on the area of this opening. We now define the lumen as follows: *The lumen is the luminous flux from a standard source with an opening of one-sixtieth of a square centimeter which falls upon one square meter of*

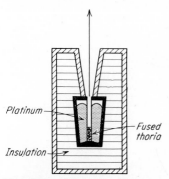

Fig. 26.9. Schematic diagram of the international standard light source.

area of a sphere of one meter radius concentric with the opening when the area is centered about the axis of the source. (The solid angle subtended by 1 m^2 of surface of a sphere of 1 m radius is called a *steradian;* thus, an opening of $\frac{1}{60}$ cm^2 in a standard source emits 1 lumen/steradian normal to the opening.) Since an area of 1 ft^2 at a distance of 1 ft subtends the same solid angle as an area of 1 m^2 at 1 m, a source of one international *candle* produces the same illumination on a surface at a given distance as a standard source with an opening of $\frac{1}{60}$ cm^2 when the surface is perpendicular to the opening.

When luminous flux from a source strikes a surface, the surface is illuminated. We define the *illuminance* (or *illumination*) E of the surface as the luminous flux incident per unit area. In the metric system we measure the illuminance in lumens per square meter; in the British system in lumens per square foot, which are sometimes called *foot-candles*.

An ideal point source of one candle produces an illumination E of 1 lumen/m^2 at a distance of 1 m. The total luminous flux from one candle passing through a sphere of 1 m radius is $4\pi R^2 E = 4\pi$ lumens. We measure the luminous intensities of other light sources in *candles* (sometimes called *candle power*). A point source of luminous intensity I candles emits a luminous flux $F = 4\pi I$ lumens. Actually, ideal point sources do not exist. Typical light sources, such as fluorescent and incandescent lamps, emit different luminous fluxes in different directions. Consequently, the apparent source intensity depends on the direction from which it is viewed. In Sec. 26.5 we describe a means of measuring the source intensity for a practical source.

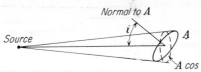

Fig. 26.10. When light falls on a surface at an angle of incidence i, the illuminance is proportional to cos i.

If we are a distance R from a source of intensity I candles, the illuminance on a surface is given by

$$E = \frac{F}{4\pi R^2} = \frac{4\pi I}{4\pi R^2} = \frac{I}{R^2} \qquad (26.1b)$$

if the light falls perpendicularly on the surface. If the angle of incidence i is the angle between the incident rays and a normal to the surface (Fig. 26.10), in general

$$E = \frac{I \cos i}{R^2} \qquad (26.2)$$

A number of instruments have been developed for measuring illuminance. One of the most common is similar to an exposure meter used by photographers. The output of a photoelectric cell is adjusted so that it reads the illuminance directly. The instrument differs from an exposure meter in that suitable filters over the cell give it a response which is proportional to the luminous flux. If the eye and the camera film had identical responses to all wavelengths, the same instrument could be used for both purposes.

Table 1 lists a few typical illuminances. Those listed for various uses are regarded as desirable levels. These figures must be regarded as approximate. One reason is that different surfaces reflect vastly different fractions of the incident light. A gray surface receiving illuminance of 50 lumens/m^2 does not

Table 1
TYPICAL ILLUMINANCES

Situation	Illuminance, lumens/m^2
Brilliant day, sun overhead....................	100,000
Overcast day...............................	8,000
Minimum recommended for fine work..........	100
Night football or baseball....................	40
Office, classrooms, reading room..............	25
Street lights................................	0.5
Full moonlight..............................	0.2
Starlight...................................	0.0003

appear as bright as a white one under the same illuminance, since more light is reflected back from the white surface.   Hence, one may find a lower illuminance acceptable for reading a book printed on good white paper than for reading a newspaper.

The *luminous efficiency* of a light source is the ratio of light flux emitted by the source to the power supplied to the source.   Table 2 lists some typical luminous efficiencies of modern light sources.   For an incandescent lamp, the higher the temperature at which the source operates, the greater the luminous efficiency.

Table 2
TYPICAL LUMINOUS EFFICIENCIES

Source, watts	Luminous flux, lumens	Efficiency, lumens/watt
Tungsten lamp:		
10.............	80	8
40.............	470	12
100............	1,600	16
1,000..........	22,000	22
Fluorescent lamp:		
6..............	210	35
10.............	380	38
30.............	1,500	50
40.............	2,300	57

26.5. The Photometer.   A photometer is a device for comparing the intensities of two sources.   To make this comparison, the distances of the sources from a screen are adjusted until they produce the same illuminance.   Under these circumstances, if I_1 is the intensity of one source, I_2 that of the other source, and R_1 and R_2 are their respective distances from the screen when they produce equal illuminance,

$$\frac{I_1}{R_1^2} = \frac{I_2}{R_2^2}$$
(26.3)

Example. A standard 32-candle lamp at a distance of 60 cm from a screen gives the same illumination as a lamp of unknown intensity at a distance of 120 cm from the screen. Find the intensity of the unknown lamp.

$$\frac{I_1}{R_1^2} = \frac{I_2}{R_2^2}$$

$$\frac{32 \text{ candles}}{(0.6 \text{ m})^2} = \frac{I_2}{(1.2 \text{ m})^2}$$

$$I_2 = 128 \text{ candles}$$

If two sources have different colors, it is impossible to obtain proper balance with a simple photometer. However, if an arrangement is made whereby a screen is illuminated first by one source and then by a second, it is possible to find a frequency of alternation such that the color difference disappears. Then the observer can adjust the source distances until both sources produce equal illuminances. A photometer which is constructed for this process is called a *flicker photometer*.

26.6. The Velocity of Light. Light travels through empty space and through air with a speed of approximately 186,000 mi/sec. In 1 sec light travels a distance more than seven times around the earth at the equator. It takes light a little over 8 min to reach us from the sun, and it requires 4 years from the next nearest star. Several methods have been devised for determining the speed of light.

Jupiter and moon

The first successful measurement of the speed of light was made by the Danish astronomer Römer about 1675. Römer studied the periods of Jupiter's moons, four of which are visible in a small telescope. The innermost of these moons revolves around Jupiter in about 42.5 hr. Römer found that as the earth moved from B to C (Fig. 26.11) the measured periods of this moon were all somewhat longer than average, while the periods were shorter than average while the earth moved from G to H. He concluded correctly that the longer periods were due to the fact that while the moon revolved around Jupiter the earth was moving farther away. The shorter periods occurred when the earth moved closer to Jupiter during the revolution of the moon. From his meas-

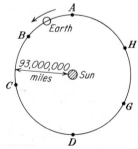

Fig. 26.11. Römer's method for determining the speed of light.

urements Römer estimated that 22 min are required for light to travel the diameter AD of the earth's orbit. Subsequent measurements show that the time required for light to traverse AD (186,000,000 miles) is 1,000 sec and that the speed of light is 186,000 mi/sec.

In Fig. 26.11 no account was taken of the motion of Jupiter which is also revolving in its orbit about the sun. This motion is an additional complication although Jupiter's speed is considerably less than that of the earth. It takes almost 12 years for Jupiter to make one revolution about the sun.

One of the most famous determinations of the velocity of light was that of Michelson. Figure 26.12 indicates a simplified diagrammatic representation of his experiment. Light from an intense source was focused by a lens and reflected from an octagonal mirror which for the moment is at rest. This mirror is adjusted so that the beam of light travels to a stationary mirror and is reflected back to the octagonal mirror and finally to the eye of an observer. In the case of Michelson's determination a stationary mirror was placed on Mount San Antonio and the rotating mirror on Mount Wilson in California. The distance between mirrors

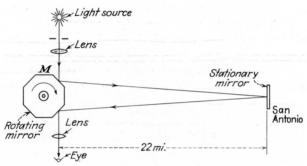

Fig. 26.12. Simplified representation of Michelson's apparatus for measuring the speed of light.

was carefully surveyed and found to be 35.4 km. Then the octagonal mirror was put into rapid rotation. Each time one of the eight sides passed the position indicated in the figure, a flash of light was sent to the stationary mirror on Mount San Antonio and returned. If, when it returned, the mirror was in some different position, the light was reflected in some direction other than that of the eye. However, when the speed of the rotation of the mirror was made great enough so that the mirror rotated through exactly one-eighth of a revolution while the light made the round trip to Mount San Antonio and return, the light was reflected to the eye and observed. When this condition was satisfied, the time for the mirror to make one-eighth of a revolution was exactly equal to the time for the light to travel 70.8 km.

Example. In Michelson's experiment the light path from a rotating mirror to a fixed mirror (Fig. 26.12) is 22 miles. If an octagonal mirror is rotated at the rate of 31,800 rev/min, the light flashes are observed for the first time. Find the speed of light.

$$\text{Time for 1 revolution} = \frac{1}{31,800} \text{ min} = \frac{60}{31,800} \text{ sec}$$

$$\text{Time for } \frac{1}{8} \text{ rev} = \frac{60}{31,800 \times 8} \text{ sec} = 2.36 \times 10^{-4} \text{ sec}$$

In this time light travels 44 miles, so that

$$c = \frac{44 \text{ mi}}{2.36 \times 10^{-4} \text{ sec}} = 186,000 \text{ mi/sec}$$

The results of the many measurements of the speed of light by many different physicists lead us to believe that the speed of light in free space is 2.9979×10^8 m/sec.

26.7. Frequency and Wavelength. The relation between frequency, velocity, and wavelength is the same for light waves as it is for sound waves. Hence,

$$c = f\lambda$$

where c is the velocity, f the frequency, and λ the wavelength. Waves of yellow light have been found to have a wavelength equal to about 590 mμ. Taking the velocity of light to be 3×10^8 m/sec, the frequency of yellow light is

$$f = \frac{c}{\lambda} = \frac{3 \times 10^8 \text{ m/sec}}{590 \times 10^{-9} \text{ m}} = 5.08 \times 10^{14} \text{ per sec}$$

The wavelength of light is usually expressed either in angstroms or in millimicrons. One angstrom $= 10^{-8}$ cm $= 10^{-10}$ m, while the millimicron is 10^{-9} m as its name implies.

PROBLEMS

1. It is desired to use a pinhole camera with a film 4 in. high to take a picture of a house 30 ft high. The film is 5 in. from the pinhole. How far should the camera be from the house to include just the full height of the house?   *Ans.* 37.5 ft

2. A lamp of unknown luminous intensity is placed at a distance of 300 cm from a 32-candle standard. The proper setting of a photometer screen placed between the sources is found by experiment to be 180 cm from the standard lamp. What is the luminous intensity of the lamp?

3. An arc lamp at a distance of 60 ft from a screen produces the same illumination as a 25-candle lamp at a distance of 5 ft from the screen. What is the luminous intensity of the arc lamp?   *Ans.* 3,600 candles

4. A 36-candle lamp is placed 30 cm in front of a screen. How far from the screen must a 120-candle lamp be placed in order that the illuminance on the screen may be four times as great as it was with the first lamp?

5. The efficiency of a 500-watt tungsten filament light bulb is given as 20 lumens/watt. If such a bulb is used as a street light, what is the illumination in foot-candles (lumens per square foot) of a surface 25 ft from the lamp, the surface being perpendicular to the line connecting it with the lamp? Assume that there is no reflector and that light is emitted equally in all directions.   *Ans.* 1.27 ft-candles

6. If it is assumed that a 120-candle incandescent lamp sends out light uniformly in all directions, how many lumens per square foot are received on a screen 4 ft from the lamp when the angle of incidence is 30°?

7. A small screen at a distance of 40 ft from a 100-candle source has its surface making an angle of 60° with the line drawn from the source.   What is the illuminance?

Ans. 0.054 lumen/ft²

8. Two lamps of 90 and 40 candles are placed 150 cm apart.   At what position between them will the illumination on both sides of an interposed screen be equal?

9. A screen is placed 90 cm from a lamp.   When a sheet of smoked glass is placed between the screen and the lamp, the lamp must be moved so that it is at a distance of 60 cm from the screen in order to produce the same illuminance on the screen. Calculate the percentage of light transmitted by the sheet of glass.   *Ans.* 44 per cent

10. The nearest star is at a distance of 4 light-years.   Express this distance in miles.

11. An astronomical unit of distance is the light-year by which is meant the distance light travels in a year.   Compute this distance in miles.   *Ans.* 5.85×10^{12} miles

12. What frequency of light will result in a wavelength of 0.00006 cm in air?

13. If the separation of the mirrors used by Michelson was 22 miles and the rotating mirror had eight sides, how rapidly was the rotating mirror turning when light was first reflected to the eye?   *Ans.* 530 rev/sec

14. What minimum speed of rotation is necessary for a twelve-sided mirror used in measuring the speed of light with Michelson's arrangement (Fig. 26.12)?

15. In measuring the velocity of light a rotating mirror having 12 sides was used. The rotating mirror was 45 km away from the stationary mirror.   What minimum speed of rotation had to be imparted to the rotating mirror?   *Ans.* 278 rev/sec

16. Light of a certain wavelength has 12,000 light waves to the centimeter in air. Find the number of waves per centimeter when the light is traveling in water if the speed of light in water is three-fourths as great as it is in air and the frequency remains constant.

17. Signals with a frequency of 600 kc are sent out by a radio station.   Find the wavelength, assuming that the waves travel with the speed of light (1,000 vib/sec = 1 kc).   *Ans.* 500 m

Reflection of Light

27.1. Laws of Reflection. When a beam of light traveling in a homogeneous medium comes to a second medium, some of the light is reflected. At a silvered surface, nearly all the light is reflected, while at the surface of clear glass, only a small part is reflected. The greater part of it enters the glass and passes through. In Fig. 27.1, AB represents the reflecting surface, MP the perpendicular or normal to this surface, OP an incident ray, and PN the reflected ray. The angle OPM between the incident ray and the normal to the surface is called the *angle*

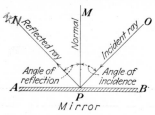

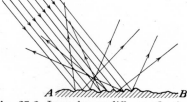

Fig. 27.1. Reflection of light from a plane mirror.

Fig. 27.2. Irregular or diffuse reflection.

of incidence. The angle MPN between the reflected ray and the normal to the surface is called the *angle of reflection.* Reflection at such a surface occurs according to the laws developed in Sec. 15.8.

First Law of Reflection. The incident ray, the reflected ray, and the normal to the surface lie in the same plane.

Second Law of Reflection. The angle of incidence is equal to the angle of reflection.

When light falls on a rough opaque surface (Fig. 27.2), the incident light is scattered in all directions. If the surface is so smooth that the distances between the successive elevations on the surface are less than about one-quarter wavelength of light, there is very little scattering of

incident — falling apon

light, and the surface is said to be *polished*. Thus, a surface may be polished for radiation of long wavelength, but not polished for light of short wavelength. A polished reflector is called a *mirror* and is said to exhibit *regular* (or specular) *reflection*. Rough surfaces produce *diffuse reflection*. Radiation that is invisible is also reflected (Fig. 27.3).

27.2. The Plane Mirror. When a luminous object such as a small candle flame, is placed in front of a plane mirror MM' (Fig. 27.4), a point O on the object sends light in all directions. Several rays which leave this point and strike the mirror are shown in the figure. To an observer in front of the mirror all the reflected rays appear to come from the same point behind the mirror. An observer, therefore, sees a bright spot which appears to be behind the mirror and which we call the *image*

Fig. 27.3. Reflection of infrared radiation. Neither the flatiron nor the cup was visible in the dark room. (*Photographed on an infrared plate by F. W. Davis, Ohio State University.*)

of the object. For every point on the luminous source there is a corresponding point on the image. The image behind the mirror is a *virtual image*, because the light rays do not actually come from that point. However, every ray of light which leaves a point on the object and is reflected from the mirror *appears to come* from the corresponding point on the image.

The ray ON (Fig. 27.4) falls normally on the mirror and is reflected directly back on itself. It is clear from the figure that the triangles ONA and INA are similar and equal triangles. Therefore, the image point is as far behind the mirror as the object point is in front.

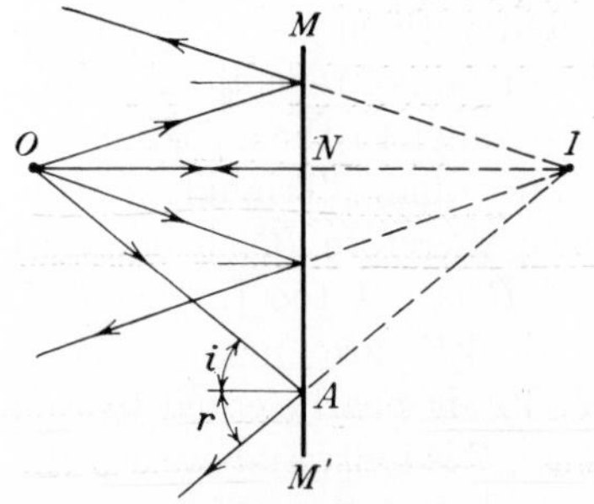

Fig. 27.4. Reflection of light from a point source by a plane mirror.

Reflection from a plane surface may also be considered in terms of a wave front of the disturbance (Fig. 27.5). At the surface AB, the direction of propagation of the disturbance is reversed. The dotted lines indicate the incident wave fronts and the continuous lines the reflected wave fronts.

Figure 27.6 shows an object in front of a mirror. It is evident from the figure that the image is as far behind the mirror as the object is in front of the mirror and that image and object have the same size. The image is, however, reversed with respect to the reflecting plane. Consequently, a right hand is reflected as a left hand.

27.3. The Concave Spherical Mirror. A concave spherical mirror is part of a spherical shell with its inner surface polished. The center C of the sphere from which the mirror was taken is called the *center of curva-*

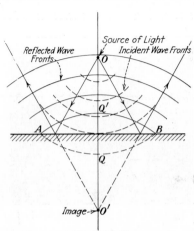

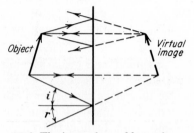

Fig. 27.5. Reflection of light from a point source by a plane mirror from the point of view of the wave front.

Fig. 27.6. The image formed by a plane mirror is the same size as the object and as far behind the mirror as the object is in front.

ture of the mirror; the radius of the sphere is called the *radius of curvature* of the mirror. The middle point V of the mirror M (Fig. 27.7) is known as the *vertex* and the straight line CV through the vertex of the mirror and its center of curvature C is the *principal axis*.

Consider a ray of light AB coming up to the mirror parallel to the principal axis. At the mirror the ray is reflected with angle of incidence equal to angle of reflection. Since AB is parallel to the axis, angles i and θ are equal. Triangle FBC is isosceles; therefore BF is equal to FC. If B is not too far from V, BF and VF are nearly equal. Hence, VF is nearly equal to FC; therefore, F is halfway between the mirror and the center of curvature C. This point F is known as the *principal focus* of the mirror. The *distance from the vertex V to the principal focus F is the focal length f of the mirror.* The focal length of a mirror is half the radius of curvature R.

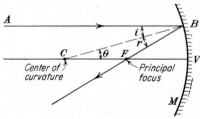

Fig. 27.7. A ray incident on the concave mirror parallel to the principal axis is reflected so that it passes through the principal focus.

$$f = \frac{R}{2}$$

(27.1)

Any ray of light which comes to the mirror parallel to the principal axis is reflected so that it passes through the principal focus F, provided the angle θ in Fig. 27.7 is small. If a ray of light passes along the line FB, it is reflected back in the direction BA. It is true in general that, if a ray takes a certain path through an optical system in one direction, a ray sent backward along the path on which the original ray leaves traverses the same path and comes out along the line on which the original ray entered.

If an object OP is placed before a concave mirror (Fig. 27.8), we may locate an image of point O by drawing a suitable ray diagram. The ray OA parallel to the principal axis is reflected back through F, the principal focus. The ray OF strikes the mirror at point B and is reflected back parallel to the principal axis CV. A ray from O through C comes to the spherical surface along the radius and is reflected directly back on itself.

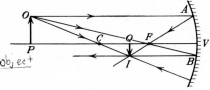

Fig. 27.8. Location of an image formed by a concave spherical mirror.

All three reflected rays pass through a common point I. Indeed, if we draw any number of rays which leave point O and are reflected by the mirror, we find that *every ray which leaves point O and strikes the mirror passes through point I.* The point I then is the image of the point O. In this case it is a *real image,* since the rays of light actually cross at this point. If we put a piece of white paper at I, we see a real image of O. A similar construction can be made for other points on the object; for each object point we can thus locate the corresponding image point. In this case the image is *inverted.*

If an object were placed at IQ, the image would be formed at OP. The points P and Q are called *conjugate points;* an object at one has an image at the other.

The distances of object and image from the mirror and the focal length f are related by a simple formula which can be derived from Fig. 27.9 as follows: The triangles OPV and IQV are similar; thus $OP/IQ = PV/QV$. Further, triangles OPC and IQC are similar and $OP/IQ = PC/QC$. Hence,

$$\frac{PC}{QC} = \frac{PV}{QV} \tag{27.2}$$

If p and q denote the distances of the object and the image, respectively, from the mirror, R denotes the radius of curvature of the mirror, and f the focal length, we have $PC = p - R$, $QC = R - q$, $PV = p$, and $QV = q$. Therefore, Eq. (27.2) becomes

$$\frac{p - R}{R - q} = \frac{p}{q}$$

from which $pq - qR = pR - pq$ or $2pq = pR + qR$. Upon dividing by pqR, we obtain $1/p + 1/q = 2/R$. Since $f = R/2$,

$$\frac{1}{p} + \frac{1}{q} = \frac{1}{f} \qquad\qquad (27.3)$$

Example. An object is situated at a distance of 80 cm from a concave mirror of radius of curvature of 60 cm. Find the position of the image.

$$p = 80 \text{ cm} \qquad f = \frac{60}{2} = 30 \text{ cm}$$
$$\frac{1}{p} + \frac{1}{q} = \frac{1}{f}$$
$$\frac{1}{80} + \frac{1}{q} = \frac{1}{30}$$
$$q = \frac{2,400}{50} = 48 \text{ cm}$$

When an object is at a great distance, $q = f$ and the image is at the principal focus. As the object is moved toward the mirror, the image moves away.

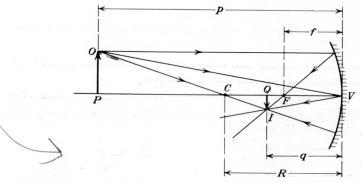

Fig. 27.9. Pictorial definition of terms used in deriving the mirror formula.

When the object distance is equal to the radius of curvature, the image distance is also the radius of curvature; object and image are identical in size. As the object is moved still closer to the mirror, the image moves away until it reaches infinity when the object is at the principal focus.

From Fig. 27.9 we observe that since the triangles OPV and IQV are similar,

$$\frac{\text{Length of image}}{\text{Length of object}} = \frac{\text{image distance}}{\text{object distance}} = \frac{q}{p} \qquad\qquad (27.4)$$

The ratio of the length of the image to the length of the object is known as the *linear magnification*.

Example. Find the size of the image of a body 2.5 cm high when placed 50 cm in front of a concave mirror whose focal length is 20 cm.

$$p = 50 \text{ cm} \qquad f = 20 \text{ cm}$$

$$\frac{1}{p} + \frac{1}{q} = \frac{1}{f}$$

$$\frac{1}{q} = \frac{1}{20} - \frac{1}{50}$$

$$q = 33.3 \text{ cm}$$

$$\frac{\text{Height of image}}{\text{Height of object}} = \frac{33.3}{50} = 0.667$$

$$\text{Height of image} = 0.667 \times 2.5 = 1.67 \text{ cm}$$

multiply magnification by height of object

If an object lies inside the principal focus of a concave mirror, a diagram such as that of Fig. 27.10 indicates that the image lies behind the

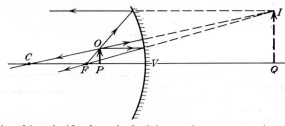

Fig. 27.10. An object inside the principal focus of a concave mirror has a virtual, erect, enlarged image.

mirror. It is *upright*, *virtual*, and *enlarged*. If we solve for q in the case in which p is less than f, we find that it is *negative*.

27.4. The Convex Mirror. In the case of the convex mirror (Fig. 27.11), a ray of light parallel to the principal axis is reflected away from the principal axis. However, if we extend the reflected ray backward, the line crosses the principal axis at the point F, which is the principal focus for this convex mirror. The principal focus is *virtual*. Rays parallel to the principal axis are reflected away from the axis in such a way that they appear to come from the principal focus. The mirror is a *diverging*

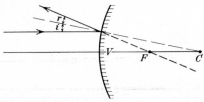

Fig. 27.11. A convex mirror has a virtual principal focus.

mirror, because rays initially parallel diverge after reflection.

If we place an object in front of a convex mirror (Fig. 27.12), the rays of light which leave a point O on the object and are reflected at the mirror never actually cross, but if we extend these rays behind the mirror, the extensions cross at point I. With a convex mirror a real object forms an *erect, virtual* image which is *reduced* in size.

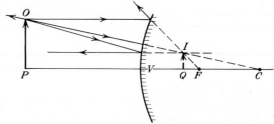

Fig. 27.12. The formation of a virtual image by a convex mirror.

Equation (27.3) is applicable to the convex mirror, provided we assign a negative sign to the focal length. Further, for a virtual image formed behind the mirror the image distance q is negative.

Example. A bright spot situated at a distance of 60 cm in front of a convex mirror forms an image 20 cm behind the mirror. Find the focal length of the mirror.

f must be negative in the answer.

$$\frac{1}{p} + \frac{1}{q} = \frac{1}{f}$$

$$p = 60 \text{ cm} \qquad q = -20 \text{ cm}$$

$$\frac{1}{60} - \frac{1}{20} = \frac{1}{f}$$

$$f = -30 \text{ cm}$$

27.5. The Standard Rays and the Sign Convention. The same formula can be used for both concave and convex mirrors if we are careful to use the proper signs for various quantities. We establish conventions for choosing these signs as follows:

1. The object distance p is positive when a ray of light parallel to the principal axis goes from the object to the mirror.
2. The focal length f is positive if this ray parallel to the principal axis strikes the mirror and is reflected so that it passes through the principal focus. If, instead of passing through the principal focus after reflection, it diverges from the principal axis, the focal length is negative.
3. The image distance q is positive if the ray from the object parallel to the principal axis passes through the image after reflection. If after reflection the ray goes away from the image, the image distance is negative.

It is of great help in solving optics problems to draw scaled ray diagrams. In such a ray diagram, the intersection of any two rays which leave a point on the object and are reflected from the mirror is sufficient to establish the corresponding point on the image. It is desirable to use three rays and thus guard against errors. We shall place emphasis on three rays, which we call the *standard rays* and which can be drawn with a ruler.   These three standard rays and their paths are as follows:

1. The ray which goes from a point on the object along the line parallel to the principal axis leaves the mirror along a line which passes through the principal focus.
2. A ray which leaves a point on the object along a line connecting that point with the principal focus is reflected along a line parallel to the principal axis.
3. A ray from a point on the object through the center of curvature of the mirror is reflected directly back on itself.

27.6. Spherical Aberration and Parabolic Mirrors. If the width of a mirror (Fig. 27.13) is comparable to its radius of curvature, parallel rays after reflection do not all meet at the single point F, the principal focus. Rays that are reflected from a limited region of the mirror in the neighborhood of its vertex M are brought to a focus at F, but the rays that strike the mirror at points distant from the vertex of the mirror cross the axis at points nearer to the mirror than F, and are not brought to a focus.   The effect of this *spherical aberration* is to destroy the sharpness of the image that would otherwise be formed by the mirror.

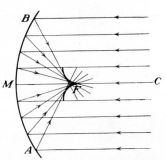

Fig. 27.13. Spherical aberration in a spherical mirror. Instead of all crossing at the principal focus, the rays parallel to the principal axis are reflected so that they cross over a surface called the *caustic* surface.

If the section of the mirror is a parabola instead of a circle, incident rays parallel to the principal axis are all focused at a single point (Fig. 27.14).   Also,

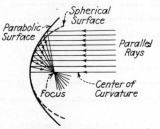

Fig. 27.14. Rays parallel to the principal axis of a parabolic mirror cross at the principal focus.

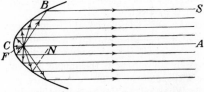

Fig. 27.15. A point source at the principal focus of a parabolic mirror gives parallel rays after reflection.

a point source of light at the focus sends out parallel rays after reflection from the surface of the mirror.   An important property of a parabola is the fact that a line FB (Fig. 27.15) through the focus and a line BS parallel to the axis make equal angles with the normal. From this, it follows that all rays parallel to the axis CA pass through the point F after reflection, and the whole beam, however large, is brought to a common focus. The distortion found in the spherical mirror is thus avoided. Since mirrors of large aperture are needed for searchlights, parabolic mirrors are often used for such purposes. If the source of light is placed

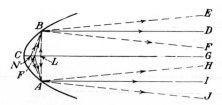

Fig. 27.16. A parabolic mirror produces diverging rays from a point source inside the principal focus and converging rays from a point source outside the principal focus.

inside the focus of a parabolic mirror (Fig. 27.16), the rays of light diverge after reflection. If it is outside the focus, the rays converge after reflection. This fact is of importance in the design of automobile headlamps.

PROBLEMS

Draw a suitable ray diagram for each problem.

1. A plane mirror lies face up, making an angle of 20° with the horizontal. A ray of light shines down vertically on the mirror. What is the angle of incidence? What will be the angle between the reflected ray and the horizontal?   *Ans.* 20°; 50°

2. A short plane mirror used for looking at shoes is placed with its lower edge against the floor. If the mirror is 4 ft from the shoes and the level of the eyes is 5 ft above the shoes, what is the greatest angle the mirror can make with the vertical?

3. An object 2 in. high is located 20 in. before a concave mirror whose radius of curvature is 10 in. Locate the image. Is it real or virtual? Is it erect or inverted? What is its size?   *Ans.* 6.67 in.; real; inverted; ⅔ in. high

4. An object is placed 12.5 cm from a concave mirror which forms an image 25 cm from the object on the side away from the mirror. What is the radius of curvature of the mirror?

5. An object 2 in. high is located 20 in. before a convex mirror with a radius of curvature of 10 in. Locate the image. Is it real or virtual? Is it erect or inverted? What is its size?   *Ans.* −4 in.; virtual; erect; 0.4 in. high

6. An object is placed 9 ft from a convex mirror which has a focal length of 2 ft. Find the position and relative size of the image.

7. A magnifying mirror has a radius of curvature of 60 cm. How far must a face be from the mirror if the image is erect, virtual, and with linear dimensions three times those of the face?   *Ans.* 20 cm

8. What will be the magnification obtained by using a concave mirror with a focal length of 1.5 ft if the mirror is held 8 in. from the face?

9. A fortuneteller uses a polished sphere of 10 cm radius. If her eye is 15 cm from the sphere, where is the image of the eye?   *Ans.* −3.75 cm from the surface

10. An incandescent lamp is located 6 ft from a wall. It is desired to throw on the wall an image magnified three diameters, using a concave mirror. What must be the radius of curvature of the mirror, and where must it be placed?

11. Where must an arc light be placed with reference to a concave mirror with a radius of curvature of 6 ft in order to have its image focused on a screen 18 ft from the mirror?   *Ans.* 3.6 ft

12. An object is placed 60 cm from a concave mirror, and an erect virtual image twice the size of the object is formed. What is the radius of curvature of the mirror?

13. An object 5 cm high is 25 cm from a concave mirror of 15 cm focal length. Find the image distance and image height. If the object is moved 5 cm closer to the mirror, how far does the image move?   *Ans.* 37.5 cm; 7.5 cm; 22.5 cm

14. An electric light bulb 5 in. long is placed at a distance of 8 in. from a concave mirror with a focal length of 4 in. Where is the image located, and how large is it?

15. An object is placed in front of a concave mirror having a radius of curvature of 25 cm. It is desired to produce both a real and a virtual image that is three times as large as the object. Find the two distances at which the object must be placed in front of the mirror.   *Ans.* 16.7 cm; 8.33 cm

16. As the position of an object used with a concave mirror of 20 cm focal length is varied, the position of the image varies. Plot the image distance as a function of the object distance, letting the latter change from $-\infty$ to $+\infty$. Where is the image real, and where virtual?

17. What is the shortest plane mirror in which a man 6 ft tall can see a full-length image of himself?   *Ans.* 3 ft

Refraction and Dispersion

28.1. Refraction. When light passes obliquely from one medium to another, there is a change in the direction of propagation. *The bending of light rays as they pass from one medium to another is called refraction.*

Refraction can be illustrated by taking a cup (Fig. 28.1) and placing a coin on the bottom at the point B, so that the far edge of the coin can just be seen when

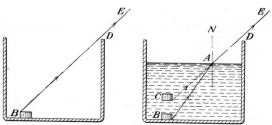

Fig. 28.1. Refraction of light. Rays bend away from the normal on leaving the water.

the eye is at E. If water is poured into the cup, the coin comes completely into view. The ray BA is bent away from the normal. Other rays are bent in a similar manner and the coin appears to be at C.

In Fig. 28.2 RS is a boundary surface separating two mediums, such as air and glass. A ray of light AO is bent as it enters the second medium and proceeds in the direction OB. The angle AON is the *angle of incidence* and the angle MOB the *angle of refraction*. When a ray of light is refracted at a surface, two laws are obeyed:

1. *The incident ray, the refracted ray, and the normal to the surface lie in the same plane.*

2. *The ratio of the sine of the angle of incidence to the sine of the angle of refraction is a constant independent of the angle of incidence.*

The ratio of sin i to sin r is called the *index of refraction of the second medium relative to the first.* The index of refraction depends on the wave-

324

length of the light, as we shall see.   The second law of refraction is called
Snell's law after its discoverer.

The correct explanation for refraction
was given by Huygens.   In Fig. 28.3 the
plane wave front AD is just reaching
the interface between air and water.
The speed of light in water V_w is less
than that in air V_a.   While the wave
front in air is moving from D to C, the
wave front in water is moving through a
smaller distance AG.   We may locate
the new wave front by applying
Huygens' principle.   If Δt is the time
required for the wave front to go from D
to C in air, we may make a circular arc
of radius $V_w\,\Delta t$ about A as center.   The
new wave front in the water must then be tangent to this arc with

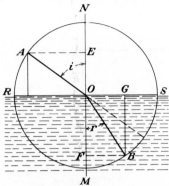

Fig. 28.2. Light is bent or refracted as it goes from one medium
to another.

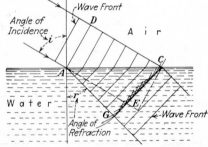

Fig. 28.3. The change in the direction of motion of the wave front at the surface of
separation of two mediums arises from the change in the speed of light as it goes from
one medium to the other.

center at A and must also pass through point C.   This leads to a new
wave front GC.   Now

$$\sin i = \frac{DC}{AC} \qquad \text{and} \qquad \sin r = \frac{AG}{AC}$$

Therefore,

$$\frac{\sin i}{\sin r} = \frac{DC}{AG} = \frac{V_a\Delta t}{V_w\Delta t} = \frac{V_a}{V_w}$$

Hence, we see the ratio of the sine of the angle of incidence to the sine
of the angle of refraction is equal to the ratio of the speed of light in the
first medium V_1 to the speed of light in the second medium V_2.

$$\text{Index of refraction} = \frac{\sin i}{\sin r} = \frac{V_1}{V_2} \tag{28.1}$$

When light goes from a medium in which its velocity is greater to one in which it is smaller, it is bent toward the normal; when it goes from a medium in which the velocity is smaller to one in which it is greater, it is bent away from the normal. Figure 28.4 shows the refraction of plane waves as they pass from a medium in which their speed is greater to one in which it is smaller.

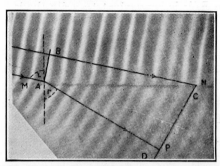

Fig. 28.4. The speed of plane waves below *MN* is less than it is above. The direction of propagation is bent toward the normal. (*From Webster, Drew, and Farwell, Physics for College Students, Appleton-Century-Crofts, Inc.*)

28.2. The Index of Refraction of a Medium. It is convenient to refer all refraction measurements to a common reference medium—a *vacuum* has been chosen as this standard medium. We define the index of refraction of any material as follows: *The index of refraction of a medium is the ratio of the sine of the angle of incidence measured in vacuum to the sine of the angle of refraction measured in the medium.* We shall indicate the index of refraction of a material by the letter *n*.

$$n = \frac{\sin i \text{ (in vacuum)}}{\sin r \text{ (in medium)}} = \frac{c}{V_m} \qquad (28.2)$$

where c is the speed of light in vacuum and V_m the speed in the material.

When we say the index of refraction of glass is 1.50 or the index of refraction of water 1.33, we are automatically implying that the light is incident from a vacuum and falls upon the material, the index of which is quoted. Table 1 lists the indices of refraction of a number of common transparent materials. It is apparent that the index of refraction of air

Table 1

INDICES OF REFRACTION

(For light of $\lambda = 589$ mμ-NaD radiation)

Substance	n	Substance	n
Air	1.00029	Glycerin	1.47
Carbon dioxide	1.00045	Water	1.333
Canada balsam	1.53	Crown and plate glass	1.52
Ethyl alcohol	1.36	Flint glass	1.63
Carbon disulfide	1.63	Heavy flint glass	1.66
Diamond	2.42	Quartz	1.54

differs very little from unity and for most practical situations we can take the index of refraction of air to be one.

If light is going from water into glass, or more generally from some medium A into some other medium B, it is convenient to write the law of refraction in the form

$$n_A \sin \theta_A = n_B \sin \theta_B \qquad (28.3)$$

where n_A and n_B are the indices of refraction of medium A and medium B, while θ_A and θ_B are the angles between the normal and the rays in medium A and medium B, respectively. This relationship applies whether the ray is going from medium A into medium B or from B to A.

If the light is going from A to B, the index of refraction of B relative to A is

$$n_{B \text{ relative to } A} = \frac{\sin \theta_A}{\sin \theta_B} = \frac{V_A}{V_B} = \left(\frac{n_B}{n_A}\right) \qquad (28.3a)$$

On the other hand, if the light goes from B to A, the index of refraction of A relative to B is

$$n_{A \text{ relative to } B} = \frac{\sin \theta_B}{\sin \theta_A} = \frac{V_B}{V_A} = \frac{n_A}{n_B} \qquad (28.3b)$$

Note that the index of refraction of A relative to B is the reciprocal of the index of B relative to A.

28.3. Refraction through Slabs with Parallel Faces.

If a ray of light AB (Fig. 28.5) falls on a plate of glass with parallel faces, it is bent toward the normal as it enters the glass. As it leaves the glass, it is bent away from the normal. Since the faces of the plate are parallel to each other, the normals to the first and second faces are parallel to each other and therefore $r = r'$. By the law of refraction, $i = i'$. Consequently, the direction of the ray on emerging from the glass is the same as its direction on entering. However, the ray is displaced laterally. In the case a ray of light passes through several parallel layers of transparent substances, the paths are as indicated in Fig. 28.6.

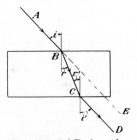

Fig. 28.5. Refraction through a slab with parallel faces. The emergent ray CD is parallel to the incident ray AB.

Whenever light goes from one transparent medium to another with different optical properties there is always a reflected beam as well as a refracted one. Figure 28.7 shows this is a schematic way. There is reflection at the lower surface of the plate as well as at the upper. The light which undergoes several reflections is said to be *multiply reflected*.

28.4. Apparent Thickness of a Transparent Body.

One of the consequences of the refraction of light is found in the fact that on looking through a transparent material the body under observation appears nearer to the observer than it actually is.   Let CA (Fig. 28.8) be a surface separating air from some more dense medium such as glass.   A ray of light coming from a luminous point O in the denser medium and striking the surface of separation at A emerges without change of direction.   A ray striking the surface at C is bent away from the

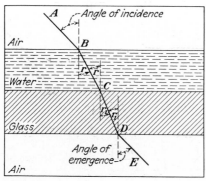

Fig. 28.6. Path of a light ray through several parallel layers of different materials.

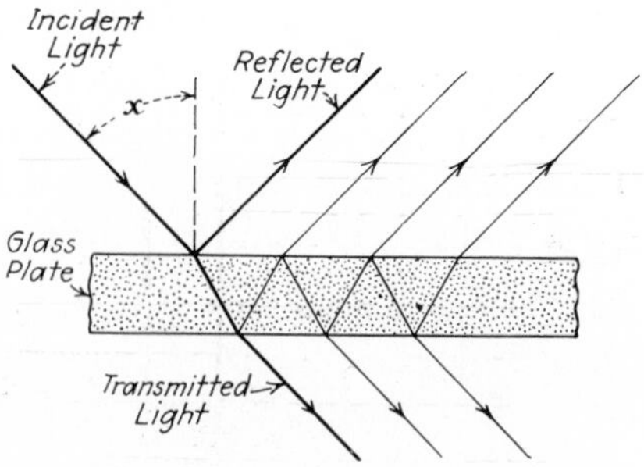

Fig. 28.7. Multiple reflection and refraction at parallel plane surfaces.

normal to the surface on entering the air.   To an eye situated in the air above the surface AC and viewing the object normally to the surface, the light appears to come from D instead of from O.   By a similar construction for the other rays coming from O and striking the surface in the neighborhood of A, it may be shown that these rays also appear to come from D.   Hence, the object O from which the rays actually come appears to be at D, which is above O.   The apparent depth of O below the surface is therefore less than its true depth. From Fig. 28.8,

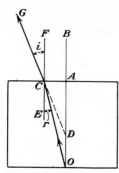

Fig. 28.8. The apparent depth of a point O in a substance such as water or glass is less than the true depth.

$$n = \frac{\sin GCF}{\sin OCE} = \frac{\sin ADC}{\sin AOC} = \frac{OC}{DC}$$

If the eye receives only rays very near the normal to the surface, we may write AO for CO and AD for CD. Then,

$$n = \frac{AO}{AD} = \frac{\text{real depth}}{\text{apparent depth}}$$

The greater the inclination at which the object is viewed, the less is its apparent depth (Fig. 28.9).   Thus the apparent depth of an object depends on the angle at which the object is viewed.

28.5. Refraction through a Prism.   A wedge-shaped portion of a refracting medium bounded by two plane surfaces is called a *prism*.   If the medium of which the prism is composed is optically denser than the surrounding medium, a ray of light incident on one of the faces is bent toward the normal to that face on entering the prism.   On emerging from the opposite face, the ray is going from a denser to a rarer medium and is bent away from the normal at that face.   The angle D (Fig. 28.10) through which the ray is deflected in passing through the prism is called the *angle of deviation*. When the angle at which the ray enters one face is equal to the angle at which it leaves the oppo-

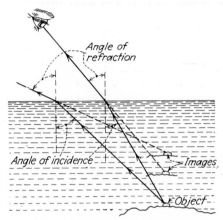

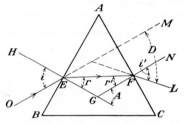

Fig. 28.9. The apparent depth depends on the angle at which light comes to the eye.

Fig. 28.10. Refraction by a prism. The angle of deviation D is minimum when the angle of incidence i is equal to the angle of emergence i'.

site face, the angle of deviation has its least value and is known as the *angle of minimum deviation*.

By observing the angle of minimum deviation and the angle between the faces of the prism, it is possible to find the index of refraction of the material of which the prism is made.   Let A be the angle of the prism, D the angle of minimum deviation, and n the index of refraction.   Since the angle between the faces of the prism is the supplement of the angle between the normals HG and NG (Fig. 28.10)

$$A = r + r'$$

The deviation at the first face is $i - r$ and at the second face $i' - r'$.   Hence, the total deviation is

$$D = i - r + i' - r' = i + i' - A$$

The angle of deviation has a minimum value when the angle of incidence is equal to the angle of emergence.   In this case, $i = i'$ and $r = r'$.   Hence, $A = 2r$ and $D = 2i - A$, and

$$i = \frac{A + D}{2}$$

From the law of refraction,

$$\text{Index of refraction} = n = \frac{\sin i}{\sin r}$$

$$n = \frac{\sin [(A + D)/2]}{\sin (A/2)}$$

Example. In a 60° glass prism, the angle of minimum deviation is found to be 48°. What is the index of refraction of the prism?

$$\text{Index of refraction} = \frac{\sin\left[(A+D)/2\right]}{\sin(A/2)}$$

$$n = \frac{\sin 54°}{\sin 30°} = \frac{0.809}{0.500} = 1.62$$

28.6. Total Reflection.
When a ray of light passes from an optically dense medium such as water to a rarer medium such as air, it is bent away from the normal so that the angle of refraction is greater than the

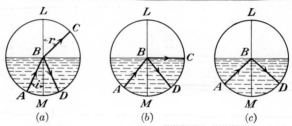

(a)   (b)   (c)

Fig. 28.11. When light goes from water to air, (a) the refracted ray is bent away from the normal; (b) at the critical angle of incidence the refracted ray is parallel to the surface; (c) the light is totally reflected when the angle of incidence exceeds the critical angle.

angle of incidence (Fig. 28.11a). If the angle of incidence is made larger, the angle of refraction increases. When the angle of incidence is increased sufficiently, the angle of refraction becomes 90° and the refracted ray travels along the surface of separation between the two mediums (Fig. 28.11b). *The angle of incidence for which the angle of refraction is 90° is called the critical angle.*

Example. The index of refraction of water is 1.33. What is the critical angle for light going from water to air?

In general for light going from medium A to medium B,

$$n_A \sin \theta_A = n_B \sin \theta_B$$

Therefore,
$$n_{\text{water}} \sin i_c = n_{\text{air}} \sin 90°$$
$$1.33 \sin i_c = 1.00 \times 1.00$$
$$\sin i_c = 0.75$$
$$i_c = 49°$$

If the angle of incidence is made larger than the critical angle (Fig. 28.11c), light no longer enters the rarer medium. Since none of the light enters the second medium, this type of reflection is known as *total reflection.* It takes place at a surface separating an optically rarer from a denser medium when the light comes from the denser to the rarer medium and the angle of incidence exceeds the critical angle (Fig. 28.12). The prism ABC (Fig. 28.13) produces total reflection of the ray OL, since the angle of incidence of 45° exceeds the critical angle for glass.

It would be erroneous to believe that when the critical angle of incidence is reached, there is a sudden transition from all light refracted to all light reflected. For any angle of incidence there is always some reflected light.   At normal incidence the fraction of the incident intensity reflected is given by $[(n_2 - n_1)/(n_2 + n_1)]^2$, where n_1 and n_2 are the indices of refraction of the first and second mediums.   As the angle of incidence is increased, a greater fraction of the incident light is reflected and a smaller fraction refracted.   It is easy to observe with

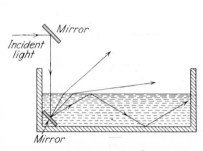

Fig. 28.12. Apparatus for demonstrating total internal reflection showing three positions of the reflected ray as the submerged mirror is rotated.

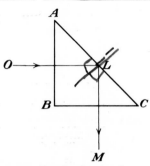

Fig. 28.13. Total reflection by an isosceles right-angled prism.

a pane of glass that as the angle of incidence becomes greater the fraction of the light reflected becomes larger.

There are many applications of total reflection.   Light can be "piped" down a bent tube of glass or lucite.   As the light goes down the tube, it strikes the surfaces at angles of incidence greater than the critical angle and is totally reflected. Thus the light is transmitted down the tube until it reaches the end, where the angle of incidence is less than the critical angle and the light emerges.   Such "light pipes" may be used to get illumination in surgical operations at places where it is difficult to operate a lamp because of the heat involved.   Light can also be piped in streams of water; colored fountains depend on total reflection to keep the light in the water stream until it finally strikes at an angle of incidence greater than the critical angle and escapes.

The lighthouse reflector is an application of total reflection.   Right-angle prisms are placed around the light (Fig. 28.14) so that they form an enclosed sphere.   The rays of light from a lamp at the center of the sphere strike one leg of the right-angle prism, enter the glass, strike the hypotenuse at an angle greater than the critical

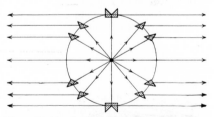

Fig. 28.14. Application of total reflection in a lighthouse reflector to send light in the directions where it is desired.

angle, and are totally reflected in such a way that the rays of light leave parallel to one another.   In automobile head lamps similar prisms are used to reflect the light to regions where illumination is desired.

28.7. Atmospheric Refraction and the Mirage.   Although the index of refraction of air under standard conditions deviates from unity by less than 0.03

per cent, there are situations in which atmospheric refraction is far from negligible. One of the most interesting occurs in the *mirage*. On hot sunny days there may be a layer of very hot air in contact with the ground. This air has a lower density and a slightly smaller index of refraction than the air above it. Light from a distant mountain or tree top approaches this layer of hot air at a large angle of incidence and is totally reflected (Fig. 28.15). The light appears to have come from the image just as though it had been reflected from the surface of a lake.

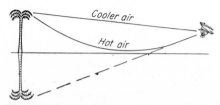

Fig. 28.15. A mirage may be observed when air near the ground is hotter than the air higher up.

Fig. 28.16. Looming occurs when the air near the surface is substantially cooler than the air above.

When the air next to the ground is substantially colder than the air somewhat higher, rays of light are deviated downward (Fig. 28.16). An image of a ship may appear above the ship itself. This phenomenon is called *looming*. It is rather common when an observer is looking over a snow field or over a body of water which is substantially colder than the air several feet above the surface. Cases have been reported where a lighthouse has been seen at a distance of 40 miles when the curvature of the earth would have completely cut off the light had there been no looming.

When one looks at an object over the hot burner of a stove or over a hot pavement, one may observe a wavy, shimmering effect. This arises from the bending of the light as it passes from colder to warmer to colder air. The twinkling of stars is in part due to similar phenomena in that the light travels through unstable layers in the atmosphere where the index of refraction is constantly changing by significant amounts.

A ray of light entering the earth's atmosphere from the sun or some other heavenly body is refracted unless it enters at zero angle of incidence. For this reason, the altitude of the sun ordinarily appears too great and must be corrected to get the true altitude (Fig. 28.17). Because of the variation in the density of the atmosphere, the correction is not easy to calculate. Ordinarily, when the sun is at the horizon, the correction is about one-half degree, which is slightly more than the angle subtended at the earth by the sun's diameter. At the horizon the sun is apparently raised by a little more than its diameter. As a consequence, the sun is really below the horizon when we watch it rise or set. When

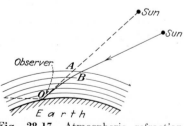

Fig. 28.17. Atmospheric refraction grossly exaggerated.

the sun (or moon) is near the horizon, the rays from the lower edge are bent more than those from the upper edge. This produces a shortening of the vertical diameter, so that the sun appears elliptical.

28.8. The Dispersion of Light by a Prism.

If a very narrow beam of white light is passed through a prism (Figs. 28.18 and 31.1) in a darkened room, the white light passing through the prism is spread out into a band of colors known as a *spectrum.* Violet light, which has the shortest wavelength of the visible, is bent most, while red with the longest wavelength is bent least. Lights with intermediate wavelengths occupy intermediate positions in the spectrum. *The separation of white light into its component colors is called dispersion.*

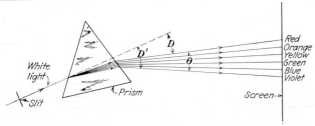

Fig. 28.18. Red light is deviated less by a prism than violet. This leads to the dispersion of light into a spectrum.

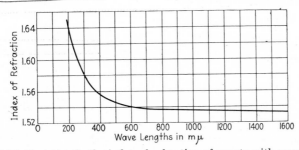

Fig. 28.19. Variation in the index of refraction of quartz with wavelength.

Since different colors are deviated different amounts by the prism, it is clear that the index of refraction of the glass is different for the various colors. Consequently, the speed of light in the glass must be different for the various colors. In ordinary crown glass red light goes approximately one per cent faster than violet. Figure 28.19 shows how the index of refraction of quartz varies with wavelength.

The question may well be raised why we did not notice dispersion in connection with experiments performed earlier with the deviation of light by a prism. In these experiments a much wider beam of light was used and the level of illumination in the room was great. Because of the large width of the beam, the blue from one part of the beam fell on the red from another, on the orange from still another part, and so forth. This led to a white core, but at the edges of the deviated beam there were doubtless evidences of dispersion. However, the colors were so dim compared with the bright central image that probably they were not noticed.

28.9. Achromatic Prism. When light of more than one color falls on a prism, the emerging beam is not only deviated but spread out into a spectrum. If a second prism is placed just beyond with its vertex at the base of the first one, the second prism tends to gather the different colors together again and combine them into white light. The net dispersion produced by the two prisms is the difference between the dispersions produced by the individual prisms. The

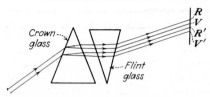

deviation produced by the second prism is opposite to that produced by the first prism and the net deviation is the difference between the two. If the two prisms were identical, the net effect would be simply that of passing the light through a parallel plate—no dispersion and no deviation. However, if the prisms are made of different kinds of glass, they may have the same net dispersion, but quite differ-

Fig. 28.20. An achromatic prism combination producing deviation without dispersion.

ent deviations. A flint-glass prism which produces the same dispersion as a crown-glass prism of larger central angle gives a smaller deviation. By placing together a crown- and flint-glass prism which have the same dispersion, it is possible to construct a prism that deviates the light without spreading it out into a spectrum (Fig. 28.20). Such a prism is called an *achromatic* prism.

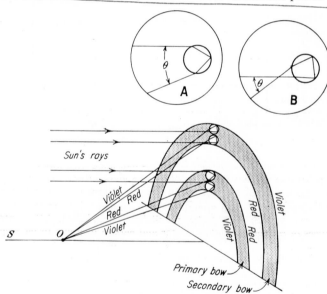

Fig. 28.21. Formation of a rainbow.

If the angle of the flint-glass prism is increased until the deviation it produces is equal to that produced by the crown-glass prism, the dispersion of the flint-glass prism is substantially greater. When two such prisms are put together, the combination produces *dispersion without deviation*. When white light passes through such a combination of prisms, it is dispersed into a spectrum, but its general direction is unchanged.

28.10. The Rainbow. No doubt the first evidence of dispersion seen by man is the rainbow. The formation of the rainbow was explained by Descartes about 1637. Let us consider a situation in which the sun is in the west and it is raining in the east. Rays of sunlight enter water droplets (Fig. 28.21) where they are refracted and dispersed. If the ray enters the drop at the proper place, it may be totally reflected at the internal surface of the drop, and leave the drop as shown in insert A of the figure. Descartes showed that when the angle θ is 42° red light is strongly reflected, while violet light appears prominently at 40°. The other colors of the spectrum are intensely reflected at angles between 40° and 42°. Each color is strongly reflected at that angle for which it can pass through the droplet with minimum deviation. If an observer stands at O and the line SO represents the direction of the incident sunlight, all those raindrops which lie on the surface of a cone of angle 40° about SO send an excess of violet light to the observer, while those which lie on a conical surface of angle 42° about SO return red light.

In addition to the primary bow which we have just discussed, there is sometimes a secondary bow in which the colors are reversed with violet on the outside and red on the inside. This secondary bow is produced by refraction, dispersion, and two internal reflections inside the raindrop as shown in insert B. For the secondary bow, the angle between the incident and emergent rays is about 51° for red and 54° for the violet.

When exceedingly tiny drops are involved, as may be the case in a garden spray, diffraction effects may become large and the structure of the bow far less simple.

PROBLEMS

1. Calculate the index of refraction of a substance for which light incident at an angle of 53° is refracted at an angle of 30°.   *Ans.* 1.60

2. Calculate the index of refraction of a substance for which light incident at an angle of 45° is refracted at an angle of 32°.

3. What is the speed of light in water? in heavy flint glass?

Ans. 2.25×10^8 m/sec or 139,500 mi/sec; 1.81×10^8 m/sec, or 112,000 mi/sec

4. Find the angle of refraction when light is incident on a water surface at an angle of 60°.

5. A glass dish with a plane parallel bottom is half filled with water. Then carbon disulfide is poured on top of the water. Finally a glass cover is placed on top of the dish, the cover being flat. A beam of light making an angle of 60° with the vertical is incident on the horizontal cover. Find the angles with the vertical made by the beam as it passes through glass, carbon disulfide, water, glass, and then into the air. Assume indices of refraction of glass, water and carbon disulfide to be, respectively, $\frac{3}{2}$, $\frac{4}{3}$ and $1\frac{3}{8}$.   *Ans.* 35.2°; 32.2°; 40.5°; 35.2°; 60°

6. The bottom of a vessel consists of a thick plate of glass that has an index of refraction of 1.55. The vessel is filled with water. At what angle will a ray of light incident at an angle of 30° on the upper surface of the water emerge from the lower surface of the glass bottom?

7. Determine the index of refraction of a substance for which the critical angle is 43°.   *Ans.* 1.47

8. Light passes from water into carbon disulfide. If the direction in the water makes an angle of 40° with the normal to the surface between the two mediums, what will be the direction in the carbon disulfide?

9. A ray of light is passed through a prism having a refracting angle of 60°. Rotation of the prism causes the ray to be deviated various amounts, the least of which is 50°. Determine the index of refraction of the glass of which the prism is made.

Ans. 1.638

10. What is the index of refraction of a glass prism which produces an angle of minimum deviation of 40°, assuming that the angle of the prism is 60°?

11. Light in passing from air into a liquid is deviated 13° when the angle of incidence is 40°. Under what conditions will total reflection occur at this surface?

Ans. i in liquid 45°

12. Find the critical angle between water and carbon disulfide.

13. A ray of light passes from oil to water. The index of refraction of oil is 1.45. What is the critical angle for light passing from oil to water? *Ans.* 67°

14. The index of refraction of glass is 1.53, and the index of refraction of water is 1.33. What is the index of refraction of glass with respect to water?

15. A ray of light makes an angle of incidence of 45° with a glass prism whose index of refraction is 1.5 and whose refracting angle is 60°. Through what angle is the ray deviated by the prism? Does this represent minimum deviation?

Ans. 37.5°; no

16. A hollow prism is made of plates of glass whose surfaces are parallel. The angle between the faces of the prism is 60°. What is the angle of minimum deviation when the sodium *D* line having a wavelength of 589 mμ is passed through the prism filled with water?

17. A fish is 5 ft below the surface of a pool. What is its apparent depth when viewed from above? *Ans.* 3.75 ft

18. Given a 45° prism of crown glass, find the angle of minimum deviation. At what angle of incidence must the light strike the prism? Find the deviation if the angle of incidence is 5° less; 5° greater.

19. Experiment shows that the index of refraction of a heavy flint glass is 1.717 for *D* light (yellow) and 1.742 for *F* light (blue). Find the angle of dispersion of these two colors produced by a 60° prism, if the light strikes the prism with an angle of incidence of 50°. *Ans.* 4.8°

20. A beam of white light is incident on a slab of flint glass at an angle of 45°. What is the angular separation of two rays of light, one of wavelength 4,860 A and the other of wavelength 6,560 A, if the index of refraction of the former is 1.67 and that of the latter is 1.65?

21. Show that the deviation produced by a thin wedge of transparent material of angle *A* is given approximately by $D = (n - 1)A$ if the angle of incidence is small. (*Hint:* For small angles, $\sin \theta = \theta$ in radians.)

Lenses

29.1. Simple Lenses. Lenses are bodies of transparent material shaped to converge or diverge a beam of light.   Simple lenses are bounded by faces which are small sections of spheres.

Consider a beam of parallel rays falling on the prism in Fig. 29.1*a*. The rays are deviated by the prism, but remain parallel to one another. If we wish to bring these rays together at a point, we must deviate the uppermost ray more than the lower one.   This can be accomplished by grinding the surfaces so that they have the cross section indicated in Fig. 29.1*b*.   If the surfaces of a glass blank are small sections of spheres, the

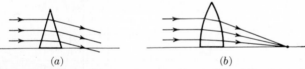

| (a) | (b) |

Fig. 29.1. Parallel rays deviated by a prism remain parallel, while a lens with spherical surfaces brings parallel rays to a focus.

upper ray is deviated more than any of the others; the higher the ray, the greater the deviation.   Of course, this does not guarantee that all incident parallel rays pass through the same point.   However, if we do not use too large a section of the spherical surfaces, the parallel rays indicated all pass very close to the same point.

If a lens takes a bundle of parallel rays and brings them together to a point focus, the lens is said to be *converging*.   If it takes such a bundle of parallel rays and makes them separate, the lens is *diverging*.   If glass or plastic lenses are used in air, they are converging if they are thicker in the middle than at the edge, diverging if they are thinner at the middle. Figure 29.2 shows six possible types of spherical lenses with their names.

Consider the lens of Fig. 29.3.   The left surface is a section of a spherical surface having point C_1 as its center, while the right surface is a portion of a sphere having point C_2 as its center.   *The principal axis of this lens is the line connecting the centers of curvature of the two lens surfaces,*

(Fig 29.3)

337

↘ $C_1 C_2$ is axis

If one of the surfaces is plane, we define the principal axis as the line which passes through the one center of curvature and is perpendicular to the plane surface.

Rays of light which approach a converging lens parallel to the principal axis are deviated so that they pass (Fig. 29.4) through a common point, the *principal focus,* on the principal axis. If rays of light parallel to the principal axis are incident from the opposite side of the lens, they

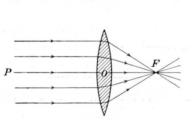

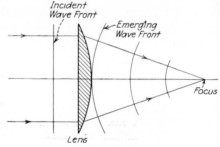

Fig. 29.2. Lens shapes. From left to right, double-convex, plano-convex, concavo-convex, convexo-concave, plano-concave, and double-concave.

Fig. 29.3. The principal axis of a lens is the line connecting the centers of curvature of the two lens surfaces.

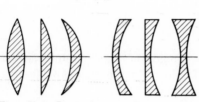

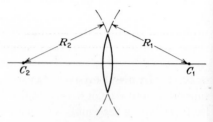

Fig. 29.4. Rays of light parallel to the principal axis are deviated by the lens so that they pass through the principal focus.

Fig. 29.5. Change in curvature of a plane wave front by a converging lens.

are deviated by the same amount and pass through the principal focus on the opposite side of the lens. Thus, a lens has *two principal foci,* one on each side. If we are dealing with thin lenses, the principal foci are equally distant from the lens. By a thin lens we mean one the thickness of which is negligible compared with the distance to the principal foci and to the objects and images concerned. In this text we confine our attention to thin lenses.

If the rays incident on a lens are parallel, the incident wave front (Fig. 29.5) is a plane perpendicular to the rays. The part of the wave front which goes through the edges emerges ahead of the central part because it has less far to go in glass where the speed is reduced. By Huygens' principle it can be shown that the emerging wave front is spherical and converges on the principal focus.

In the case of a diverging lens, rays parallel to the principal axis are bent as shown in Fig. 29.6. These rays never intersect but they all appear to come from the virtual principal focus F.

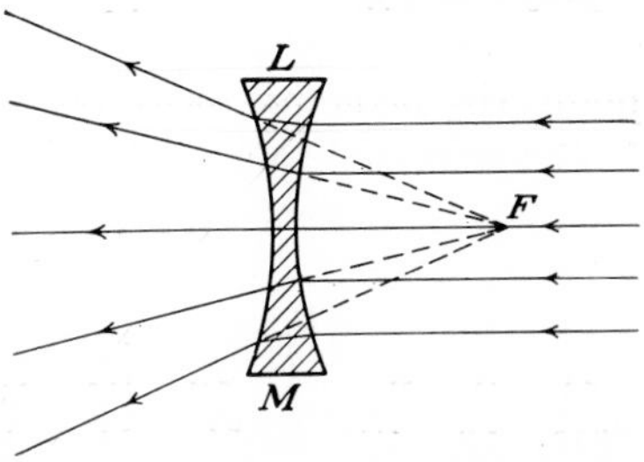

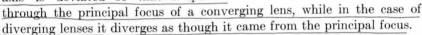

29.2. Standard Rays for Lenses.
Whenever we are concerned with the problem of tracing a ray through lenses, there are three standard rays which we can use. These rays are directly analogous to the ones we have discussed for mirrors.

Fig. 29.6. Rays parallel to the principal axis of a diverging lens are deviated so they appear to come from a virtual focus.

1. A ray parallel to the principal axis is deviated so that it passes through the principal focus of a converging lens, while in the case of diverging lenses it diverges as though it came from the principal focus.

2. A ray of light which approaches the lens along a line which passes through the principal focus for parallel rays coming from the opposite side of the lens is deviated so that it leaves the lens parallel to the principal axis.

3. A ray through the optical center of the lens passes through the lens undeviated. In a thin lens we may take the optical center to be the center point of the lens.

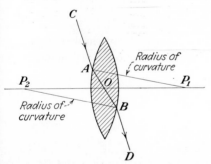

Fig. 29.7. The optical center of a thick lens is at O where the ray AB crosses the principal axis.

For a thick lens the optical center must be defined more carefully; however, for every lens there is some point such that rays passing through it are not deviated. For example, the ray $CABD$ (Fig. 29.7) emerges from the lens in the same direction in which it entered, although slightly displaced. This may be seen by drawing tangent planes at A and at B which are parallel to each other. The lens behaves for rays that enter at A and leave at B as a plate of glass with parallel faces. Such a plate causes only a displacement of the ray without a change in direction. *The optical center of the lens is the point at which an undeviated ray crosses the principal axis in passing through the lens.*

29.3. Converging Lenses.
If we have an object OP before a converging lens (Fig. 29.8), every ray of light which leaves point O on the object and passes through the lens crosses at the point I. In the figure we have

Fig 29.8

shown only the three standard rays, but any ~~other~~ ray which leaves point O and passes through the lens must pass through point I.   Therefore, at point I we have an image of point O.   For the entire object OP we find a corresponding image IQ.   This image is real and inverted.

If we place an object at IQ, the image is at OP.   The points P and Q are *conjugate points* for the lens.   Figure 29.9 shows how the wave fronts which diverge from a point on an object are made to converge by the lens to the corresponding point on the image.

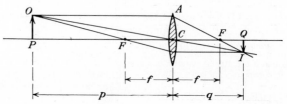

29.8. The image of an object formed by a converging lens.

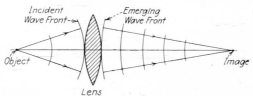

Fig. 29.9. Reversal of curvature of a spherical wave by a converging lens.

Let us denote the distance from the object to the lens by p and that from the image to the lens by q.   The distance from the lens to either principal focus is the focal length.   It is easy to show that the equation

$$\frac{1}{p} + \frac{1}{q} = \frac{1}{f} \tag{29.1}$$

applies equally as well to lenses as to mirrors.

Equation (29.1) can be derived as follows: The triangles OPC and IQC (Fig. 29.8) are similar and hence $OP/IQ = CP/CQ = p/q$.   Also, the triangles ACF and IQF are similar, so that $AC/IQ = FC/FQ = f/(q - f)$.   Since $AC = OP$, we have $AC/IQ = OP/IQ = p/q = f/(q - f)$.   Therefore $pq - pf = qf$.   If we divide by pqf and rearrange, we have $1/p + 1/q = 1/f$.

We note further that $IQ/OP = q/p$.   Since IQ is the length of the image and OP the length of the object, we have

$$\text{Linear magnification} = \frac{\text{length of image}}{\text{length of object}} = \frac{q}{p} \tag{29.2}$$

If an object is inside the principal focus of a converging lens, the image formed is *erect, virtual*, and *enlarged* (Fig. 29.10).   In this case, the image distance is negative.

29.4. Diverging Lenses.   If a real object is placed before a diverging lens, an erect, virtual, and reduced image is formed (Fig. 29.11).   If we

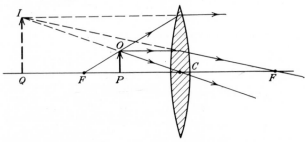

Fig. 29.10. The image of an object inside the principal focus of a converging lens is erect, virtual, and enlarged.

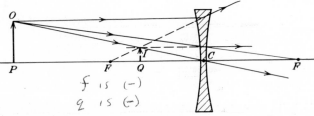

Fig. 29.11. The image of a real object formed by a diverging lens is erect, virtual, and reduced in size.

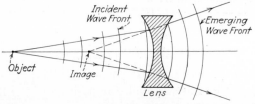

Fig. 29.12. Change of curvature of a spherical wave front by a diverging lens.

apply the general lens formula to the diverging lens, the focal length is taken as *negative*.   In Fig. 29.11 the image distance is also *negative*. Figure 29.12 shows how a wave front is affected by a diverging lens.

29.5. The Lens Maker's Equation.   The focal length of a lens depends on the material of which the lens is made and on the radii of curvature of the two surfaces.   It can be shown that the focal length is given by

$$\frac{1}{f} = (n - 1)\left(\frac{1}{R_1} + \frac{1}{R_2}\right)$$ (29.3)

where R_1 and R_2 are the radii of curvature of the two lens surfaces and n is the index of refraction of the *lens material relative to its surroundings.* In this relationship R_1 is the radius of curvature of the surface upon which the light is incident, while R_2 is the radius of curvature of the surface by which the light leaves the lens. R_1 is *positive when the surface is convex* and *negative when the surface is concave.* The same rule applies for R_2. Thus, for a double-convex lens the two radii are positive, while for the double-concave lens both are negative.

Example. A double-convex lens is made of glass having an index of refraction of 1.5. The front surface has a radius of curvature 10 cm, and the back surface has a radius of curvature of 20 cm. Find its focal length.

$$\frac{1}{f} = (n - 1)\left(\frac{1}{R_1} + \frac{1}{R_2}\right)$$

$$\frac{1}{f} = (1.5 - 1)(\tfrac{1}{10} + \tfrac{1}{20})$$

$$= \tfrac{1}{2}\,(\tfrac{3}{20}) = \tfrac{3}{40}$$

$$f = \tfrac{40}{3} = 13.3 \text{ cm}$$

The reciprocal of the focal length of a lens in meters is the power of the lens measured in diopters. Thus, a lens of focal length 50 cm has a power $P = 1/0.5 = 2$ diopters. Note that the power is given in diopters only when the focal length is measured in meters. The powers of lenses used in typical eye glasses range from about 0.2 to 4 diopters.

One of the great advantages of using the powers of lenses is associated with the fact that when two thin lenses are in contact the power of the combination is equal to the sum of the individual powers. If f represents the focal length of the combination of two thin lenses in contact,

$$\frac{1}{f} = \frac{1}{f_1} + \frac{1}{f_2} \tag{29.4}$$

where f_1 and f_2 are the focal lengths of the two lenses.

29.6. Combinations of Lenses. Whenever light passes first through one lens and then through a second, the position of the final image can be calculated by repeated use of the general lens equation. *The object for the second lens is the image formed by the first.* If there is a third lens, the image formed by the second lens acts as its object. The final image formed by a very complicated optical system, such as that of a submarine periscope, can be located by successive applications of the relations governing simple lenses and mirrors. In every case the object for any single component is the image formed by the preceding one.

In carrying out such calculations, great care must be taken to ensure that the proper signs are taken for object distances, image distances, and focal lengths. The sign convection used in this text for both lenses and mirrors is as follows:

1. *If the direction of an incident ray is from the object toward the lens (or mirror), the object distance is positive; if its direction is from the lens toward the object, p is negative.* In Fig. 29.13 the object distance for the first lens is positive, but for the second lens the object distance is negative, since the second lens is interposed ahead of the image which the first lens would produce if it acted alone.

2. The focal length is positive for a converging lens (or mirror) and negative for a diverging lens (or mirror).

3. The image distance is positive if a ray goes from the lens (or mirror) toward the image. It is negative if the ray goes away from the image when it leaves the lens (or mirror).

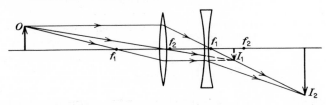

Fig. 29.13. The image formed by a pair of lenses which are separated.

Example. An object 5 cm high is 30 cm from a lens of 10 cm focal length. A diverging lens of focal length -8 cm is placed 9 cm beyond the converging one (Fig. 29.13). Find the position and height of the final image.

For the first lens $\dfrac{1}{p} + \dfrac{1}{q} = \dfrac{1}{f}$

$$\frac{1}{30} + \frac{1}{q} = \frac{1}{10} \qquad \frac{\text{size of image}}{\text{size of object}} = \frac{15}{30}$$

$$q = 15 \text{ cm} \qquad \text{size of image} = 2.5 \text{ cm}$$

For the second lens $p = -6$ cm

$$\frac{1}{-6} + \frac{1}{q} = \frac{1}{-8} \qquad \frac{\text{size of image}}{\text{size of object}} = \frac{24}{6}$$

$$q = 24 \text{ cm from second lens} \qquad \text{size of final image} = 10 \text{ cm}$$

Example. If the diverging lens of the preceding example had been only 4 cm from the first lens, where would the final image have been located? The image which would be formed by the first lens is still 15 cm from the first lens. The image distance for the second lens is now -11 cm.

$$\frac{1}{p} + \frac{1}{q} = \frac{1}{f}$$

$$\frac{1}{-11} + \frac{1}{q} = -\frac{1}{8}$$

$$q = -29.3 \text{ cm}$$

Example. An object is 25 cm from a diverging lens of 15 cm focal length. A converging lens of focal length 10 cm is 5 cm beyond the diverging lens (Fig. 29.14). Find the position of the final image.

For the first lens $\dfrac{1}{p} + \dfrac{1}{q} = \dfrac{1}{f}$

$$\dfrac{1}{25} + \dfrac{1}{q} = \dfrac{1}{-15}$$

$$q = \dfrac{-75}{8} \text{ cm}$$

For the second lens $p = {}^{75}\!/_{8} + 5 = {}^{115}\!/_{8}$ cm

$$\dfrac{1}{p} + \dfrac{1}{q} = \dfrac{1}{f}$$

$$\dfrac{8}{115} + \dfrac{1}{q} = \dfrac{1}{10}$$

$$q = 33 \text{ cm}$$

29.7. The Telephoto Lens. An interesting application of two lenses in series is found in the telephoto lens (Fig. 29.15). In order to produce a large

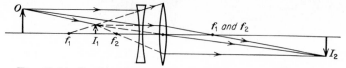

Fig. 29.14. Combination of a diverging and a converging lens.

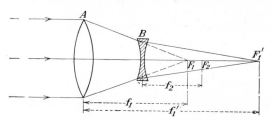

Fig. 29.15. A telephoto lens.

image of a distant object, with a single lens, the focal length must be large. This fact makes it necessary that a camera of inconvenient length be used, since the length of the camera must be approximately equal to the focal length of the lens. This difficulty can be avoided by a telephoto lens, which consists of a combination of a converging lens A and a diverging lens B placed at a distance d from each other. The converging lens A would form an image of a distant object just outside its focus F_1, but the lens B causes the image to be formed at F'_1. The image formed at F'_1 is larger than the one that would have been formed at F_1. The magnification of the lens system is increased without increasing the length of the camera too much.

Example. The telephoto lens of Fig. 29.15 is used for taking an action shot at a football game. Lens A has a focal length 12 cm and lens B a focal length of -6 cm; they are separated by a distance of 8 cm. If the action is 100 m away, find the position of the final image and the magnification of the system. What focal length single lens would produce an image of the same size? How long would the camera have to be in this case?

For lens A $\dfrac{1}{100} + \dfrac{1}{q} = \dfrac{1}{0.12}$

$$q = 0.1202 \text{ m} = 12.02 \text{ cm}$$

and the size of the image is $0.12/100$ that of the object.

For lens B, $p = -4.02$ cm and $f = -6$ cm

$$\frac{1}{-4.02} + \frac{1}{q} = \frac{1}{-6}$$

$$q = 12.2 \text{ cm}$$

Size of second image $= \dfrac{12.2}{4.02}$ size of first image

$$= \frac{12.2}{4.02} \times \frac{0.12}{100} \text{ size of original object}$$

Magnification $= 0.00364$

Film is $(8 + 12.2) = 20.2$ cm from lens A

For a single-lens camera to produce the same size image, $p = 100$ m and $q = 0.00364p$
$= 0.364$ m

$$\frac{1}{p} + \frac{1}{q} = \frac{1}{f}$$

$$\frac{1}{100} + \frac{1}{0.364} = \frac{1}{f}$$

$$f = 0.362 \text{ m}$$

Minimum length of camera is distance from lens to film $= 36.4$ cm; therefore this camera is almost twice as long as the one using the telephoto lens.

29.8. Defects of Lenses. If we had an ideal lens, every ray of light from any given point on the object would cross at exactly the same point on the image. Further, the image would be similar to the object in every respect. Any circle on the object would be a perfect circle on the image, and any square on the object would lead to a perfect square on the image. If the object were all in one plane, the image would be all in one plane. Actually no such ideal lens exists. For a single lens, the rays from a point on the object ordinarily fall over a small region of the image. If most of the rays from a point on the object cross at the desired image point but some of them cross off on one side, a defect called *coma* occurs. With some lenses a rectangular object (Fig. 29.16) is distorted so that it is *barrel-shaped;*

Object   Pincushion   Barrel

Fig. 29.16. Pincushion and barrel distortion.

in other cases it may look like a *pincushion.* The detailed explanation of these defects is beyond the scope of this book, but there are three types of image defect which can be readily explained.

Spherical Aberration. When rays of light parallel to the principal axis of a spherical lens pass through zones near its edges, they cross the axis nearer the lens than those which pass through nearer to the center. Instead of converging to a sharp focal point (Fig. 29.17) they cross the axis at slightly different points and form a blurred image. This defect is known as *spherical aberration.* It can be minimized by using only a small portion of the lens; for a lens of small aperture and long focal length, spherical aberration becomes small. Spherical aberration can be reduced by a proper choice of the curvatures of the lens surfaces. In general, the spherical aberration is minimized when the bending is roughly the same at each lens surface. In this case deviation is minimum and so is spherical aberration.

Chromatic Aberration. When rays of white light parallel to the principal axis pass through an ordinary lens, they are refracted in such a way that different colors are brought to focus at different distances from the lens (Fig. 29.18).

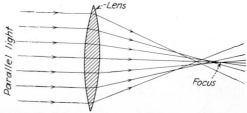

Fig. 29.17. Spherical aberration in a converging lens.

Since violet rays are bent more than the red ones, the focal length for violet light is smaller than that for red light. Such a lens cannot bring all the rays of white light from a point on the object to a single point on the image. As a result the image is not sharp and is likely to have colored rings or markings associated with it. This image defect is called *chromatic aberration.* It may be largely corrected by combining a converging lens of crown glass with a diverging lens of flint glass. These lenses are chosen so that the dispersion of one is just equal and opposite to that of the other. In this way no major separation of light into colors occurs.

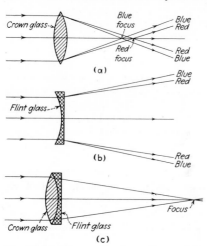

On the other hand, the bending or refractive power of one of the lens exceeds that of the other; thus there is a resultant bending of the rays in spite of the fact that one of the lenses deviates the rays in one direction and the other in the opposite direction. Lenses which are free from dispersion are called *achromatic lenses.* If two lenses

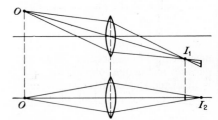

Fig. 29.18. Chromatic aberration and its correction by use of two lenses of compensating dispersion to form an achromatic doublet.

Fig. 29.19. Astigmatism and astigmatic focal lines.

are combined to form the achromatic lens, it is called an *achromatic doublet.* Actually an achromatic doublet can bring only two colors to exactly the same focus; the other colors are not perfectly corrected. If one wants to correct better for chromatic aberration, one must use more lenses.

Astigmatism. Rays of light from an object point far from the principal axis pass through the lens obliquely and do not converge to a common image point.

Figure 29.19 shows side and top views of several rays from the object point O. Rays in the vertical plane converge on I_1, while those on the horizontal plane converge on I_2. Thus, the rays from this single point at O focus in two lines I_1 and I_2 which are called *focal lines*. At a point midway between I_1 and I_2, a roughly circular patch of light corresponds to the closest approximation to a point image which is available. In quality optical systems astigmatism is corrected by the use of two or more lenses with the proper separation between them.

In a high-quality camera or microscope a combination of several lenses is utilized to perform the function which a single *ideal* lens might do. The different kinds of glass used in these lenses, their radii of curvature, and their separations are carefully chosen by the optical designer to minimize the many kinds of image defects.

PROBLEMS

Draw ray diagrams whenever appropriate.

1. A converging lens has a focal length of 12 cm. An object 4 cm high is placed 20 cm in front of the lens. Find the position and height of the image.
Ans. 30 cm; 6 cm

2. An object 15 cm from a lens has a real image 30 cm from the lens. Find the focal length of the lens.

3. An object 4 cm high is placed 20 cm from a diverging lens of focal length −12 cm. Find the position and the height of the image. *Ans.* −7.5 cm; 1.5 cm

4. A candle is placed at a distance of 2 m from a diverging lens with a focal length of −1 m. Where is the image located, and how large is it relative to the object?

5. The image formed by a converging lens is erect, virtual, and three times as high as the object. If the focal length of the lens is 25 cm, find the object and image distances. *Ans.* 16.7 cm; −50 cm

6. A metric scale is placed at a distance of 25 cm from the eyes and observed with one eye unaided, the other looking at a similar scale through a converging lens placed close to the eye. It is seen that a magnified millimeter division appears the same size as 6-mm divisions seen with the naked eye. Find the focal length of the lens.

7. A lens, made of glass whose index of refraction is 1.5, has surfaces whose radii of curvature have magnitudes 10 and 20 cm. If this is a double-convex lens, what is its focal length? If double-concave, what is the focal length?
Ans. 13.33 cm; −13.33 cm

8. The radii of curvature of a double-concave lens are 40 and 25 cm, respectively. It is made of glass which has an index of refraction of 1.5. Find its focal length.

9. A double-convex lens has radii of curvature of its surfaces of 30 and 50 cm, respectively. It is made of glass with index of refraction 1.5. An object is placed 75 cm before the lens. Locate the image. *Ans.* 75 cm

10. A plano-convex lens is used to form a virtual image of an object. The image is 12 cm from the lens. The glass of which the lens is made has an index of refraction of 1.6, and the convex surface has a radius of curvature of 15 cm. Find the position of the object.

11. A double-convex lens made of glass of index of refraction 1.5 has surfaces whose radii of curvature are both 10 in. An object 1 in. high is placed 5 in. before the lens. Locate the image. What is its height? *Ans.* −10 in.; 2 in.

12. A double-convex lens is used to form the image of an object 40 cm from the lens. The front surface of the lens has a radius of curvature of 15 cm and the back surface of 18 cm. The glass has an index of refraction of 1.6. Find the position of the image.

13. A plano-concave lens is made of glass of index of refraction 1.5. The curved surface has a radius of 12 in. An object is placed 60 in. before the lens. Where is the image? What is its size relative to the object?

Ans. −17.1 in.; ⅖ size of object

14. A double-convex lens has radii of curvature which are equal in magnitude. The index of refraction of the glass is 1.5 and the strength of the lens is 4 diopters. What is the radius of curvature of the convex surfaces?

15. The index of refraction of a double-convex glass lens is 1.65. Its radii of curvature are 12 and 25 cm, respectively. Where will it produce an image of an object which is 28 cm in front of it?   *Ans.* 22.5 cm from lens

16. A glass lens having an index of refraction of 1.65 and radii of curvature of +10 and +20 cm, respectively, is cemented to another glass lens having an index of refraction of 1.56 and radii of curvature of +5 and −10 cm, respectively. Find the focal length of the combination.

17. A double-convex lens is made of glass of index of refraction 1.5 and with radii of curvature of 15 and 30 cm, respectively. Find the focal length of this lens in air and its focal length when immersed in water.   *Ans.* 20 cm; 80 cm

18. A plano-convex lens is made of flint glass, which has an index of refraction of 1.69 for violet light and 1.64 for red light. If the radius of curvature of the curved surface of the lens is 20 cm, what is the difference in focal length of the lens for these two colors?

19. Two double-convex lenses have focal lengths of 50 cm. These are separated by 25 cm. An object 5 cm high is placed 100 cm before the first lens. Find the position of the image formed by the system of two lenses. How high is the image?

Ans. 30 cm beyond second lens; 2 cm

20. A beam of sunlight falls on a diverging lens of focal length 10 cm; 20 cm beyond this is placed a converging lens of 15 cm focal length. Find where a screen should be placed to receive the final image of the sun.

21. A converging and a diverging lens are placed 16 cm from each other. Where will this combination of lenses produce an image of a distant object if the converging lens has a focal length of 20 cm and the diverging lens a focal length of −6 cm?

Ans. +12 cm

22. A converging lens with a focal length of 18 cm is placed 40 cm in front of a diverging lens having a focal length of −30 cm. An object is placed 24 cm in front of the converging lens. Both lenses have the same principal axis and the object is located on the axis. Find the position and linear magnification of the image produced by the two lenses.

23. A converging lens that has a focal length of 30 cm is in contact with a diverging lens that has a focal length of −50 cm. What is the focal length and power of the combination of lenses?   *Ans.* 75 cm; 1.33 diopters

24. A distant object is viewed through a diverging lens that has a focal length of 30 cm and a converging lens that has a focal length of 60 cm. The lenses are 25 cm apart and have the same principal axis. If the converging lens is nearer to the eye than the diverging lens, what is the position of the image formed by these two lenses?

25. A long camera uses a telephoto lens system (Fig. 29.15) with a converging lens of 20 cm focal length separated from a diverging lens of −10 cm focal length by a distance of 12 cm. If the camera is used to photograph an object 100 m away, how far is it from the converging lens to the film? How far would it be from the lens to film in a camera using a single lens if the final image is the same size?

Ans. 53 cm; 102 cm

26. Prove that when two thin lenses are in contact the power of the combination is the sum of the powers of the two lenses. (*Hint:* Assume a distant object and use the fact that the image formed by the first lens acts as object for the second.)

Optical Instruments

30.1. The Photographic Camera. One of the simplest applications of lenses is in an ordinary photographic camera (Fig. 30.1). In a quality camera a combination of lenses in one end of the camera acts as a single ideal lens and produces a real image of an external object on a photographic film at the other end. The distance between the lens and the

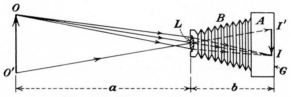

Fig. 30.1. Photographic camera.

photographic film can be altered to focus the image on the plate. In some cameras this adjustment is made by a bellows and in some by sliding one tube inside another.

For a distant object the image is formed in the focal plane, which contains the principal focus. Therefore, if two cameras of different focal lengths are set up to take the same picture, the lengths of the images of any object are directly proportional to the focal lengths of the cameras. If both cameras are using the same kind of film, the total amount of light which must reach unit area on both films for proper exposure is the same. The luminous flux entering the camera is directly proportional to the area of the lens opening which in turn is proportional to the square of the diameter of the circular opening. Consequently, the exposure times for the two cameras are the same if the ratios of focal length to diameter of the opening are the same. The *ratio of focal length to diameter of the opening is called the f number.* If a camera is set at $f/3$, the diameter of the lens opening is one-third the focal length of the camera. If the opening is reduced to $f/6$, for the same exposure a time four times as great is required. If a picture must be taken in a very short time, a lens with a small f number must be used and this in turn means a large opening. To produce a lens with a large aperture for which the various lens defects have been satisfactorily corrected is an expensive process. For this reason a camera with an $f/1.5$ lens may cost several times as much as one with an $f/3$ lens.

The smaller the opening through which light is admitted, the greater the depth of focus for a camera. A smaller cone of rays is used to form the image of a point when the opening is small; therefore the circle on which they fall is smaller when a point is not quite in focus. On the other hand, a smaller opening calls for a longer exposure. If one is taking pictures of fast action such as that in a football game, a compromise between short exposure time and great depth of focus must be made.

30.2. The Projection Lantern. In the projection lantern the fundamental optical parts are essentially those of a camera. Now we are trying to produce a large image at some distance of a small object close by. All the light which forms the image must come from the object. Since the image has a much greater area than the object, it is necessary that the object be strongly illuminated if a bright image is desired. Basically, the projection lantern consists of a powerful source of light S (Fig. 30.2), a large condensing lens NP, and an objective lens LM. The condensing lens NP collects the light from the source S and sends it through the slide OI, so that this slide is brilliantly illuminated. The objective LM then

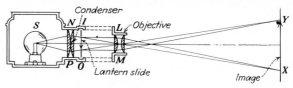

Fig. 30.2. Projection lantern.

produces a real image of the slide OI on the screen XY. Since the slide OI is just outside the principal focus of the lens LM, the image on the screen is enlarged, real, and inverted. The magnification produced by the lantern is obtained from an application of the law for the magnification of a lens.

Example. Find the focal length of a lens which must be used in a lantern to produce the image of a slide 8 cm square upon a screen 3 m square at a distance of 10 m from the lantern. Assume that the image covers the entire screen.

$$\text{Magnification} = \frac{q}{p} = \frac{300}{8}$$

Since $q = 1,000$ cm

$$\frac{q}{p} = \frac{1,000}{p} = \frac{300}{8} \quad \text{and} \quad p = 26.7 \text{ cm}$$

$$\frac{1}{p} + \frac{1}{q} = \frac{1}{f}$$

$$\frac{1}{26.7} + \frac{1}{1,000} = \frac{1}{f}$$

$$f = 25.9 \text{ cm}$$

30.3. The Eye. Like the camera, the eye can be looked upon as a lighttight enclosure having a lens at one end and a sensitive film of nerve fibers at the other end.   To understand how the eye works, it is desirable to have some appreciation of its anatomy.   The eyeball is a hollow sphere of dense fibrous tissue (Fig. 30.3).   In front there is a small transparent tissue called the *cornea*.   Its radius of curvature is much less than that of the remainder of the eyeball; the principal bending of light occurs when it enters the cornea.   Light passes through the cornea into a clear fluid called the *aqueous humor* from which it enters the *lens*. The index of refraction of the lens is somewhat greater than that of the aqueous humor on one side and the jellylike substance known as the *vitreous humor* on the other.

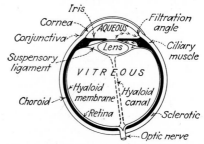

Fig. 30.3. Anatomy of the human eye.

The light is brought to focus on the *retina*, which plays the role of a sensitive screen.   The amount of light which enters the eye is regulated by a circular diaphragm called the *iris*.   It is this diaphragm which is responsible for color of the eye.   It is provided with muscles which diminish or dilate the *pupil*, which is the opening through which the light enters the lens.   When the eye is relaxed, the lens is in its thinnest shape and has surfaces of maximum radii of curvature.   Under these circumstances

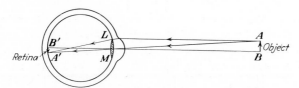

Fig. 30.4. Normal eye.   The image is focused on the retina.

a normal eye is in focus for distant objects.   For a close object the image would fall behind the retina if no adjustment were made.   However, the muscles of the ciliary body which encircles the lens contract, thereby changing the shape of the lens and making the radii of curvature smaller, particularly that of the front surface.   Thus the focal length of the lens is reduced and the image focused on the retina (Fig. 30.4).

The remarkable ability of the eye to adjust its focal length is called *accommodation*.   The greatest and shortest ranges at which a given eye can see distinctly are called the *far point* and *near point*, respectively. For a normal eye the far point is at infinity; the near point may be 6 cm for a child and usually increases with age.

30.4. Defects of Vision.   If the image formed by a distant object falls in front of the retina, an eye is *nearsighted* or *myopic* (Fig. 30.5).

This may occur because the lens has too short a focal length, because the eyeball is too long, or for some other reason. Such an eye may see a near object distinctly since the image moves back as the object approaches. To correct for *myopia*, a diverging lens is placed in front of the eye. The image formed by this lens serves as the object for the eye.

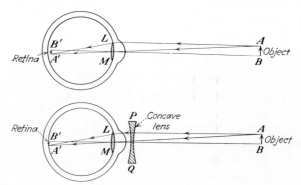

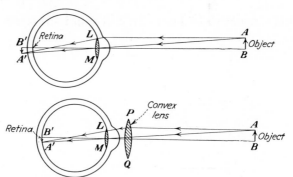

Fig. 30.5. Nearsighted eye. The image of a distant object falls in front of the retina. A diverging lens provides the correction.

Fig. 30.6. Farsighted eye. The image of a close object falls behind the retina. A converging lens provides the correction.

Example. A nearsighted eye cannot see objects clearly when they are more than 3 m distant. Find the power of the weakest correcting lens which will just allow this eye to form a sharp image of the moon on the retina.

The image formed by the lens serves as object for the eye. The lens desired must form an image of a distant object 3 m from the eye. Therefore, $p = \infty$ and $q = -3$ m.

$$\frac{1}{p} + \frac{1}{q} = \frac{1}{f}$$

$$\frac{1}{\infty} + \frac{1}{-3} = \frac{1}{f}$$

$$f = -3 \text{ m}$$

$$\text{Power} = -\tfrac{1}{3} = -0.33 \text{ diopter}$$

In the *farsighted* or *hyperopic* eye the image of a nearby object is formed behind the retina (Fig. 30.6). This defect may arise because the lens is too flat or the eyeball too short. As the object is moved far away, the image moves nearer to the retina so this eye may see distant objects clearly. To correct for farsightedness, a converging lens is placed in front of the eye. This makes the equivalent focal length of the eye shorter.

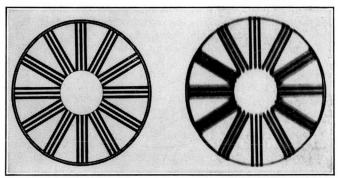

Fig. 30.7. To the normal eye all the spokes of the wheel at the left appear equally sharp. To the astigmatic eye the radial lines differ in sharpness. The image at the right was formed with a cylindrical lens in the optical system to illustrate astigmatism. (*Courtesy of Glenn A. Fry, School of Optometry, Ohio State University.*)

Example. The near point of an eye is 90 cm. What is the lowest power lens which will permit this eye to see print clearly at a distance of 25 cm?

The image formed by the lens acts as object for the eye. The lens must produce an image of the print at 25 cm at a distance of 90 cm in front of the eye.

$$p = 25 \text{ cm} \qquad q = -90 \text{ cm}$$
$$\frac{1}{p} + \frac{1}{q} = \frac{1}{f}$$
$$\frac{1}{25} + \frac{1}{-90} = \frac{1}{f}$$
$$f = 34.8 \text{ cm}$$
$$\text{Power} = \frac{1}{0.348} = 2.89 \text{ diopters}$$

Another common defect of the eye is *astigmatism*. This defect occurs when the lens or the cornea does not have a truly spherical surface. The curvature is not the same in different planes containing the axis of the eye. Then the focal length is not the same in different planes. Rays of light from a vertical luminous wire do not come to a focus at the same place as the rays from a horizontal luminous wire. When light from some luminous area is received by the eye, there is an attempt by the eye to adjust so that light from all parts of the object forms sharp images. With an astigmatic eye this is not possible, because the optical system has different focal lengths for light in different planes. Consequently, the image formed is indistinct (Fig. 30.7) and the eye is strained in forming the image. This defect may be overcome by using lenses that have cylindrical surfaces.

30.5. Luminous Flux and the Eye.   The eye has two mechanisms by which it adjusts for changes in the level of illumination.   The first is by varying the diameter of the *pupil* through the motion of the iris.   In bright light the pupil closes down; in dim light it opens.   However, this adjustment covers only a relatively minor range and the total amount of light entering the eye can be changed by only a factor of about 16 by changes in the iris.   The eye, however, can see in brilliant sunlight and in dim moonlight, a range of illumination which covers a factor of many millions.   The principal mechanism which the eye uses to adapt for changes in illumination is that of changing the sensitivity of the retinal surface.   To understand this, we must consider the retina in more detail.

Just under the surface of the retina is a mosaic of photosensitive cells, of which there are two kinds named *rods* and *cones* after their shapes.   The cones are responsible for color vision; the rods give only achromatic perceptions of white, gray, and black.   The rods are grouped in bunches with each bunch having a connection to the brain, while each cone usually has a private line to the brain.

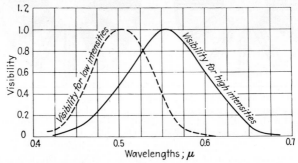

Fig. 30.8. Relative illuminances produced for equal intensities of monochromatic radiation of visible wavelengths.   Solid curve is for cones and dashed curve for rods.

Cones are largely concentrated in the central region of the retina, the *fovea*.   As we go away from this central region, the number of cones per unit area decreases. The number of rods per unit area increases to a maximum at 20° from the optic axis and then decreases slowly.

The cones of the foveal area give us acute and color vision under conditions of high to adequate illumination.   The solid line of Fig. 30.8 shows how cones respond to equal intensities of various wavelengths.   For equal amounts of light energy a yellow-green light of $\lambda \approx 0.56\mu$ appears brightest to the normal light-adapted eye.   One watt of radiant energy at this wavelength corresponds to 680 lumens of luminous flux.   Under illuminances lower than about 0.5 lumens/m² the cones do not respond well.   The rods are sensitive to very small amounts of radiant energy.   The dotted curve of Fig. 30.8 shows that the rods have maximum sensitivity at $\lambda = 0.51\ \mu$; they are relatively more sensitive to blues and less sensitive to reds than the cones.   This is one reason for using blue lights for aisles of theaters and darkened railroad trains.

On the rods the eye builds a photosensitive pigment called *rhodopsin* or *visual purple*.   When light strikes a rod, rhodopsin is bleached and a signal goes to the brain.   In bright daylight little rhodopsin is present.   In darkness the rhodopsin is built up in the rods and the eye becomes *dark adapted*.   It takes about 30 min to build up a maximum concentration.   When this has been accomplished, the eye is very sensitive to light.   This accounts for the blinding effect of bright head lamps from an approaching car at night; these same lights would produce no problem at all in daytime when little rhodopsin is present.

30.6. Convergence and Divergence. When the eyes are focused on near objects, there is a movement of the eyeballs, causing the visual axes to converge from the normal parallel position toward the middle line (Fig. 30.9). Such a movement is necessary in order that the images in both eyes may fall on the correct area of the retina. The amount of convergence varies inversely as the distance of the object. In normal circumstances the visual axes are in parallel adjustment for objects at infinity. Because of the distance between the eyes, objects are viewed from slightly different angles by each eye. Each retina receives a slightly different picture; this helps us judge distances and solidity.

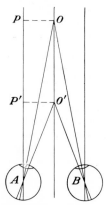

30.7. Simple Microscope. When an object is placed inside the principal focus of a converging lens, an eye brought up to the lens sees a virtual, erect, and magnified image $A'B'$ (Fig. 30.10). A lens used in this way constitutes a simple microscope. To obtain the greatest advantage, the eye should be as near as possible to the lens. In this way, the

Fig. 30.9. Convergence of the optical axes of the eyes.

field of view is made as large as possible. For most distinct vision, an object must be about 25 cm from a normal eye. If an object is placed at a greater distance, the image on the retina is smaller and its details are not seen so distinctly. When the object is placed nearer than 25 cm, the image on the retina is blurred.

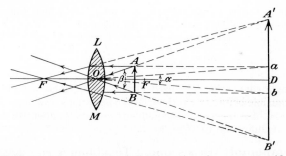

Fig. 30.10. A simple microscope produces a virtual, erect, magnified image.

When an object is examined with the aid of a magnifying glass, the object is brought nearer to the eye than would be possible for distinct vision without the magnifying glass. In Fig. 30.10 the angles subtended at the center of the lens by the object AB and the image $A'B'$ are the same. But OD is the distance of distinct vision, and, if the lens were absent, the eye could not see AB distinctly until it is removed to ab. Hence by using the lens, the visual angle has been increased from α to β.

The *angular magnification* of the simple microscope is defined as the ratio β/α.

$$M = \text{angular magnification} = \frac{\beta}{\alpha} = \frac{A'B'/25}{AB/25} = \frac{q}{p}$$

For most distinct vision $q = -25$ cm, and since $1/p + 1/q = 1/f$

$$\frac{25}{p} = +\frac{25}{f_{\text{cm}}} + 1$$

Hence, the angular magnification M is given by

$$M = \frac{25}{f_{\text{cm}}} + 1$$

if the image is at the distance of most distinct vision and the eye is placed as close as possible to the lens.

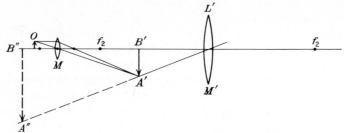

Fig. 30.11. Simplified diagram of the optical parts of a compound microscope.

It is usually less tiring to use a simple microscope if the final image is at infinity, since then the eye muscles are relaxed. In this case

$$M = \frac{A'B'/q}{AB/25} = \frac{AB/f_{\text{cm}}}{AB/25} = \frac{25}{f_{\text{cm}}}$$

With a single converging lens used at the eye, angular magnifications up to about 4 are possible before aberrations become a serious problem. By using eyepieces composed of two lenses it is possible to correct for aberrations and increase the angular magnification to 15 or 20.

30.8. Compound Microscope. To obtain great magnification, a compound microscope is used. It utilizes a group of lenses, acting as an ideal single converging lens M of short focal length (Fig. 30.11). This lens, called the *objective*, produces a real, magnified image $A'B'$ of a small object placed just outside its focus. The image $A'B'$ is viewed through the eyepiece $L'M'$, which acts as a simple microscope. The eyepiece produces an enlarged, virtual image $A''B''$ of the real image $A'B'$.

The magnification of a compound microscope (Fig. 30.12) depends on the focal lengths of objective and eyepiece. The objective might have a focal length of

5 mm and form a real image at a distance of 20 cm from the objective. Since the object is near the focus of the objective, the object distance may be taken as almost equal to 5 mm. The linear magnification produced by this lens is then

$$\frac{q}{p} = \frac{20}{0.5} = 40$$

If now the eyepiece has a focal length of 2.5 cm and is adjusted for a final image at infinity, the angular magnification is $25/f = 10$. The over-all angular magnification is $40 \times 10 = 400$ times.

30.9. Astronomical Telescope.

The principle of the astronomical telescope is the same as that of the compound microscope. The objective lens LM is modified to meet the fact that the instrument is used to view distant objects. The objective, which is a large converging lens of long focal length, forms a real, inverted image $A'B'$ of a distant object AB. This real image is formed at the focus of the eyepiece NP

Fig. 30.12. A binocular compound microscope. (*Bausch and Lomb Optical Co.*)

by which an enlarged virtual image $A''B''$ of the real image $A'B'$ is produced at infinity.

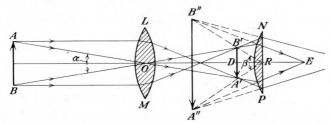

Fig. 30.13. Diagrammatic representation of an astronomical telescope, not drawn to scale. Actually $A'B'$ is formed at the principal focus of the objective lens LM and the final image $A''B''$ is placed at infinity by adjusting the eyepiece NP so that $A'B'$ is at its principal focus.

Because of the great distance of the object from the telescope, the rays from any point are essentially parallel when they reach the objective. Hence, the image formed lies essentially in the focal plane of the objective. The angular magnification of the telescope is determined by the angles that the object subtends and appears to subtend at the eye (Fig. 30.13). The angle that the object AB subtends at the eye when no lenses are present is $AOB = B'OA'$. The angle that the image $A''B''$ subtends at the eye is $B''RA'' = A'RB'$.

$$\text{Angular magnification} = \frac{A'RB'}{A'OB'} = \frac{A'B/RD}{A'B'/OD} = \frac{OD}{RD}$$
$$= \frac{\text{focal length of objective}}{\text{focal length of eyepiece}}$$
$$= \frac{F}{f}$$

The image formed by an astronomical telescope is inverted. For terrestrial uses of the telescope it is desirable that the image be erect. This condition is realized by inserting a third convex lens between the objective and the eyepiece in such a way that the image $A'B'$ formed by the objective is again inverted before it is viewed by the eyepiece.

Example. The focal length of the objective of a telescope is 150 cm and the focal length of the eyepiece is 2 cm. Find the angular magnification of the telescope for distant objects.

$$\text{Angular magnification} = \frac{\text{focal length of objective}}{\text{focal length of eyepiece}}$$
$$= {}^{150}\!/_{2} = 75$$

In very large telescopes the objective lens is replaced by a concave mirror. One possible arrangement of this mirror and the eyepiece is evident from Fig. 30.14. The mirror in use at the Mount Palomar Observatory has a diameter of 200 in.

30.10. Prism Binoculars. A terrestrial telescope of reasonable field and magnification becomes unreasonably long. The prism binocular has largely replaced the old "spy glasses."

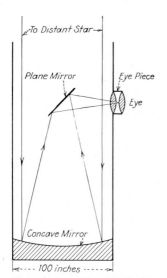

Fig. 30.14. Simplified diagram of a reflecting telescope.

Each side of the binocular achieves a long optical path by making the light traverse almost three times the length of the binoculars (Fig. 30.15). The beam of light OB from the objective is reflected internally at B and C by a right-angled prism. In this way, its direction is reversed, and it travels back to a second right-angled prism which is placed at right angles to the first one. Here it is again reflected internally at D and E and then passes through the eyepiece. The reflections at B and C interchange the two sides of the image so that it is no longer perverted like the image in an ordinary plane mirror. Reflection by the second prism at D and E makes the image upright. Hence, the image after the reflections by the two right-angled prisms is restored completely to its natural position. The eyepiece then magnifies this image, serving as a simple microscope.

30.11. Opera Glass or Galilean Telescope. The opera glass uses an objective *LM* which converges the rays from a distant object toward an image *TS* (Fig. 30.16). Before they reach this image they pass through the diverging lens *NP* which acts as eyepiece. In passing through this lens, rays that were converging are made to diverge. To an eye on the right-hand side of lens *NP*, the rays appear to have come from the virtual, erect image *A'B'*.

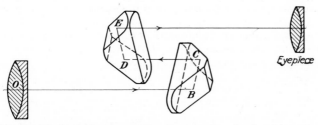

Fig. 30.15. Optical components of one ocular of prism binoculars.

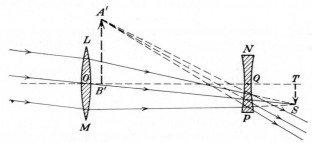

Fig. 30.16. Optical components of the opera glass, not to scale. The final image *A'B'* is usually placed at infinity in which case *T* is at one of the principal foci of the diverging lens *NP*.

To have the opera glass in focus, the lens *NP* is adjusted so the rays emerging from it are parallel and the final image is at infinity. Then,

$$\text{Angular magnification} = \frac{\text{focal length of objective}}{\text{focal length of eyepiece}} = \frac{F}{f}$$

The length of the opera glass is $F - f$; thus the glasses need not be as long as a telescope of comparable magnifying power. A major disadvantage of the opera glass is its small field of view.

PROBLEMS

1. A camera has a lens of 50 mm focal length. When it is set at $f/3$, what is the diameter of the lens opening? If the iris setting is changed to $f/4.5$, how much longer exposure time is required?   *Ans.* 16.7 mm; 2.25 times

2. The lens of an aerial camera has a focal length of 9 in. What will be the dimensions on the plate of 1 square mile of the earth's surface, photographed from a height of 3 miles?

3. The lens of a camera has focal length of 8 in. It is used to photograph an object that is 10 ft from it, and then to photograph an object that is 100 ft from it. How much must the lens of the camera be moved?   *Ans. 0.51 in.*

4. If a camera with a focal length of 6 in. produces a sharp image of a distant object, how far must the lens be moved to have the camera in focus for an object 8 ft away?

5. A double-convex lens whose focal length is 2 in. is used as a magnifier. If held close to the eye to form an image 10 in. from the eye, where should the object be located? What is the angular magnification?   *Ans. 1.67 in.; 6*

6. A converging lens used as a reading glass has a focal length of 5 cm. What is the angular magnification if the lens is used to produce an image at a distance of 25 cm from the eye?

7. A microscope consists of an objective of 0.5 in. focal length and an eyepiece of 1 in. focal length. These lenses are placed 6 in. apart. A person uses it to form an image at infinity. Where must the object be placed?   *Ans. 0.56 in.*

8. The objective of a compound microscope has a focal length of 0.5 cm, and its eyepiece has a focal length of 1.5 cm. If the distance between the objective and the eyepiece is 25 cm, what is the angular magnification of the microscope when the image is at infinity?

9. A nearsighted person can see objects which are placed no more than 7.5 in. from his eyes. What is the focal length of the weakest lens which will permit him to see distant objects?   *Ans. −7.5 in.*

10. A nearsighted person cannot see objects clearly when they are more than 50 cm from his eyes. Find the power of the weakest lens which will permit him to see distant objects distinctly.

11. A farsighted eye has a near point of 60 cm. Find the power of the lens which will bring the near point to 20 cm.   *Ans. 3.3 diopters*

12. The closest distance of distinct vision for a certain eye is 2 m. What kind of lens will permit this eye to see clearly an object that is 40 cm from the eye? State the minimum power of the lens in diopters.

13. A farsighted person can see distinctly objects which are no closer than 36 in. A plano-convex lens made of glass whose index of refraction is 1.5 is used to enable him to see an object located 10 in. away. What should be the radius of the curved surface?   *Ans. 6.93 in.*

14. An enlarging camera has a lens with a focal length of 8 in. It is used to enlarge a negative that is 3 in. on each side. How far from the lens must the negative be placed in order that each side of the negative may be 9 in.?

15. A compound microscope has an objective lens of focal length 4 mm, which forms an image 20 cm from the lens. The eyepiece produces a magnification of 10. What is the total magnification?   *Ans. 490*

16. A camera with a lens of 6 in. focal length is used to take a picture of an object 12 ft away. How far from the eye must the picture be held so that the image will subtend the same angle at the eye as the object subtended at the lens of the camera?

17. A projection lantern is desired which will throw an image 6 ft wide on a wall 30 ft distant of a slide 3 in. wide. What must be the focal length of the projecting lens selected?   *Ans. 1.2 ft*

18. A projection lantern is to be placed at a distance of 20 ft from a screen on which an image with a height of 4 ft is desired of a slide 3 in. high. What should be the focal length of the projecting lens?

19. The objective lens of an astronomical telescope has a focal length of 8 ft and the eyepiece a focal length of 2 in. Calculate the angular magnification obtained when the telescope is used for viewing distant objects.   *Ans. 48*

20. A telescope which consists of an objective that has a focal length 75 cm and an eyepiece with focal length of 1.5 cm is used to view an object that is 600 cm from the objective.   What must be the distance between the eyepiece and the objective for the final image at infinity?

21. The objective lens of an astronomical telescope has a focal length of 48 in.   The focal length of the eyepiece is 0.60 in.   It is desired to produce a real image of a distant object on a screen that is 8 in. from the eyepiece.   How far must the objective lens be placed from the eyepiece?   *Ans.* 48.65 in.

CHAPTER 31

Skip

Spectra and Color

31.1. Spectroscopy. When a beam of white light is passed through a prism, the light is dispersed into a spectrum (Sec. 28.8). If we use an incandescent lamp bulb or a candle as a light source, we observe all the

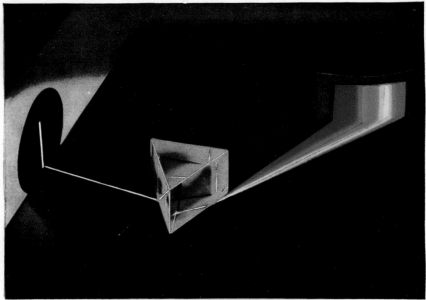

Fig. 31.1. Prismatic spectrum. A beam of white light is dispersed into its component colors.

colors of the rainbow (Fig. 31.1). However, if we put salt in the flame of a bunsen burner, the light emitted is yellow. If a lithium salt is put in the flame, a bright red is produced.

The systematic examination of the spectra from various light sources was initiated by Kirchhoff about a century ago. The spectra of elements gave us one of the most important clues in the development of

362

modern atomic theory. To this day spectroscopy is one of the most active branches of physics; industrial applications are legion. Spectroscopy involves the observation and interpretation of spectra. It deals not only with visible light but also with electromagnetic waves of longer and shorter wavelengths including radio, radar, infrared, ultraviolet, x-ray, and gamma-ray waves. The wavelength regions of these radiations are suggested below and in Fig. 31.2. Actually there is substantial overlapping of regions and most of the boundaries are not sharp.

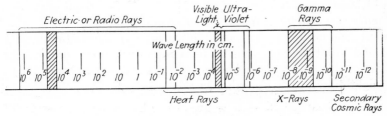

Fig. 31.2. The electromagnetic spectrum.

As an example of how potent a tool spectroscopy is, consider the spectrum of the element *helium* which was observed in light from the sun some 25 years before helium was discovered on the earth. Thanks to study of spectra of the stars, we know a great deal about their chemical composition, even though no sample has ever been placed in the hands of a chemist. In the next few sections we shall discuss some important types of spectra and how they may be studied. In spectral measurements we are concerned directly with the wavelengths of the radiation, which range from many kilometers for radio waves to far less than a billion billionth of a meter. Some of the common units in which wavelengths are reported are given in Table 2.

Table 1

Kinds of waves	Limit of wavelengths
Waves from oscillatory circuits	10^4 km to 10^{-4} m
Infrared radiation	10^{-3} to 7×10^{-7} m
Visible spectrum	7×10^{-7} to 4×10^{-7} m
Ultraviolet radiation	4×10^{-7} to 10^{-8} m
X-rays	10^{-8} to 10^{-14} m
Gamma rays	10^{-10} to 10^{-12} m
Secondary cosmic rays	10^{-10} m to —

Table 2

Name of unit	Abbreviation	Value, m
Micron	μ	10^{-6}
Millimicron	$m\mu$	10^{-9}
Angstrom	A	10^{-10}
X unit	xu	10^{-13}

31.2. The Spectrometer.   For the study of optical spectra a spectroscope or a spectrometer is used.   One essential part of a typical spectrometer (Fig. 31.3) is the collimator, which consists of a tube with a slit at one end and a converging lens at the other.   The slit is located at the principal focus of the lens so that the light rays which emerge from the lens when the slit is illuminated are parallel. These rays pass through a prism which disperses the light to a telescope mounted so that it can rotate about the vertical axis of the instrument.   The angle through which the telescope is rotated is read on a divided circle.

31.3. Types of Emission Spectra.   There are several different ways in which spectra may be classified.   We shall divide them as follows.

Continuous Spectra.   When the spectrum of the light from an incandescent solid or liquid is examined, it shows no regions of darkness (Figs. 31.1 and Frontispiece).   Spectra from an incandescent lamp or a carbon arc are of this kind and are known as *continuous spectra*, since they contain light of every wavelength over a broad region.

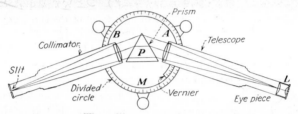

Fig. 31.3. A spectrometer.   The collimator produces parallel rays, which the telescope brings to a focus.

Bright-line Spectra.   If a solution of some salt such as lithium chloride is introduced into the flame of a bunsen burner, the light emitted consists of a number of *narrow bright lines* (Frontispiece) with wavelengths characteristic of the element that emits them.   Such spectra are known as *bright-line* spectra.   Each substance has its own characteristic spectrum.

Since each element has a unique spectrum, an examination of the light emitted by a substance gives direct evidence of its composition.   This method is very useful in detecting small quantities of a substance.   It is a rapid and sensitive method of analysis.   The spectrum of an element can be excited in a variety of ways, among which are passing an electrical discharge through a gas containing the element, heating the material in a furnace, or introducing it into an electric arc.   The characteristic spectral lines are radiated when an electron of an element is excited from its normal state (Chap. 48).

When radiation is emitted by excited molecules, the spectrum often appears in the form of bands of light with regions of darkness between.   Such molecular spectra are often referred to as *band spectra*.   However, when band spectra are studied in spectrometers of great resolving power, it is found that the bands result from a large group of lines which are close together.   The overlapping of these lines gives rise to the band structure.

31.4. Dark-line Spectra; Fraunhofer Lines.   The spectrum of the sun is crossed by a number of fine dark lines (Frontispiece), known as

Fraunhofer lines. They are produced by absorption in the atmospheres of the sun and of the earth. The core of the sun emits white light. Surrounding this central part is an atmosphere of cooler vapors and gases. When light passes through this solar atmosphere, the wavelengths corresponding to the light that would be emitted by these luminous vapors is absorbed by them. For example, sodium vapor in the sun's atmosphere absorbs those wavelengths which sodium vapor emits when luminous. These wavelengths are therefore almost absent when the solar spectrum is examined. From the Fraunhofer lines it has been possible

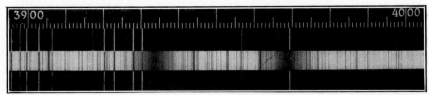

Fig. 31.4. Emission spectrum of iron and the spectrum of the sun (center), showing that many Fraunhofer lines correspond to absorption by iron vapor. The wavelength region covered here is from 3,900 to 4,000 A. (*Courtesy of Mt. Wilson Observatory.*)

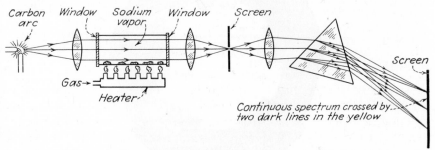

Fig. 31.5. Schematic diagram of a method of producing a dark-line spectrum by absorption of light in sodium vapor.

to determine what elements are abundant in the sun's atmosphere. Figure 31.4 compares the emission spectrum of iron with the solar spectrum, showing that iron vapor is present in the solar atmosphere. It is possible to produce a dark-line spectrum of sodium vapor by passing white light from a carbon arc through sodium vapor (Fig. 31.5).

31.5. The Doppler Effect. When a sound source is moving toward or away from an observer, the frequency observed is different from the source frequency (Sec. 17.7). An effect similar to this is observed in light. The Doppler effect provides a means of determining the motions of distant luminous bodies, such as planets and stars. If a star is moving away from the earth, the frequency of a spectral line observed at the earth is lower than the emitted frequency so that the observed wavelength is greater than normal; if the star is approaching the earth, the wavelengths are shifted toward smaller values. By measuring the displacements of the lines, the speed of the moving star can be determined.

The Doppler effect of light waves differs in one very important respect from that for sound waves. For sound waves it is the velocity of the source (or of the observer) *relative to the air* which is of importance. In the case of light waves there is no comparable medium. So long as the velocity of the light source relative to the observer is small compared with the speed of light,

$$\frac{f_{\text{observed}}}{f_{\text{source}}} = \frac{c}{c - v} \tag{31.1}$$

where c is the speed of light and v the velocity of source toward observer.

The Doppler effect is used for measuring speeds of missiles and of automobiles. For example, when a radar transmitter on a police car sends out very high-frequency waves, these waves are reflected by oncoming automobiles. The reflected

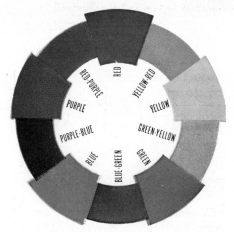

Fig. 31.6. Hue circle showing the principal hues.

waves have a different frequency and are "beat" (Sec. 16.9) against the initial frequency, yielding a *beat frequency* equal to the difference between the two. In this case the source is the image of the transmitter reflected from the vehicle which acts as a plane mirror. Therefore, the speed of the source is twice the speed v of the oncoming vehicle. Let the frequency emitted by the radar be f and that received be f_r. Then Eq. (31.1) yields

$$\frac{f_r}{f} = \frac{c}{c - 2v}$$

The beat frequency F is given by

$$F = f_r - f = \frac{2vf}{c - 2v} = \frac{2vf}{c}$$

since $2v$ is negligible compared with c.

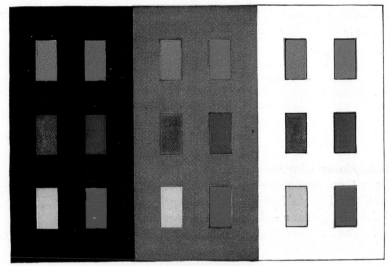

Fig. 31.7. A contrast of hues showing effect of background on color. (*From F. A. Osborne, Physics of the Home.*)

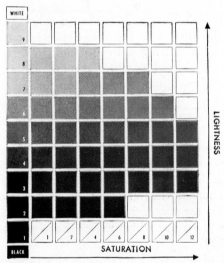

Fig. 31.8. Sample page of a Munsell color atlas (with the designation of the coordinates changed.)

Example. A radar transmitter sends out a signal at 100 megacycles. An automobile is approaching and the beat frequency observed is 19 beats per second. Find the speed of the approaching car.

$$F = \frac{2vf}{c}$$

$F = 19$ beats per second $f = 10^8$ cycles/sec
$$c = 186,000 \text{ mi/sec}$$
$$19 = \frac{2v \times 10^8}{186,000}$$
$$v = 1.77 \times 10^{-2} \text{ mi/sec}$$
$$= 64 \text{ mi/hr}$$

31.6. Color Classification. When we look at a group of colored objects, there are three psychophysical characteristics in terms of which we can make a qualitative color description. They are *hue, saturation,* and *lightness* (or for a self-luminous object such as a light bulb, the *brightness*). The *hue* we can give in terms of the color which the object most closely resembles, such as blue, orange, purple, or yellow-green in the hue circle of Fig. 31.6. In the system of color notation developed by Munsell the complete hue circle consists of 100 hues. The apparent hue depends somewhat on the background against which it is observed (Fig. 31.7).

The term *saturation* has to do with the extent to which the hue is influenced by the addition of other colors. If blue is the only color present, the saturation approaches unity. On the other hand, if other colors are present, but enough blue so that the object has a blue hue, the saturation is low (Fig. 31.8). In mixing paints, a paint of lower saturation can always be made by mixing white with the color. Thus, it is easy to produce a wide range of variations in saturation for the same hue. As we go from zero to 100 per cent in saturation, we go from whites and grays to pure colors. Whites and grays are *achromatic* and correspond to zero saturation.

Lightness is connected with the relative amount of light which reaches the eye from the object. If the object is illuminated by white light and it reflects all the incident light, it has maximum lightness and appears white; if it reflects none of the light, it is black. It is possible to arrange achromatic grays in a scale of brightness and to match against these grays samples of a given hue which reflect the same fraction of the incident light (Fig. 31.8).

One simple way of representing colors is in a three-dimensional color cylinder or color tree (Fig. 31.9) in which the lightness (or brightness) is plotted, going from black to grays to brilliant white along an axis. Around this axis can be drawn concentric circles with the various hues given by the angles and the saturations by the distance from the central white-black axis.

31.7. Color Vision.   Color vision is known to arise from the stimulation of the cones in the retina.   The processes which occur in color vision are not completely understood, but a reasonable explanation can be built upon the assumption that there are three types of cone response, each of which is excited to some extent by the whole visual spectrum (Fig. 31.10). However, the blue response is particularly strong for wavelengths around 450 mμ, the green around 550 mμ, and the red response around 600 mμ.

When all three types of response are aroused about equally, the sensation of white light is produced.   It is not necessary that all wavelengths be present to get the sensation of white light.   Indeed, properly chosen amounts of radiation of only two wavelengths can excite all responses sufficiently so that a sensation of perfect white light is created.   Two wavelengths (or two colors) which when mixed together give white light are said to be *complementary*.   Red and blue-green are complementary and so are blue and yellow.   The complementary of green is reddish-purple (magenta) which is not a spectral color.

Purples arise from excitation of the blue and red sensations without any substantial amount of green.   Purple is not a spectral color, but a mixture of spectral colors.   Yellow is a true spectral color; nevertheless, the simultaneous excitation of the red and green sensations in roughly equal amounts gives the eye the sensation of yellow, even though none of the "yellow wavelengths" are present.

31.8. The Measurement of Color.   Suppose that we have a projector (Fig. 31.11) which throws on the screen S_1 an arbitrary color X. Let us now illuminate the adjacent area S_2 by means of three lanterns, each of which sends out a light of a single narrow wavelength region, A at 425 mμ (blue), B at 551 mμ (green), and C at 650 mμ (red).   For almost any color we can find one and only one combination of relative intensities of these three lights which exactly matches the color X.   We can then describe color X in terms of the values of these amounts of light from A, B, and C.   Thus, we can describe this color by three specific numbers.

Although we may match almost all colors in this way, there are some which we cannot match by adding everything on the screen at the right. Colors which we cannot match are outside the *gamut* of these *primaries*. However, if we move the proper one of the lamps to the other side and add its light to the unknown color, it is possible to achieve a match.   For example, if we try to match a pure green of $\lambda = 500$ mμ with the lamps above, we find that we always have too much red, but if we move lamp C to the other side, we find that we can match $\lambda = 500$ mμ plus some red from C with light from lamps A and B.   One way of saying this is to say we can match $\lambda = 500$ mμ with light from A and B and a *negative* amount of light from C. This, however, introduces the complication of negative numbers for specifying some colors.

We have chosen for our illuminants blue, green, and red, because with them we can match the widest gamut of colors.   In this sense red, green, and blue are primary colors.   However, if we use any three different

Fig. 31.9. Color tree showing the three-dimensional relationship between lightness, hue, and saturation. (*Reproduced, with permission, from the Kodak Data Book Color as Seen and Photographed.   The color tree was produced by Allcolor Company, Inc., New York.*)

wavelengths, we can still match any color if we include the use of negative contributions and if we assume that the sources A, B, and C can be varied in intensity over an infinite range.

To avoid the difficulties associated with negative numbers and for other reasons, the International Commission on Illumination agreed in 1931 on a standard *operational procedure* for determining the color of a surface. (This method can be shown to be equivalent to the type of experiment in which we match the color with three primary sources, except that the sources chosen do not exist in the realm of *real colors*.)   The surface is placed in a spectrophotometer.   This instrument contains an optical system in which the light from a standard lamp is dispersed into a spectrum by a prism.   One narrow range of wavelengths at a time is allowed to

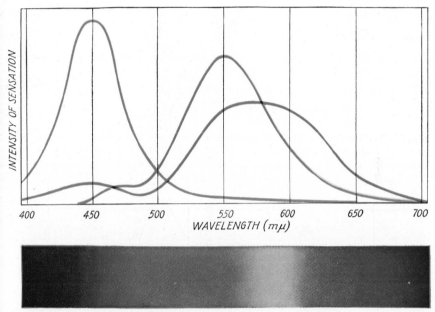

Fig. 31.10. Approximate response curves of the normal color vision according to the three-component theory with the spectrum of daylight (to which the curves pertain) suggested beneath.

fall upon the surface under test and the amount of light reflected is compared with the amount of the same wavelength range reflected from a standard white surface.   A plot is made of the relative reflectance of the surface under test as a function of wavelength.   Several such *spectral reflectance* curves are shown in Fig. 31.12.   From the spectral reflectance curve it is possible to calculate the coordinates x and y for the color of the surface on the ICI *chromaticity diagram* (Figs. 31.13 and 31.14).

The horseshoe-shaped boundary (Fig. 31.14) is called the *spectrum locus,* since here we find the pure colors of the continuous spectrum. Point B on the diagram represents a white surface illuminated by sunlight at noon, while point C represents average daylight from an overcast sky.   The other points on the inner curve represent the colors of black bodies at the temperatures indicated on the diagram. Point C is ordinarily chosen as the illumination standard.

Any color above the dotted lines in Fig. 31.15 may be regarded as a mixture of illuminant C and a single spectral frequency. Thus the point marked N in this figure could be reached by mixing daylight and sodium D radiation. The line CN extended to the spectrum locus gives us 589.3 mμ, which is called the *dominant wavelength* for the color specified by N. Since the yellow of point N lies between C and the spectrum

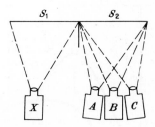

Fig. 31.11. Almost any color thrown on screen S_1 by lamp X can be matched by adding on screen S_2 three homogeneous primaries in carefully chosen amounts.

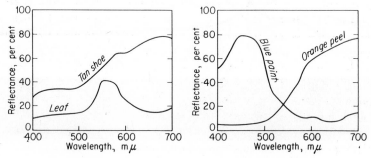

Fig. 31.12. Spectral reflectance curves for various objects.

color, it is not *saturated yellow* as is the spectrum color. The ratio of the distance from the point C to N divided by distance from C to the spectrum locus gives the *purity* of the color. In this particular case the purity is 40 per cent.

The point P below the dotted line is a purple and not a spectral color. If we extend the line CP, it reaches the spectral curve at 500 mμ. Point P is said to have the coordinate 500c, where the (c = complementary) is added to indicate that the point P is on the opposite side of C from the 500 mμ spectral color to which it is complementary. We may assign a purity to the color represented by P if we use a straight line connecting the end points of the visible region as the analogue of the spectrum locus.

By use of the ICI chromaticity diagram it is possible to specify measurable physical quantities, dominant wavelength, and purity which correspond to the psychological *hue* and *saturation*. From the spectral reflectance curve for a surface it is possible to compute the *luminous reflectance* where the word *luminous* means that the value takes into account the visual response of a standard observer and the color characteristics of the light source. The luminous reflectance is the physical analogue of *lightness*.

For color television phosphors are available which give the primaries R, G, and B of Fig. 31.15 when they are bombarded by the electron beam. The screen is made up of these phosphors. By appropriate variations in intensities, all the colors in the triangle RBG can be attained. Although this triangle does not include all visible colors, it covers a sufficiently wide range so that rich color communication is possible.

31.9. Color of Bodies. Thus far we have discussed the color of surfaces from which light from a standard illuminant is reflected. Of course, the color of the object depends on the spectral distribution of the incident light. If a white surface is illuminated with red light, it appears red because it reflects only red light to the eye. Since no other colors are present to be reflected, the color of the body is completely determined by this reflected red light. An object that appears red in white light is also red in red light, but it is black in any light which it does not reflect or transmit. Bodies that have the same color when viewed in daylight may not have the same color in lamplight. Light from an ordinary incandescent lamp is richer in red rays than in blue.

A piece of glass which appears blue may actually reflect and transmit other colors such as the neighboring green and violet (Fig. 31.16). Similarly, a yellow glass plate may transmit red and green. If both glasses are placed in a beam of white light, the only color which can pass through both is green. This is an example of color by the *subtractive* process in which we start with white light and remove various wavelength regions by absorption. The mixing of pigments is another example of a subtractive process. Mixing suitable yellow and blue pigments may give rise to a green paint just as green light passes through the combined filters of Fig. 31.16.

31.10. Fluorescence. Although many bodies return only those visible wavelengths which fall upon them, some bodies absorb light of one wavelength and emit light of longer wavelength. This process is called *fluorescence*. Many dyes emit vivid visible radiation when ultraviolet light is incident. Fluorescence is used in a wide variety of applications ranging from the theater to the identification of ores in mining.

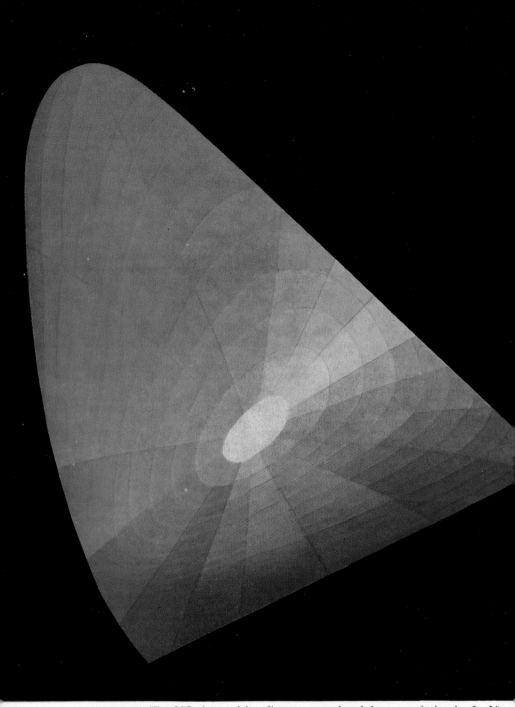

Fig. 31.13. The ICI chromaticity diagram reproduced from a painting by L. M. Condax of the Eastman Kodak Company. The boundaries between segments separate the various hues, while the oval boundaries represent lines of constant saturation. The horseshoe-shaped outer boundary corresponds to the positions of the pure spectrum colors. (*Courtesy of L. M. Condax and the Eastman Kodak Company. This painting was first reproduced in The Science of Color by the Committee on Colorimetry of the Optical Society of America, Thomas Y. Crowell Company, 1953.*)

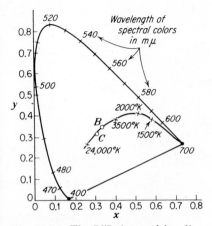

Fig. 31.14. The ICI chromaticity diagram showing the spectrum locus and the colors of black bodies at the temperatures indicated. Point *C* represents average daylight from an overcast sky and is chosen as the illumination standard.

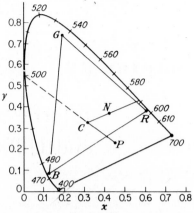

Fig. 31.15. An ICI chromaticity diagram showing method of specifying a color in terms of dominant wavelength and purity. The phosphors of color television screens give the primaries *R*, *B*, and *G* and permit the production of any color in the triangle *RBG*.

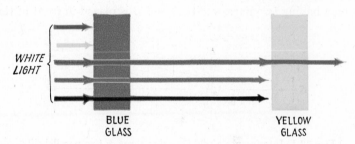

Fig. 31.16. Transmission and absorption of white light by yellow and blue glass. (*From Weber, White, and Manning, College Technical Physics, McGraw-Hill Book Company, Inc.*)

In fluorescent lamps ultraviolet light from an electrical discharge in mercury vapor is absorbed by fluorescent materials, called *phosphors*, which coat the inside of the tubes. By suitable choice of phosphors a wide range of colors of fluorescent light is available.

Some materials continue to emit visible light for some time after exposure to ultraviolet light. Such materials are said to be *phosphorescent.*

Interference
and Diffraction

32.1. Double-slit Interference. In 1801 Thomas Young performed a celebrated experiment which led to the general acceptance of the wave theory of light. Huygens and others had advanced the wave theory much earlier, but their arguments were inconclusive.

In order to understand Young's experiment, consider a source of light placed behind the screen containing a narrow slit S (Fig. 32.1). A second screen having two narrow slits A and B is placed in front of the first

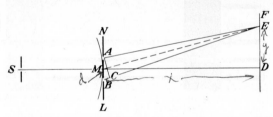

Fig. 32.1. Interference of light passing through two parallel slits.

screen in such a way that the openings are equally illuminated by the light from S. If the illumination on a third screen DF is examined, it is found that a series of light and dark bands (Fig. 32.2) results. At point D, where we might expect the center of a shadow, there is a bright line. This, of course, means that light from the source S arrives at the screen at a point which it could not reach if light travels in perfectly straight lines. Thus, any explanation requires that light bends, to some extent at least, around obstacles. *The bending of light when it passes an obstacle is called diffraction.*

To explain the pattern of Fig. 32.2, we accept the tentative hypothesis that light is a wave motion and that Huygens' principle is applicable. Then we can understand the origin of the bright and dark lines by the following reasoning: A wave front from S reaches slits A and B. Each

376

point on this wave front acts as a new source of Huygens' wavelets. Since A and B are equidistant from S, the Huygens' sources at A and B both send out crests at the same time and half a cycle later both send out troughs.   The waves from A and B arrive at the screen DF in such a way that at some points crests meet crests (Fig. 32.2a) and troughs meet troughs, thereby giving constructive interference and a bright line.   At

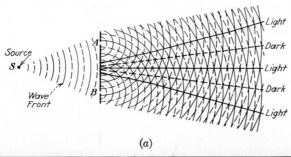

(a)

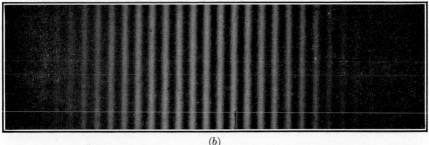

(b)

Fig. 32.2. (a) Interference of light from two identical slits A and B.   (b) Interference fringes produced in the double-slit experiment.   (*From Jenkins and White, Fundamentals of Physical Optics, McGraw-Hill Book Company, Inc.*)

other points the troughs meet crests and crests meet troughs, resulting in destructive interference or darkness.   The bright and dark bands on the screen are called *interference fringes*.

The experiment which we have just described with slits differs from that of Thomas Young in that he used pinholes in the screens rather than slits.   In his experiment, interference fringes were also formed, but these fringes were not straight lines.

Let us now see how we can find the wavelength of light waves from the interference pattern observed.   Note that a bright fringe is produced at D which is in the heart of the shadow of the slit.   This bright line arises from the constructive interference of the light coming through slits A and B.   The waves from these two slits arrive in phase, since the light travels exactly the same distance in both cases.   For the first bright fringe above D the light must travel one wavelength farther from slit B than from slit A.   For the nth bright fringe above D the light from B

goes n wavelengths farther than from A.   Suppose for the moment that the nth bright fringe is formed at point E.   For this particular case the distance BC is n wavelengths if $CE = AE$.   On the other hand, for a dark fringe at E the path difference BC must be some odd number of half wavelengths so that the waves interfere destructively.

We can calculate the path difference BC as follows: Let d represent the distance between slits A and B, X represent the distance MD from the double slit to the screen DF, and y represent the distance ED.   Then

$$(AE)^2 = X^2 + \left(y - \frac{d}{2}\right)^2 \quad \text{and} \quad (BE)^2 = X^2 + \left(y + \frac{d}{2}\right)^2$$

$$(BE)^2 - (AE)^2 = X^2 + y^2 + yd + \frac{d^2}{4} - X^2 - y^2 + yd - \frac{d^2}{4}$$

$$= 2yd$$

$$(BE - AE)(BE + AE) = 2yd$$

$$BE - AE = \frac{2yd}{(BE + AE)} = \frac{2yd}{2X}$$

since BE and AE are almost exactly equal to X.   Therefore, we have

$$\text{Path difference} = BC = \frac{yd}{X} \tag{32.1}$$

For bright fringes, the central one at D occurs for zero path difference. Counting this fringe as zero, the nth bright fringe in either direction comes when the path difference BC is $n\lambda$, which we know from Eq. (32.1) to be yd/X.   For the dark fringes, on the other hand, the difference in distance traversed from the two slits must be some odd integer number of half wavelengths.   The first dark fringe occurs for $yd/X = \lambda/2$, the second for $yd/X = 3\lambda/2$, and so forth.

We have required that our slit S be illuminated with monochromatic light.   If we use white light, we have the red wavelengths interfering constructively at different places than the blue.   As a result, we observe white light at the central point D and there is a spectrum on each side of D where the path difference is one wavelength, then another spectrum where the path difference is two wavelengths, and so forth.   However, in a short distance the spectra overlap seriously and the illumination appears uniform.

Example.   The distance between the slits A and B in Young's interference experiment is 0.25 cm.   The distance X to the screen on which the fringes are formed is 100 cm from the slits and the distance from the central bright fringe to the third dark one is 0.059 cm.   Find the wavelength of the incident light.

For the third dark fringe the path difference BC must be 2.5λ.

$$2.5\lambda = \frac{yd}{X}$$

$$= \frac{0.059 \times 0.25}{100}$$

$$\lambda = 5.9 \times 10^{-5} \text{ cm}$$

32.2. Coherent Sources. Shortly after Young's work, Fresnel was able to produce interference fringes similar to those of Fig. 32.2 in other ways. One of his methods involves placing a source of light behind a biprism (Fig. 32.3) and finding interference fringes in the crosshatched region where the light which went through the upper prism and the light through the lower prism overlapped. Still another method devised by Fresnel involved the use of two mirrors set so that the angle between their surfaces is very near to zero. The Fresnel double-mirror arrangement is shown in Fig. 32.4.

In Young's experiment and in the two interference experiments of Fresnel, light must come from a single source. No interference would be observed in Young's experiment, for example, if one light source were placed behind slit A and another behind slit B. Each source sends out a very large number of waves with completely random phases. At one

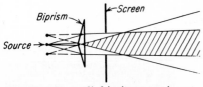

Fig. 32.3. Fresnel's biprism experiment. Interference occurs in the crosshatched region.

Fig. 32.4. The Fresnel double-mirror method of producing interference.

instant the crest of one wave might meet the trough of another, but an instant later crest might be meeting crest. The light reaching any area would be the sum of that contributed by each of the sources if it acted alone. When two sources send out waves in such a way that there is no regular phase relationship between these waves, the sources are *incoherent*. If there is a regular phase relationship between the waves, the sources are *coherent*.

In the interference experiments which we have discussed light comes from a single source. A single wave front is separated into two parts, one of which travels one path and the other a second path. When the parts are recombined, interference results. In order to produce interference, there must be two "apparent" sources initiating light waves which are in phase. This cannot be achieved with separate light sources. The only way it can be done is to start with a single source and send different portions of the wave front by different paths.

32.3. The Michelson Interferometer. An interesting example of a device in which part of a wave front is sent along one path and part along a different one is the Michelson interferometer (Figs. 32.5 and 32.6). Light emerging from a source S falls on a glass plate A, which reflects half and transmits the remainder. The reflected part goes to mirror C, by which it is reflected, and returns along its original path. The part which went through plate A passes through a second glass plate B, is reflected at mirror D, and returns to mirror A. There it is reflected in such a way that its direction coincides with the direction of the ray which was reflected at mirror C and which subsequently passed through the glass plate A. The wave front from source S has been split into two wave fronts. Both are received by the eye, one of them after reflection at C and the other after reflection at D. The plane parallel glass plate B is introduced to compensate for the extra thickness of glass through which the ray reflected at C has passed in

Fig. 32.5. A Michelson interferometer.   (*The Gaertner Scientific Corp.*)

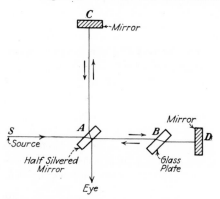

Fig. 32.6. Optical paths in a Michelson interferometer.

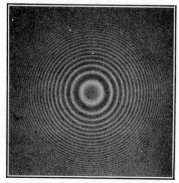

Fig. 32.7. Interference fringes produced with a Michelson interferometer using one of the lines of neon ($\lambda = 5{,}852$ A). (*After Babcock.*)

reaching the eye. In this way, the thickness of glass through which the two rays have passed in reaching the eye is the same.

If the distance from plate A to mirror C is the same as the distance from plate A to mirror D, the two rays of light travel the same distance, and they are therefore in phase. Under these conditions, the central rays reinforce each other. If, however, the distance AD is greater than the distance AC by a distance equal to one-quarter of a wavelength of the light, the central rays are out of phase and destroy each other. Rays which make small angles with the central ray travel slightly different distances and interfere alternately constructively and destructively (Fig. 32.7). If mirror D is moved along the line AD, the light and dark circles interchange position for each quarter wavelength the mirror is moved.

32.4. Lloyd's Mirror and Phase Change at Reflection.   Lloyd was

able to obtain interference fringes with a light source and a single mirror
in the manner indicated in Fig. 32.8.   Light coming directly from the
source and light reflected from the plane mirror overlap in the crosshatched region.   If a screen is placed at the end of the mirror, one might
expect a bright fringe at point P where the screen and mirror come in
contact.   However, a dark fringe is observed at this point.   This fact is
explained by a change in phase of
one-half wavelength (or 180°) which
occurs when light is reflected at a
medium which is optically more
dense.   *When light in a less dense
medium is reflected at the surface of
an optically denser medium, there is a*

Fig. 32.8. The Lloyd's mirror experiment.

*half wavelength phase shift; there is no phase shift when light in a denser
material is reflected at the surface of a less dense material.*[1]

It may be helpful to consider an analogue to this phase shift at reflection.   If a

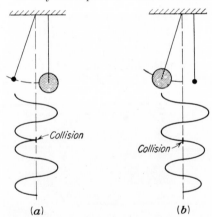

small mass m is set into vibration as a
pendulum bob, the x component of the
displacement as a function of time is
given by the sine wave of Fig. 32.9a.
If, as m swings through the equilibrium
position, it collides at P with a larger
mass M, the laws of conservation of
momentum and of energy lead to a
recoil of m.   From the figure we can
see that the small mass has missed one-
half of an oscillation; one-half wavelength is missing.   On the other hand,
if we have a large mass M serving as
the bob of the pendulum and if it has a
collision with a smaller mass m as it
swings through the equilibrium position
(Fig. 32.9b), the larger mass continues
in its original direction with somewhat
reduced amplitude.   There is no phase

Fig. 32.9. Mechanical analogue for the
180° phase shift in reflection.

shift when the larger mass collides with the smaller one, but a half wavelength
change in phase when the smaller mass collides with the larger.

32.5. Interference in Thin Films.   Consider the thin air film

between two optically plane pieces of glass when the plane surfaces touch
at one edge and are slightly separated at the other end (Fig. 32.10).
When monochromatic light falls normally from above on this air wedge,
part of the light is reflected at the upper surface of the wedge and part

[1] This is an oversimplification which leads to correct results in any situation discussed in this text.

of the light passes to the bottom of the air wedge, where some of the light is reflected, this time with a change in phase of half a wavelength. If the air wedge is viewed from above, a series of light and dark bands (Fig. 32.11) is observed.

In the region where the two plates touch there is a dark band, because although the two reflected waves go the same total distance, there is a

change in phase at the reflection in which the light goes from air to glass. The first light fringe occurs when the air wedge is one-fourth wavelength thick. The wave reflected from the lower plate goes one-half wavelength farther than the wave reflected at the upper surface and there is a half wavelength phase shift at the lower reflection. Therefore, the wave reflected at the two sides of the air wedge meet in phase and a light band occurs. When the thickness of the air wedge is one-half wavelength, the wave reflected at the lower plate goes one wavelength farther, but

Fig. 32.10. A thin air wedge illuminated from above p o- duces fringes due to the interference of light reflected from the two edges of the wedge.

the half wavelength change in phase on reflection again puts the two waves out of phase by half a wavelength and a dark band results. When the air wedge is three-quarters of a wavelength thick, constructive interference occurs once more, and so forth. There is a bright band when-

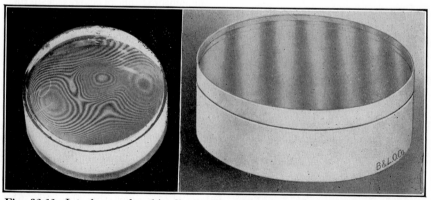

Fig. 32.11. Interference by thin films. The irregular pattern at the left indicates the surfaces are not plane, while the parallel, equispaced fringes show the air wedge at the right has plane surfaces.

ever the thickness of the air wedge is an odd number of quarter wavelengths and a dark band whenever the thickness of the air wedge is an even number of quarter wavelengths. If n represents the number of a bright fringe, counting the first bright fringe after the point of intersection of the planes as one, the thickness of the wedge at the nth bright fringe is given by $(2n - 1)\lambda/4$.

The interference of light waves is used when a working gauge block for checking vernier and micrometer calipers with great accuracy is compared with a master block. The two blocks are placed next to each other on a flat surface and an optically flat glass plate is placed on top of them (Fig. 32.12). If the two are exactly the same height, the optical flat is in contact with both blocks across their entire upper surfaces and no interference fringes are observed. If the working block is shorter than the master block, parallel fringes are observed and the amount by which the working block is low can be calculated.

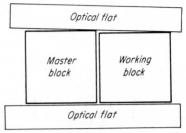

Fig. 32.12. Use of interference to test gauge blocks.

Example. When the optical flat of Fig. 32.12 is viewed from above with helium yellow light of $\lambda = 587.6$ mμ, there is a dark fringe where the flat touches the working block, a second dark fringe one-third the way across the block, a third one two-thirds the way across, and a fourth one just before the master block is reached. Find how much too short the working block is.

At the line of contact the separation is a negligible fraction of a wavelength. At the second dark fringe the air wedge is $\lambda/2$ thick, at the third λ, and at the last $3\lambda/2$. Therefore, the working block is $3\lambda/2$ shorter than the master block.

$$\frac{3\lambda}{2} = \frac{3}{2} \times 587.6 = 881 \text{ m}\mu$$

If a plano-convex lens is placed on an optical flat and illuminated with monochromatic light from above, a series of light and dark rings almost like those of Fig. 32.7 is observed. This pattern is known as Newton's rings. These light and dark rings are analogous to the light and dark straight fringes observed with plane surfaces. In the region where the lens touches the optical flat, there is destructive interference. Where the thickness of the air film is one-quarter wavelength, a bright circular fringe exists, while there is a dark circle where the thickness is $\lambda/2$, etc.

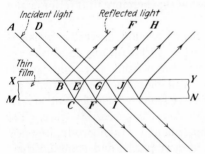

Fig. 32.13. Interference of light produced by differences in path of light reflected from the two surfaces of a thin film.

Consider a very thin film of transparent material with surfaces parallel to each other (Fig. 32.13). If one of these surfaces is illuminated by a beam of light of a single wavelength, light is reflected from the upper and lower surfaces. An incident ray like AB is partly reflected from the upper surface, but most of the light enters the film and a small part of it is reflected at C. In a similar manner, part of the ray DE is reflected at E and the remainder of the light enters the film.

Some of it is reflected at F, etc. If rays parallel to AB and DE illuminate the upper surface XY of the film, parallel rays EF, GH, etc., are reflected from the upper surface. There are also rays which are parallel to EF, GH, etc., which are reflected from the lower surface MN of the film. The rays reflected from the lower surface MN are superposed on those reflected from the upper surface XY. These two sets of reflected beams have nearly the same brightness but differ in phase, because those which are reflected from the lower surface of the film have traveled a distance equal to BCE farther than those reflected at the upper surface, while the latter have undergone a phase shift of one-half wavelength. The two sets of beams may interfere constructively or destructively, depending on the angle of incidence, on the wavelength of light, and on the thickness and refractive index of the film. The condition for destructive interference does not occur at the same place for different wavelengths. Hence, when the film is illuminated by white light, certain wavelengths reinforce each other where light of other wavelengths destroy each other. The result is a series of colored fringes giving the appearance of a rainbow. The colors of thin films of oils are an illustration of this type of interference.

32.6. Diffraction. When light passes an obstacle, it does not proceed in exactly straight lines, but spreads out somewhat into the geometrical shadow. Ordinarily this effect is small for light waves. However, light does bend slightly around the corners of an obstacle in much the same way that water waves bend around the corners of an object. *This spreading of a wave motion into the geometrical shadow of an object is called diffraction.* The effect is large when the wavelength of the wave motion is large compared with the size of the obstacle; it is small when the wavelength is short compared with the size of the obstacle. Thus, radio waves and sound waves, which have relatively long wavelengths, bend readily around objects. The wavelengths of visible light are small compared with the sizes of ordinary obstacles; therefore diffraction is not prominent for light waves.

To account for the fact that light bends around obstacles, we need only invoke Huygens' principle, which tells us that for any kind of wave motion we may regard each point on a wave front as a new source. Whenever we are dealing with diffraction phenomena, we are treating a case in which various parts of the same wave front act as coherent sources and the secondary wavelets from these coherent sources interfere. For interference in a Young's double-slit experiment we take two limited sections of a wave front, send them by different paths, and combine them to get constructive and destructive interference. In diffraction much larger sections of the wave front are involved. The basic theory calls for finding the net interference effect for a large number of waves with a continuous variation in phase passing a given point at a given time. The mathematical treatment of diffraction phenomena is more difficult than that for interference. For this reason we discuss diffraction in a qualitative way, except for the case of the diffraction grating.

32.7. Diffraction by a Straight Edge. Suppose that light is diverging from a narrow slit L (Fig. 32.14a) and that it passes by the straight edge of an opaque screen AB. If the light were propagated exactly in straight lines, there would be uniform illumination on the screen above

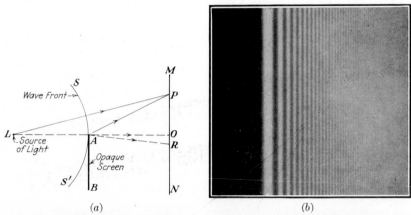

(a) $\qquad\qquad\qquad\qquad\qquad$ (b)

Fig. 32.14. Diffraction by a straight edge: (a) light passing a straight edge bends into the geometrical shadow; (b) diffraction pattern due to a straight edge. (*Courtesy of M. E. Hufford, University of Indiana.*)

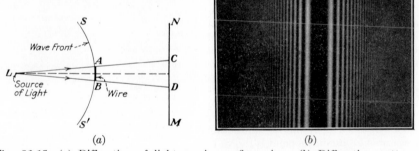

(a) $\qquad\qquad\qquad\qquad\qquad$ (b)

Fig. 32.15. (a) Diffraction of light passing a fine wire. (b) Diffraction pattern produced by a fine wire. (*Courtesy of M. E. Hufford, University of Indiana.*)

the line LAO and complete darkness below it. However, the illumination does not become zero immediately below O, but fades away continuously. There is almost complete darkness at a small distance below O. Immediately above O the illumination is not uniform, but shows a series of bright and dark bands parallel to the edge AB. The appearance of the fringes thus produced is seen in Fig. 32.14b.

Consider now the case of a fine wire AB (Fig. 32.15a) placed in front of a narrow slit L. The shadow of this wire on the screen MN is found to be bounded on each side by a system of parallel fringes (Fig. 32.15b). Each edge of the wire behaves like a straight edge.

32.8. Diffraction through a Narrow Slit. If light from a narrow slit at O falls on a second narrow slit which is parallel to the first slit, a bright central band appears on the screen MN (Fig. 32.16).

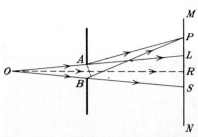

Fig. 32.16. Diffraction of light passing through a narrow slit.

On each side of this central band, there are alternate bright and dark bands which become wider as the slit O is decreased in width. By an application of Huygens' principle, these bands can be explained by the interference of light from different parts of the wave front coming through the slit AB. The light that reaches the points on the screen between L and S comes from points on the wave front in such a way that the light is nearly in the same phase and there is reinforcement at all points. Light that has come from points on the wave front illuminates points on the screen above L or below S in such a way that in some cases there is reinforcement and in other cases there is destructive interference. Hence, alternate bright and dark bands are produced above L and below S. If the edges of the slit are not parallel, the diffraction bands have the form shown in Fig. 32.17. Diffraction patterns produced by wire screens of different meshes are shown in Fig. 32.18.

32.9. Diffraction by a Circular Aperture. Another striking illustration of diffraction is observed when light from a luminous point passes through a small circular aperture like a pinhole. When this aperture is viewed by means of a magnifying glass, there appears a brilliant spot which is surrounded by a series of bright rings. The size and appearance of these rings are altered as the eye is moved closer to the opening or farther from it. Such a system of diffraction rings about a luminous point is shown in Fig. 32.19. When images are formed in any kind of optical instrument, even the most perfect optical parts cannot produce

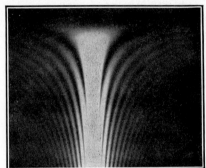

Fig. 32.17. Diffraction of light produced by a wedge-shaped opening; the narrow end of the opening corresponds to the widest separation of the fringes. (*Courtesy of M. E. Hufford, University of Indiana.*)

a point image of a point source. Instead there is a diffraction pattern consisting of a bright circle surrounded by a series of light and dark rings. Ultimately these diffraction patterns limit the angular separation of two sources which can be distinguished as separate.

32.10. Diffraction Grating. If a series of very fine equidistant parallel slits is ruled on a plate of glass with a fine diamond point, we have a *diffraction grating*. Where the diamond point has made a furrow on the glass, the light cannot pass through regularly. Between the furrows where the surface of the glass has been undisturbed, the glass is transparent, and light can pass through regularly. The plate of glass is then somewhat like a picket fence.   In effect, there is a strip through which the light can pass followed by a strip through which it cannot pass.

Let AB (Fig. 32.20) represent such a grating on which parallel light is falling so that the direction of the rays is perpendicular to the plane of

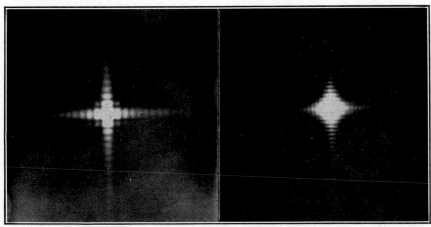

Fig. 32.18. Diffraction patterns produced by screens with rectangular openings; at the left smaller, and at the right larger openings. (*Courtesy of M. E. Hufford, University of Indiana.*)

the grating.   Figure 32.21 shows the secondary wave fronts that start out from these slits.   These wavelets destroy or reinforce each other, according to whether they are in phase or out of phase at a given point.

Through the slits in the grating come beams of parallel light.   If these rays coming in the direction perpendicular to the plane of the grating are brought to a focus on the screen PS by the lens LM, a bright line is formed at K.   If the light is viewed in a direction making an angle θ with the normal to the grating, parallel rays of light emerging from the slits in this direction travel unequal distances to reach the screen, and when they are brought to a focus at N by the lens LM, they may either reinforce or destroy each other.   If the angle θ is made such that a ray of light from one slit is one-half wavelength behind the corresponding ray

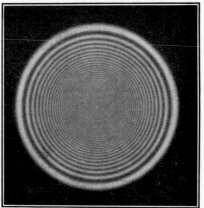

Fig. 32.19. Diffraction pattern produced by a circular opening. (*Courtesy of M. E. Hufford, University of Indiana.*)

from the adjacent slit, then the rays from one slit are out of phase with the rays from the adjacent slit and destroy each other. Hence, there will be darkness. If the angle between the normal to the grating and the ray is increased, the rays from the lower slits will be more and

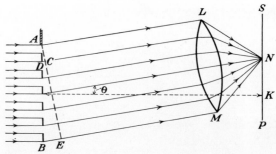

Fig. 32.20. Diffraction grating. For reinforcement $n\lambda = d \sin \theta$.

more behind the rays from the upper slits. When the difference in path between corresponding rays from adjacent slits amounts to one wavelength, wavelets from all the slits are again in phase and interfere constructively. When these rays are focused by the lens LM, another bright image of the slit is formed on the screen. When

$$DC = AD \sin \theta = n\lambda \qquad n \text{ is an integer}$$

the rays from different slits reinforce each other, and the screen is illuminated.

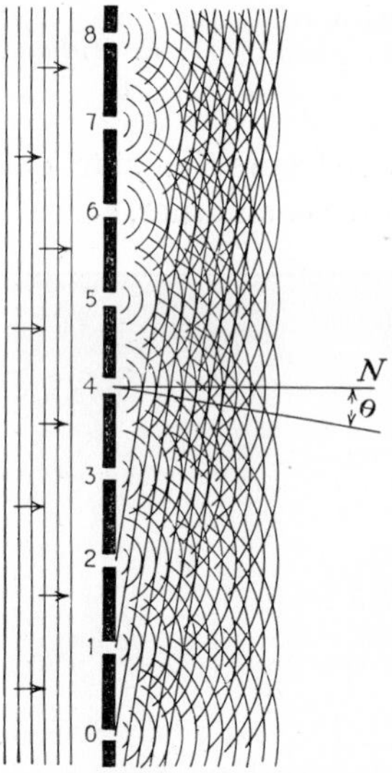

The angle θ_1 at which reinforcement is again obtained after leaving the central band K can be easily measured on the divided circle of a spectrometer. The number of rulings per centimeter of the grating is given by the maker. From this, the distance d between the slits on the grating can be computed. For the first reinforcement, $DC = \lambda$ and

Fig. 32.21. Wave fronts from a diffraction grating.

$$\lambda = d \sin \theta_1 \qquad (32.2)$$

Since all the quantities in this equation are known except λ, the wavelength of the light can be calculated. This is a very accurate method of measuring the wavelength.

Reinforcement also occurs at other angles θ_n which satisfy the equation

$$n\lambda = d \sin \theta_n \qquad (32.3)$$

The integer n gives the *order* of the spectrum.   When $n = 2$, the waves from each slit go two wavelengths farther than those from the adjacent slit.   In the third order n is 3 and $DC = 3\lambda$.

Example.   In using a grating to determine the wavelength of light, it was observed that the angular separation of the second-order spectrum from the central image was 45°.   The number of lines per inch on the grating was 14,500.   What was the wavelength of the light?

$$2\lambda = d \sin \theta_2$$

$$\lambda = \frac{d}{2} \sin \theta_2$$

$$= \frac{1}{2} \times \frac{0.0254 \text{ m/in.}}{14,500/\text{in.}} \times 0.707$$

$$= 621 \times 10^{-9} \text{ m} = 621 \text{ m}\mu$$

Example.   For a certain color of yellow light, the angular separation between the central image and the first-order spectrum produced by a plane grating was 17°. The grating has 5,000 rulings to the centimeter.   What is the wavelength of the light?

$$\text{Wavelength} = d \sin \theta_1$$

$$\lambda = \frac{1 \text{ cm}}{5,000} \times \sin 17°$$

$$= \frac{1}{5,000} \times 0.292$$

$$= 0.0000584 \text{ cm, or } 5840 \text{ A}$$

PROBLEMS

1. Green light of wavelength 5,000 A from a single source is passed through two narrow slits separated by 1 mm.   On a screen 150 cm away, there is formed an interference pattern.   Calculate the separation of intensity maxima in this pattern.
Ans. 0.75 mm

2. The two parallel slits used in Young's interference experiment were 0.25 mm apart.   The screen on which the fringes were projected was 1 m from the slits.   What is the distance between the fringes for monochromatic light of wavelength 589 mμ?

3. Two flat glass plates which are almost parallel produce interference fringes by successive reflections from the surfaces.   If the light with which the plates are illuminated normally has a wavelength of 6,000 A, what is the difference in thickness that would be indicated in passing from one bright fringe to the next?   *Ans.* 3,000 A

4. Monochromatic light from a narrow slit illuminates two parallel slits 0.2 mm apart.   On a screen 80 cm away interference bands are observed 3 mm apart.   Find the wavelength of the light.

5. Newton's rings are observed by reflected light of wavelength 580 mμ.   The central area is dark and is surrounded by light and dark circles.   Find the thickness of the air film at the first and fifth bright circles.   *Ans.* 145 mμ; 1,305 mμ

6. Two pieces of optical glass are pressed together at one edge and separated by a fine wire at the other edge.   The distance between the wire and the edges of glass that are in contact is 10 cm.   When light of wavelength 0.000060 cm is incident normally on the surface of one of the pieces of glass, interference fringes are observed.   If these fringes are 0.15 cm apart, what is the diameter of the wire?

7. If 6,000 A radiation falls on a grating ruled with 4,000 lines per centimeter, how many orders may be observed on each side of the direct beam?   Determine the angles of diffraction for orders on one side of the zeroth order.
Ans. 4; about 14°, 29°, 46°, 74°

8. A glass grating is ruled with 4,300 lines to the centimeter. Yellow light striking the grating normally is seen to form a second-order image diffracted at an angle of 30° from the normal. What is the wavelength of the yellow light?

9. In observing the spectrum of a certain color with a grating that has 300 lines to the millimeter, the angular deviation of the second-order spectrum from the central image is 15° when the incident light is normal to the grating. Find the wavelength of the light. *Ans.* 432 mμ

10. The fourth-order spectrum contains a certain color diffracted at an angle of 65°. If the grating is ruled with 200 lines to the millimeter, what is the wavelength of the light?

11. Two spectral lines of different colors are observed by means of a grating, and it is seen that the third-order image of one line coincides with the fourth-order image of the second line. What is the ratio of the wavelengths for the two colors? *Ans.* 4 to 3

12. A diffraction grating having 14,000 lines to the inch is used with a spectrometer in such a way that light of wavelength 0.000059 cm falls normal to its surface. What angle must the telescope of the spectrometer make with the normal to the grating so that the first order of the spectrum can be observed?

13. A grating is ruled with 5,000 lines per centimeter. Calculate the angles of diffraction for first-order red and blue light, the wavelengths being, respectively, 7,000 and 4,000 A. Determine the angular separation in radians. A lens of 50 cm focal length is placed in the path of light just beyond the grating. Determine the linear separation of the red and the blue spots. (This is essentially the basis for a grating spectrometer.) *Ans.* 20.5°; 11.5°; 0.16 radian; 8 cm

14. A transmission grating has 440 lines to the millimeter. It is used with light of wavelength 5,000 A. If the incident light is normal, what is the angle between a ray to the undeviated image and a ray to the second-order spectrum?

15. When the movable mirror of a Michelson interferometer is moved 0.10 mm, how many fringes pass the reference mark if light of wavelength 5,900 A is used? *Ans.* 339

16. When a Michelson interferometer was used to measure the wavelength of monochromatic light, it was found that 250 fringes passed the observing microscope when the movable mirror was displaced 0.074 mm. What is the wavelength of the light?

CHAPTER 33

Skip

Polarization

33.1. Polarization. The phenomena of interference and diffraction show that light has wave properties. We ask whether these waves are longitudinal, like sound waves, or transverse, like waves in a stretched string. There are certain phenomena which show that light waves are transverse, i.e., that the vibrations take place at right angles to the direction in which the wave is traveling. The following experiment with two crystals of tourmaline shows the nature of this evidence most simply.

When a crystal of tourmaline (Fig. 33.1) is cut parallel to the crystallographic axis and a ray of light passes through it, the transmitted beam in no way differs from the incident beam so far as the unaided eye can detect. If the light that has passed through one tourmaline crystal is allowed to pass through another with its axis parallel to the first, the light is almost completely transmitted by the second crystal. If now the second crystal is rotated around the ray of light as an axis so that the axes of the two crystals are inclined to each other, the intensity of the transmitted light decreases. When the axes of the crystals are at right angles to each other, none of the light from the first crystal passes through the

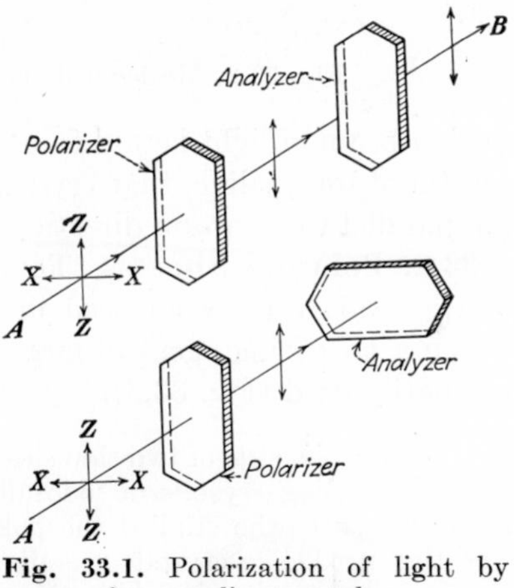

Fig. 33.1. Polarization of light by means of tourmaline crystals.

second. If the rotation of the second crystal is continued until the axes of the crystals are again parallel, the light from the first crystal is transmitted through the second. It is evident that light in passing through the first crystal has acquired properties that ordinary light does not possess.

To understand this experiment, consider a stretched string (Fig. 33.2) in which the particles are vibrating perpendicular to the length of the string. If a block

391

of wood with a slot in it is placed over the string, the vibrations are not affected when the slot is parallel to the direction of vibration. However, when the slot is at right angles to this direction, the vibrations do not pass beyond the slot. If the slot makes various angles with the direction of vibration of the string, the component of the vibratory motion which is parallel to the slot passes through. If a second slot is placed over the string, the vibrations that pass the first slot also pass the second when the two slots are parallel. When the slots are perpendicular to each other, the vibrations that pass the first slot do not pass the second.

The action of the tourmaline may be understood if we consider ordinary light to consist of a transverse wave motion in which the vibrations take place in all directions in a plane perpendicular to the direction in which the light is traveling. When such a beam passes through a tourmaline crystal, the crystal absorbs one component of the vibrations and transmits the other component. Consequently the emerging beam differs from the ordinary light in that all the vibrations are in one direction.

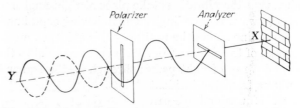

Fig. 33.2. Mechanical analogue of the polarization of light.

Such a beam of light is said to be *plane-polarized*. If it falls on a second crystal of tourmaline, that crystal transmits only those vibrations which are parallel to a certain direction.

33.2. Polaroid Sheets. Tourmaline crystals are somewhat colored and are not very often used in the study of polarization phenomena. When a polarizing agent of large aperture is desired, polaroid sheets are ordinarily used (Fig. 33.3).

A polaroid consists of two thin sheets of plastic with a thin layer of ultramicroscopic polarizing crystals of iodosulfate of quinine (also known as *herapathite* after Herapath who studied the polarizing properties in 1852) between them. The tiny needlelike crystals are aligned with their axes parallel by subjecting them to a strong electric field as the plastic in which they are embedded solidifies.

When unpolarized light passes through a polaroid, one component of the vibration is absorbed and the other transmitted. The vibrations of the transmitted light all lie along one axis. When ordinary light falls on a polarizing agent and plane-polarized light is produced, we call the agent a *polarizer* (Fig. 33.4). To determine whether a beam of light is polarized or not, we pass the light through a second polarizing agent such as a polaroid. When this polaroid is rotated, there is no change in the transmitted intensity if the light is unpolarized, while the intensity goes from the maximum to zero if the beam is plane-polarized. A polarizing agent used in this way is called an *analyzer*. If the incident light is partially plane-polarized, the intensity is maximum for one orientation of the

Fig. 33.3. Two polaroid sheets crossed so the light transmitted by one is absorbed by the other. (*Polaroid Corp.*)

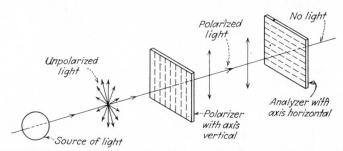

Fig. 33.4. A polarizer and analyzer with their planes of transmission at right angles to each other.

analyzer and minimum for another, but there is no zero. When two polarizing agents are arranged with their axes perpendicular so that they cut out all light, they are said to be *crossed*.

Actually a pair of crossed polaroids is not perfectly effective for eliminating the far red and far violet radiations, so that one can see a little deep purple through crossed polaroids.

33.3. Light Vibrations. Light is a complex system of wave motions, consisting of alternating electric and magnetic fields at right angles to each other.

In a plane-polarized wave the electric vibrations all lie in the same plane, while the magnetic vibrations are in a plane at right angles to the one containing the electric vibrations. In discussing polarized light, it is necessary to consider only one of these types of vibration; it is customary to focus attention on the *electric vibrations* since most common optical phenomena are due to the interaction of the electric vector with the charged particles in matter. The plane of vibration is defined as the plane determined by the electric vibrations and the direction of propagation.

A beam of ordinary light consists of a very large number of waves, each with its own plane of vibration, with every direction of vibration perpendicular to the

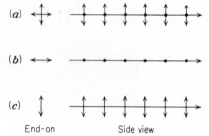

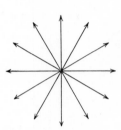

Fig. 33.5. Ordinary light coming out of the plane of the paper has a random array of electric vibrations in the plane of the paper.

Fig. 33.6. Pictorial representation of (a) ordinary light, (b) plane-polarized light with electric vibrations horizontal, and (c) plane-polarized light with electric vector vertical.

rays having equal probability. We represent such a beam, looking head on, by Fig. 33.5. When we pass such a beam through a tourmaline crystal, it comes out plane-polarized. Only an infinitesimal part of unpolarized light beam contains vibrations in any single direction. However, if we have a polarizer set to transmit only vertical vibrations, approximately half of the incident intensity is transmitted. Those vibrations which are not exactly vertical also contribute to this beam. Actually, a polarizer transmits all *components* which are parallel to its select direction. We can look on a beam of unpolarized light as being composed of two equal beams plane-polarized at right angles to one another. Any vibration which is not in one or other of these two directions can be resolved into two components, one in each direction. Hence, we

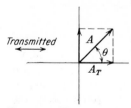

Fig. 33.7. The resolution of the amplitude of the electric vector into rectangular components.

sometimes represent unpolarized light by showing only two of these many directions of vibrations (Fig. 33.6a). We use a dot to represent vibration perpendicular to the plane of the paper and arrows to indicate vibrations in this plane. In this same figure there are representations of plane polarized light; in Fig. 33.6b the vibrations are perpendicular to the plane of the paper and in Fig. 33.6c they are in the plane.

If a beam of plane-polarized light falls on an analyzer set to transmit a plane of vibrations making an angle θ with that of the incident beam, a portion of the incident beam is transmitted. To calculate the fraction transmitted, we proceed as follows: We resolve (Fig. 33.7) the vibration amplitude A of the incident beam into two components, one parallel to the preferred plane of the

analyzer and the other perpendicular.   The polarizer passes the parallel component and rejects the perpendicular one.   The amplitude transmitted A_T is given
by

$$A_T = A \cos \theta \qquad (33.1)$$

Since the intensity is proportional to the square of the amplitude, the fraction of
the incident intensity I transmitted is given by

$$\frac{I_T}{I} = \frac{A_T^2}{A^2} = \cos^2 \theta \qquad (33.2)$$

Example.   An analyzer is set to transmit vibrations at 37° to those of an incident
plane-polarized beam.   Find what fraction of the incident intensity is transmitted.

$$A_T = A \cos \theta$$
$$= A \cos 37°$$
$$= 0.8A$$
$$\frac{I_T}{I} = \frac{A_T^2}{A^2} = 0.64$$

33.4. Polarization by Reflection.   When a beam of unpolarized
light is reflected at the surface of glass or water, the reflected beam is
unpolarized for normal incidence
and for grazing incidence.   For any
other angle of incidence, the reflected ray contains more vibrations
parallel to the reflecting surface,
while the transmitted beam contains more of the vibrations in the
plane of incidence (Fig. 33.8a).
If the angle of incidence is about
45° and the reflected light is examined by use of an analyzer, some

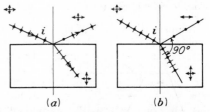

Fig. 33.8.   (a) Partial polarization by
reflection and refraction.   (b) The reflected beam is plane-polarized only at
the polarizing angle.

light is transmitted for every orientation of the polarizer, but the intensity is maximum when the analyzer passes electric vibrations parallel to
the reflecting surface.

When the angle of incidence is such that the angle between the reflected
and refracted rays is 90° (Fig. 33.8b), the reflected beam is completely
plane-polarized.   We call the angle of incidence the *polarizing angle* and
indicate it by i_p.   For this case the angle of refraction r is the comple-
ment of the angle of incidence i_p so that $\sin r = \cos i_p$.   If n is the index
of refraction of the reflecting material relative to the air, we have

$$n = \frac{\sin i_p}{\sin r} = \frac{\sin i_p}{\cos i_p} = \tan i_p \qquad (33.3)$$

The relation $n = \tan i_p$ is known as *Brewster's law.*

Although the reflected beam is completely plane-polarized for incidence at the polarizing angle, the refracted beam is only partially plane-polarized. Most of the intensity is associated with the transmitted beam, which includes all vibration components in the plane of incidence and part of those perpendicular to this plane.

Light reflected from metallic and other conducting surfaces is not polarized. A well-silvered mirror may reflect 98 per cent of the incident light; both types of polarization are reflected. In order to have plane polarization by reflection, we must have a dielectric medium which is not a good conductor of electricity.

Sunlight reflected from the surface of a lake or from an asphalt pavement is partially plane-polarized. Glasses equipped with polaroid lenses oriented so that they transmit only vertical vibrations cut out most of the reflected light and only half of unpolarized light. It is for this reason that polaroid glasses reduce glare which is due primarily to reflected light.

33.5. Double Refraction. If a crystal of calcite (often called *Iceland spar*) is placed over a page of print, two images are seen in the calcite. If these images are examined through a polaroid analyzer, it is found that each of the images is produced by plane-polarized light with their planes of vibration at 90° to one another. Thus, ordinary light entering the crystal is split into two plane-polarized beams which travel through the crystal in different directions. This phenomenon, known as *double refraction*, is shown by many transparent crystals.

Suppose that a flash of light is created at point P inside the calcite and that we look at the wave front a very short time Δt later. In glass or water the wave front is expected to be a sphere with the radius $V \Delta t$, where V is the speed of light in the medium. In calcite, however, there are two wave fronts (Fig. 33.9), one due to light with its vibration perpendicular to the page and the other with vibrations in the plane of the page. One of these wave fronts is spherical and is called the *ordinary* wave front, while the other is an ellipsoid of revolution and is called the *extraordinary* wave front. In calcite there is one direction in which these two wave fronts travel with the same speed. This direction is called the *optic axis*. In other directions the two wave fronts have different speeds and double refraction results.

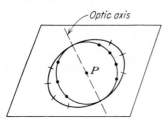

Fig. 33.9. There are two wave surfaces in calcite, the circular one formed with electric vibrations perpendicular to the plane of the paper and the ellipsoidal ones by electric vibrations in the plane of the paper.

In order that a crystal show double refraction it must be *anisotropic;* i.e., it must have different properties in different directions. Calcite and quartz are examples of anisotropic crystals. Water and glass have the same properties in all directions and are therefore *isotropic*. However, a piece of glass can be made anisotropic if it is subjected to stress.

For a calcite crystal the optic axis for a typical cleavage crystal is oriented as shown in Fig. 33.9. If we now use Huygens' principle to trace light through a calcite crystal, the Huygens' wavelets for the extraordinary wave are ellipsoidal rather than spherical (Fig. 33.10). To find the new wave front for the extraordinary wave, we find the surface which is tangent to these wavelets. This is a

plane in the crystal parallel to the ordinary wave front, but the light which enters
the crystal at point A in the figure moves along
the line AX which represents the path of the
extraordinary ray. The construction for the
ordinary ray is just as it would be for an isotropic medium. Thus, an ordinary ray goes
straight through the crystal, while the extraordinary ray moves off to one side. If we place
a calcite crystal over a dot on a piece of paper
and rotate the crystal, the image formed by the
ordinary ray stands still, while the image due to
the extraordinary ray rotates about it.

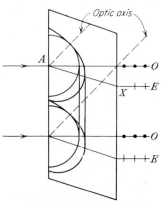

Fig. 33.10. Double refraction in
calcite, showing the Huygens'
wavelets and the paths of ordinary and extraordinary rays.

33.6. Nicol Prism. One method of separating the ordinary from the extraordinary ray is
by use of a *Nicol prism* (Fig. 33.11). A rhomb
of Iceland spar $AMBN$ is cut into two parts by
a plane MN, which makes an angle of about
$22°$ with MB. When the cut surfaces have been
polished, they are cemented together with
Canada balsam, the index of refraction of which
is less than that of calcite for the ordinary ray
and greater than that of calcite for the extraordinary ray. The refractive indices
are Canada balsam 1.55, ordinary ray in calcite 1.658, and extraordinary ray 1.468.

The ray of light LC entering the face of the rhomb at C is broken up into the
ordinary and extraordinary rays which are polarized at right angles to each other
as indicated by the dots and crosslines in the figure. When the ordinary ray

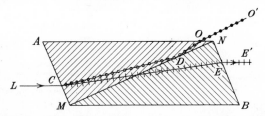

Fig. 33.11. Nicol prism. The ordinary ray is eliminated by total reflection.

reaches the surface of separation of the Iceland spar and the Canada balsam at D
at an angle greater than the critical angle, it is totally reflected and emerges from
the rhomb in the direction OO'. This surface of the rhomb is ordinarily painted
black and the ray is absorbed in this black coating. The extraordinary ray is
transmitted in the direction CE and emerges from the rhomb at the face BN.
In this way, there is obtained a beam of light that is plane-polarized.

33.7. Polarization by Selective Absorption. We have introduced
polarization phenomena with the aid of tourmaline crystals and polaroid
sheets. These materials produce plane-polarized light by the phenomenon of *selective absorption*, which is exhibited by a number of minerals
and organic compounds. Materials which yield polarized light by selective absorption are not only *anisotropic* and double refracting, but in addi-

tion they strongly absorb one of the polarized beams while they transmit the other.

33.8. Polarization by Scattering. When light rays pass through the air, they interact with air molecules and dust particles. Part of the energy is scattered. Particles with dimensions much smaller than a wavelength of the radiation scatter short wavelengths more strongly

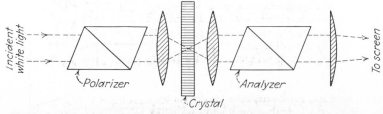

Fig. 33.12. Apparatus for producing interference by means of converging polarized light. The crystal between the polarizer and analyzer is double refracting.

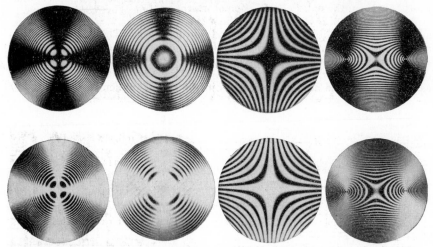

Fig. 33.13. Interference patterns from crystals placed in convergent monochromatic polarized light. (*From Jenkins and White, Fundamentals of Physical Optics, McGraw-Hill Book Company, Inc.*)

than long ones. Indeed, the scattering is proportional to the fourth power of the frequency. Since the violet part of the light from the sun has a frequency approximately double that of the red waves, the violet rays are scattered about $2^4 = 16$ times as strongly as the far red.

Light from the sun is scattered in passing through the atmosphere and some of this scattered light is rescattered to our eyes. Since this scattered light is much richer in blues and violets than in the longer wavelengths, the sky is blue. By the same token the sun, even at mid-day, looks far more orange than it would if it were viewed from a rocket ship above the earth's atmosphere. Much of the blue and violet has been scattered out before the light reaches the earth's surface. At sunrise and at sunset the sun's rays go through far greater thicknesses of atmosphere; for this reason the sun appears redder at these times.

If the light of the sky is examined through a polaroid, it is found that this light is partially plane-polarized if the sky is viewed from almost any angle. Light scattered at an angle of 90° with the incident rays is plane-polarized.

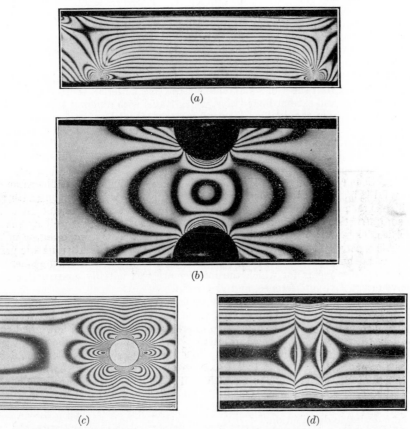

(a)

(b)

(c) (d)

Fig. 33.14. Stress distributions photographed by means of polarized light. (a) Stresses in a beam supported at both ends. (b) Tensile stresses in a member with a semicircular groove. (c) Stress pattern for a circular shaft with a transverse hole when shaft is under tension. (d) Same shaft as in (c), but rotated through 90° so that light is perpendicular to axis of the hole. *(Courtesy of M. M. Frocht, Carnegie Institute of Technology.)*

33.9. Rotation of the Plane of Polarization. When a beam of monochromatic plane-polarized light passes through certain substances, the plane of polarization is rotated.   Thus, if a plate of quartz cut so that the faces are perpendicular to the axis of the crystal is placed between crossed Nicol prisms, the light is no longer extinguished by the second Nicol prism. If, however, the second Nicol prism is rotated, a new position can be found at which the light is again extinguished. Rotation of the plane of polarization is called *optical activity*.

This angle through which the plane of polarization is rotated depends on the kind of substance interposed between the Nicol prisms, on the thickness of the substance, on the wavelength of the light, and on the temperature. The rotation may be either clockwise or counterclockwise. In this respect there are two kinds of quartz. One kind rotates the plane of polarization clockwise; the other rotates it counterclockwise. Some liquids and gases also cause a rotation of the plane of polarization. Molecules in which a carbon atom is attached by valence bonds to four different atoms or groups of atoms often show optical activity. Optical activity is a matter of importance in organic chemistry and has established the foundations of stereochemistry.

33.10. Interference with Polarized Light. If plane-polarized light is incident on a thin sheet of some double-refracting material, the beam is spread into ordinary and extraordinary rays, which travel with different speeds. When they emerge from the double-refracting material, the vibrations are likely to be out of phase. If the light is now passed through an analyzer which transmits only horizontal vibrations, this analyzer selects only the horizontal components of the vibrations from both ordinary and extraordinary rays. These horizontal components may interfere with one another either constructively or destructively. In particular, if highly convergent light is passed through the double-refracting crystal (Fig. 33.12), the paths of various rays in the crystal differ in length, and there is then constructive interference for a given wavelength for some directions and destructive interference for others. Consequently, interference patterns are formed (Fig. 33.13). If the original light contains all the wavelengths in the visible spectrum, the interference pattern is vividly colored. If either the polarizer or analyzer is rotated through 90°, the colors change to the complementary ones, because colors for which the interference was initially constructive then have destructive interference, and vice versa.

When a sheet of cellophane is placed under stress, it becomes double refracting. Interference colors may be observed when such a sheet is placed between two polaroids. It is possible to determine where the stresses are and how great they are by careful analysis of such an interference pattern. One of the most useful methods of studying the stresses in various structural shapes involves making a plastic model, subjecting it to external stresses, and studying the interference patterns (Fig. 33.14) produced. Such studies permit a fairly complete analysis of the stress distributions. Once one knows what stress distribution is most likely to cause difficulty, he can change the shape in such a way as to produce a more desirable distribution.

PROBLEMS

1. Determine the angle of incidence (polarizing angle) for which reflected light is plane-polarized when reflected from glass of index of refraction 1.6.   *Ans.* 58°

2. Find the angle of incidence for which light reflected from water is plane-polarized.

3. Light reflected from a glass surface is plane-polarized when the angle of incidence is 56.5°. What is the index of refraction of the glass?   *Ans.* 1.51

4. Sir David Brewster determined that light reflected from the surface of a refracting medium will be plane-polarized if the angle of incidence is such that there is exactly 90° between the reflected ray and the refracted ray. From this, show that the reflected light is plane-polarized if the angle of incidence, i_p is such that $\tan i_p = n$, the index of refraction.

5. Determine the critical angle for the ordinary ray passing from calcite to Canada balsam in a Nicol prism.   *Ans.* 69°

6. Determine the critical angle for the extraordinary ray passing from Canada balsam to calcite in a Nicol prism.

7. Two polaroids are crossed. If the analyzer is now rotated through an angle of 40°, what fraction of the plane-polarized light from the polarizer is transmitted, assuming the polaroid is a perfect transmitter of one polarization and a perfect absorber of the other? What fraction of the ordinary light incident on the polarizer is transmitted through the analyzer?   *Ans.* 41.3 per cent; 20.7 per cent

8. Light of a certain wavelength passes through a Nicol prism and is thus polarized. It then passed through a second Nicol prism whose plane of vibration makes an angle of 60° with the plane of vibration of the first Nicol prism. What percentage of the light incident on the second Nicol prism emerges from it?

9. Two Nicol prisms have their planes of vibration parallel to each other. One of the Nicol prisms is then turned so that its plane of vibration makes an angle of 40° with that of the other Nicol prism. What percentage of the light that is incident on the second Nicol prism is transmitted by it?   *Ans.* 58.6 per cent

10. Proposals have been made for the use of Polaroid for reducing the dangers of night driving by elimination of blinding headlights. Explain how this could be done. What are the disadvantages of such a system?

PART V

Electricity

CHAPTER 34 *important*

Electric Charges at Rest

34.1. Electricity in Modern Life. The twentieth century may well be called *the age of electricity.* Developments in the nineteenth century made it possible to generate, deliver, and control vast amounts of electrical energy at a reasonable cost. The results are everywhere apparent. Electrical energy is used for lighting, cooking, refrigeration, washing, drying, ironing, and air circulation in many modern homes. Electrical energy dominates the world of communication; the telephone, telegraph, radio, and television are direct outgrowths of advances in our understanding of electricity.

Less obvious, but no less important, is the role of electricity in our economic development. The automobile and the aluminum industries, to mention only two, could not have evolved in their present form until man learned how to generate and control electrical energy. So important is electricity in our everyday life that our standard of living would be tremendously lowered without it. Electrical servants have replaced human servants in the average home. In the short course of less than a century the science of electricity has developed from a curiosity to a dominant position in our technology.

Although most of the common uses of electrical phenomena involve electric charges in motion, the fundamental concepts are best developed by considering first *electrostatics*, the science of stationary electric charges. Electrostatics is both the historical and the logical starting point in the study of electricity.

34.2. Charges by Contact and Separation. As early as 600 B.C. it was known that amber rubbed with fur had the interesting property of attracting light pieces of straw or paper. A rubber comb run through the hair may also exhibit this same property. Such bodies are said to be *electrified*, a term derived from the Greek word for *amber*. Experiments reveal that it is possible to electrify any kind of material by rubbing it with a suitable second material and then separating the two. An electrified body is said to bear an *electric charge*. When a charged body

405

and an uncharged one are brought together, a portion of the charge is likely to be transferred to the uncharged body.

If a small pith ball is charged by contact with an electrified glass rod, the rod and ball repel each other.   Similarly, if a pith ball is charged by contact with an electrified rubber rod, they repel one another.   However, a ball charged by contact with the electrified *glass* rod is attracted by the electrified *rubber* rod, while the charged *glass* rod attracts a pith ball charged by contact with the electrified *rubber* rod.   This simple experiment suggests (see Fig. 34.1) that there are *at least* two different kinds of electric charge.   Exhaustive experiments with many different kinds of substances have led to the conclusion that there are *only* two kinds of charges.   The charge on a glass rod rubbed with silk is called *positive*, while that on a rubber rod rubbed with cat's fur is *negative*. From a number of experiments it is possible to establish the qualitative laws of electrostatic reaction: *Like charges repel one another; unlike charges attract one another.*

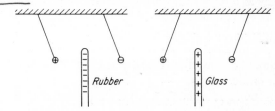

Fig. 34.1. Like charges repel; unlike attract.

34.3. The Electrical Structure of Matter.   The idea that all matter is composed of tiny particles called *atoms* is well known.   Although the word *atom* means "indivisible," atoms have a complex structure. Practically all the mass of an atom is concentrated in a tiny core called the *nucleus*.   The nucleus bears a *positive* charge, the magnitude of which depends on the atom in question.   All nuclei of a given element bear the same charge.   The nucleus with the smallest charge is that of the hydrogen atom, which carries one positive atomic unit equal in magnitude to the negative charge on the electron.   The nucleus of the hydrogen atom has a special name, the *proton*.   Every other type of atom has a nucleus bearing some integral number of atomic units.   All oxygen nuclei have 8 atomic charges; all copper nuclei 29 charges.   Indeed, the atomic number of the atom is a measure of how many atomic units of charge its nucleus bears (i.e., of how many protons it contains).

Outside the nucleus of a neutral atom are *electrons*, the number of electrons being equal to the number of positive charges in the nucleus.   It is sometimes convenient to think of an atom as sort of a submicroscopic solar system, with the nucleus as the sun and with the electrons rotating about it much as the planets revolve around the sun.

For an atom which has several electrons there is abundant evidence to indicate that some of the electrons are close to the nucleus and others much farther away.   Sodium has eleven electrons, of which two are ordinarily close to the nucleus, eight are at a somewhat greater distance, and the eleventh is usually much farther from the nucleus, as indicated schematically in Fig. 34.2. This "outside" electron is not very tightly held by the atom; it can be removed readily, which accounts for many of the interesting chemical properties of sodium. In general, any atom which has several electrons will have some which are very difficult to remove and one or at most a few electrons which are comparatively easy to take away from the atom. The outer electrons of some atoms, such as lithium and sodium, are particularly easy to remove, while those of other atoms, such as neon and argon, are relatively tightly held. The chemical properties of elements are intimately related to their electronic structures.

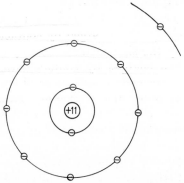

Fig. 34.2. Grossly oversimplified schematic diagram of a sodium atom, showing its nucleus with eleven positive atomic units of charge surrounded by eleven electrons, each of which bears one negative atomic charge unit.

If two substances are brought into intimate contact with one another, it is almost certain that one has a greater affinity for electrons than the other.   As a result, some of the electrons are transferred to the substance with the greater electron affinity. This leaves one substance with an excess of electrons or negatively charged, while the other is left with a deficiency of electrons and a corresponding positive charge. The transfer of charges does not go on indefinitely because, as the substance with the greater electron affinity accumulates electrons, the excess negative charge repels other electrons while the other substance with its excess positive charge attracts them.

34.4. Conductors and Insulators. In some materials, notably the metals, a small fraction of the electrons are not bound to any one nucleus, but are free to wander among the atoms. Materials in which electrons are free to move about are called conductors. On other hand, in many other materials each electron is held by one or two atoms. A material in which charges are not free to move about is called a *nonconductor* or *insulator*. As might be expected, the line between conductors and insulators is not a sharp one. For example, a piece of damp wood is neither a good conductor of electricity nor a good insulator.

In most solid conductors the transfer of charge is by movement of electrons.   However, there are many situations in which charges are not conducted by electrons.   A solution of sodium chloride in water is a good conductor of electricity, because the molecules break into two parts, a sodium atom with an electron missing and a chlorine atom with one additional electron.   These charged particles are called *ions*.   The conduction is by the movement of both positively charged sodium ions and negatively charged chlorine ions.   In liquids and gases, the transfer of charge by ions, both positive and negative, is common.

The early observations of electric charges were made on materials such as amber and glass, which are nonconductors.   A piece of glass rubbed with silk obtains a positive charge which does not escape readily because the glass is a good insulator.   If a copper rod is rubbed with silk, it also becomes charged, but, unless it is carefully insulated, the charge is rapidly conducted away.   If one holds the copper rod in his hand, the charges have no difficulty in traveling along the copper conductor and escaping through the human body, since the body is a fairly good conductor, especially when the skin is moist.

It is possible to charge one end of a hard rubber rod positively and the other end negatively by rubbing one end with a material of great electron affinity and the other end with a material of low electron affinity.

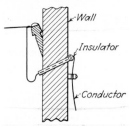

Fig. 34.3. Use of conductors and insulators.

Because the rubber is a good insulator the charges remain on the ends.   However, if one tries to do this to a metal rod, the charges do not stay on the ends; rather, there is an immediate flow of electrons.   Similarly, if a wire of conducting material is connected between a positively charged metal sphere and a negatively charged sphere, there is a flow of charges.   Such a flow is called an *electric current*.   In sending electric energy from one point to another, it is standard practice to produce a flow of charges; since this requires some sort of conducting medium, one finds wires of good conductors, usually copper or aluminum, connecting homes with power-generating stations (Fig. 34.3).

34.5. The Law of Conservation of Charge.   Since electrification by contact and separation always involves a transfer of charges from one body to another, the amount of positive charge which appears on one is equal to the negative charge which appears on the other.   Whenever a certain positive charge appears on one body, an equal negative charge must appear on some other body or bodies.

Charge is one of the fundamental properties of matter.   *The total net charge of any isolated system never changes.*   This statement expresses the *law of conservation of charge,* one of the basic laws of nature.   This law and the laws of conservation of energy and of momentum are of great importance in the interactions of atoms and in the reactions of atomic nuclei.

34.6. Coulomb's Law. In 1785 the French physicist Coulomb used a torsion balance (Fig. 34.4) to measure the force between two small charged spheres as a function of the distance between them. He found that the force between two charges in air varies inversely as the square of the distance between the charges and that the force is directly proportional to the product of the magnitude of the two charges.

$$F = k \frac{Q_1 Q_2}{r^2} \quad = newtons \tag{34.1}$$

Coulomb's law is directly applicable only in situations where the distance between the charges is very large compared to the dimensions of the charged bodies. Then we may consider all the charge as being concentrated at a point and we speak of it as a "point charge."

Charge may be measured in a number of units, four of which have been widely used. We shall work with only two.

1. The atomic unit of charge is the charge on a single proton; the charge on the electron has the same magnitude, but is negative in sign. The atomic unit of charge is exceedingly minute, far too small to be convenient for use in most practical problems in electricity. It is, however, a truly basic unit in that no smaller charge has ever been observed and all larger charges are believed to be an integral number of atomic units.

2. The *coulomb* is the practical unit of charge. We shall take it as a new fundamental unit, which with the meter, kilogram, and second will permit us to formulate the laws of electricity and magnetism in a self-consistent manner. The

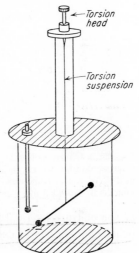

Fig. 34.4. A torsion balance of the type used by Coulomb in his research on the law of force between electric charges.

formal definition of the coulomb in terms of the operations required for a precise measurement of charge involves the use of concepts which are developed in subsequent chapters. We can, however, compare the coulomb with the atomic unit of charge.

1 coulomb = 6.242×10^{18} atomic units

or   1 atomic unit = 1.6019×10^{-19} coulomb

3. The electrostatic unit of charge, sometimes called the statcoulomb, is especially convenient for dealing with electrostatic problems. It is defined in terms of Coulomb's law as follows: The electrostatic unit of charge is that charge which repels an identical charge one centimeter away in vacuum with a force of one dyne (10^{-5} newton).

$$1 \text{ coulomb} = 3 \times 10^9 \text{ electrostatic units of charge}$$

4. The electromagnetic unit of charge, sometimes called the *abcoulomb*, is defined in terms of the magnetic field produced at the center of a circular coil by a current.

$$1 \text{ coulomb} = 0.1 \text{ electromagnetic unit of charge}$$

Complete systems of electrical units have been built around both the electrostatic and the electromagnetic units of charge. For handling certain special problems these systems are particularly convenient. However, it is difficult to learn three distinct systems of electrical units; therefore we shall use only the practical system in the problems for this text. In electrostatics we seldom meet charges as great as 1 coulomb; we therefore use submultiples such as the microcoulomb (μcoulomb).

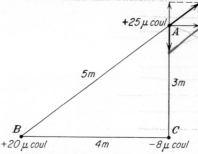

When the charges Q_1 and Q_2 are in coulombs, the force in newtons, and the distance in meters, the constant k of Eq. 34.1 is 9×10^9 newton-m^2/coul^2 for air or vacuum[1] and Eq. 34.1 becomes

$$F = 9 \times 10^9 \frac{Q_1 Q_2}{r^2} \quad (34.1a)$$

Fig. 34.5. Charges of $+25$, $+20$, and -8 microcoulombs are at the corners A, B, and C of a right triangle with sides of lengths 3, 4, and 5 m.

When several charges are present in one region, the force on any one of the charges is equal to the vector sum of the forces which each of the other charges would exert on the first one if it acted independently.

Example. Charges A, B, and C of $+25$, $+20$, and -8 μcoulombs, respectively, are arranged as shown in Fig. 34.5. Find the magnitude of the force on charge A.

$$F_{AB} = 9 \times 10^9 \frac{20 \times 10^{-6} \times 25 \times 10^{-6}}{25}$$

$$= 0.180 \text{ newton}$$

$$F_{AC} = -9 \times 10^9 \frac{25 \times 10^{-6} \times 8 \times 10^{-1}}{9}$$

$$= -0.200 \text{ newton}$$

The vertical component of $F_{AB} = \frac{3}{5} \times 0.180 = 0.108$ newton. The horizontal component of $F_{AB} = \frac{4}{5} \times 0.180 = 0.144$ newton.

[1] More exactly, $k = 8.987 \times 10^9$ newton-m^2/coul^2 for vacuum. For air, it is less by 1/1.0006. For problems in this book, these small corrections may be neglected.

The vertical component of the resultant force on A is $-0.200 + 0.108 = -0.092$ newton. The horizontal component of the resultant is 0.144 newton. The magnitude of the resultant is then

$$\sqrt{(0.144)^2 + (0.092)^2} = 0.171 \text{ newton}$$

34.7. Electric Field Intensity. Any region in which electric forces may be detected is called an *electric field*.

The *intensity* (or *strength*) **E** of an electric field at any point is defined as the ratio of the force **F** acting on a small test charge q at that point to the charge q.

$$E = \frac{F}{q} \qquad (34.2)$$

To measure the electric field at a point it is desirable that a very small test charge be chosen, since a large test charge would change the charge distribution which creates the field and thus distort the very thing it is being used to measure. Clearly, the electric field strength is a vector quantity. Its direction is the direction of the force on a *positive* charge.

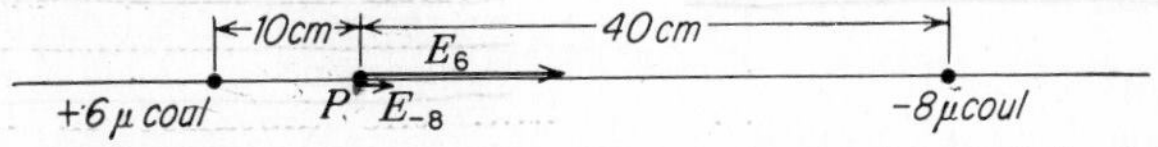

Fig. 34.6. The electric field strength at point P is the resultant of the fields due to the $+6$- and the -8-microcoulomb charges.

The intensity of the electric field at a distance r from an isolated point charge Q is obtained by performing an imaginary experiment in which a small test charge q is placed at the point where the intensity is desired. By Coulomb's law the force on this test charge is $F = 9 \times 10^9 Qq/r^2$. Since $E = F/q$, we conclude that the electric intensity at a distance r from a point charge Q is given by

$$E = 9 \times 10^9 \frac{Q}{r^2} \quad \text{newtons/coul} \qquad (34.3)$$

If an electric field is due to two or more charges, the electric intensity **E** at any point is given by the resultant of the electric intensities due to each charge taken individually.

Example. Find the magnitude of the electric intensity at A of Fig. 34.5 due to the charges at B and C.

We have found the magnitude of the force on a charge of 25 μcoulombs at this point to be 0.171 newton. By Eq. (34.2),

$$E = \frac{F}{q} = \frac{0.171 \text{ newton}}{25 \text{ }\mu\text{coulombs}} = 6{,}840 \text{ newtons/coul}$$

Example. Find the electric field strength at the point P of Fig. 34.6 which is 10 cm from a charge of $+6$ μcoulombs and 40 cm from a charge of -8 μcoulombs.

E is a vector quantity

The electronic field due to the $+6$-μcoulombs charge has a magnitude $9 \times 10^9 \times 6 \times 10^{-6}/(0.1)^2 = 54 \times 10^5$ newtons/coul. The field due to the -8-μcoulomb charge has a magnitude $9 \times 10^9 \times 8 \times 10^{-6}/(0.4)^2 = 4.5 \times 10^5$ newtons/coul. The fields due to both charges are in the same direction—to the right. Therefore, the resultant has a magnitude 58.5×10^5 newtons/coul and is directed toward the right.

34.8. Lines of Force. The electric field in the vicinity of one or more charged bodies is frequently represented by drawing *lines of force* as an aid in visualizing the field. *An electric line of force is a line which is*

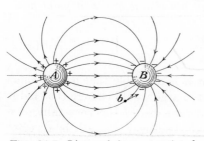

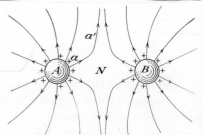

Fig. 34.7. Lines of force associated with a pair of equal and opposite charges.

Fig. 34.8. Lines of force associated with two identical positive charges. At the point N the field is zero; for this reason it is called a *neutral point*.

drawn so its tangent at every point has the direction of the electric intensity at that point. Some of the lines of force associated with a pair of equal and opposite charges are shown in Fig. 34.7, while some due to two identical positive charges are indicated in Fig. 34.8. Lines of force always begin on positive charges and terminate on negative ones. The lines of Fig. 34.8 terminate on negative charges which might, for example, be on the walls of the room.

We may draw as many lines of force as we wish in picturing an electric field. A reasonable number of lines can give us a visualization of the direction of the force on a small $+$ test charge any place in the field. The line of force through a point tells us the direction of the electric intensity at that point, but nothing of its magnitude. However, a qualitative estimate of the magnitude of the field can be obtained from a plot if lines of force are drawn close together where the field is strong and far apart where it is weak.

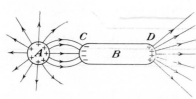

Fig. 34.9. Opposite charges are induced at C and D when an uncharged conductor B is brought into the electric field of a positive charge A.

34.9. Electrostatic Induction. If an uncharged conductor B (Fig. 34.9) is brought into the electric field of a positively charged conductor A, the attractive forces due to the excess positive charge on A

cause the electrons in B to be pulled toward end C, leaving the farther end D with a deficit of electrons and therefore charged positively.   Since B was originally neutral (i.e., contained as much positive as negative electricity), in spite of this displacement of electrons, it still has as much positive as negative electricity.   The positive charge on end D is just equal to the negative charge on end C.

If the conductor B is connected to the earth by means of a wire, enough electrons come from the earth to the conductor B to neutralize the posi-

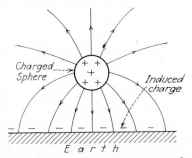

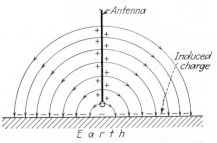

Fig. 34.10. A positively charged sphere induces a negative charge on the earth.

Fig. 34.11. Lines of force connecting the positively charged antenna with the negative induced charge on the earth.

tive charge at D.   Meanwhile the electrons on the other end C are held fast by the attractive force due to the positive charge on A.   If the connection to the earth is now broken and B removed from the presence of A, B will have an excess of electrons and therefore be charged nega-tively.   If B is now connected again to the earth, this excess of electrons will flow to the earth, leaving it uncharged.

A charged sphere in the neigh-borhood of the surface of the earth (Fig. 34.10) induces a charge on the surface of the earth below it.   A

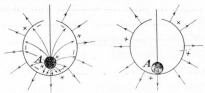

Fig. 34.12. The Faraday ice-pail experi-ment.   The charge induced on the inside of the cavity is equal in magnitude to the inducing charge on A.

charged antenna in the neighborhood of the surface of the earth (Fig. 34.11) has a similar effect.

Another illustration involving electrostatic induction is seen in Fig. 34.12.   If a metal sphere, charged positively, is introduced into an uncharged hollow sphere that is insulated, some of the electrons of the hollow sphere are drawn to its inner surface, leaving the outer surface charged positively.   If the metal sphere A is placed in contact with the inner surface of the hollow sphere, the electrons from the inner surface of the hollow sphere go over to the sphere A and just compensate the deficit of electrons.   This leaves both the sphere A and the inner surface of the hollow sphere without a charge, while the outer surface of the hollow sphere has too few electrons and is therefore charged positively.   If the outer surface is now connected to the earth, it gains a sufficient number of electrons to compensate for its deficit and it is left uncharged.   By experiments of this type Faraday was able to show that the charge induced on the outside of an almost closed hollow conductor is equal to an inducing charge on the inside.   As his hollow conductor Faraday used a small ice pail and the operations described in this paragraph are often referred to as the "Faraday ice-pail experiment."

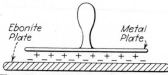

Fig. 34.13. The electrophorus.   A positive charge is induced on the bottom of the metal plate by the negative charge on the ebonite; the corresponding negative charge produced on the upper side of the metal plate goes to the ground when the metal plate is touched.

If an ebonite plate (Fig. 34.13) is charged negatively by rubbing it with cat's fur, a positive charge is induced on the bottom of a metal plate placed above the ebonite and an equal negative charge is induced on the upper surface.   If the metal plate is grounded for an instant, electrons flow from the metal plate, leaving it with a net positive charge.   The metal plate may be removed, carrying with it the positive charge.

34.10. The Electroscope.   A useful instrument for studying electrostatic phenomena is the electroscope, one form of which consists of two thin gold leaves attached to a metal rod which is terminated at the other end by a metal sphere (Fig. 34.14).   When the metal sphere is charged, part of the charge goes to the gold foils, which are repelled by each other and therefore diverge.   The greater the charge on the leaves, the greater the divergence.   The electroscope may be used to give a semiquantitative indication of the charge on the leaves.

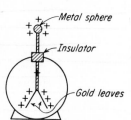

Fig. 34.14. A gold-leaf electroscope.   The leaves repel each other when a charge is placed on the metal sphere.

In actual practice it is customary to use only one gold leaf for the electroscope and to let the rigid and flattened extension of the central rod serve as the other leaf.   In this case only the leaf made of foil moves.

An electroscope can be charged positively or negatively by touching the knob with either a positive glass rod or a negative rubber rod, but there is a substantial danger that so much charge may be transferred that the gold leaf will be torn off.   A safe way to charge an electroscope is by induction.   To charge an electroscope positively by induction, one brings a negatively charged rod near the knob, as shown in the first part of

Fig. 34.15.   Electrons in the knob are repelled by the rod and descend to the leaves.   The knob is then grounded by touching it, and the excess electrons on the leaves run off.   The connection to ground is then removed, leaving a net positive charge on the electroscope knob.   When

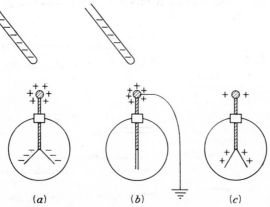

Fig. 34.15. Charging an electroscope by induction.   When the negative rod is brought near, the charges rearrange themselves in the electroscope, as shown in (a). When a connection to the ground is made in (b), negative charges flow off, leaving a positive charge held on the knob by attraction for the negative rod.   The connection to the ground is then broken, the charged rod removed, and the positive charges on the electroscope rearrange themselves as shown in (c).

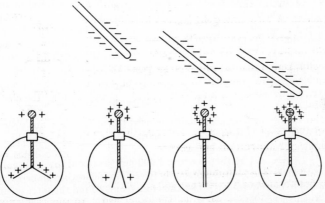

Fig. 34.16. The effect of bringing a negatively charged rod nearer and nearer to a positively charged electroscope.   Note how the charge distribution changes, although the total charge on the electroscope remains constant.

the negative rod is removed, these charges rearrange themselves so that both the knob and leaves are positively charged.

If a negatively charged rod is brought near a positively charged electroscope, some of the electrons on the metal sphere are repelled and move to the leaves where they reduce the net positive charge and reduce the divergence of the leaves (Fig. 34.16). As the negative rod is brought still nearer, more electrons go to the leaves which eventually lose all their net charge and converge. On bringing the negative rod still closer, even more electrons go to the leaves, causing them to diverge once more. In this case, although the total charge on the electroscope is positive, the leaves bear a negative charge.

PROBLEMS

1. Charges -3 and $+2$ μ coulombs are 2 m apart. Find the force between them.
Ans. 0.0135 newton

2. A point charge of 6×10^{-9} coulomb is located 20 cm from a point charge of 8×10^{-9} coulomb. Find the force exerted on each charge by the other.

3. Find the force on a charge of 3×10^{-9} coulomb if it is placed in a field of intensity 20,000 newtons/coul.
Ans. 6×10^{-5} newton

4. The force on a charge is 2×10^{-6} newton when the charge is placed in an electric field of intensity 5×10^5 newton/coul. Find the magnitude of the charge.

5. How many electrons must be removed from a small pith ball to give it a charge of 10^{-9} coulomb?
Ans. 6.24×10^9

6. If 50 billion electrons are added to a small neutral sphere, what charge does the sphere bear?

7. In a Bohr model of the hydrogen atom an electron revolves in a circular orbit of radius 5×10^{-11} m about a nucleus which bears a positive charge equal in magnitude to the electronic charge. Find the force on the electron which provides the centripetal acceleration for the uniform circular motion.
Ans. 9.2×10^{-8} newton

8. Two point charges repel each other with a force of 0.004 newton when they are 30 cm apart. Find the force if the distance between them is reduced to 10 cm.

9. A small test charge of 10^{-9} coulomb experiences a force of 4×10^{-4} newton when it is 2 m from a point charge of unknown magnitude. Find the electric intensity at the test charge due to the unknown charge and the magnitude of the unknown charge.
Ans. 4×10^5 newton/coul; 1.78×10^{-4} coulomb

10. A small sphere is charged with 6×10^{-9} coulomb of negative electricity. When another similar sphere is brought to a distance of 40 cm from the first sphere, the second sphere is attracted with a force of 6×10^{-5} newton. Find the charge on the second sphere.

11. A point charge of 0.02 μcoulomb is placed 0.8 m from a point charge of 0.05 μcoulomb. What force is exerted on each charge? Find the electric field strength at the point midway between the charges.
Ans. 1.4×10^{-5} newton; 1,690 newtons/coul toward smaller charge

12. The electric intensity in the region between two deflecting plates of an electrostatic deflection television tube is 40,000 newtons/coul. Find the force on an electron passing between these plates.

13. An unknown charge and a charge of -6 μcoulombs are 1 m apart. The electric field strength is zero at a point 60 cm from the unknown charge on the line connecting the two charges. Find the unknown charge.
Ans. -13.5 μcoulomb

14. Three charges of $+5$, -5, and $+5$ μcoulombs are placed in the same straight line 10 cm apart. What force acts on each charge because of the other two charges?

15. Two small pith balls, each weighing 0.001 newton, are hung from a common point by nylon threads 10 cm long. When the pith balls are given equal positive charges, they repel one another and stand 12 cm apart, so that the supporting threads make an angle of 37° with the vertical. Find the charge on each pith ball.
Ans. 3.46×10^{-8} coulomb

16. Two small equally charged spheres, each with a mass of 0.15 g, are suspended from the same point by silk fibers 90 cm long. The repulsion between them keeps them 6 cm apart. What is the charge on each sphere?

17. Charges of +2, −3, and +4 μcoulombs are placed on the corners of a square with sides 20 cm long. Find the magnitude of the electric field strength at the fourth corner diagonally opposite the −3-μcoulomb charge. *Ans.* 6.96 × 10⁵ newtons/coul

18. Three charges A, B, and C are located on the same straight line. The distance from A to B is 30 cm and that from B to C is 40 cm. The charge at A is 0.03 μcoulomb, that at B is 0.04 μcoulomb, and that at C is 0.05 μcoulomb. What force is exerted on A by the charges at B and C if all the charges are positive? What is the electric intensity midway between B and C?

19. Charges of 1 × 10⁻⁹ coulomb are placed at opposite ends of the hypotenuse of a right triangle with sides 3, 4, and 5 m. Find the magnitude of the electric intensity at the other vertex.   *Ans.* 1.15 newtons/coul

20. Two small spherical pith balls are charged with positive electricity and placed 20 cm apart. One of them has a charge of 1.2 × 10⁻⁸ coulomb and the other a charge of 1.8 × 10⁻⁸ coulomb. Find the force on a positive charge of 1.5 × 10⁻⁸ coulomb located 15 cm from the larger charge in a direction perpendicular to the line joining the charges.

21. Charges of −2 and +4 μcoulombs are placed at two of the vertices of an equilateral triangle with sides 10 cm in length. Find the magnitude of the electric intensity at the third vertex, and of the force which would act on a charge of 2 × 10⁻⁸ coulomb at that vertex.   *Ans.* 3.12 × 10⁶ newtons/coul; 0.0624 newton

22. What is the magnitude of the electric intensity at the intersection of the bisectors of the angles of an equilateral triangle when a charge of 2 × 10⁻⁹ coulomb is located at each vertex and the sides of the triangle are 20 cm?

23. Can two lines of force ever cross? Explain your answer carefully.

CHAPTER 35 important

Potential

35.1. Potential Energy in an Electric Field. When a small test charge $+q$ is moved about in the field of a fixed charge $+Q$ (Fig. 35.1) work must be done to move the test charge closer to Q. This work goes into increasing the potential energy of the test charge. On the other hand, as q moves away from Q, the electric field does work and the potential energy of q decreases. In discussing the movement of electric charges, the concept of electric potential energy plays a very important role, since many problems in

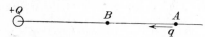

Fig. 35.1. Work must be done to move a small positive test charge q from point A to point B against the electric field of charge Q.

electricity involve the law of conservation of energy and the electric potential energy is one of the forms which must be taken into consideration.

In expressing the electric potential energy of a charge quantitatively, it is necessary to specify some point at which the potential energy is zero, just as it is necessary to specify a zero position in dealing with any other form of potential energy. For example, in treating the potential energy of a given mass relative to the earth (Chap. 7), it is shown that the potential energy is proportional to the elevation h. In this case it is necessary to decide from what level h is measured. The potential energy of a 1-kg mass 2 m above a table is different depending on whether one wishes to use the table or the floor as the point of zero potential energy. In dealing with the particular situation illustrated in Fig. 35.1, it is common to consider the potential energy of q to be zero when it is infinitely far from Q. This choice is arbitrary.

Having once chosen a point of zero potential energy, one may define the potential energy of a charge $+q$ at point P as the work necessary to move the charge from the point at which its potential energy is zero to the point P. If the potential energy of a charge q at a given point is W joules, the potential energy of a charge $3q$ at this same point is $3W$ joules, and in general for charge nq the potential energy at this point is

nW.   Since the potential energy of the charge at a given point is directly proportional to the charge, it is convenient to introduce the concept of *potential energy per unit charge*.   The ratio of the potential energy of a charge at a given point to the charge is called the *potential at the point*. In electrostatics the zero of potential is almost invariably chosen to be at infinity.   For this choice the following definition applies: *The potential at a point P is the ratio W/q, where W is the work required to move a small test charge $+q$ from infinity to the point P.*

The practical unit for measuring potential, the joule per coulomb, is called the *volt*, in honor of Alessandro Volta, whose pioneering work with the battery was a major contribution to the infant science of electricity in 1800.   *The potential at a point is one volt when it requires one joule of work to move a charge of $+$ one coulomb from a point of zero potential to the point in question.*

35.2. The Potential Due to a Point Charge.

The potential at a distance R from a point charge of Q coulombs is the *work per coulomb* required to bring a positive test charge from an infinite distance to the point in question.   If q is the test charge which is being transferred, the force on this charge at a distance r from Q is kQq/r^2.   The small element of work ΔW required to move q a small distance $-\Delta r$ (Fig. 35.2) toward Q is $\Delta W = -(kQq/r^2)\,\Delta r$. (The minus sign arises from the fact that q is being moved in such a direction as to decrease r and consequently the change in r is negative.)   Since the force on q changes as the charge is moved toward Q, it is necessary to call upon more advanced mathematical techniques to compute the total work done in moving q from infinity to a point R m from Q.   An exact calculation[1] of this work shows that it is given by $W = kQq/R$.   The potential at this point is then

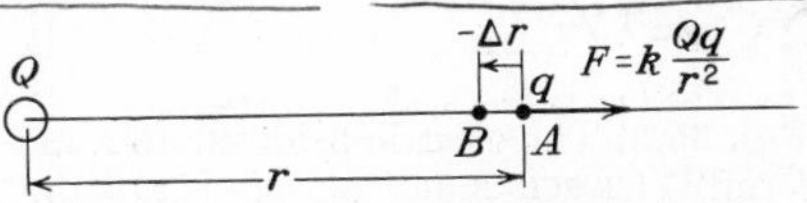

Fig. 35.2. The work ΔW required to move a test charge Q a distance $-\Delta r$ (from A to B) is given by

$$\Delta W = -F\,\Delta r = (-kQq/r^2)\,\Delta r$$

$$V = \frac{kQ}{R} = volts \qquad V = \frac{W}{q} = 9 \times 10^9 \frac{Q}{R} \text{ volts} \qquad (35.1)$$

when Q is in coulombs and R in meters.   The potential 1 m from a charge of 1 coulomb in vacuum is 9×10^9 volts.

Example.   Find the potential two meters from a charge of $+6$ μcoulombs.

$$V = \frac{9 \times 10^9 Q}{R} = \frac{9 \times 10^9 \times 6 \times 10^{-6}}{2} = 27{,}000 \text{ volts}$$

When there are a number of charges in a region, the potential at any point is the sum of the potentials due to each charge acting alone.   Thus if there

---

[1] It is assumed that all operations in this chapter are carried out in air or *in vacuo*.

are three charges Q_1, Q_2, Q_3 in a region, the potential at a point which is at distance of R_1 from Q_1, R_2 from Q_2, and R_3 from Q_3, is simply given by

$$V = 9 \times 10^9 \left(\frac{Q_1}{R_1} + \frac{Q_2}{R_2} + \frac{Q_3}{R_3} \right) \qquad (35.2)$$

The contribution of a negative charge to the potential is negative, because the electric field does work in bringing a positive test charge toward a negative charge. A great advantage of working with potential in preference to electric intensities arises from the fact that potential is a scalar quantity while the electric intensity is a vector.

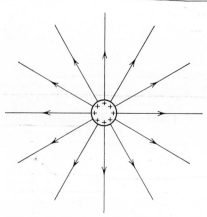

Fig. 35.3. The electric field due to a uniformly charged spherical shell is radial at all points outside the sphere.

35.3. The Isolated Sphere. Consider a metal sphere of radius R, far away from all other bodies and bearing a charge of Q coulombs. The electric field (Fig. 35.3) associated with this charged sphere is everywhere radial and for all points outside the sphere is indistinguishable from the electric field which would be associated with a point charge Q located at the center of the sphere. Thus, a uniformly charged sphere behaves, *so far as all external points are concerned,* exactly as though all its charge were con-

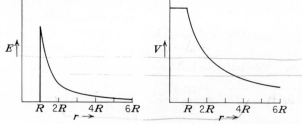

Fig. 35.4. The electric field intensity and the potential at a distance r from the center of a uniformly charged, conducting sphere of radius R.

centrated at the center. The work necessary to bring a unit charge from infinity to the surface of the sphere is the same as the work which would be required to bring the same unit charge from infinity to the distance R from a point charge Q. The potential of the sphere is therefore given by

$$V = 9 \times 10^9 \frac{Q}{R} \qquad (35.3)$$

Within the sphere the electric field is zero (see Sec. 35.7). Therefore, no work is required to carry a small test charge from any point on the surface of the sphere to any point within the sphere. *The potential at all points inside the sphere is the same as the potential at the surface.* The electric field and the potential are plotted as a function of r in Fig. 35.4.

35.4. Surface Charge Density. When a sphere of radius R bears a charge of Q coulombs, the charge per unit area is given by

Sigma

$$\sigma = \frac{Q}{4\pi R^2} \qquad (35.4)$$

where σ is known as the *surface charge density*.

If a large sphere and a small one are far apart but connected by a conductor and a charge is placed on the system, there is a flow of charges until both spheres come to the same potential V. If the charges on the two spheres are then Q and q and the radii of the two spheres are R and r, respectively, V is given by

$$V = \frac{9 \times 10^9 Q}{R} = \frac{9 \times 10^9 q}{r}$$

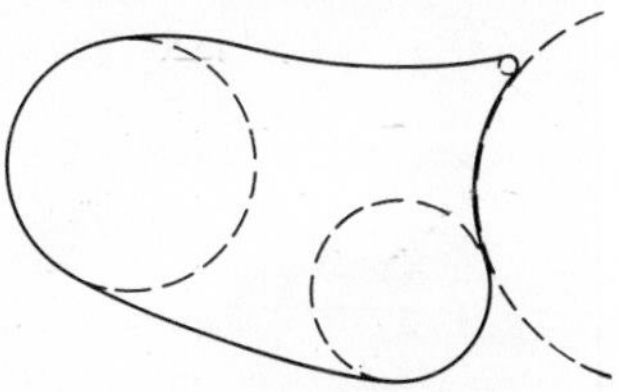

Let σ_R and σ_r be the charge densities on the respective spheres. Then

$$V = 9 \times 10^9 \frac{4\pi R^2 \sigma_R}{R} = 9 \times 10^9 \frac{4\pi r^2 \sigma_r}{r}$$

and

$$R\sigma_R = r\sigma_r \qquad (35.5)$$

Fig. 35.5. The surface of a conductor may be thought of as being made up of a number of small sections of spherical surfaces.

For spheres at the same potential, the charge density is inversely proportional to the radius.

The surface of any conductor may be regarded as composed of a large number of spherical segments (Fig. 35.5) of different curvatures. Where the surface has the greatest curvature (i.e., the smallest radius), the surface charge density is greatest. When a conductor terminates in a sharp point, the surface density at the point is so great that the molecules of air in the neighborhood of the point may become charged with electricity. Since like charges repel, the charged molecules are repelled from the point, and the body to which the point is attached is discharged. The ionized molecules may emit light which is readily visible in a darkened room. Such a discharge is called a *corona*

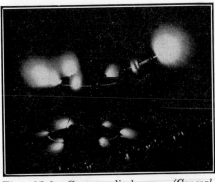

Fig. 35.6. Corona discharge. (*General Electric Co.*)

discharge (Fig. 35.6). If the field is sufficiently great, flashover occurs (Fig. 35.7).

The fact that charged points allow the electricity to escape from them is used in electrostatic machines (Fig. 35.8), where rows of metallic points are used to conduct electricity from moving to fixed parts of the machine. This fact is also important in the design of lightning rods. The pointed conductors on the rod bring about a silent and gradual discharge from the rod to the clouds. The escape of electricity from these points prevents the accumulation of enough electricity on the building on which the lightning rod is mounted to result in a dangerous disruptive discharge.

35.5. Potential Referred to the Earth.

In dealing with problems associated with potential, it is convenient to assign zero potential to some convenient conducting body just as it is convenient to refer the height of a building to the ground level, while the height of a mountain is ordinarily referred to mean sea level. In many situations the potential of

Fig. 35.7. Flashover on a sealed bushing. (*General Electric Co.*)

Fig. 35.8. An electrostatic machine. (*Central Scientific Co.*)

the earth is taken as zero. When one speaks of a 110-volt lighting circuit or of a 180,000-volt transmission line, one ordinarily implies that the earth is taken as zero potential. In a radio or television receiver the chassis is usually regarded as being at zero potential; often it is actually tied to the ground by a direct conductor. In dealing with the electrical circuits of an automobile, it is convenient to regard the frame of the car as being at zero potential, although it is ordinarily insulated from the earth by the tires.

In general, one may assign the potential zero to any convenient point. Then the potential at any other point is the ratio W/q, where W is the work required to move a small charge q from the point at zero potential to the point in question.

35.6. Potential Difference.

One of the most important concepts in all of electrical theory is that of potential difference. Let W be the external work done against an electric field in moving a small *positive* test charge q from one point to another. The potential difference V between these two points is defined as the ratio of W to q,

$$V = \frac{W}{q} \tag{35.6}$$

The potential difference between two points is the work per unit positive charge required to move a small test charge from one point to the other. Potential difference, as well as potential, is commonly measured in volts (joules per coulomb). *The potential difference between two points is one volt if it requires one joule of external work to move each coulomb of charge from one point to the other.* The potential difference across the terminals of an ordinary automobile battery is 12 volts; this means that 12 joules of external work are required to transfer 1 coulomb of positive charge from the negative terminal to the positive terminal. This energy is supplied by the chemical reaction within the cells, so that chemical energy is converted into electrical energy.

The potential difference between two points A and B is equal to the potential at A minus the potential at B, just as the term *potential difference* implies. Thus, $V_{AB} = V_A - V_B$. Alternatively, *the potential difference between points A and B is the external work per unit charge done against the electrostatic field in moving a small test charge from B to A.* The potential difference is independent of the zero of potential. For example, the potential difference between the positive and negative terminals of an ordinary dry cell is 1.5 joules/coul, regardless of whether the earth or some other point is taken as the zero potential reference. The sign of the potential difference depends on which way the charge is moved. The potential difference *between the positive and the negative terminals* of the cell is +1.5 volts, while the potential difference *between the negative and the positive terminals is* −1.5 volts.

In any electrostatic field, external work is required to move a positive charge from a point of lower to a point of higher potential, since the electric field is directed from points of higher to points of lower potential. If a small positive test charge is moved from B to A against an electric field and then returned to B, external work is required to transfer the charge from B to A; when the charge returns to B, work is done on the charge by the electric field. Since the force on a negative charge in an electric field is opposite to that on a positive charge, the field moves negative charges from points of lower toward points of higher potential; external work must be done to carry a negative charge from a point of higher to one of lower potential.

35.7. Equipotential Surfaces. It is often convenient to represent the potential distribution in an electric field by means of equipotential surfaces. An equipotential surface is defined as a surface, all points of which are at the same potential.   Some of the equipotential surfaces for a spherical charge distribution are shown in Fig. 35.9.   In this particular

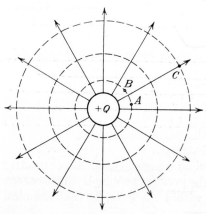

case the equipotential surfaces are spheres, while the lines of force are radial.   The lines of force are perpendicular at every point to the equipotential surfaces.   This follows immediately from the fact that it takes no work to move a small test charge from one point to another on the same equipotential surface.   Therefore, the electric field has no component in the direction of the surface and hence must be perpendicular to it.

Fig. 35.9. Lines of force (radial) and equipotential surfaces (spheres) for a spherical charge distribution.

In Fig. 35.9, A and B lie on the same equipotential surface, while C lies on another equipotential surface.   In moving a small test charge from A to B along the equipotential surface, no work is done since the displacement is at all points perpendicular to the force on the charge. However, if a charge is moved from C to A work must be done; regardless of what path is chosen the force due to the field must have a component in the direction of this displacement for at least some part of the movement.   The work required to move a charge from one point to another is independent of the path.   The work required to move a small test charge from C to A is the same whether one goes first along the line of force to the equipotential surface AB and then to A, or from C to A along a straight line, or to B and then over to A.

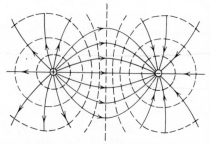

Fig. 35.10. Lines of force (solid lines) and equipotential surfaces (dashed lines) near two equal, but opposite, charges.

The lines of force and equipotential surfaces are shown in Fig. 35.10 for the region around two equal point charges of opposite sign.

In a conductor there is a flow of charge if there is a potential difference between any two points.   This flow stops as soon as all points in the conductor are at the same potential.   In electrostatics, charges are at rest and therefore there is no potential difference between points in the conductor.   The entire conductor is an equipotential surface.   Since there can be no electric field within the conductor, there is no net charge within the conductor. *The entire net charge of the conductor resides on the surface. Any excess or deficiency of electrons is at the surface.* Since the surface of a conductor is an equipotential surface and since lines of force are always perpendicular to equipotential surfaces, *lines of force always leave perpendicular to the surface of a conductor.*

35.8. The Potential Gradient. Consider two large parallel plates, one bearing a charge $+Q$ while the other bears a charge $-Q$ (Fig. 35.11). The electric field between the two plates (reasonably far from an edge) is constant, both in magnitude and direction. Such a field is said to be *uniform*. If a charge q is carried from the lower plate

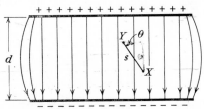

Fig. 35.11. The electric field between two parallel charged plates is uniform so long as one stays far from the edges where "fringing" of the field becomes important.

to the upper one, the work done against the field is $-Eqd$, where d is the displacement from the lower plate. The minus sign appears because E and the displacement are in opposite directions. The potential difference V between the plates is $W/q = -Ed$. Solving for E yields

$$E = -\frac{V}{d} \tag{35.7}$$

If the test charge q is moved from X to Y (Fig. 35.11) the work done is

$$W = -qEs \cos \theta$$

and the potential difference is $V = -Es \cos \theta$ or

$$E \cos \theta = -\frac{V}{s} \tag{35.8}$$

The ratio of the potential difference V between two neighboring points along a line of force to the distance d between the points is a vector called the *potential gradient*. The electric intensity **E** is the negative of the potential gradient (Eq. 35.7). The component of the potential gradient in any direction is the negative of the component of the electric intensity in that direction (Eq. 35.8). E may be measured in terms of potential difference divided by distance as well as in terms of force divided by charge. Electric field strengths are often expressed in volts per meter, rather than in the equivalent newtons per coulomb. (An electric intensity of one volt per meter is exactly the same as an electric intensity of one newton per coulomb.)

35.9. Atmospheric Electricity and Lightning. On a clear day the surface of a level field, freely exposed to the sky, is negatively charged so that there is an electric field downward. In good weather the electric field strength is about 100 volts/m. This potential gradient at the surface of the earth is continually varying. In addition to local variations, there are well-defined annual and diurnal variations, which differ at different parts of the surface of the earth. The diurnal variations of the potential gradient for two seasons of the year are shown in Fig. 35.12. As we go up above the earth's surface, the potential gradient diminishes and at a height of about 10 km it approaches zero, a fact which is explained by the rapid increase in the conductivity of the atmosphere as we go to high altitudes.

The earth's negative charge is believed to come largely from lightning and point discharges under clouds. During thunderstorms the violent, ascending air cur-

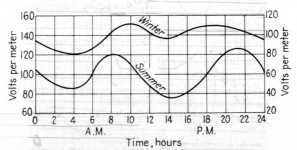

Fig. 35.12. Variation of potential gradient in the atmosphere for different hours of the day.

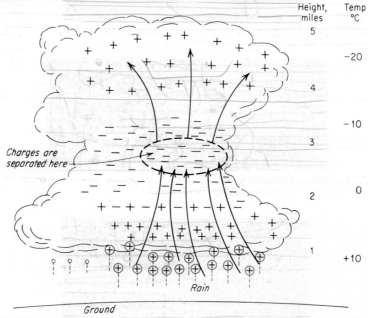

Fig. 35.13. Ascending air currents in thunderheads lead to the charging of clouds by contact and separation to give charge distribution shown.

rents in thunderheads (Fig. 35.13) break large raindrops into small ones. In this process the water droplets become positively charged and the air molecules negatively charged. Electrification occurs particularly strongly in the area of the thunderhead where the temperature is a few degrees below zero and tiny ice crystals abound. Water droplets are driven against ice crystals; the ice crystals

Fig. 35.14. Lightning discharge in the atmosphere.   (*Underwood and Underwood.*)

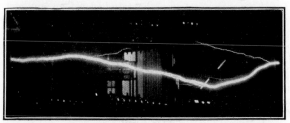

Fig. 35.15. Artificial lightning produced in the high-voltage laboratory of the General Electric Company.   (*Underwood and Underwood.*)

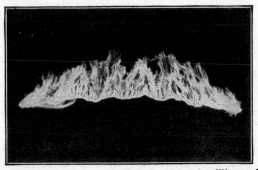

Fig. 35.16. A 60-cycle arc between points 25 ft apart; 2 million volts were required to arc this distance.   Current in the arc was about 1.5 amp and duration of the arc about 2 sec.   (*Courtesy of J. A. Carrol, Stanford University.*)

become strongly negative, while the residue of the water droplets is positive. These tiny charges are carried to great elevations where they freeze.   The result is that the top of the thunderhead has a large positive charge which eventually spreads out in the upper atmosphere.   The region near the 0°C isotherm is strongly negative, while the falling raindrops are positively charged.   Most of the lightning flashes (Fig. 35.14) to earth are from the lower negative center to ground and these flashes bring the earth its negative charge.   The earth would require 500,000 coulombs of negative charge to produce a potential gradient of 100 volts/m over its entire surface.   The gradient is not the same all over the earth and it is actually reversed over substantial areas during lightning storms.

Not only do we have lightning strokes between charged clouds and the earth, but discharges between the lower negative charge center and the upper positive region also occur.   With special transformers or other sources of high voltage it is possible to produce artificial lightning (Figs. 35.15 and 35.16) on a small scale in the laboratory.

PROBLEMS

1. Find the potential at a point 2 m from a charge of 8 μcoulombs.   How much work is required to bring a 1-μcoulomb charge from infinity to this point?
                                                          Ans. 36,000 volts; 0.036 joule

2. Four joules of work are done in carrying a charge of 80 μcoulombs from infinity to a point.   Find the potential of this point.

3. How much work is required to move a charge of 2 μcoulombs from a point where the potential is -3 volts to one where the potential is $+200$ volts.   *Ans.* 406 μjoules

4. The potential difference between the terminals of an automobile battery is 12 volts.   How much work is done by the battery in transferring 500 coulombs from one terminal to the other?

5. Find the potential and electric intensity midway between point charges of -8 and $+5$ μcoulombs if they are separated by a distance of 4 m.
               Ans. $-13,500$ volts, 29,300 newtons/coul toward -8 charge

6. Find the potential and electric intensity at a point midway between charges of $+2$ and -4 μcoulombs if they are separated by a distance of 1 m.

7. The potential of a sphere of radius 6 cm is 3,000 volts.   Find the charge on the sphere and the potential at a distance of 1 m from the center of the sphere.
                                                    Ans. 2 $\times$ 10^{-8} coulomb; 180 volts

8. A sphere of radius 2 cm bears a charge of 6 $\times$ 10^{-9} coulomb.   Find the electric intensity and the potential at the surface of the conducting sphere.

9. How much work is required to move a charge of 10^{-9} coulomb from a point 2 m to a point 0.5 m from a point charge of 5 μcoulombs?   What is the potential difference between these points?   *Ans.* 6.75, $\times$ 10^{-5} joule; 67,500 volts

10. Find the potential difference between two points, one 3 m and the other 2 m from a point charge of 6 $\times$ 10^{-9} coulomb.

11. How much work is required to carry a charge of 2 $\times$ 10^{-9} coulomb from an infinite distance to a point midway between two identical 4-μcoulomb charges 20 cm apart?   How much if one of the charges is -4 μcoulombs?
                                                      Ans. 1.44 $\times$ 10^{-3} joule; zero

12. Two points differ in potential by 75,000 volts.   How much work is required to carry 2 $\times$ 10^{-9} coulomb from the point of lower to the point of higher potential?

13. Find the potential at the center of a ring of radius 3 cm which bears a charge of 2 $\times$ 10^{-9} coulomb.   *Ans.* 600 volts

14. Find the potential at a point due to three charges of 0.02, 0.03, and 0.04 μcoulomb which are at distances of 10, 15, and 25 cm from the given point.

15. The potential difference between two clouds is 8 million volts. How much electrical energy is dissipated if a lightning stroke involving 60 coulombs leaps from one cloud to the other? Assume that the potential difference between the clouds remains constant. *Ans.* 480,000,000 joules

16. Charges of -1, 2, -3, and 4 μcoulombs are placed at the corners of a square 20 cm on a side. Find the potential at the center of the square.

17. It requires 0.003 joule to carry a charge of $+6$ μcoulombs from one parallel plate to another. Find the potential difference and the electric intensity between the plates if they are 2 cm apart. *Ans.* 500 volts; 25,000 newtons/coul $=$ 25,000 volts/m

18. The uniform electric field between two parallel plates has an intensity of 7,000 newtons/coul. How much work would be required to carry a charge of $+5$ μcoulombs from the negative to the positive plate if the separation of the plates is 4 cm?

19. A charge of 0.09 μcoulomb is placed on a conducting sphere of radius 10 cm. This sphere is then connected temporarily by a copper wire to an uncharged conducting sphere of radius 8 cm. Find the charge on each sphere.

Ans. 0.05 μcoulomb on 10-cm sphere; 0.04 μcoulomb on 8-cm sphere

20. A metal sphere having a radius of 8 cm carries a charge of 0.05 μcoulomb. It is temporarily connected to a second uncharged metal sphere having a radius of 12 cm. The two spheres are then separated. Find the charge on each sphere.

21. A rectangle is 4 by 3 m. If charges of $+8$ and -6 μcoulombs are placed at corners separated by 4 m, find the potential of the other two corners and the potential difference between them. *Ans.* 13,200 volts; $-3,600$ volts; 16,800 volts

22. Two large parallel plates are 5 cm apart. If the potential difference between them is 500 volts, calculate the electric intensity between the plates and the force on a 2-μcoulomb charge placed anywhere between the plates.

23. A hollow copper sphere has a radius of 3 cm. If it bears a charge of 6×10^{-9} coulomb, find the potential and the electric intensity (*a*) inside the sphere, (*b*) at the surface of the sphere, and (*c*) at a point 2 m from the center.

Ans. (*a*) 1,800 volts, 0; (*b*) 1,800 volts, 6×10^4 newtons/coul; (*c*) 27 volts, 13.5 newtons/coul

CHAPTER 36 *Important* cap. in series and parallel
especially

Capacitance
and Dielectrics

36.1. Capacitors. A device on which electric charges may be stored is called a *capacitor* or a *condenser*. Capacitors are important components in radio and television circuits, in the ignition system of an automobile, and in other electrical equipment. The term condenser originated in the erroneous idea that electricity was a fluid which could be stored in a suitable container. An early form of condenser is the Leyden jar (Fig. 36.1), which consists of a glass jar with a coating of tin foil on the inside and another on the outside.

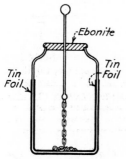

Ebonite

Tin Foil

Tin Foil

Fig. 36.1. A Leyden jar, a simple form of capacitor.

Capacitors have many different forms. A typical capacitor consists of two conductors, one of which is charged positively and the other negatively. Charging is usually accomplished by transferring the charge from one conductor to the other by means of a battery or other source of potential difference. The charge gained by one conductor is equal to that lost by the other. When we refer to the charge on a capacitor, we mean the magnitude of the charge on either conductor. Since the two conductors bear equal and opposite charges, the net charge is zero.

Let $+Q$ be the charge on the positive conductor, $-Q$ that on the negative conductor, and V the potential difference between the two conductors. *The capacitance C is defined as the ratio of the charge to the potential difference.*

$$C = \frac{Q}{V}$$

(36.1)

From the definition it follows that capacitance may be measured in coulombs per volt. This unit has been named the *farad* in honor of

430

Michael Faraday.   *The farad is that capacitance for which a charge of one*
coulomb will produce a potential difference of one volt.   The farad is a very
large unit of capacitance; a capacitance of a few microfarads (written
μf or mfd) is typical and capacitances of the order of a few micromicro-
farads (μμf), i.e., 10^{-12} farad, are common in radio and television circuits.
   The capacitance of a capacitor is independent of the charge.   If the
charge is doubled, the potential difference between the two conductors is
also doubled.   The capacitance depends on the size and shape of the conductors, on their relative positions, and on the character of the insulating
material between them.   Before we develop equations for the capacitance

of various arrangements of conductors, it is desirable to consider the
reason that the insulating material
affects the capacitance.

36.2. The Dielectric Constant.

If two parallel metal plates are insulated from one another and connected to an electroscope (Fig. 36.2),
there is a potential difference between the plates if they are charged
so that one bears $+Q$ and the other
$-Q$ coulombs.   The potential difference V may be measured in a
variety of ways, e.g., by the divergence of the electroscope leaves.
If a sheet of glass is inserted between
the two plates, the potential differ-

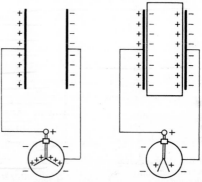

Fig. 36.2. A capacitor before and
after the insertion of a glass plate.
The surface charge induced on the
glass plate by polarization reduces the
potential difference between the two
conductors as the electroscope shows.

ence between the two plates becomes smaller and the divergence of the
electroscope leaves is reduced.   Since no charge escaped from the plates
while the potential was reduced, the capacitance Q/V of the system with
the glass plate in place must be greater than the capacitance without the
glass plate.
   To understand this phenomenon, it is necessary to consider what happens to the glass plate.   The plate is composed of electrically neutral
atoms.   When it is placed in the electric field, the electrons are attracted
by the positively charged conductor and the nuclei by the negatively
charged conductor.   The electrons in the glass are not free and cannot
leave the atoms to which they are attached, but they can undergo slight
displacements toward the positive plate, while the nuclei have similar displacements toward the negative plate.   The net effect of these minute
displacements throughout the glass is to produce a layer of negative
charge on one side and a layer of positive charge on the other.   The
presence of the glass results in a layer of negative charge close to the

positive metal plate.   This negative charge layer reduces the potential of the plate (see Sec. 35.2).   Similarly, the positive surface layer near the negative metal plate raises the potential of the latter.   The potential difference between the metal plates is decreased.   The glass plate increases the capacitance of the capacitor because it places a layer of negative charge close to the positive conductor and a layer of positive charge close to the negative conductor.   In a very real sense it reduces the *effective* charge on the conductors, although the actual charge is not changed.

A material is said to be *polarized* when the electrical "center of charge" of the electrons and of the nuclei of a material do not coincide.   As a consequence of the polarization, there is a "bound" charge on the surface of the polarized material.

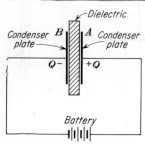

Fig. 36.3. A dielectric between the plates of a capacitor.

Suppose the space between the metal plates of Fig. 36.3 is completely filled with some material and the capacitance is measured. It is found that introducing this material increases the capacitance over its value when the region between the plates is evacuated. *The ratio of the capacitance of a capacitor with a given material filling the space between conductors to the capacitance of the same capacitor when the space is evacuated is the dielectric constant[1] of the material.*   The dielectric constants of several materials are listed in Table 1.

Table 1
DIELECTRIC CONSTANTS AND DIELECTRIC STRENGTHS

Material	K	Dielectric strength, volts/m	Material	K	Dielectric strength, volts/m
Vacuum	1		Barium titanate		
Air (1 atm)	1.0006	3×10^6	(25°)	1,200	
Ammonia (liquid)	22		Glass	4.8–10	30×10^6
Ethyl alcohol (0°C)	28.4		Mica	4.5–7.5	200×10^6
Transformer oil	2.1	$5–15 \times 10^6$	Paraffined paper	2	40×10^6
Water (18°C)	81		Polystyrene	2.6	20×10^6
Amber	3		Porcelain	6	15×10^6
			Rubber (hard)	3	21×10^6

36.3. Piezoelectricity.   We have seen that when a slice of dielectric material is placed between two charged plates (or more generally, in an electric field) there

[1] Some authors prefer the name *specific inductive capacity* and others use the name *relative permittivity*.

is a polarization of the medium.   In some materials, such as quartz and rochelle salt, this displacement of electric charges is accompanied by small changes in the size and shape of the crystal slice, an effect called *electrostriction*.   Electrostriction effects depend on the orientation of the crystal axes relative to the direction of the electric field.

In view of the fact that the shape of some crystals changes when the internal charges are displaced by an electric field, it is not surprising that changing the shape of the crystal may result in a redistribution of charges.   If a thin slice of quartz is compressed (Fig. 36.4), one face becomes positive and the other negative. If the crystal is stretched, instead of compressed, the charges on the faces are reversed.   Compressing or elongating the crystal results in a potential difference between the faces.   This potential difference may be hundreds or even thousands of volts.   This phenomenon is known as *piezoelectricity* (*piezo* means "pressure").

If an alternating voltage is applied to a properly sliced quartz crystal, the crystal faces oscillate.   By proper choice of the thickness of the slice, the mechanical oscillations can be made to have any desired frequency over a wide range. If a radio-frequency circuit has the same natural frequency as the mechanical oscillations of a quartz crystal, a sharp resonance may be obtained and the electrical oscillations may be accurately controlled by the mechanical frequency of the quartz crystal.   Quartz crystals are often used to control the frequencies of radio and television transmitters.

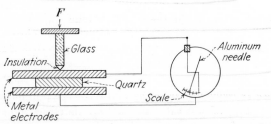

Fig. 36.4. A piezoelectric cell.   Pressure on the crystal faces produces a potential difference between them.

36.4. The Capacitance of an Isolated Sphere.   Consider a single sphere of radius R in vacuum, removed sufficiently far from other bodies so that their influence may be neglected.   Let this sphere be charged with Q coulombs, presumably brought to the sphere from an infinite distance away.   (In this case the second conductor of the capacitor is a sphere of infinite radius, which now bears a charge $-Q$).   According to Eq. (35.3) the potential of the sphere is given by $V = 9 \times 10^9 Q/R$.   Since $C = Q/V$, it follows immediately that

$$C = \frac{R}{9 \times 10^9} \qquad (36.2)$$

where C is in farads when R is in meters.

If we imagine all space to be filled with a medium of dielectric constant K, we have

$$C = \frac{KR}{9 \times 10^9} \qquad (36.3)$$

Obviously, the charge Q has not changed; therefore the increase in C must arise from a decrease in V. The potential of the sphere under these conditions is given by

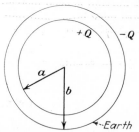

$$V = \frac{9 \times 10^9 Q}{KR} \qquad (36.4)$$

Fig. 36.5. A capacitor formed by two concentric spheres.

36.5. Capacitance of Spherical Capacitor.

Figure 36.5 shows a capacitor consisting of two concentric spheres. Let a be the radius of the inner sphere, b the radius of the outer sphere, $+Q$ the charge on the inner sphere, and $-Q$ the charge on the outer sphere, and let the region between the spheres be filled with a medium of dielectric constant K. The potential V_b of the outer sphere is, by Eq. (35.2),

$$V_b = \frac{9 \times 10^9 Q}{Kb} - \frac{9 \times 10^9 Q}{Kb} = 0$$

Similarly, the potential of the inner sphere is given by

$$V_a = \frac{9 \times 10^9 Q}{Ka} - \frac{9 \times 10^9 Q}{Kb} = \frac{9 \times 10^9 Q}{K}\left(\frac{1}{a} - \frac{1}{b}\right)$$

Since the potential of the outer sphere is zero, the potential difference V between the spheres is just the potential of the inner sphere V_a and the capacitance of the two concentric spheres is

$$C = \frac{Q}{V} = \frac{Kab}{9 \times 10^9 (b - a)} \qquad (36.5)$$

36.6. Capacitance of Two Parallel Plates.

If the radii of the two concentric spheres considered above are allowed to increase until they are very large while the difference $(b - a)$ remains constant, the surfaces of the spheres become approximately plane. The product ab becomes almost equal to a^2, since a and b are almost equal when both a and b are very large.

Let S be the area of the sphere of which a is the radius ($S = 4\pi a^2$) and let d ($= b - a$) be the distance between the spheres (kept constant) as a and b approach infinity. Then

$$C = \frac{Kab}{9 \times 10^9 (b - a)} = \frac{Ka^2}{9 \times 10^9 d}$$
$$= \frac{KS}{9 \times 10^9 \times 4\pi d}$$

If this relation is true for the entire spherical capacitor, it is also true for a small portion of it, provided the area of that portion is used instead of the entire area of the sphere. If the spheres are very large, and only a small portion of area A is cut out of the spherical surfaces, the capacitor obtained in this artificial way consists of two parallel plates at a distance d apart, each plate with area A. The capacitance in farads of such a capacitor is

$$C = \frac{KA}{9 \times 10^9 \times 4\pi d} \tag{36.6}$$

when A is in square meters and d is in meters.

Example. Find the capacitance of a capacitor consisting of two parallel plates that are 0.5 cm apart. Each of the plates has an area of 100 cm². The space between the plates is filled with a medium whose dielectric constant is 3.

$$\text{Capacitance} = \frac{\text{area} \times \text{dielectric constant}}{(4\pi \times \text{distance between plates}) \times 9 \times 10^9}$$

$$C = \frac{AK}{4\pi d(9 \times 10^9)}$$

$$= \frac{(0.01) \times 3}{0.005 \times 4\pi \times 9 \times 10^9}$$

$$= 54 \times 10^{-12} \text{ farad, or } 54 \ \mu\mu\text{f}$$

36.7. Practical Capacitors. Most of the practical capacitors in everyday use represent some modification of the parallel-plate capacitor. A good example is the familiar type used for tuning radio and television circuits (Fig. 36.6). The capacitance is varied by changing the effective area of the plates, which is that area close to a plate bearing the opposite charge. Alternate plates are connected together so that there are only two conductors; several plates are used to get a large area in a reasonable space. A further favorable factor in giving a large area is that both sides of all but the outermost plates are used.

Another common form of capacitor consists of two thin foils of aluminum with a thin sheet of wax-impregnated paper between them. Since both the paper and the foil are flexible, the whole arrangement may be rolled up to form a small compact cylinder. From Eq. (36.6) it follows that the thinner the layer between the conducting plates, the greater the capacitance. However, there is a practical limitation to how thin the insulating separator may be, because if it is too thin a spark may jump through it. The maximum potential difference which an insulating layer can stand may be computed from a knowledge of the thickness and of the *dielectric strength* of the material. *The dielectric strength is the potential gradient at which electrical breakdown occurs.*

Fig. 36.6. Parallel-plate capacitor with variable capacitance. (*General Radio Co.*)

Among the materials which are used as insulators in capacitors are impregnated papers, mica, plastics, ceramic materials, glass, and oils. Air is used in the variable capacitor of Fig. 36.6; because of the low dielectric constant, air capacitors have relatively small capacitance for a given area.

In the circuit diagram of radio and other electric circuits capacitors are commonly represented by the symbols of Fig. 36.7. An arrow drawn through the capacitor symbol indicates that it is variable; when no arrow is shown, it is implied that the capacitor has a fixed value.

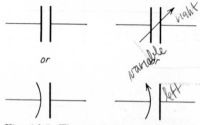

or

Fig. 36.7. The symbols used to represent fixed (left) and variable (right) capacitors.

A common and very inexpensive form of capacitor is the electrolytic capacitor. Such a capacitor has one plate of aluminum, the dielectric is a very thin coating of aluminum oxide on the surface of the plate, and the other conductor is a conducting solution. In such a capacitor d is exceedingly small and therefore a relatively large capacitance can be provided in a rather small space. However, these capacitors break down at relatively low voltages; furthermore, it is important that the aluminum terminal be made positive, since the aluminum oxide layer conducts if the aluminum is negative.

36.8. Energy Stored in a Capacitor. In charging a capacitor, it is necessary to do work to carry the electric charge from one terminal to the other. At the beginning, the two conductors of the capacitor are at the same potential. As charge is transferred from one plate to the other, the difference of potential between the two increases. Suppose that the final potential difference V between the terminals of the capacitor is attained after Q coulombs of electricity have been transferred from one terminal to the other. At the beginning of the process of charging, the difference of potential is zero; and at the end of the charging, the difference of potential is V. The average difference of potential during the charging is $V/2$. The work done is equal to the product of the average difference of potential and the quantity of electricity transferred. The energy W stored in the capacitor is given by

$$W = \tfrac{1}{2}QV \qquad\qquad (36.7)$$

This energy is released when the capacitor is discharged. If the capacitor is allowed to discharge through a wire, the energy is converted to heat in the wire.

Example. A condenser having a capacitance of 2 μf is charged with 10^{-3} coulomb of electricity. How much energy is stored in it?

$$\text{Energy} = \frac{1}{2}\,QV = \frac{1}{2}\frac{Q^2}{C}$$
$$= \frac{1}{2} \times \frac{10^{-3} \times 10^{-3}}{2 \times 10^{-6}}$$
$$= 0.25 \text{ joule}$$

36.9. Capacitors in Parallel. When two or more capacitors are connected in such a way that all the positive conductors are at the same potential V^+ and all the
negative conductors are at potential V^-, the capacitors are said to be connected *in parallel*. If a number
of capacitors having capacitances C_1, C_2, C_3, . . .
(Fig. 36.8) are connected in parallel, the system will
have a capacitance C which is equal to the sum of the
separate capacitances. This result can be proved as
follows:

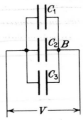

Fig. 36.8. A
group of three
capacitors con-
nected in parallel.

The capacitors are all charged to the same difference
of potential. Let V denote this difference of potential
and let Q_1, Q_2, and Q_3 be the charges on the capacitors
C_1, C_2, and C_3, respectively. Let Q be the total charge on all the capacitors. . Then

$$Q = Q_1 + Q_2 + Q_3 \cdots$$
and
$$Q_1 = C_1V \qquad Q_2 = C_2V \qquad Q_3 = C_3V$$
and
$$Q = CV$$

Substituting these values yields

$$CV = C_1V + C_2V + C_3V$$

Dividing by V gives

$$C = C_1 + C_2 + C_3 \tag{36.8}$$

Hence, to find the equivalent capacitance of a number of capacitors connected in parallel, it is only necessary to add together the separate
capacitances.

36.10. Capacitors in Series. Two or more capacitors are said to be
in series when they are connected as shown in Fig. 36.9. If a potential
difference V is applied between points A and B, a
charge $+Q$ appears on the positive plate of C_1 and
a corresponding charge $-Q$ on the negative plate
of C_1. The electrons which produce the negative charge on C_1 must come from the plate of
C_2 and leave it with a charge $+Q$. The negative plate of capacitor C_2 has a charge $-Q$ which
comes from the positive plate of capacitor C_3,
which is left with a charge $+Q$. Finally, the
negative plate of C_3 bears a charge $-Q$. Thus,
*when capacitors are connected in series, the same
charge is stored on each capacitor.* The poten-
tial difference across the combination of capacitors in series is equal to
the sum of the differences of potential of the individual capacitors.

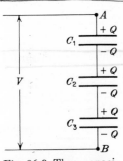

Fig. 36.9. Three capaci-
tors connected in series.

Let Q be the charge on each capacitor, C the equivalent capacitance of the capacitors when joined in series, and V_1, V_2, and V_3 the differences of potential between the terminals of C_1, C_2, and C_3, respectively. Since the total difference of potential is equal to the sum of the separate differences of potential,

$$V = V_1 + V_2 + V_3$$

If we divide both sides of this equation by Q, we have

$$\frac{V}{Q} = \frac{V_1}{Q} + \frac{V_2}{Q} + \frac{V_3}{Q}$$

Since $Q = Q_1 = Q_2 = Q_3$, we have

$$\frac{V}{Q} = \frac{V_1}{Q_1} + \frac{V_2}{Q_2} + \frac{V_3}{Q_3}$$

Since V/Q is the reciprocal of the capacitance,

$$\frac{1}{C} = \frac{1}{C_1} + \frac{1}{C_2} + \frac{1}{C_3} \tag{36.9}$$

Example. A capacitance of 4 μf is connected in series with one of 5μf. What is the equivalent capacitance of the combination? If 100 volts is the potential difference across the combination, find the potential difference across the 4-μf capacitor.

$$\frac{1}{C} = \frac{1}{C_1} + \frac{1}{C_2}$$
$$= \tfrac{1}{4} + \tfrac{1}{5} = \tfrac{9}{20}$$
$$C = \tfrac{20}{9} = 2.22 \ \mu f$$
$$Q = CV$$
$$= 2.22 \times 100$$
$$= 222 \ \mu coulombs$$
$$V_4 = \frac{Q}{C} = \frac{222 \ \mu coulombs}{4 \ \mu f}$$
$$= 55.5 \ volts$$

36.11. Groups of Capacitors. When several capacitors are connected in such a way that part are connected in parallel and others in series (Fig. 36.10),

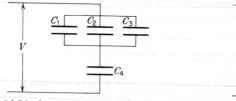
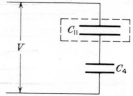

Fig. 36.10. A group of three capacitors in parallel are connected in series with a single capacitor.

Fig. 36.11. When the three capacitors in parallel of Fig. 36.10 are replaced by the equivalent 24-μf single capacitor, the circuit reduces to a series one.

one may replace any parallel group by the equivalent single capacitor of value given by Eq. (36.8). Once this is done for the parallel group (or groups), we are left with a problem in series capacitors.

Example.   The four capacitors of Fig. 36.10 are 6, 8, 10, and 12 μf, respectively. They are charged to a potential difference V of 120 volts.   Find the charge and potential difference for each individual capacitor.

The capacitance of the three parallel capacitors is given by $C_\| = 6 + 8 + 10 = 24$ μf.   If we replace these capacitors by their equivalent, our circuit reduces that of Fig. 36.11.   The capacitance of a 24- and a 12-μf capacitor in series is C_s, where

$$\frac{1}{C_s} = \frac{1}{24} + \frac{1}{12} = \frac{1}{8} \quad \text{or} \quad C_s = 8 \ \mu\text{f}$$

The charge on each capacitor of Fig. 36.11 is therefore given by $Q = C_sV = 8 \times 120 = 960$ μcoulombs. $V_{24} = {}^{960}\!/_{24} = 40$ volts and $V_{12} = {}^{960}\!/_{12} = 80$ volts. Note that these potential differences add to 120 volts.   The 24-μf capacitor, which is the equivalent to the 6-, 8-, and 10-μf capacitors in parallel, has a potential difference of 40 volts and so must the three individually.   The charges are given as follows: $Q_6 = 6 \times 40 = 240$ μcoulombs, $Q_8 = 8 \times 40 = 320$ μcoulombs, and $Q_{10} = 10 \times 40 = 400$ μcoulombs.   Note that these charges add to 960 μcoulombs.

PROBLEMS

1. What is the difference of potential between the terminals of a capacitor that has a capacitance of 25 μf when the charge on the capacitor is 0.05 coulomb?

Ans. 2,000 volts

2. A charge of 0.006 coulomb is stored in a capacitor at a potential of 1,200 volts. What is the capacitance of the capacitor?

3. Capacitors of 6, 6, and 3 μf, respectively, are arranged so that they may be connected in series or in parallel.   What capacitance is obtained in each case?

Ans. 1.5 μf; 15 μf

4. What is the capacitance of three capacitors of 5, 4, and 20 μf, respectively, when they are all joined in series?

5. An 8-μf capacitor is charged to a potential of 550 volts.   Find the charge on the capacitor plates and the energy stored.   *Ans.* 0.0044 coulomb; 1.21 joules

6. A capacitor whose insulation can withstand an applied potential of 6,500 volts has a capacitance of 30 μf.   What is the maximum energy the capacitor can have?

7. Find the capacitance of the earth if it is approximately a sphere of 6,400 km radius.   *Ans.* 7.1 $\times$ 10^{-4} farad

8. What is the capacitance of a sphere of radius 1 m?

9. A parallel-plate capacitor consists of two sheets of aluminum each of area 0.6 m^2 separated by a thin layer of a plastic insulation of dielectric constant 2.5 and thickness of 0.1 mm.   Find the capacitance and the charge stored when this capacitor is charged to a potential difference of 150 volts.   *Ans.* 0.133 μf; 19.9 μcoulombs

10. A capacitor consists of two parallel plates which are separated by a sheet of mica which is 0.2 cm thick.   The area of each plate is 500 cm^2.   The capacitor is charged to 5,000 volts.   Find the energy stored in the capacitor.   Dielectric constant of mica is 6.0.

11. A parallel-plate capacitor has a capacitance of 6 $\mu\mu$f with air between the plates and a capacitance of 45 $\mu\mu$f with glass between the plates.   What is the dielectric constant of the glass in question?   *Ans.* 7.5

12. A capacitor is made of two sheets of tin foil in contact with a plate of glass. If the area of each sheet of tin foil is 50 cm^2 and the thickness of the glass is 0.2 cm, what is the capacitance of the capacitor? What energy is stored in it when it is charged to a potential of 600 volts? Assume that the dielectric constant of glass is 5.5.

13. Three capacitors of capacitances 7, 18, and 40 μf are connected in parallel across a 110-volt potential difference. Find the total capacitance and the charge on each capacitor.   *Ans.* 65 μf; 0.00077, 0.00198, and 0.0044 coulomb

14. A 20-μf capacitor is connected in parallel with a 5-μf capacitor across a 250-volt potential difference. Find the total energy stored.

15. Three capacitors of capacitances 20, 30, and 60 μf are connected in series across a 100-volt source. Find the charge and potential difference associated with each capacitor.   *Ans.* 0.001 coulomb; 50, 33.3, and 16.7 volts

16. Two capacitors of capacitances 12 μf and 4 μf are connected in series across a potential difference of 200 volts. Find the charge and potential difference for the 12-μf capacitor.

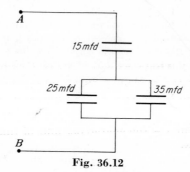

Fig. 36.12

17. Three capacitors are connected as shown in Fig. 36.12. Find the capacitance of this combination. If a potential difference of 120 volts were applied between *A* and *B*, find the charge and the potential difference for the 25-μf capacitor.
Ans. 12 μf; 24 volts; 600 μcoulombs

18. Solve Prob. 17 for the case in which the 15- and 35-μf capacitors are interchanged.

19. A 40-μf capacitor is charged to a potential difference of 150 volts. It is then disconnected from the source of potential difference, but not discharged. Find the new potential difference if this capacitor is connected in parallel with an uncharged 20-μf capacitor.   *Ans.* 100 volts

20. When a capacitor that has a capacity of 360 μf and a charge of 0.036 coulomb is connected in parallel with a second capacitor, the resulting potential difference is 40 volts. Find the capacitance of the second capacitor.

21. A capacitor is made up of 200 sheets of tin foil, each 25 by 20 cm. These sheets of tin foil are separated by sheets of paraffined paper which are 0.15 mm thick and which have a dielectric constant of 2. What is the capacity of the capacitor when alternate sheets of tin foil are joined together?   *Ans.* 2.35 μf

CHAPTER 37 *very important*

Electric Current
and Resistance

37.1. Currents and Their Effects. If two metallic spheres, one charged positively and the other negatively, are connected by a copper wire, electrons flow until there is no longer a potential difference between the two spheres. Such a flow of charge is called an electric *current*. The magnitude of the current I is the charge per unit of time that passes any cross section of the wire.

$$I = \frac{Q}{t} \qquad (37.1)$$

Current is commonly measured in coulombs per second or *amperes*, named for the French physicist André Marie Ampère. *The ampere is the current when one coulomb per second passes any cross section of a conductor.*

Electric currents are of great practical importance because of the many ways in which we can use the three principal kinds of effects they produce: (1) heating, (2) chemical, and (3) magnetic effects. *—effects produced by currents*

Heating by electric currents is utilized in making the filaments of incandescent lamps luminous, in operating electric stoves, and in hundreds of other ways. There are cheaper ways to obtain thermal energy, but none easier to control and handle than electrical energy.

The electroplating industry is based on chemical effects of electric currents. We depend on electric currents to produce aluminum, to charge batteries in automobiles, and to purify many metals.

The magnetic effects of currents are used in giant electromagnets and in tiny electrical relays in telephone circuits. The interaction between currents and magnetic fields is fundamental to electric motors and to "drawing" the picture on a television receiver.

37.2. The Direction of a Current. The charges which are primarily responsible for the current in metallic conductors are negative electrons. However, early in the nineteenth century there was no way to know

441

whether it was negative or positive charges (or both) which were in motion.   About 1820 Ampère introduced the *convention* that the *direction of the current is the direction in which a positive charge would move under the influence of the electric field.*   This convention is still in use by the vast majority of physicists and engineers.   By definition then, the *conventional* current in a wire flows from a point at higher potential to a point at lower potential, as though the current represented a movement of positive charge.   Actually, *in metallic conductors* the positive nuclei are not free to move and the transfer of charge results from a flow of electrons in a direction opposite to that of the conventional current.   In liquid and gaseous conductors, both positive and negative ions are in motion.   In some of the modern high-energy accelerators, such as Van de Graaff generators and cyclotrons, the current may be a movement of positive charges.   Obviously no convention could be most convenient for handling every possible situation.   It is perhaps unfortunate that Ampère did not call the direction of the current the direction in which negative charges flow, but the Amperian convention is so well entrenched now that any effort to replace it would produce much confusion.

When a constant potential difference is maintained between two points in a conductor, a constant flow of charge results. The current is always in the same direction and is said to be a *direct current*.   On the other hand, when the flow of charges is first in one direction and then in the opposite direction, the flow of charge is called an *alternating current*.   In the next five chapters, discussion is confined to direct currents.

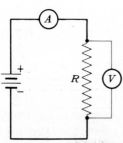

Fig. 37.1. A current, read by the ammeter *A*, is produced in the long conductor represented by the saw-toothed symbol marked *R* by the application of the potential difference *V*. The resistance of the battery, ammeter, and the heavy connecting leads are all negligible.

37.3. Ohm's Law for a Resistor.   To produce a steady current through a conductor, such as the filament of a lamp, it is necessary that an electric field be established in the conductor.   Since the natural flow of charges in a conductor is always such as to eliminate the electric field, a *steady* current can result *only* if some device such as a battery or generator maintains the field.   In this agency, called a source of *electromotive force* (emf), some other form of energy is converted into the electrical energy needed to keep the charges flowing.   Various sources of emf are discussed in the chapters which follow.

Consider a conductor across which a constant potential difference is maintained by a battery, as indicated in Fig. 37.1.   In this figure the symbol *A* represents an ammeter, an instrument for measuring electric currents, while V represents a voltmeter, an instrument for measuring potential differences.   The common forms of ammeters and voltmeters depend on the magnetic effects of electric currents for their operation. These effects are discussed in Chap. 40.   In using the ammeter and the voltmeter, the two terminals of the voltmeter are connected to the two points between which one wishes to know the potential difference, while the ammeter is connected so that all the charges which pass through the device in which the current is to be measured also pass through the ammeter.   (In Fig. 37.1 the ammeter passes not only the current through the wire, but also the current through the voltmeter; the latter is assumed to be negligible in this case.   It is not always negligible.)   Let the current through the conductor be I_1 amperes (amp) when the potential difference across it is V_1 volts.   If the battery is replaced by a different one, the potential difference and current may again be read and found to be V_2 and I_2.   If V_2 is double V_1, I_2 is double I_1.   Indeed, so long as the temperature of the wire is constant, the ratio of the potential difference to the current is constant.   The ratio

$$R = \frac{V}{I} = \frac{V_1}{I_1} = \frac{V_2}{I_2} \tag{37.2}$$

is called the *resistance* of the wire.   The resistance is commonly expressed in *ohms*.   *The ohm is that resistance in which a potential difference of one volt produces a current of one ampere.*   This unit is named in honor of Georg S. Ohm who discovered (1825) that the current in a wire is proportional to the potential difference between the ends.   Much of our knowledge about resistance is due to the pioneering work of Ohm, who made his own batteries, wires, and meters in the early nineteenth century and used them to discover much of the information presented in this chapter.   The symbol Ω (Greek capital omega) is often used as an abbreviation for *ohms*.

The relation

$$I = \frac{V}{R} \tag{37.2a}$$

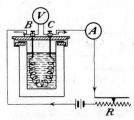

Fig. 37.2. A calorimeter for measuring the heat generated by an electric current.

is *Ohm's law for a single resistor*.   Ohm's law is obeyed within wide limits for metallic conductors.   For many nonmetallic conductors the current is *not* proportional to the potential difference.

37.4. Joule's Law of Heating.   When a potential difference V produces a current I through a conductor of resistance R, electrical energy is converted into thermal energy (Fig. 37.2).   The potential difference V represents the energy per unit charge converted from electrical to ther-

lost

mal energy in the conductor.   The total energy W dissipated in the wire is given by

$$W = VQ \tag{37.3}$$

Since by Eq. (37.1) the charge Q is the product of the current and the time, we may rewrite Eq. (37.3) in the form

$$W = VIt = I^2Rt \tag{37.3a}$$

The fact that the amount of heat produced by an electric current in a conductor is proportional to the square of the current, to the resistance, and to the time was reported by Joule and the relation

$$W = I^2Rt \tag{37.3b}$$

is known as Joule's law of heating.   Clearly, this formula gives the heat in joules when I is in amperes and R in ohms.   If one wishes to obtain the heat in calories, one may use the relation 4.183 joules = 1 cal.

Power is defined as the ratio of W/t; thus the power is equal to VI.   The power is given in watts when the current is in amperes and the potential difference in volts (volt-amperes = joules per coulomb × coulombs per second = joules per second = watts).   With the aid of Ohm's law, we may express the power in the forms

$$P = VI = I^2R = \frac{V^2}{R} \tag{37.4}$$

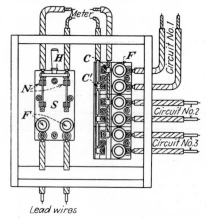

Lead wires

Fig. 37.3. Fuses in a wiring system melt when an excessive current is drawn.

37.5. Electric Fuses.   It is desirable to have some sort of device to protect electric machines and appliances from excessive currents.   One method of furnishing this protection is by means of fuses (Fig. 37.3).   A typical fuse consists essentially of a wire that has a low melting point.   When an excessive current passes through this fuse wire, the heat generated is sufficient to melt the wire, and the circuit in which the wire was inserted is opened.   The size of the fuse is so chosen that it melts when the current becomes greater than a preselected amount. The fuse is enclosed in some material like asbestos or porcelain so that there is no danger from fire when the fuse is melted.

37.6. Resistivity.   In his studies of resistance Ohm made wires of various materials, lengths, and areas.   He was able to show that for a wire of given material at constant temperature *the resistance is directly proportional to the length and inversely proportional to the cross-sectional area of the conductor.*   This fact may be expressed by the equation

$$R = \rho \frac{l}{A} \tag{37.5}$$

where ρ is called the *resistivity* (or *specific resistance*) of the material. The resistivity depends on the material in question and on its temperature. In the metric system the resistivity of a material is numerically equal to the resistance of a piece of the material one meter in length and one square meter in cross-sectional area. The resistivities of several materials are recorded in Table 1.

Table 1
RESISTIVITIES AND TEMPERATURE COEFFICIENT OF RESISTANCE
(Approximate values at 20°C)

Material	Resistivity,* ohm-meters	Temperature coefficient, per C°
Aluminum	2.6×10^{-8}	0.0040
Carbon	$3,500 \times 10^{-8}$	−0.0005
Constantan	49×10^{-8}	0.000002
Copper	1.7×10^{-8}	0.00393
Iron	9.7×10^{-8}	0.0058
Manganin	48×10^{-8}	0.0
Silver	1.6×10^{-8}	0.0038
Tungsten	5.5×10^{-8}	0.0047
Glass	Approx. 10^{13}	
Quartz	Approx. 10^{17}	

(handwritten annotation: 1m long – 1m² area)

* To obtain ρ in ohms per mil-foot, multiply ρ in ohm-meters by $6 \times 10.^{8}$

In the British engineering system *resistivity* is numerically equal to the resistance of a piece of the material one foot long and with an area of one circular mil. A circular mil is defined as the area of a circle one one-thousandth of an inch in diameter. The units are usually written as *ohms per (circular) mil-foot*, which is dimensionally incorrect and misleading. The British engineering unit has an advantage of convenience for circular conductors in that the area of a wire d thousandths of an inch is d^2 cir mils.

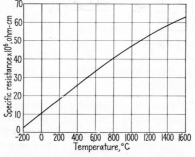

Fig. 37.4. Resistivity (or specific resistance) of platinum as a function of temperature.

37.7. Temperature Coefficient of Resistance.
The resistance of most conductors increases as the temperature is increased. Figure 37.4 shows how the resistivity of platinum varies with temperature. For a few materials, such as carbon, the resistance decreases as the temperature is increased. In almost every case the change in the resistance of a con-

ductor is roughly proportional to the change in the temperature and to the original resistance R.

$$\Delta R = \alpha R \, \Delta t \qquad (37.6)$$

where ΔR represents the change in the resistance and Δt the change in temperature. The proportionality constant α is called the *temperature coefficient of resistance* and is defined as the change in resistance divided by the product of the original resistance and the change in temperature. If R_0 represents the resistance at $0°C$ and α_0 the temperature coefficient at $0°C$, the resistance R_t at temperature t may be written in the form

$$R_t = R_0(1 + \alpha_0 t) \qquad (37.7)$$

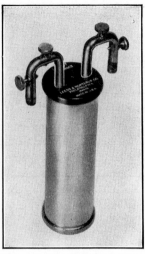

Fig. 37.5. Standard resistor made of manganin wire. (*Leeds and Northrup Co.*)

For materials which decrease in resistance as the temperature is raised, the temperature coefficient α is negative. The values of temperature coefficients of resistance of several metals and alloys are listed in Table 1. For most pure metals the temperature coefficient of resistance lies in the neighborhood of 0.004 per C°, while for most alloys α is much smaller. Indeed, for constantan and manganin, the temperature coefficients of resistance are very near zero. For this reason these two alloys are often used for resistors (Fig. 37.5) for which it is essential that the resistance be nearly independent of temperature.

37.8. Resistance Thermometers. Since the resistance of a wire changes with the temperature, it is possible to infer the change in temperature from observations on the change of resistance.

A resistance thermometer using platinum wire can be used to determine temperatures over a wide range up to the melting point of platinum. When properly calibrated, such a thermometer gives high precision in the measurement of temperatures. Figure 37.6 shows the essential components of a resistance thermometer.

Comparison leads,   Resistance coil,

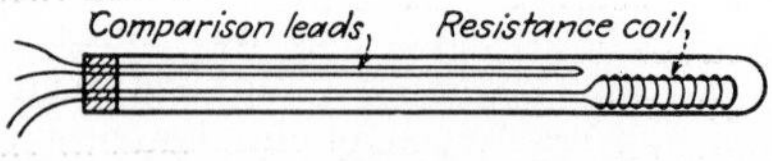

Fig. 37.6. A resistance thermometer shows change of temperature by change of its resistance.

Example. In using a resistance thermometer made of platinum wire, the resistance in a mixture of ice and water at $0°C$ was found to be 10 ohms, and in a furnace of unknown temperature it was found to be 50 ohms. If the temperature coefficient of the resistance of platinum is $0.004/C°$ what was the temperature of the furnace?

$$\text{Temperature of furnace} = t = \frac{R_t - R_0}{\alpha R_0}$$

$$= \frac{50 - 10}{0.004 \times 10} = \frac{40}{0.04}$$

$$= 1000°C$$

37.9. Superconductivity. At very low temperatures the resistivities of all metals are very much smaller than at room temperature. At a temperature of a few degrees Kelvin the resistivities of some materials drop suddenly to an immeasurably small value. The drop in resistance occurs over an exceedingly small temperature range, as is shown in Fig. 37.7. Metals in which the resistance has vanished at very low temperatures are called *superconductors* and are said to be in the *superconducting* state. By no means all metals become superconducting as the temperature approaches absolute zero. Metals such as gold, platinum, sodium, potassium, and iron have curves of resistivity as a function of temperature which show no such abrupt changes (Fig. 37.8).

37.10. Qualitative Considerations in Conduction. In general, metals have low resistivities and high temperature coefficients of resistance; on the other hand, alloys ordinarily have higher resistivities and lower temperature coefficients. In a crude qualitative way these facts can be explained as follows: The

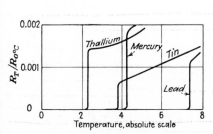

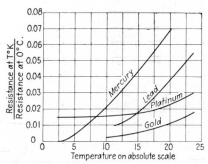

Fig. 37.7. Disappearance of electric resistance at very low temperatures.

Fig. 37.8. Resistance of four metals at low temperatures.

atoms in a pure metal are arranged in a crystal and there is an abundant supply of free electrons. Ideally, the resistance of a perfect crystal lattice should be zero, if there is no movement of the atoms. It is the energy lost by electrons in collisions with atoms which shows up as the Joule heat discussed in the Sec. 37.3. As the temperature of the metal is increased, movements of the atoms become greater; the chances of an electron colliding with an atom increases and so does the resistance. In alloys, on the other hand, one may assume that the crystal array is less favorable for free movement of electrons; consequently, the resistivity is greater, especially at very low temperatures. However, as the temperature increases, the thermal vibrations of the atoms in the alloy are almost as likely to move a given atom out of the way of a moving electron as to move it into the way. Consequently, the resistance is considerably less temperature sensitive than it is in the case of a pure metal.

Most nonmetallic solids are poor conductors and good insulators. An important exception is carbon which is a good conductor, particularly at high temperatures. The temperature coefficient of resistance of carbon is negative; the higher the temperature, the lower the resistance.

The temperature coefficients of fairly good insulators are usually negative. Indeed, materials such as glass which are good insulators at room temperature are conductors at higher temperatures. The negative temperature coefficients of many insulators may be explained by recalling that there are very few free electrons available for carrying the current in insulating materials. When such a material is heated, the atoms have more energy and the increased thermal energy gives rise to larger numbers of free electrons. This phenomenon is of great importance in connection with the oxides and sulfides of many metals. For example, copper oxide has a resistivity at 70°C which is only one-tenth of its resistivity at room temperature (20°C). The increase in conductivity is presumably due to the rapid increase in the number of free electrons as the temperature is raised.

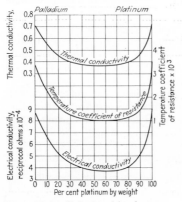

Fig. 37.9. Relationship between electrical and thermal conductivities for palladium-platinum alloys.

37.11. Relation of Electric to Thermal Conductivity. It is a well-known fact that good conductors of electricity are also good conductors of heat, and that nonconductors of electricity are poor conductors of heat. The Wiedemann-Franz law states that the ratio of the thermal conductivity to the electric conductivity of metals is a constant which is independent of the nature of the metal and depends only on the temperature. The intimate relationship between electrical and thermal conductivities is strong evidence that free electrons are the chief agency in thermal conductivity of metals as well as in electrical conductivity. That the Wiedemann-Franz law is approximately true for alloys is evident from Fig. 37.9.

37.12. Resistors in Series. The battery and the resistors of Fig. 37.10 are connected *in series*. Two circuit elements are in series whenever all the charge passing through one of the elements passes through the second. Every electron which passes through the battery of Fig. 37.10 passes through R_1, through R_2, through R_3, and returns to the battery. The current through each resistor is the same. The current I is the same in all the series resistors.

The work necessary to move a coulomb from A to D is the work necessary to move it from A to B plus the work necessary to move it from B to C plus the work from C to D. Thus, the potential difference across the combination of resistors in series is the sum of the potential differences across the individual resistors.

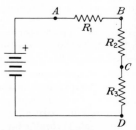

Fig. 37.10. Three resistors connected in series.

$$V = V_1 + V_2 + V_3$$

The resistance of the combination is by definition the ratio of the potential difference V across the combination to the current I.

$$R = \frac{V}{I} = \frac{V_1 + V_2 + V_3}{I} = R_1 + R_2 + R_3 \qquad (37.8)$$

Thus, *the resistance of any combination of resistors connected in series is equal to the sum of the individual resistances.*

37.13. Resistors in Parallel. The resistors of Fig. 37.11 are connected *in parallel.* When several conductors are connected between two points so that the current divides between them and then rejoins, they are said to be in *parallel.* An electron in going from B to A of the figure may pass through R_1, R_2, or R_3. The potential difference across each resistor is the same, because the work required to move a charge from A to B is independent of the path chosen. If V is the potential difference between A and B and V_1, V_2, and V_3 are the potential differences across R_1, R_2, and R_3, respectively,

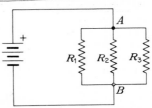

Fig. 37.11. Three resistors connected in parallel.

$V = V_1 = V_2 = V_3$. The current I splits at point A, part going through each of the parallel resistors. The total charge reaching B each second is equal to that leaving A each second. Therefore,

$$I = I_1 + I_2 + I_3$$

The resistance between A and B is by definition the ratio of V to I.

$$R = \frac{V}{I} = \frac{V}{I_1 + I_2 + I_3}$$

or
$$\frac{1}{R} = \frac{I}{V} = \frac{I_1 + I_2 + I_3}{V} = \frac{I_1}{V_1} + \frac{I_2}{V_2} + \frac{I_3}{V_3}$$

and
$$\frac{1}{R} = \frac{1}{R_1} + \frac{1}{R_2} + \frac{1}{R_3} \tag{37.9}$$

When resistors are connected in parallel, the reciprocal of the total resistance is equal to the sum of the reciprocals of the individual resistances.

PROBLEMS

1. Find the current drawn by, and the resistance of, a 550-watt 110-volt toaster.
Ans. 5 amp; 22 ohms

2. An electric toaster carries a current of 6 amp at 110 volts. How much heat is given off per hour, and what is the cost per hour at the rate of 3 cents per kw-hr?

3. A transmission line has a resistance of 3 ohms. It carries a current of 25 amp. How much power is dissipated in the line? *Ans.* 1,875 watts

4. What is the difference of potential between the ends of the feeder for a trolley bus when a current of 400 amp is flowing if the resistance of the feeder is 0.068 ohm?

5. A copper bus bar is 1 cm thick, 2 cm wide, and 50 cm long. Find its resistance and the potential difference between its ends when it bears a current of 800 amp.
Ans. 4.25×10^{-5} ohm; 0.034 volt

6. A ribbon of silver, 6 cm long and 1 mm wide, is to be made into a resistance of 0.5 ohm. How thick must it be?

7. A potential difference of 50 volts is applied across a resistance of 40 ohms for a period of 2 min. Calculate the charge which passes through the resistor. How many joules of energy does each coulomb lose in the resistor? *Ans.* 150 coulombs; 50 joules

8. If a lamp filament made of tungsten wire with a diameter of 0.08 mm is to have a resistance of 6.6 ohms at 20°C, how long must it be?

9. A platinum resistance thermometer is used to determine the temperature of a special oven. If the temperature coefficient of resistance of platinum is 0.0037 per C° and the resistance of the platinum coil is 120 ohms at 0°C, find the temperature when the coil has a resistance of 600 ohms.   *Ans.* 1080°C

10. A platinum resistance thermometer is used to measure the resistance of a furnace. The resistance of the thermometer is 250 ohms at 0°C and 1,800 ohms at the temperature of the furnace. If the temperature coefficient of resistance for platinum is 0.0037 per C°, what is the temperature of the furnace?

11. A piece of wire has a resistance of 34.175 ohms at 40°C and of 32.000 ohms at 0°C. What is the temperature coefficient?   *Ans.* 0.0017 per C°

12. The resistance of a copper wire that is known to be 18.42 ohms at 0°C is observed to be 22.08 ohms. What is the temperature?

13. The resistance of a tungsten-lamp filament is 9 ohms at 20°C. The temperature coefficient of tungsten at 20°C is 0.0047 per C°. If the filament operates at 2220°C, find its resistance. How many times as great is the resistance at operating temperature as the resistance at room temperature?   *Ans.* 102 ohms; 11.3

14. What is the greatest length of copper wire having a resistance of 1.8 ohms per 1,000 ft that can be used to carry 8 amp, allowing a drop of 4 volts in the wire?

15. The field coil of a motor draws a current of 0.5 amp from a 110-volt line when the motor is started and the coil is at 0°C. What is the resistance of the coil at 0°C? If the potential difference across the coil does not change, what current is drawn by the copper field coil at its normal operating temperature of 60°C?

Ans. 220 ohms; 0.40 amp

16. A piece of wire, 8 m long and 0.5 mm in diameter, has a resistance of 2 ohms. What length of wire of the same material 0.4 mm in diameter will have a resistance of 2.5 ohms?

17. A copper wire of resistance 10 ohms is drawn through a die so that its length is tripled and its cross section is reduced to one-third of its previous value. Find the new resistance.   *Ans.* 90 ohms

18. Two wires of the same length and material have resistance of 12 and 16 ohms, respectively. If the diameter of the first wire is 0.8 mm, what is the diameter of the second wire?

19. If 1 g of copper and 1 g of aluminum are used to make uniform wires each of which is 10 m long, find the ratio of the resistance of the copper wire to that of the aluminum wire.   *Ans.* 2.2

20. A copper rod, which was 1 cm in diameter and 1 m long, was drawn out into a wire which was 1 mm in diameter. Find the resistance of the wire produced in this way.

21. When the light switch on a car is pulled on, two head lights, two tail lamps, and a dash light are connected in parallel with the 6-volt battery of negligible internal resistance. If each head light has a resistance of 1.5 ohms, each tail lamp a resistance of 6 ohms, and the dash light has a resistance of 8 ohms, find the current through the battery.   *Ans.* 10.75 amp

22. The electric resistance of a platinum wire is 20 ohms at 20°C and 27.8 ohms at 120°C. What is its resistance at 160°C, if the resistance of platinum varies linearly with the temperature?

23. A 2,000-watt heating unit in a hot-water heater is on 3 hr per day. If electrical energy costs 2 cents per kw-hr, how much does hot water cost each 30-day month?

How many kilograms of water would be heated from 10° to 70°C each day if all the heat dissipated in the heater is effective in warming the water? *Ans.* $3.60; 86 kg

24. A 60-watt electric lamp is immersed in a vessel containing 80 liters of water. What fraction of a degree rise in temperature of the water is caused by operating the lamp for 8 min?

25. Six resistances of 60 ohms each are arranged in two groups. One group contains four resistances in parallel and the other group has two resistances in parallel. The two groups are then connected in series across a 120-volt line. Find the current flowing through each of the resistances. *Ans.* 1.33 amp; 0.67 amp

26. An electrocalorimeter contains 300 g of water. A change from 11 to 19°C is produced in 12 min by a certain current flowing through a resistance of 6 ohms immersed in the water. Find the current.

27. A heating coil with a resistance of 6 ohms is used to evaporate water at the boiling point at the rate of 1.8 g/sec. What potential difference must be applied to the coil? *Ans.* 156 volts

28. An electric iron weighing 1.5 kg has an average specific heat of 0.10 cal/(g)(C°). The heating unit takes 5.5 amp from a 110-volt line. If half of the heat is lost by radiation, how long will it take to bring the iron to a temperature of 160°C, if it is at 15°C originally?

29. Two wires, one having a resistance of 6 ohms and the other a resistance of 12 ohms, are connected in parallel and then in series with another resistance of 2 ohms. How many watts are generated in each resistance when the combination is connected to an 8-volt battery? *Ans.* 4.74, 2.37, and 3.56 watts

30. Four 120-volt 60-watt electric lights are connected in parallel. The group is then connected in series with a coil of wire having a resistance of 45 ohms. How much power is dissipated in each lamp and in the coil of wire when the combination is connected across a 220-volt battery?

31. An ammeter in series with a battery and a rheostat having a resistance R reads 6 amp. When an additional resistance of 3 ohms is inserted in series with the other resistance, the reading of the ammeter is reduced to 4 amp. Find the resistance of the rheostat. The resistances of the battery and ammeter are negligible.
Ans. 6 ohms

32. An oven requires 10 amp to heat it to the desired temperature when the applied voltage is 110 volts. How much resistance must be inserted in series with the oven in order to keep it at the same temperature if the voltage is increased to 120 volts? How much power is wasted in the resistance?

CHAPTER 38 *very important –* *especially Kirchhoff's Laws and Wheatstone bridge*
Electric Circuits

38.1. Electromotive Force. To maintain a steady current in a conductor, it is necessary to maintain a steady potential difference between the two points. This potential difference can be supplied only if some device transforms some other form of energy into electrical energy. Such a device is called a *source of electromotive force* (abbreviated *emf*).

There are many kinds of emf. In batteries chemical reactions occur and chemical energy is converted into electrical energy. In the giant generators of our electric power plants mechanical energy is converted into electrical energy. In a thermocouple it is heat energy, while in the photoelectric cell it is radiant energy which is transformed.

When a charge q receives an energy W in passing through a battery or some other source of electrical energy, the emf $\mathcal{E}$ is given by

$$\mathcal{E} = \frac{W}{q} \tag{38.1}$$

When W is in joules and q in coulombs, the emf is in joules per coulomb, or volts.

When a charge of one coulomb receives one joule of energy upon passing through a source, the source is said to have an electromotive force of one volt. A 12-volt battery delivers 12 joules of energy to each coulomb which passes through it. Electromotive force and potential difference are measured in the same units. An emf is a particular kind of potential difference; namely, one which arises through the possible transformation of some other form of energy into electrical energy.

In a source of emf not only may some other form of energy be transformed into electrical energy, but the reverse process may also occur—electrical energy may be converted into another form. For example, in charging a battery, charges are forced through the battery in a direction opposite to that in which they go when the battery is discharging; these charges deliver electrical energy to the battery where it is converted into and stored as chemical energy.

452

38.2. The Conservation of Energy in a Simple Circuit. Consider the circuit of Fig. 38.1 in which a battery is connected in series with three resistors. A charge q which passes through the battery gains an amount of energy $\mathcal{E}q$ joules. In passing through the resistance R_1, this charge loses energy $V_1 q$ joules. In passing through resistors R_2 and R_3 this charge loses amounts of energy $V_2 q$ and $V_3 q$, respectively. In going once around the complete circuit, the charge loses exactly the same amount of energy as it gains. Therefore,

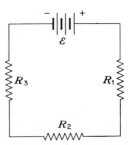

$$\mathcal{E}q = V_1 q + V_2 q + V_3 q \qquad (38.2)$$
$$\mathcal{E} = V_1 + V_2 + V_3$$

or $\qquad \mathcal{E} = IR_1 + IR_2 + IR_3 \qquad (38.3)$

If Eq. (38.3) is solved for I, we obtain

$$I = \frac{\mathcal{E}}{R_1 + R_2 + R_3} \qquad (38.4)$$

Fig. 38.1. When a coulomb goes around the complete circuit, the energy it gains in passing through the battery is equal to the energy it loses in the three resistors.

In a simple series circuit the current is equal to the ratio of the emf to the sum of the resistances in the circuit. This statement represents a simplified form of *Ohm's law for a complete circuit*.

38.3. The Resistances of Sources of Electromotive Force. Any source of emf, such as a battery or electrical generator, has some internal resistance. As a consequence, a current through a battery produces some heating. When the battery is being discharged, the total energy given to a charge q is $\mathcal{E}q$, but a portion of this energy is converted into heat within the battery. If the internal resistance is r, the potential drop in the battery resistance is Ir. The net potential gain V_t is the potential difference between the terminals of the battery.

$$V_t = \mathcal{E} - Ir \qquad (38.5)$$

The terminal potential difference is $\mathcal{E}$ only when no current is being drawn.

The decrease in the terminal potential difference of a battery when the current drawn is changed is illustrated by the dimming of automobile head lights when the starter is activated. The starter draws a large current from the battery. As a consequence of the increased Ir drop within the battery, the terminal potential is reduced and the potential difference across the lamps of the car is lower. For an automobile battery of emf about 12 volts, the internal resistance may be about 0.005 ohm. The current drawn by the lights is approximately 6 amp; thus, when current is being drawn only for the lights, the terminal potential difference of the battery is only a few hundredths of a volt less than the emf. If the current drawn from the battery is increased to 150 amp by operating the starter motor, V_t

becomes $12 - 0.75$ or 11.25 volts. The brightness of the lamps is reduced by such a decrease in terminal potential difference.

For practical purposes we may assume that the real battery is made up of a pure emf and a series resistor as suggested in Fig. 38.2. Ohm's law for a complete circuit is applicable, but the internal resistance of the battery must be included in the total resistance.

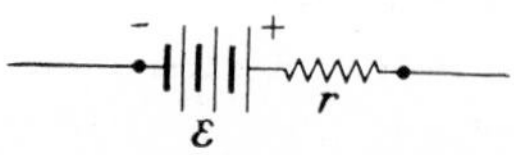

Fig. 38.2. A real battery may be looked upon as an ideal resistanceless battery with a series resistor.

Example. A 45-volt battery has an internal resistance of 0.6 ohm. It is connected in the circuit as indicated in Fig. 38.3. Find the current in each resistor.

First, the series equivalent of the two parallel resistors must be found.

$$\frac{1}{R_{\parallel}} = \frac{1}{12} + \frac{1}{8} = \frac{5}{24}$$
$$R_{\parallel} = 4.8 \text{ ohms}$$

Now applying Ohm's law for the complete circuit yields

$$I = \frac{E}{R} = \frac{45}{0.6 + 20 + 4.8 + 7}$$
$$= \frac{45}{32.4} = 1.389 \text{ amp}$$

This is the current through the battery, the 20-, and the 7-ohm resistors. The potential difference across the parallel resistors is $1.389 \times 4.8 = 6.667$ volts. Therefore, the current in the 8-ohm resistor is $6.667/8 = 0.833$ amp, while that through the 12-ohm resistor is $6.667/12 = 0.556$ amp. Note that the sum of these currents is 1.389 amp.

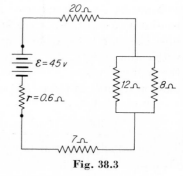

Fig. 38.3

38.4. Charging a Battery. The terminal potential difference of a battery as it is discharged is given by $\varepsilon - Ir$. While the battery is being charged, the terminal potential difference is greater than the emf by an amount Ir, as can be seen from consideration of the energy transformations. In charging the battery, electrical energy is converted into chemical energy; the energy per unit charge is ε. The charging current produces heat in the battery and the energy per unit charge required to produce this heating effect is Ir. Thus, the total electrical energy which must be delivered to the battery per unit charge is

$$V_t = \varepsilon + Ir \tag{38.6}$$

Regardless of the direction of the current through a cell or other source of emf, Joule heat is always produced.

38.5. Cells in Series.   When two or more sources of emf are connected in series, the net emf is the algebraic sum of the individual emfs. If two cells are connected in series in such a way that both would produce a current in the same direction, the emf is the simple sum of the two emfs; on the other hand, if the two are connected in series in such a way that they would send currents in the opposite directions, the net emf is the difference of the two.   In the first case the cells are said to be connected in *series aiding;* in the second case in *series opposing.*   When a battery is to be charged, it must be connected in series opposing with some other source of emf which supplies electrical energy to be transformed into chemical energy.

When several identical cells are connected in series, the total emf is equal to the number of cells multiplied by the emf of a single cell, while the resistance of the battery is equal to the resistance of an individual cell times the number of cells.   The type of cell used in ordinary automobile batteries has an emf of approximately 2 volts; in order to obtain an emf of 6 volts three cells are connected in series; for 12 volts, six cells are required.

When several identical sources of emf are connected in parallel, the emf of the combination is the emf of a single source.   The net resistance of this combination is equal to the resistance of a single cell divided by the number of cells, since effectively all the resistances are in parallel.

When cells which are not identical in emf are connected in parallel, we use Kirchhoff's laws (Sec. 38.7) to find the current and terminal potential difference for each cell.   Cells with different emfs are seldom connected in parallel.

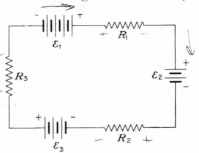

Fig. 38.4. A series circuit containing several sources of emf.

38.6. Ohm's Law for a Complete Circuit.   In Fig. 38.4 several batteries of negligible resistance are connected in series with a number of resistors.   For this circuit one may again apply the fundamental principle that the total energy gained by a charge in going around the complete circuit is equal to the total energy lost.

If a small test charge is carried clockwise around the circuit of Fig. 38.4, the net change in potential energy for the complete circuit is zero, or

$$\mathcal{E}_1 - IR_1 - \mathcal{E}_2 - IR_2 + \mathcal{E}_3 - IR_3 = 0 \qquad (38.7)$$

It is often convenient to mark plus and minus signs at the appropriate ends of all resistors and batteries.   The potential change may be con-

sidered positive when the test charge is moved from the minus terminal
of a circuit element to the positive one and negative when the charge
goes from plus to minus.   It is not necessary that the charge be carried
around the circuit in the direction in which the current flows.   Indeed,
if the direction of motion is reversed, all signs in Eq. (38.7) are changed
and the sum is still zero.   In the case of the circuit of Fig. 38.4 battery 2
is being charged by the other batteries.

The total current, which is the same in all parts of the circuit, may be
obtained by solving Eq. (38.7) to obtain

$$I = \frac{\mathcal{E}_1 - \mathcal{E}_2 + \mathcal{E}_3}{R_1 + R_2 + R_3} = \frac{\Sigma \mathcal{E}}{\Sigma R} \tag{38.8}$$

This equation represents Ohm's law for a complete series circuit which
may be stated as follows:

*The current in any series circuit is given by the ratio of the algebraic sum
of the emfs to the total series resistance of the circuit.*

Ohm's law for a complete circuit is to be distinguished from Ohm's law for a
single resistor.   The law for a single resistor involves only the potential difference
across the resistor, while the law for the complete circuit involves the algebraic
sum of the emfs in the circuit and the total resistance of the series circuit.   In a
series circuit the algebraic sum of the emfs is equal to the sum of the IR drops in
the resistors.   This follows directly from the law of conservation of energy.

When one applies Ohm's law to a complete circuit in which there are
parallel resistors, each group of parallel resistors is first replaced by the

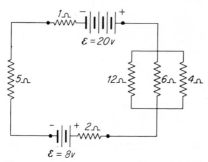

equivalent series resistor.   Then
Ohm's law for the circuit is applied
directly.

Example.   A battery of emf 20 volts
and internal resistance 1 ohm is connected
in series with a 5-ohm resistor, a second
battery of emf 8 volts and internal resistance 2 ohms which is in series opposing,
and a group of three resistors of 12, 6, and
4 ohms resistance in parallel as shown in
Fig. 38.5.   Find the current in each resistor
and the terminal potential difference of
each battery.

Fig 38.5. A circuit containing two
batteries connected in series opposing.

We first replace the three parallel resistors by the equivalent single resistor; $R_{\parallel} = 2$
ohms from $1/R_{\parallel} = \frac{1}{12} + \frac{1}{6} + \frac{1}{4}$.   We next apply Ohm's law for the circuit, which
gives

$$I = \frac{20 - 8}{1 + 5 + 2 + 2} = \frac{12}{10} = 1.2 \text{ amp}$$

for the current in each battery and in the 5-ohm resistor.   The potential drop across
$R_{\parallel}$ is given by $IR_{\parallel} = 1.2 \times 2 = 2.4$ volts, which remains unchanged if we replace $R_{\parallel}$

by the original three resistors. The currents in these resistors are given by V/R as follows: $I_{12} = 2.4/12 = 0.2$ amp; $I_6 = 2.4/6 = 0.4$ amp; and $I_4 = 2.4/4 = 0.6$ amp. Note that the sum is 1.2 amp, the current in the main circuit.

Terminal potential difference for the 20-volt battery is $\mathcal{E} - Ir = 20 - 1.2 \times 1 = 18.8$ volts, while the terminal potential difference for the 8-volt battery which is being charged is $\mathcal{E} + Ir = 8 + (1.2 \times 2) = 10.4$ volts.

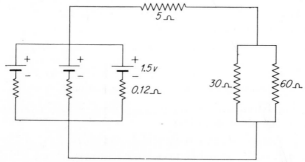

Fig. 38.6. A circuit containing three identical cells in parallel.

Example. Three identical dry cells with $\mathcal{E} = 1.5$ volts and $r = 0.12$ ohms are connected in parallel to the circuit of Fig. 38.6. Find the current in each cell and in each resistor.

The emf of the three identical cells in parallel is 1.5 volts and the resistance of the combination is 0.04 ohm (three 0.12-ohm resistors in parallel). The resistance of the 30- and 60-ohm parallel combination is 20 ohms. Application of Ohm's circuit law yields

$$I = \frac{1.5}{0.04 + 5 + 20} = \frac{1.5}{25.04} = 0.060 \text{ amp}$$

The potential drop across the 30- and 60-ohm resistors is (20×0.060), or 1.2 volts. Therefore, $I_{30} = 1.2/30 = 0.04$ amp and $I_{60} = 1.2/60 = 0.02$ amp. The current through each of the three identical cells is one-third of 0.06 amp, or 0.02 amp.

38.7. Kirchhoff's Laws. Circuits ranging from the simplest to very complex networks with many branches and many emfs can be handled by application of two fundamental principles which are known as Kirchhoff's laws. These laws, which apply once a steady state has been reached, have been used in previous discussions, although they have not been specifically named. Kirchhoff's two laws are:

1. *The sum of all currents arriving at any point in a circuit is equal to the sum of the currents leaving that point.*

2. *In going around any closed loop, the sum of the potential rises is equal to the sum of the potential drops.*

The first law must apply if we are to avoid an accumulation of charge at any point in the circuit or a continuing disappearance of charge at that point. If Kirchhoff's first law were not true and the sum of the currents reaching a point exceeded the currents leaving it, the charge would build up at this point and the potential of the point would change continuously.

Kirchhoff's second law is a special statement of the law of the conservation of energy. If a charge gained more energy in going around a closed path than it lost, it would be able to gain more and more energy by repeated traversing of this path. This is obviously not permissible. Once the charge returns to its starting point, its potential energy is exactly the same as when it started.

If a man takes a hike in the mountains and eventually returns to his starting point, we know that he has climbed up exactly as many feet as he has descended, since he ends at the same altitude at which he started. Kirchhoff's second law is the electrical analogue of this mechanical illustration.

In applying Kirchhoff's laws to a problem, it is convenient to carry out the following steps in order: •

1. *Assign a direction and a symbol to the current in each independent branch of the circuit.* It is not necessary to worry about which direction to assign the current in a given branch, since if the incorrect assignment is made, the current will turn out to be negative.

2. *Place appropriate plus and minus signs at the terminals of every source of emf and of every resistor in the circuit.* Remember that in a resistor the current is from the + to the − terminal; thus the choices of current directions in the first step determine the + and − terminals of all resistors.

3. *Apply Kirchhoff's first law at enough junctions so that each current appears in an equation.* Be sure that each junction equation contains at least one current which has not appeared in earlier equations.

4. *Apply Kirchhoff's second law to closed loops until once again every current has been included in at least one equation.* When we go through a circuit element from − to +, potential is gained; from + to − it is lost. Once again be sure that every new loop equation involves at least one current which has not appeared in a previous loop equation.

5. *Solve the equations for the desired unknowns.*

A familiarity with the use of Kirchhoff's laws is best obtained by studying one or more examples and then by practice on additional problems.

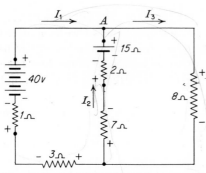

Fig. 38.7. A circuit in which there are three different currents.

Example. Find the current in all branches of the circuit of Fig. 38.7.

1. Let us designate the currents by I_1, I_2, and I_3 and assume them to be in the **directions** indicated by the arrows.

2. We place a + on the higher potential end of each circuit component and a − on the lower potential end.

3. At point A, $I_1 + I_2 = I_3$ by Kirchhoff's first law.

4. If we start at point A and apply Kirchhoff's second law to the left loop going clockwise, we obtain

$$-15 + 2I_2 + 7I_2 - 3I_1 - I_1 + 40 = 0$$

By going clockwise from A around the right loop we obtain $-8I_3 - 7I_2 - 2I_2 + 15 = 0$.

5. We now have the equations

$$
\begin{aligned}
I_1 + I_2 - I_3 &= 0 \\
4I_1 - 9I_2 \quad\;\; &= 25 \\
9I_2 + 8I_3 &= 15
\end{aligned}
$$

The solutions are $I_1 = 4$ amp, $I_2 = -1$ amp, and $I_3 = 3$ amp. The fact that I_2 is negative means that the current I_2 is in the direction opposite to the one assumed. The 15-volt battery is being charged.

38.8. The Wheatstone Bridge. An accurate and simple method of measuring resistances employs the Wheatstone bridge. The circuit for this bridge is shown in Fig. 38.8. A and B are fixed resistors, the values of which are known. The resistance X whose value is to be determined is connected in the third arm of the bridge, while a variable resistance R is connected in the fourth arm. The resistance R is varied until there is no current between c and d as indicated by the galvanometer G, an instrument for detecting small currents. When the galvanometer shows no current between c and d, the bridge is said to be *balanced*.

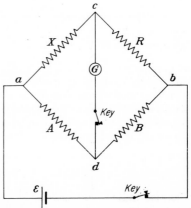

Fig. 38.8. A Wheatstone bridge.

The condition that there be no current in the galvanometer is that the potential difference between points c and d be zero. For this to be true, the potential drop across resistor A must be equal to the potential drop across X, since one end of the two resistors is at the potential of point a and the other ends must be at the same potential if the galvanometer current is zero. If I_A is the current in A and I_X the current in X, the condition for no current in the galvanometer is that $V_{ac} = V_{ad}$ or $I_x X = I_A A$. Similarly, the fall of potential from c to b must be equal to the drop in potential from d to b, which gives $I_R R = I_B B$. The current in R and in X is the same when no current flows through the galvanometer. Similarly, the current in A is the same as that in B. Therefore $I_x X / I_R R = I_A A / I_B B$, or

$$\frac{X}{R} = \frac{A}{B} \qquad (38.9)$$

In the slide-wire Wheatstone bridge the resistors A and B are segments of a wire of uniform cross section and resistivity. The ratio A/B is determined by the position of the movable contact along this wire. In high-quality commercial Wheatstone bridges, the ratio of A to B can be set at one of several values and the final balance made by varying R.

38.9. The Potentiometer. The potentiometer occupies an important place in electrical measurements because it can be used to measure potential differences with great accuracy and *without drawing any current*. This feature is of great importance in working with sources of emf of high internal resistance and low current capabilities.

A schematic diagram of a potentiometer is shown in Fig. 38.9. The wire *ab*, which is of uniform cross section, carries a current maintained constant by the working battery *B*. There is a progressive drop in potential along the wire from

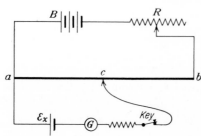

Fig. 38.9. A simple potentiometer circuit.

a to b, which is directly proportional to the distance from *a*. To measure an emf whose value $\mathcal{E}_x$ is unknown, this emf is placed in series with a galvanometer and connected as shown in Fig. 38.9, in which point *c* represents a movable contact. It is important that the emf $\mathcal{E}_x$ oppose the current which the working battery *B* would produce if $\mathcal{E}_x$ were zero. If the potential difference between *a* and *b* is greater than $\mathcal{E}_x$, there is some point *c* at which the potential difference across *ac* is equal to $\mathcal{E}_x$. This point can be found by moving the sliding contact until the current through the galvanometer is zero. The potentiometer is then *balanced*.

In the usual application of the potentiometer a standard cell of known emf $\mathcal{E}_s$ is first used in place of $\mathcal{E}_x$ and the balance point is found at some point *d*. The unknown emf $\mathcal{E}_x$ is substituted for $\mathcal{E}_s$ and the balance point *c* is found. Then $\mathcal{E}_x$ can be calculated from the relation

$$\frac{\mathcal{E}_x}{\mathcal{E}_s} = \frac{ac}{ad}$$

where *ac* and *ad* represent the length of conductor from *a* to *c* and from *a* to *d*, respectively.

PROBLEMS

1. A battery of emf 3 volts and internal resistance 0.2 ohm is connected in series with two resistors, one of 4.8 ohms and another of 10 ohms. Find the current, the potential difference across each resistor, and the terminal potential difference of the battery.

Ans. 0.2 amp; 0.96 volt; 2 volts; 2.96 volts

2. Three cells of a storage battery, each with a resistance of 0.02 ohm and an emf of 2.0 volts, are connected in series with a coil having a resistance of 3.94 ohms. Find the current.

3. The resistors in Fig. 38.10 are a portion of a complete circuit. The current through the 6-ohm resistor is 0.5 amp. Find the current through the 8-ohm resistor and the potential difference between *A* and *B*.

Ans. 1.5 amp; 15 volts

4. Solve Prob. 3 for the case in which the 3-ohm resistor is replaced by a 12-ohm resistor The current through the 6-ohm resistor remains 0.5 amp.

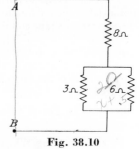

Fig. 38.10

5. A battery having an internal resistance of 0.2 ohm and emf of 6 volts is used to send a current through a 3-ohm resistance connected in series with two resistances, one of 1 ohm and the other of 4 ohms, in parallel. Find the current in each of the resistances. *Ans.* 1.5 amp; 1.2 amp; 0.3 amp

6. An automobile battery has an emf of 6.3 volts and an internal resistance of 0.008 ohm. What potential difference is necessary to charge it with a current of 15 amp?

7. A circuit has three parallel branches with resistances of 30, 40, and 50 ohms, respectively. When a current of $3\frac{1}{3}$ amp is flowing in the 30-ohm branch, how much current is flowing in each of the other branches? *Ans.* 2.5 amp; 2.0 amp

8. If a 20-ohm resistor bears a current of 0.4 amp when it is connected in parallel with a 6-ohm resistor, find the current in the latter.

9. A 24-volt battery with an internal resistance of 1 ohm is to be charged at the rate of 8 amp from a 120-volt source. What resistance must be connected in series with the battery? What will be the terminal potential difference of the battery during the charging process? Assuming that the emf arises entirely from the conversion of chemical to electrical energy, find at what rate electrical energy is converted into chemical energy. At what rate is electrical energy converted into heat in the battery? In the series resistor?
Ans. 11 ohms; 32 volts; 192 watts; 64 watts; 704 watts

10. A storage battery having an emf of 24 volts and an internal resistance of 1.5 ohms is to be charged by connecting it to a 110-volt generator. What resistance must be introduced in series with it in order that the charging current may not exceed 10 amp?

11. When an external resistance of 10 ohms is connected to the terminals of a battery, the current is found to be 0.36 amp. When this resistance is increased to 36 ohms, the current drops to 0.12 amp. Find the emf and the internal resistance of the battery. *Ans.* 4.68 volts; 3 ohms

12. Ten storage batteries, each of three cells with an emf of 2 volts and an internal resistance of 0.015 ohm per cell, are to be charged in series at the rate of 10 amp from a 110-volt line. How much resistance must be inserted in series with the batteries?

13. In Fig. 38.11 $\mathcal{E}_1 = 10$ volts, $r_1 = 1$ ohm, $\mathcal{E}_2 = 6$ volts, $r_2 = 2$ ohms, $R_1 = 3$ ohms, and $R_2 = 4$ ohms. Find the current, the terminal potential difference of each battery, and the potential difference between points A and B.
Ans. 0.4 amp; 9.6 volts; 6.8 volts; 8.4 volts

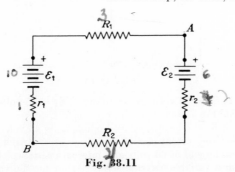

Fig. 38.11

14. In Fig. 38.11 $\mathcal{E}_1 = 20$ volts, $r_1 = 2$ ohms, $\mathcal{E}_2 = 8$ volts, $r_2 = 1$ ohm, $R_1 = 7$ ohms, and $R_2 = 14$ ohms. Find the current, the terminal potential difference of each battery, and the potential difference between points A and B.

15. Find the current through the batteries of Fig. 38.12 and the current through the 6-ohm resistor. Find the terminal voltages of the two batteries and the potential difference between points A and B.

Ans. 2 amp; 0.67 amp; 26 volts; 8 volts; 4 volts

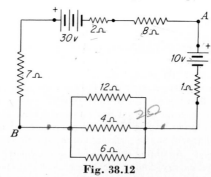

Fig. 38.12

16. Without referring to the text draw a Wheatstone bridge, and derive the relationship between the resistors when the bridge is balanced.

17. Eight cells, each with an internal resistance of 0.16 ohm, are connected in parallel to send a current through an external resistance of 0.28 ohm. How much current will be obtained in the external resistance if each cell has an emf of 1.2 volts?

Ans. 4 amp

18. Twelve cells, each with an internal resistance of 1.2 ohms, are connected so as to have four parallel groups of three cells in series. A current of 2.1 amp is sent through an external resistance of 1.1 ohms. What is the emf of each cell?

19. In Fig. 38.13 $\mathcal{E}_1 = 30$ volts, $R_1 = 3$ ohms, $\mathcal{E}_2 = 16$ volts, $R_2 = 2$ ohms, and $R_3 = 6$ ohms. Find the current in each element in the circuit.

Ans. 4 amp; 1 amp; 3 amp

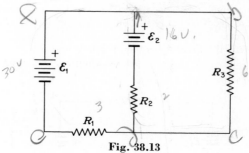

Fig. 38.13

20. In Fig. 38.13 $\mathcal{E}_1 = 50$ volts, $R_1 = 15$ ohms, $\mathcal{E}_2 = 35$ volts, $R_2 = 5$ ohms, and $R_3 = 4$ ohms. Find the current in each branch.

21. In Fig. 38.13 $\mathcal{E}_1 = 52$ volts, $R_1 = 4$ ohms, $\mathcal{E}_2 = 46$ volts, $R_2 = 5$ ohms, and $R_3 = 6$ ohms. Find the current in each branch. *Ans.* 4 amp; 2 amp; 6 amp

22. A battery has an emf of 60 volts and internal resistance of 3 ohms. Find the power dissipated in a variable external series resistor for the values 1, 2, 3, 4, and 5 ohms. Plot a rough curve of power dissipated in the load as a function of load resistance to confirm the fact that maximum power is supplied to the load when the load resistance is equal to the internal resistance of the battery.

Chemical and Thermal
Electromotive Forces

39.1. Electrolysis. If two copper plates are inserted into a beaker filled with water and connected to the terminals of a battery (Fig. 39.1), an ammeter in the circuit shows no current. However, if a little copper sulfate ($CuSO_4$) is poured into the beaker, there is a current through the solution. When the copper sulfate dissolves in water, many of the molecules split (or dissociate) into Cu^{++} and $SO_4^=$ ions. The $SO_4^=$ ion carries two excess electrons, while the copper ion has two less electrons than a neutral copper atom. The positively charged copper ions migrate to the negatively charged plate, while the negatively charged sulfate ions move to the positive plate.

After a current has passed between the two copper electrodes for some time and the electrodes are removed from the solution, the *cathode* (the electrode by which the conventional current leaves) has gained weight and is bright. The *anode* (by which current enters) has lost weight. There has been not only a transfer of electricity through the solution, but copper has been carried from one plate to the other. The Cu^{++} ions which reach the cathode obtain two electrons there and are deposited as neutral copper atoms, while each sulfate ion which goes to the anode gives it the two excess electrons and joins with an atom of copper. The copper sulfate so formed goes into solution, thus keeping the amount of $CuSO_4$ constant. The net effect is a gain of copper by the cathode and a loss of copper by the anode.

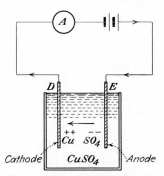

Fig 39.1. Electrolysis of copper sulfate. The copper ions migrate to the cathode and the sulfate ions to the anode.

463

The addition of almost any common acid, base, or salt to the water in the beaker makes it conducting, provided the solute dissociates into ions.

When a current is passed between two platinum electrodes in a very dilute solution of sulfuric acid in water (Fig. 39.2), hydrogen is released at the negative electrode, and oxygen at the positive electrode. The water is decomposed into its constituents. The volume of the hydrogen released is twice that of the oxygen. A simplified explanation of the process by which the water is decomposed is as follows: A sulfuric acid molecule in the solution splits up into one SO_4^- and two H^+ ions. The H^+ ions are attracted to the cathode where they receive electrons to form neutral hydrogen atoms. Two atoms promptly form a hydrogen molecule which rises to the top of the collecting tube. The SO_4^- ions give up their two excess electrons at the positive terminal and then unite with two atoms of hydrogen to form sulfuric acid. These atoms of hydrogen are taken from water and oxygen is set free. Two atoms of oxygen unite to form a molecule of oxygen gas. The sulfuric acid formed at the anode goes into solution; consequently, the amount of sulfuric acid in the water does not change.

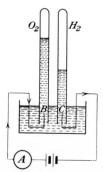

Fig. 39.2. Electrolysis of water.

39.2. Faraday's Laws of Electrolysis. To understand the quantitative laws of electrolysis, consider a number of electrolytic cells connected in series (Fig. 39.3). Assume that all the electrodes are made of platinum so that there are no secondary reactions between the electrodes and the ions in solution. Now let these cells be connected to a battery so that the same current flows through each cell for the same time. Suppose A contains a solution of silver nitrate, B a solution of hydrochloric acid, C a solution of copper sulfate, and D a solution of nickel chloride. There are liberated at the respective cathodes silver, hydrogen, copper, and nickel. By determining the amount of sub-

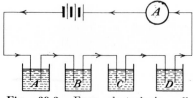

Fig. 39.3. Four electrolysis cells connected in series.

stance liberated at each cathode as a function of the charge transported, it is possible to confirm two laws of electrolysis, which were discovered by Michael Faraday.

1. *The mass of any substance liberated is proportional to the charge which passes through the cell.* Hence, the mass liberated is proportional to the product of the current and the time.

2. *The masses of different elements liberated by a given charge are proportional to the ratios of atomic weights to valences.*

Suppose that in cell B the current exists until 1 g of hydrogen is liberated. Then, in cell A 108 g of silver are deposited, in cell C 31.5 g of copper, and in cell D 29 g of nickel. Whatever current is chosen and whatever the length of time it exists, the masses deposited at these cathodes always bear the same ratio to each other and are proportional to the quotient obtained by dividing the atomic weight by the valence.   The ratio of the atomic weight to the valence of an element is called the chemical equivalent, or combining weight.   When an element is monovalent, the chemical equivalent is equal to the atomic weight.   If the element is divalent, the chemical equivalent is equal to one-half of the atomic weight.

It requires 96,520 coulombs to deposit one gram-equivalent weight of any element.   A charge of 96,520 coulombs is called 1 *faraday*.   Faraday's two laws of electrolysis can be summarized by the relation

$$m = \frac{Q}{96,520} \frac{A}{v} \tag{39.1}$$

where m is the mass of the element liberated, Q is the total charge, A is the atomic weight of the element, and v its valence.

The mass deposited is directly proportional to the charge.   *The electrochemical equivalent of any substance is defined as the ratio of the mass of the substance deposited to the charge transferred.*   It is denoted by the symbol Z.   From Eq. (39.1),

$$Z = \frac{m}{Q} = \frac{A}{96,520v} \tag{39.2}$$

One of the most accurate methods we have for measuring the electric charge which passes through a circuit is to insert an electrolytic cell containing a solution of silver nitrate.   The mass of silver deposited is a measure of the total quantity of charge passed.   Indeed, for many years the ampere was defined as that current which would deposit 0.001118 g/sec from a standard solution of silver nitrate. Since 1948 the ampere has been defined in terms of the interaction between two current-carrying conductors (*National Bureau of Standards Circular* C 459).

39.3. Applications of Electrolysis.   Electrolysis is of great commercial importance.   The chromium plating of automobile parts and the silver plating of tableware are examples of the wide variety of commercial plating operations. Practically all of our aluminum is produced by the electrolysis of aluminum oxide from a molten mixture.   It takes 10 kw-hr of electrical energy to produce a single pound of aluminum.   Chlorine and many other commercially important elements are obtained by electrolytic processes.

By no means all electrolytic processes are desirable ones.   Electrolysis is an important factor in limiting the life of underground pipes.   When a steel pipe is laid near an electrified railroad, the current may find its way into the pipe instead of traveling from the generator to the motors directly through the track.   At certain points the water pipe may be eaten away as is the anode in the electrolysis of copper sulfate.   The electrochemical action is complex but as part of the process, iron is removed from the pipe in regions where it serves as anode.

39.4. Chemical Electromotive Forces.   Electrical energy used to send electric current through a solution can produce chemical reactions, such as the liberation of hydrogen and oxygen from water. The reverse process of using chemical reactions to provide electrical energy also occurs. This fact was discovered about 1800 by the Italian physicist Volta, who built the first batteries.

Most batteries are composed of several cells connected in series. In each cell a chemical reaction converts chemical energy into electrical energy. A relatively simple cell to understand is one in which a zinc plate and a lead plate are immersed in a dilute solution of sulfuric acid (Fig. 39.4). When this is done, zinc ions leave the metal and go into solution. Each zinc ion bears two units of positive charge by virtue of the fact that it leaves two electrons with the metal. As zinc ions go into solution, the zinc metal becomes negatively charged. As the zinc becomes more negative, it attracts the positive zinc ions in the solution. Eventually equilibrium is reached in which the rate of loss of zinc ions

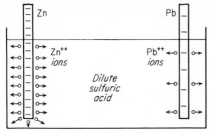

Fig. 39.4. A zinc-lead–sulfuric acid cell.

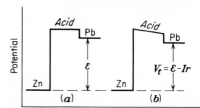

Fig. 39.5. Variation of potential in a zinc-lead–sulfuric acid cell: (a) when no current exists and (b) when a current is drawn.

is equal to the rate of return. When this occurs, the potential of the zinc is lower than the potential of the solution.

Similarly, lead ions leave the lead plate and go into solution. They bear two unit positive charges and leave the lead plate negative relative to the solution. However, equilibrium for the lead ions is established when the lead is less negative than the zinc plate. There is now a potential difference between the zinc plate and the lead plate, as shown in Fig. 39.5a. If a wire is connected between the zinc and lead plates, electrons flow through the wire from the zinc to the lead. When there is a current through the cell, there is a potential drop in the solution due to its resistance (Fig. 39.5b).

As electrons leave the zinc plate, it becomes less negative; the equilibrium is disturbed so that more zinc ions go into solution. At the same time the lead plate becomes more negative and positive ions are attracted back.

Chemical cells can be made from a large number of different materials. The emf depends on the particular materials involved. Generally speaking, the most active chemical metal forms the negative terminal.   Table 1 shows the electromotive series of metals.   It indicates the potentials of various metals relative to a hydrogen electrode formed by bubbling hydrogen gas over a spongy platinum conductor.   The values in the table are for standard ion concentrations.

Table 1

THE ELECTROMOTIVE (OR ELECTROCHEMICAL) SERIES

(All potential differences are referred to a standard hydrogen electrode taken as zero and are for a temperature of 25°C)

Element	Potential difference, volts	Element	Potential difference, volts
Li	−2.96	Cd	−0.40
Rb	−2.93	Ni	−0.23
K	−2.92	Sn	−0.14
Ca	−2.76	Pb	−0.12
Na	−2.71	H	0
Mg	−2.40	Cu	0.34
Al	−1.70	Ag	0.80
Zn	−0.76	Hg	0.80
Fe	−0.44	Au	1.5

An *ideal* cell utilizing any two of these elements as electrodes has an emf given by the difference between the voltages listed in Table 1 for the elements in question.   For example, the potential of the copper-zinc cell can be predicted by observing that zinc relative to hydrogen has a potential of −0.76 while copper has a potential of +0.34.   A copper-zinc cell will then be expected to have a potential difference of approximately 1.10 volts.

The emf of a cell is determined primarily by the energy released in the chemical reactions per coulomb of charge transferred through the cell.   However, it would be erroneous to assume that the only energy transformations occurring are between chemical and electrical energy.   When some cells are discharged, part of the chemical energy is transformed into heat; when such cells are charged, this heat is retransformed to chemical energy.

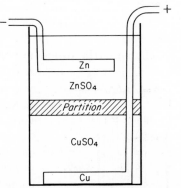

Fig. 39.6. The Daniell cell was one of the earliest practical cells.

Other cells transform heat energy into electrical energy during discharge and electrical energy into heat energy when they are being charged.

39.5. The Daniell Cell and Polarization.   One of the earliest practical sources of emf was the Daniell cell, of which the basic components are shown in Fig. 39.6.   It consists of a copper electrode submerged in copper sulfate and a zinc electrode in zinc sulfate.   A porous partition separates the zinc sulfate from the copper sulfate so that charges can pass through but the chemicals do not mix readily.   In such a cell the zinc electrode becomes negative and the copper plate positive.   When the plates of the Daniell cell are connected through a resistance, electrons flowing through the wire reduce the negative charge on the zinc terminal and permit more zinc to go into solution.   The potential of the copper electrode is reduced and copper ions are deposited from the solution.   The net effect of the reaction is to convert zinc and copper sulfate into zinc sulfate plus copper.   In this reaction chemical energy is transformed into electrical energy.

In the early days of telegraphy the Daniell cell was the standard source of emf.   Its output is about 1.1 volts, but the terminal potential difference of a cell is somewhat less when current is drawn.   The *volt* as the practical unit of potential difference originated with the use of Daniell cells in early telegraph circuits, when the "voltage" was just the number of Daniell cells connected in series.

The Daniell cell is by no means the only type of cell in which zinc and copper electrodes may be used.   If a zinc strip and a copper one are inserted in a juicy lemon, the juice serves as electrolyte and we can observe a potential difference between the zinc and the copper.   Another possibility is that of making a simple cell by immersing a zinc plate and a copper one in a dilute solution of some acid such as H_2SO_4.   This zinc-copper–sulfuric acid cell does not perform very satisfactorily as a source of emf because as current is drawn, hydrogen ions are deposited on the copper.   This reduces the emf, since the positive electrode is now essentially hydrogen rather than copper.   Further, hydrogen bubbles on the surface of the plate form an insulating layer and greatly increase the resistance of the cell.   This is an example of an effect called *polarization*.   (This should not be confused with polarization of a dielectric.)   Polarization can occur in many ways in a cell, but its net effect is always to reduce the observed emf to a value below that which would be expected on the basis of the electrochemical series.

39.6.   Primary and Secondary Batteries.

Among the many possible kinds of chemical reactions which may be used for batteries, a few are reversible.   In most cases the chemical reaction cannot be reversed by changing the direction of the current.   A cell in which the chemical

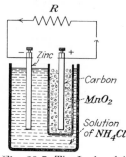

Fig. 39.7.   The Leclanché cell.

reaction is irreversible is a *primary* cell, while one which can be charged and discharged repeatedly is known as a *secondary* cell.   The simple zinc-copper–sulfuric acid cell discussed above is a primary cell.   If one attempts to reverse the chemical process by making the zinc electrode positive, the zinc ions do not plate out.   Rather, copper and hydrogen ions are deposited and the zinc stays in solution.   The reaction is not reversible.

There are, however, a number of reversible cells which are useful for batteries.   Prominent among them are the lead storage cell (Sec. 39.8) and the Edison cell (Sec. 39.9), which can be charged and recharged many times.

39.7.   The Dry Cell.

The Leclanché cell (Fig. 39.7) is a primary cell of interest because a later modification, known as a *dry cell*, is widely used.   This cell consists of a zinc rod which dips into a solution of ammonium chloride. The other electrode of the cell is a carbon rod. The ammonium chloride in the electrolyte dissociates into NH_4^+ and Cl^-. The interaction of the Cl^- ions with the zinc leaves the zinc plate negative. When the plates are connected externally, electrons flow to the carbon rod. The NH_4^+ ions go to the carbon and there give up their charge, breaking down into NH_3 and hydrogen. The hydrogen collects on the electrode and the NH_3 is absorbed by the water. If the hydrogen remained on the electrode, the cell would soon be polarized. To prevent this, the carbon electrode is surrounded by a cup filled with manganese dioxide and graphite. The MnO_2 reacts chemically with the hydrogen to produce water and thus acts as a *depolarizer*. The graphite serves to keep the material in the cup conducting. Since the action of the depolarizer is slow, the cell is adapted to work in which it is used for a short time and then allowed to stand. This type of cell has an emf of about 1.5 volts.

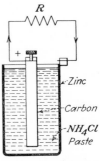

Fig. 39.8. A dry cell.

The dry cell (Fig. 39.8) differs from the Leclanché cell only in the fact that the electrolyte is in the form of a paste of ammonium chloride instead of the solution. The negative electrode is the zinc can that contains the carbon and paste. The zinc on the inside of the can is covered with several layers of blotting paper, and the space around the carbon rod that forms the positive electrode is filled with a mixture of carbon, manganese dioxide, and sawdust saturated with a solution of ammonium chloride. The top is sealed with wax to prevent evaporation of the moisture in the paste. (When a dry cell is really dry, its conductance is so low that it is useless.)

39.8. Lead Storage Cell. In the lead storage cell, both the positive and negative plates are made of heavy lead grids full of holes or grooves filled with the active material. The positive plates contain lead peroxide and the negative plates spongy lead. A cell is usually formed of a number of such plates, alternately negative and positive, covered with sulfuric acid. The negative plates are connected together and act as one terminal of the battery, and the positive plates are connected together to form the other terminal. It is customary to have one more negative plate than positive so that every positive plate lies between two negative ones. In this way, both sides of the positive plates are charged or discharged. During the process of recharging, there is a restoration of the peroxide which is accompanied by an increase in volume, causing a swelling of the plate. Since this swelling takes place equally on both sides of the positive plate, there is little tendency for the plates to warp. If the plates are close together and if, through the use of a large number of plates, the area is large, the cell has a small internal resistance. By increasing the number of plates and making the areas larger, the current capacity of the cell is increased.

When a lead storage cell is delivering a current, both the lead peroxide on the positive electrode and the spongy lead on the negative electrode are converted to lead sulfate. As this occurs, the emf of the cell gradually decreases, as shown in Fig. 39.9. In order to charge the battery and make it ready for further use, it is only necessary to maintain an electric current in it in a direction opposite to that in which the current flows when the cell is in use. During this process the lead sulfate on the negative plate is reduced to spongy lead, while the lead sulfate on the positive plate is reconverted to lead peroxide. After a sufficient time of charging, the original condition of the battery is restored. The chemical action taking place during the process of charging and discharging may be represented by the following equations:

Charging:

At positive plate, $PbSO_4 + SO_4 + 2H_2O \rightarrow PbO_2 + 2H_2SO_4$
At negative plate, $PbSO_4 + H_2 \rightarrow Pb + H_2SO_4$

Discharging:

At positive plate, $PbO_2 + H_2SO_4 + H_2 \rightarrow PbSO_4 + 2H_2O$
At negative plate, $Pb + SO_4 \rightarrow PbSO_4$

It is seen from these equations that, during the process of charging, sulfuric acid is formed. Since the specific gravity of H_2SO_4 is greater than that of water, the density of the electrolyte rises when a battery is being charged. During discharge, sulfuric acid disappears and water is formed. For this reason, the density of the electrolyte decreases during discharge (Fig. 39.10). By measuring the density of the electrolyte, it is possible to find the state of charge of the battery.

39.9. Edison Storage Cell. A storage battery composed of Edison cells is lighter, more rugged, and longer-lived than a lead storage battery. In the

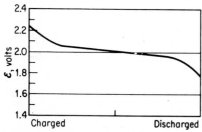

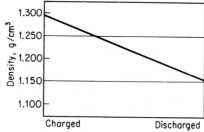

Fig. 39.9. Electromotive force of a lead cell as a function of the state of charge.

Fig. 39.10. Density of sulfuric acid in a lead cell as a function of the state of charge.

Edison cell the negative plate is a nickel-plated steel grid with a large number of pockets filled with powdered iron oxide (FeO). The positive plate is a nickel-plated steel grid with perforated steel tubes filled with alternate layers of nickel hydroxide and flaked nickel. The flaked nickel is added to reduce the internal resistance of the cell. The electrolyte is a 21 per cent solution of potassium hydroxide.

When the cell is discharging, the nickel peroxide is reduced to a lower oxide (Ni_2O_3) and the iron oxidized to form iron oxide (FeO). The net reaction is

$$2NiO_2 + Fe \rightarrow Ni_2O_3 + FeO$$

When the cell is being charged, the reaction is reversed. The electrolyte enters into intermediate reactions. Its effect in charging and discharging is to transfer oxygen from one plate of the cell to the other. Its density changes only slightly during the reactions. The normal emf of an Edison cell is about 1.2 volts, varying from 1.4 volts to 0.9 volt as the cell discharges. This variation of emf and relatively high cost are major disadvantages of Edison cells.

39.10. Weston Standard Cell. Standard cells offer a means of obtaining definite, known, and constant potential differences. The most widely used of these standard cells is the cadmium or Weston cell (Fig. 39.11). Its emf changes very little with the temperature, which is one of the reasons the Weston cell is considered the best standard available. At 20°C its emf is 1.0183 volts and the emf decreases about 4×10^{-5} volt for each centigrade degree the temperature is raised.

39.11. Thermoelectricity—The Seebeck Effect.

When two different materials are in contact, there is ordinarily a potential difference between them. In electrostatics this phenomenon permits us to produce charges by contact and separation. In batteries the potential differences between metals and solutions give rise to the emfs. When two metals are placed in contact, there is a potential difference between them which depends both on the metals used and on the temperature of the junction.

When two wires of dissimilar metals (e.g., copper and iron) are joined together at the ends to form a closed circuit and one of the junctions

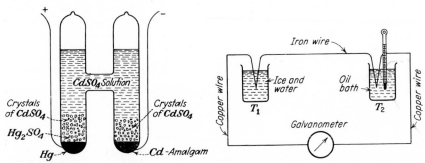

Fig. 39.11. Weston standard cell.

Fig. 39.12. A thermal emf exists when the temperatures of the two copper-iron junctions are different.

thus formed is maintained at a different temperature than the other (Fig. 39.12), an electric current is established in the circuit. This effect was discovered in 1821 by Seebeck. The magnitude of the emf producing the current depends on the two kinds of wire and on the temperatures of the two junctions. If the two junctions are at the same temperature, the emfs established at the junctions are exactly equal and opposite, so that there is no net emf.

Consider first a thermocouple made of iron and copper (Fig. 39.12). If one of the junctions is kept at 0°C while the other is heated, a net thermoelectromotive force is produced. When the temperature of the hot junction is raised, the thermal emf first increases at a nearly uniform rate (Fig. 39.13). As the temperature is raised further, the rate of increase becomes less. When the temperature of the hot junction becomes 275°C, a further increase in temperature results in a decrease in the thermal emf. The temperature at which the emf reaches its maximum is the *neutral temperature,* so named because there is neither increase nor decrease of thermal emf with temperature. When the temperature of the hot junction is raised above the neutral temperature, the thermal emf decreases and finally becomes zero at approximately 550°C. If the temperature of the hot junction is still further increased, the current in the circuit reverses direction. The temperature at which the thermal emf passes through zero is called the *inversion temperature*. The curve obtained by plotting thermoelectromotive force as a function of the temperature of one junction (the second junction is kept at constant temperature) has the shape of a parabola.

For some materials, such as chromel and alumel, the emf increases continuously as the temperature of the hot junction is raised. For these materials the neutral temperature and the inversion temperature are reached by cooling the variable-temperature junction rather than by warming it.

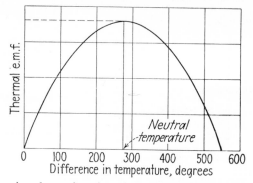

Fig. 39.13. Thermal cmf as a function of the temperature of the hot junction of a copper-iron thermocouple.

Thermocouples are convenient for measuring temperatures, since the emf depends on the temperature difference between the junctions in a known way. Ordinarily, one junction is kept at a constant temperature, usually in an ice bath at 0°C. The hot junction need not be anywhere near the cold junction. It may be installed at some inaccessible point where it would be impossible to place and read a standard mercury thermometer. Thermocouples can be used for measuring temperatures roughly up to the melting point of the materials involved, which is as high as 2900°F for some couples. Further, they can be made much smaller than glass or metal expansion thermometers, so that they can be used to measure the temperatures of very small objects, such as insects or twigs of trees.

For any thermocouple it is likely that one would want to make connection to a galvanometer by means of copper wires fastened to the ends of the thermocouple elements. Adding other materials in the circuit has *no effect so long as the junctions of the other metals are all at the same temperature.* Electromotive forces exist at the new junctions but the algebraic sum of the emfs in the circuit remains the same. The lengths of the wires also have no effect on the emf (although they do influence the resistance of the circuit).

The emfs involved in the Seebeck effect are ordinarily very small, usually of the order of millivolts. To obtain higher emfs, a number of thermocouples are connected in series, thus producing a *thermopile* (Fig. 39.14).   Thermopiles are often used for measuring radiant energy.

39.12. The Peltier and Thomson Effects.   We have seen that when two dissimilar metals are placed in contact, electrons diffuse from one metal to the other and an emf exists between the surfaces.   This potential difference is called the Peltier emf.   It depends on the metals in contact and upon the temperature of the junction.

If two ends of a wire of any material are at different temperatures, electrons are likely to diffuse more rapidly in one direction than in the other.   This unequal diffusion produces a potential difference called the Thomson emf.   The Seebeck effect, discussed in Sec. 39.11, arises as the result of the Thomson emfs between opposite ends of wires of the same material which are at different temperatures and of the Peltier emfs at the junctions of the metals.   Usually the Peltier emfs greatly exceed the Thomson emfs.

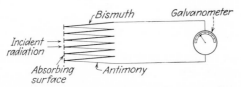

Fig. 39.14. Thermopile consisting of a number of thermocouples connected in series.

When a current is passed through a thermocouple by connecting a battery in the circuit, the Peltier emf at one junction is aiding the battery while the Peltier emf at the second junction is in series opposing.   At the junction where the Peltier emf is in opposition, heat is evolved not only because of the I^2Rt heating effect, but also because of the work done against the emf at the junction.   At the other junction thermal energy is absorbed and converted into electrical energy. The temperature of this junction may be reduced substantially.   When a current is passed through a thermocouple made of bismuth and antimony, one of the junctions is heated and the other is cooled.   Heat is developed at one junction and absorbed at the other.   This is known as the *Peltier effect*.

PROBLEMS

1. How long will be required for a current of 12 amp to plate 2 g of silver on a knife?
Ans. 149 sec

2. A copper plate weighing 109.265 g is placed in an electroplating bath.   A steady current is sent through the bath for 20 min, and the weight of the plate is increased to 110.490 g.   What was the current in amperes, assuming copper is divalent?

3. Find what volumes of hydrogen and oxygen under standard conditions are released by the electrolysis of acidulated water for a period of 10 min by a current of 0.6 amp.
Ans. 41.8 cm³; 20.9 cm³

4. An object that has a surface of 16 cm² is to be plated with silver.   What will be the average thickness of the silver when a current of 0.15 amp flows for 24 hr?

5. Find the electrochemical equivalent of platinum if a current of 0.080 amp deposits 0.584 g in 2 hr.
Ans. 0.001012 g/coul

6. Find the electrochemical equivalent of oxygen which is bivalent.

7. A current of 6 amp flows for 4 hr through a series of cells containing nickel nitrate, copper sulfate ($CuSO_4$), and silver nitrate, respectively.   Find the quantity of nickel, copper, and silver deposited.
Ans. 26.2 g; 28.4 g; 96.5 g

know the right hand rules.

Magnetic Fields
of Currents

40.1. Magnets. Small pieces of the mineral lodestone (Fe_3O_4) have the ability to attract other small pieces of the same mineral or small pieces of iron. This fact was known in the seventh century B.C. How much earlier it had been discovered we do not know. Lodestones turn with the same side toward the north when they are suspended from cords or floated on corks in water. This special property led to the important invention of the mariner's compass sometime before the twelfth century.

When a steel knitting needle is stroked from one end to the other with a piece of lodestone, the needle may acquire the property of attracting iron filings and of setting itself along a north-south line when suspended by a string. Such a needle is said to be *magnetized* and is commonly called a *magnet*. Most materials cannot be magnetized in this way; relatively few show attraction for a lodestone or a small magnet. Iron and some of its alloys are by far the best known of magnetic materials, although cobalt, nickel, and a number of alloys exhibit strong magnetic properties.

One end of a magnetized needle, suspended by a cord so that it is free to rotate in any direction, normally points in a northerly direction. This end of the needle is commonly called the *north pole* (N pole), an abbreviation for the more fully descriptive *north-seeking pole*. The opposite end of the needle is called the *south pole* (S pole).

If this magnetized needle is dipped into soft-iron filings, the filings cling tenaciously to the ends; relatively few stick to the middle. It is often convenient to think of all the magnetic properties of the needle concentrated in the two ends or poles, although this is an oversimplification.

When two magnetized needles are brought near one another, the two north poles repel one another as do the two south poles. On the other hand, there is an attractive force between the north pole of one magnet

474

and the south pole of the other.   Such observations lead to the conclusion: *like poles repel; unlike poles attract.*

40.2. Interactions of Currents and Magnets.   In 1819 Oersted discovered that a magnet in the neighborhood of a current-bearing wire undergoes a deflection.   A magnetized needle held above a straight wire carrying a current is deflected as shown in Fig. 40.1.   If the magnet is held below the wire, the N pole is deflected in the opposite direction.   The direction in which a north pole points may always be found by the application of a simple rule, illustrated in Fig. 40.2.

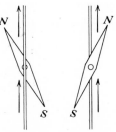

If the right thumb is pointed in the direction of the conventional current and the fingers are allowed to curl, the direction in which the fingers point is the direction in which the north pole of the needle is deflected by the current.

If a long cylindrical coil of wire (called a solenoid) is produced by winding fine wire on a match stick and current is passed through it, the solenoid behaves like a small magnet of the same shape.   While current is passing

Fig. 40.1. The deflection of a magnetic needle by a current toward the north. When the needle is below the wire, the deflection is opposite to that when the needle is above the wire.

through the solenoid, it will pick up small iron filings.   It has a north and a south "pole," which exert forces on other poles.   The fact that a current-bearing solenoid behaves like a magnet of the same dimensions

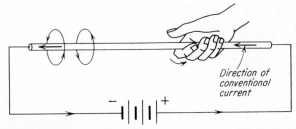

Direction of conventional current

Fig. 40.2. If the right thumb is pointed in the direction of the conventional current, the fingers curl in the direction of the magnetic field, which is the direction of the force on the N pole of a magnetic needle.

led Ampère to suggest in 1820 that the forces between iron magnets arise from electric currents in the iron.   This point of view has been substantiated by later research and is discussed in Chap. 41.

Magnetic interactions occur between moving charges, whether they be currents in wires, a beam of electrons in a television tube, or the electrons in magnetic materials.   The forces so produced are of tremendous practical importance.   Electric motors depend on them, as do most of our meters for measuring electric currents and potential differences.

40.3. The Magnetic Field.   A magnetic field is any region in which forces may be observed to act on small magnets or on small current-bearing elements.   *The direction of the magnetic field at any point is the direction of the force experienced by the north-seeking pole of a small test magnet when the test magnet is placed at the point.*   A small current-bearing solenoid could be substituted for the test magnet.

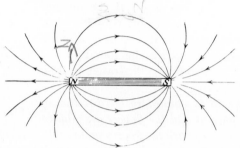

Fig. 40.3. The magnetic field in the vicinity of a bar magnet.

One may readily explore the magnetic field associated with a large bar magnet by taking a small compass needle and finding in what direction the N pole points at various places in the field.   A plot of the magnetic field associated with a magnet is shown in Fig. 40.3.   In discussing magnetic fields, it is convenient to make use of the idea of magnetic lines of force which are defined as lines whose tangents give the direction of the magnetic field at every point in the field.   It is customary to draw the lines close together where the field is strong, farther apart as the field becomes weaker.   The lines of force for a bar magnet are identical with those for a suitably chosen current-bearing solenoid (Fig. 40.4).   The magnetic field associated with a straight current-bearing conductor is shown in Fig. 40.2.   The lines of force in this case are circles concentric with the wire.

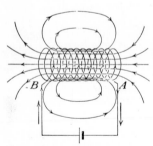

Fig. 40.4. The magnetic field of a solenoid is like that of a bar magnet of the same shape.

The magnetic field at any point is characterized not only by a direction, but also by a strength.   The vector which describes the field at a point is called the *magnetic induction, magnetic flux density*, or *magnetic intensity*.   It is represented by the symbol **B**.   To measure **B**, we make use of the fact that there is a force on a current element in a magnetic field.

Consider first the special case of the uniform magnetic field between the pole pieces of the large magnet of Fig. 40.5.   If a straight wire bearing a current I is placed perpendicular to the lines of magnetic force and if l

represents the length of the part of the wire in the magnetic field, there
is a force **F** on the wire in the direc-
tion indicated. We define the magnetic intensity **B** by the equation

$$B = \frac{F}{Il} \qquad (40.1)$$

In practical units **F** is measured in
newtons, I in amperes, and l in
meters and **B** has the dimensions
newtons per ampere-meter.

In the preceding discussion we
stated that the wire must be perpendicular to the direction of the magnetic field. This is very important;
indeed, if the wire lies along the lines

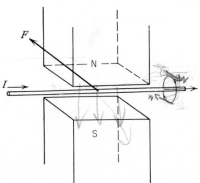

Fig. 40.5. A current-bearing conductor lies perpendicular to a uniform
magnetic field.

of force, there is no force at all. If the wire makes an angle θ with the
field, the force is given by

$$F = IlB \sin \theta \qquad (40.2)$$

Many magnetic fields are not uniform, but vary from point to point. The
field intensity **B** at any point is then the limit of the ratio $\Delta F / I \, \Delta l$ as Δl is made
smaller and smaller. Here ΔF represents the small force on a small element of
length Δl. The result of using any finite length l of wire is to measure the average intensity over the region covered by l. In actual practice it is often difficult
to determine the force on a small element of a current-bearing conductor; therefore other means are ordinarily used to measure **B**.

The direction of the force on a current-bearing wire is perpendicular
both to the length of the wire and to the magnetic field. For the particular situation of Fig. 40.5 the direction of this force may be found as
follows: The lines of flux associated with the
current are concentric circles as indicated.
The magnetic field of the wire exerts a force
on the north pole out of the paper and on
the south pole also out of the paper. Since
the wire pushes outward on the magnet, the
force exerted by the magnet on the current
must be inward in accord with Newton's
third law.

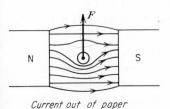

Current out of paper

Fig. 40.6. The force on a current-bearing conductor in a
magnetic field is from the
stronger toward the weaker
resultant field.

The origin of some magnetic fields, such
as that of the earth, may not be obvious.
In such a case one can find the direction of
the force on the wire by observing that on one side of the wire the magnetic field due to the current (Fig. 40.6) reinforces the field already

present, while on the other side of the wire the two fields are opposite in direction.   The force on the wire is directed from the stronger field toward the weaker one, or from the side on which the two fields reinforce to the side on which the two fields oppose.

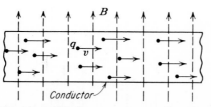

Fig. 40.7. The force on a current-bearing conductor in a magnetic field results from the forces acting on the individual moving charges.

40.4. Magnetic Force on a Moving Charge. The force exerted on a current-bearing conductor in a magnetic field is the resultant of the forces which act on individual moving charges in the conductor. Let us consider a conductor in which there are n charged particles per unit length, each with a charge q and a velocity $\mathbf{v}$ perpendicular to a magnetic field $\mathbf{B}$, as shown in Fig. 40.7.   The current through the plane PP' is just the charge passing per second, which is

$$I = qnv$$

The force on a length l is given by $IlB = qvnlB$.   The number of particles in the length l is nl and the force on each particle is

$$F = qvB \tag{40.3}$$

Equation (40.3) gives the force on a single charged particle moving perpendicular to the magnetic intensity $\mathbf{B}$.   It is one of the basic equations of particle physics.   If θ represents the angle between the directions of the vectors $\mathbf{B}$ and $\mathbf{v}$, the force is given by

$$F = qvB \sin \theta \tag{40.3a}$$

The force is perpendicular to the plane defined by $\mathbf{B}$ and $\mathbf{v}$.

The deflection of charged particles by magnetic fields has many uses. The electron beam which sketches the pictures on a television tube is usually directed by magnetic forces.   In cyclotrons, betatrons, and synchrotrons, accelerated charged particles are restrained to roughly circular paths by magnetic fields.   Electron microscopes and mass spectrographs use magnetic forces to control beams of charged particles.   Some of these important instruments are described in later chapters.

40.5. The Magnetic Moment of a Coil. Consider a rectangular loop of wire bearing a current I and placed in a uniform magnetic field of intensity $\mathbf{B}$ with one side of the rectangle perpendicular to the field and the other side lying along the field (Fig. 40.8).   Let y represent the length of the side perpendicular to the magnetic field and x the length of the side parallel to the magnetic field.   Under these circumstances there are no forces on the sides marked x, but the force on each of the wires perpendicular to the field is given by $F = BIy$.   The lever arm about the axis OO' for one of the vertical sides is $x/2$ and the torque L on this one side is given by $L = BIyx/2$.   The net torque acting to rotate the loop is just twice this great, or $BIyx$.   The product yx is equal to the area A of the rectangle and the torque on the coil is equal to BIA.   If a rectangular coil is made by winding N turns around the loop, the torque on the coil will be increased by a factor N and

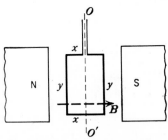

$$L = BNIA \qquad (40.4)$$

Fig. 40.8. A rectangular loop of wire bearing a current is subject to a torque in a magnetic field.

The magnetic moment **M** *of the coil is the ratio of the torque to the magnetic field strength when the plane of the coil is parallel to the magnetic field.*   For the rectangular coil we have, from Eq. (40.4),

$$M = \frac{L}{B} = NIA \qquad (40.4a)$$

The dimensions of magnetic moment are ampere-meters^2.   While Eq. (40.4) has been derived for a rectangular coil, it applies to coils of any

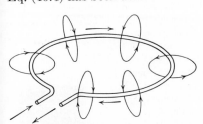

shape.   The magnetic moment is a vector perpendicular to the plane of the coil and in the direction in which a right-handed screw would advance if turned in the direction of the current I.   The magnetic field due to a coil is shown in Fig. 40.9.

The torque **L** on a coil of magnetic moment **M** is given by BM when **M** is perpendicular to **B**.   When **M** and **B** are parallel, the torque is zero.   In general, if the angle between **M** and **B** is θ, the torque is given by

Fig. 40.9. The magnetic field associated with a current-bearing loop.

$$L = BM \sin \theta \qquad (40.5)$$

If there is no opposing torque, the loop shown in Fig. 40.8 rotates under the influence of the magnetic field until the magnetic moment is aligned in the direction of the field.

40.6. The Moving-coil Galvanometer.   If a coil such as the one of Fig. 40.10 is suspended between the poles of a permanent magnet and a small current is passed through the coil, the coil rotates until the restoring torque exerted by the suspension is equal to the torque due to the interaction of the current and the magnetic field. This latter torque is proportional to the current. Therefore, the angular deflection of the coil is proportional to the current, provided the restoring torque is proportional to the angular displacement and the magnetic field is perpendicular to **M** for all displacements. This latter condition is reasonably well satisfied for angles up to 30° for the magnet of Fig. 40.10. Thus, a single loop of wire suspended by an elastic suspension in a magnetic field can be used to detect and measure currents. The sensitivity of the instrument can be changed by making the coil of several turns of wire instead of using a single loop. Such a coil, suspended in a magnetic field, is called a galvanometer when it is used to detect and measure very small currents. A small pointer or mirror attached to the coil is ordinarily used to measure the angular deflection.

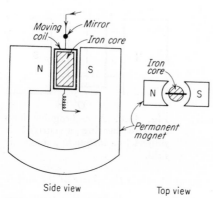

Fig. 40.10. Schematic diagram of a moving-coil galvanometer.

Figure 40.10 shows a schematic diagram for a moving coil galvanometer. The magnet NS is often made in the shape of a horseshoe which is favorable for producing a strong magnetic field. A typical coil may be wound on a very light frame and be suspended by means of fine phosphor bronze wire between the poles of the magnet. The bottom of the coil is connected to a binding post by means of a fine wire or a ribbon wound in the form of a spiral. Figures 40.11 and 40.12 show two common types of moving coil galvanometers, known as D'Arsonval galvanometers.

40.7. Ammeters and Voltmeters. When a galvanometer and its scale are so adjusted that the scale readings indicate the current passing through some portion of a circuit in amperes, the meter is called an *ammeter*. A common form of ammeter is shown in Fig. 40.13. It consists of a coil of fine copper wire wound on a light frame which is mounted on jeweled bearings between poles of a permanent magnet. When a current exists in the coil, it rotates between the poles of the magnet. Two spiral springs, one at the top and the other at the bottom, carry the current into and out of the coil and they provide a restoring torque proportional to the angular displacement.

Fig. 40.11. Wall-type D'Arsonval galvanometer. (*Leeds and Northrup Co.*)

Since a very small fraction of an ampere through the coil of an ordinary ammeter produces a full-scale deflection, it is necessary to use a low-resistance *shunt* to carry a large fraction of the current which passes through the ammeter. (A shunt is a resistance connected in parallel with a circuit element.) Because the current flowing in the movable coil is always a constant fraction of the full current entering the instrument, the scale can be calibrated so that the pointer indicates the entire current passing through the instrument. Any galvanometer can be made to operate as an ammeter by the use of a suitable shunt. By choice of some other shunt, the galvanometer can be made into an ammeter of different range.

A galvanometer can also be made into a *voltmeter* by the proper appli-

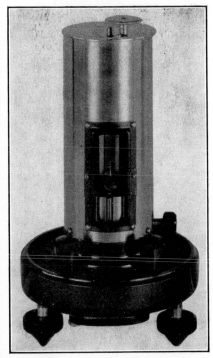

Fig. 40.12. A sensitive D'Arsonval galvanometer. (*Leeds and Northrup Co.*)

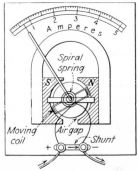

Fig. 40.13. An ammeter consisting of a coil in a magnetic field. The deflection of the coil is proportional to the current.

cation of an additional resistance. A voltmeter, as its name implies, is an instrument used to measure potential difference. By connecting a high resistance in series (Fig. 40.14) with the galvanometer coil the current passing through the coil can be limited to a value which will not exceed full-scale deflection. Since for a given resistance the current is directly proportional to the potential difference across the instrument, the deflection of the pointer is proportional to the potential difference. Then the scale may be calibrated to read potential difference directly in volts. By the suitable choice of the series resistance one can make a voltmeter which gives full-scale deflection for any desired potential difference across the terminals of the voltmeter.

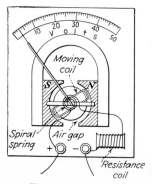

Fig. 40.14. A voltmeter. (*Weston Electrical Instrument Corp.*)

Example. A galvanometer requires 0.00015 amp to produce a full-scale deflection. The coil has a resistance of 60 ohms. What shunt resistance is needed to convert this galvanometer into an ammeter reading 2 amp full scale?

Of the 2 amp which enter the ammeter for a full-scale deflection, 0.00015 amp must pass through the galvanometer and the remainder $(2 - 0.00015 = 1.99985$ amp) go through the shunt. Since the shunt and galvanometer are in parallel, the potential difference across each is the same

$$V_G = V_S \quad \text{and} \quad I_G R_G = I_S R_S$$
$$0.00015 \times 60 = 1.99985 R_S$$
$$R_S = \frac{0.009}{1.99985} = 0.0045 \text{ ohm}$$

Example. What series resistance R is needed to convert the galvanometer of the preceding example into a voltmeter reading 6 volts full scale?

When 6 volts are impressed across the voltmeter, a current of 0.00015 amp must pass through the coil and the series resistance if the deflection is to be full scale. The total resistance of the voltmeter must be

$$R_V = \frac{6}{0.00015} = 40,000 \text{ ohms}$$

But $R_V = R$ plus the resistance of the galvanometer; therefore

$$R = 40,000 - 60 = 39,940 \text{ ohms}$$

40.8. The Magnetic Field of a Long Straight Wire. In Sec. 40.3 it is shown that a long straight wire carrying a current has associated with it a magnetic field. The lines of force are concentric circles about the wire. When the wire lies in air (or some other nonmagnetic material), the magnetic intensity **B** at any point is proportional to the current I and inversely proportional to the distance r from the wire. It can be shown that $B = 2kI/r$, where k is a constant which has the value 10^{-7} newton/amp². The magnetic field strength **B** at a distance r from a long straight wire carrying a current I is given by

$$B = \frac{2I}{10^7 r} \tag{40.6}$$

When two long wires parallel to one another bear currents I_1 and I_2 in the same direction, there is an attractive force between them.   If the wires are separated by a distance r, the magnetic field at the first wire due to the current in the second is given by $2I_2/10^7r$.   Therefore, the force on a length l of the first wire is given by

$$F = I_1lB = \frac{2I_1I_2l}{10^7r} \qquad (40.7)$$

The force per unit length is $2I_1I_2/10^7r$.   That the force is attractive can be seen by study of Fig. 40.15.   If the directions of the currents in the two wires are opposite, the force between the wires is repulsive.

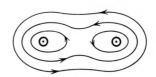

Although Eq. (40.7) has been derived for long straight wires, there is an attractive force between any two neighboring conductors which are carrying currents in the same direction.   One of the most accurate methods of measuring current involves the determination in an instrument known as the "current balance" of the attractive force between two precisely made, parallel coils carrying the same current.   In the absolute system of units, officially adopted by the United States (*National Bureau of Standards Circular* C 459, 1947), the ampere is defined in terms of

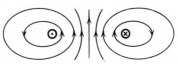

Fig. 40.15. Two parallel wires attract one another when they bear currents in the same direction and repel one another when the currents are opposite.

measurements made with a current balance.   The coulomb is then derived from the ampere as the charge which is carried by a current of one ampere in one second.   (For pedagogical reasons we have introduced the coulomb first and then defined the ampere; our units are consistent with those adopted by the National Bureau of Standards.)

When coils carry an alternating current, neighboring turns are attracted to one another by forces which change as the alternating current increases and decreases.   The turns may vibrate, moving together and then apart.   This leads to the familiar and annoying hum associated with many coils carrying alternating currents.

40.9. The Magnetic Field for Other Current Configurations. The magnetic field due to any current configuration can be found by finding the vector sum of the contributions to the magnetic field due to the current in each minute element of length Δl.   The contribution $\Delta \mathbf{B}$ to the magnetic field due to the current in a small element of length Δl (Fig. 40.16) is given by

$$\Delta B = \frac{kI \, \Delta l \sin \theta}{r^2} \qquad (40.8)$$

where θ is the angle between the element $\Delta \mathbf{l}$ and the vector $\mathbf{r}$ connecting $\Delta \mathbf{l}$ to the point at which $\Delta \mathbf{B}$ is to be measured, and k is 10^{-7} newton/amp^2.

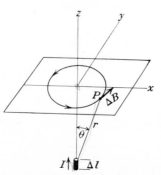

Fig. 40.16. The contribution to the magnetic field at point P due to the current bearing element of length Δl is given by Ampère's law.

This equation is an expression of a fundamental rule known as *Ampère's law.* Equation (40.8) is applicable only if the wire is in a nonmagnetic medium. It should be emphasized that the contribution $\Delta \mathbf{B}$ from each element of length $\Delta \mathbf{l}$ is a vector which must be added vectorially to all the other $\Delta \mathbf{B}$'s if one wishes to find the resultant magnetic intensity.

The magnetic field at the center of a circular loop of wire (Fig. 40.9) of radius a is readily computed by use of Eq. (40.8). Since the contributions of the tiny elements of length Δl are all in the same direction and are exactly equal in size, addition of the components simply gives $B = Il/10^7 a^2$. The length of the wire l is $2\pi a$, so that this equation reduces to

$$B = \frac{2\pi I}{10^7 a}$$

If the circular loop is replaced by a circular coil having N turns, the contributions of these turns are all in the same direction. Accordingly, at the center of the circular coil the magnetic intensity $\mathbf{B}$ is given by

$$B = \frac{2\pi N I}{10^7 a} \tag{40.9}$$

One of the common current configurations in magnetic circuits is that of the solenoid, often used for windings on electromagnets. The solenoid provides a uniform field over its entire central section. If it is long compared with its diameter, the magnetic field is almost the same at all points inside the solenoid except at distances less than one diameter from the ends. At the ends the field falls off. In the central section of the solenoid the magnetic field $\mathbf{B}$ is given by the relation

$$B = \frac{4\pi n I}{10^7} \tag{40.10}$$

where n is the number of turns per meter. It is important to note that n represents the *number of turns per unit length*, while N is used to represent the total number of turns; $n = N/l$, where l is the length of the solenoid. Equation (40.10) is applicable no matter what the cross-sectional shape of the solenoid may be.   Solenoids with square or rectangular cross section are common.

The magnetic fields of a solenoid, a coil and a single straight wire are shown in Figs. 40.4, 40.9, and 40.2, respectively.   In every case *magnetic lines of flux are continuous.   They never begin or end;* rather they follow closed curves which encircle the current-bearing conductors.   In this respect magnetic lines of force are different from electrical lines of force, which always begin and end on electric charges.

PROBLEMS

1. A long wire bearing a current of 7 amp lies perpendicular to a uniform magnetic field between the poles of a large magnet.   If 15 cm of the wire lie in the field and if the force on this length is 0.035 newton, find the magnetic intensity B.
Ans. 0.033 newton/amp-m

2. Find the force on 8 cm of conductor bearing a current of 3 amp if it lies perpendicular to a magnetic field of intensity 0.007 newton/amp-m.

3. Find the force on and the acceleration of an electron moving 3×10^7 m/sec at right angles to a magnetic field of intensity 0.0008 newton/amp-m in a television picture tube.   The charge on the electron is 1.6×10^{-19} coulomb and its mass is 9×10^{-31} kg.   *Ans.* 3.84×10^{-15} newton; 4.26×10^{15} m/sec^2

4. A rectangular galvanometer coil is 2 cm high, 1 cm long, and has 50 turns of wire.   Find its magnetic moment when it bears a current of 10^{-7} amp.

5. A coil of 20 turns of wire has an area of 2.5 cm^2.   It carries a current of 4×10^{-6} amp.   Find the magnetic moment of the coil.   If the magnetic moment is perpendicular to a magnetic field of intensity 0.12 newton/amp-m, calculate the torque on the coil.   *Ans.* 2×10^{-8} amp-m^2; 2.4×10^{-9} newton-m

6. A coil of magnetic moment 4×10^{-8} amp-m^2 experiences a torque of 6×10^{-9} newton-m when it is placed in a magnetic field with the magnetic moment normal to the field.   Find the magnetic intensity.

7. Find the magnetic intensity a distance of 6 cm from a long straight wire bearing a current of 15 amp.   *Ans.* 5×10^{-5} newton/amp-m

8. A long straight wire bears a current of 4 amp.   At what distance from the wire is the magnetic field 2×10^{-5} newton/amp-m?

9. Two straight, long, parallel wires are 8 cm apart.   A current of 5 amp flows through one wire and a current of 8 amp through the other.   If the two currents flow in the same direction, what is the magnetic intensity at a point midway between the wires?   Find the attractive force per meter of length between the wires.
Ans. 1.5×10^{-5} newton/amp-m; 1×10^{-4} newton/m

10. How many turns of wire must be placed on a solenoid 1.5 m long, in order that a current of 4 amp may produce a magnetic field of 0.003 newton/amp-m at its center?

11. A solenoid is 30 cm long.   It is wound with 6,000 turns of copper wire.   What current must be sent through the windings to produce a magnetic intensity of 0.005 newton/amp-m?   *Ans.* 0.199 amp

12. What is the intensity of the magnetic field in a coil of wire wound in the form of a solenoid having 200 turns to the centimeter when a current of 4 amp is flowing through the coil?

13. Find the magnetic intensity at the center of a circular coil of 40 turns of 5 cm radius when the coil bears a current of 6 amp.   *Ans.* 0.003 newton/amp-m

14. A current in a circular loop of wire with a diameter of 10 cm produces a field strength of 8×10^{-5} newton/amp-m at the center of the coil. What is the current?

15. A cylindrical solenoid of 3,600 turns, 15 cm in diameter and 180 cm long, is placed with its axis parallel to the lines of the earth's field. If the latter has an intensity of 2×10^{-5} newton/amp-m, what current must flow through the coil in order to make the magnetic field at its center zero? *Ans.* 0.008 amp

16. In two concentric solenoids the currents flow in opposite directions. The inner one has 300 turns per centimeter, and the outer one 160 turns per centimeter. What current in the outer one will be necessary in order to have the field at the center zero when the inner coil is carrying 4 amp?

17. A galvanometer has a moving coil with a resistance of 124 ohms and a sensitivity of 1 mm deflection for 10^{-7} amp. What shunt will be needed to produce 1 mm deflection for 0.001 amp in the main circuit? *Ans.* (124/9,999) ohm

18. A solenoid of 600 turns is wound on a cylinder 80 cm long and 1 cm in diameter. What is the magnetic field intensity near the center when there is a current of 0.20 amp?

19. The moving element of a voltmeter has a resistance of 5.0 ohms, and a full deflection is produced when 0.050 volt is applied to the coil. Calculate the series resistances needed to use the voltmeter for 3 volts full scale and for 150 volts, respectively. *Ans.* 295 ohms; 14,995 ohms

20. A milliammeter has a resistance of 1 ohm and its full-scale reading is 100 ma. Find the resistance of a shunt that must be used in order to convert it into an ammeter on which the full-scale reading is 10 amp.

21. A galvanometer of 12 ohms resistance requires a current of 0.0015 amp to produce a full-scale deflection. What resistance is required to convert this galvanometer into an ammeter reading 3 amp full scale? What resistance is required to convert this galvanometer to a voltmeter reading 5 volts full scale? *Ans.* (0.018/2.9985) ohm; 3,321 ohms

22. The full-scale reading of a certain voltmeter is 5 volts. It requires 15 ma to produce this deflection. What resistance must be inserted in series with this voltmeter in order that its full-scale reading may correspond to 500 volts?

23. The resistance of the coil of a moving-coil galvanometer is 12.5 ohms. It requires 0.00012 amp to produce a full-scale deflection in it. What resistance must be used as a shunt to transform it into an ammeter that gives a full-scale deflection when the current is 0.05 amp? *Ans.* 0.0301 ohm

24. The resistance of a certain ammeter is 0.008 ohm, and the full reading of its scale is 15 amp. What must be the resistance of a shunt for this ammeter in order that the full-scale reading may be 150 amp?

CHAPTER 41 ~~important~~

Magnets

41.1. The Magnetic Moment of a Magnet. In Chap. 39 we saw that a coil placed in a magnetic field of strength **B** with its magnetic moment **M** perpendicular to the field experiences a torque equal to BM. Similarly, a current-bearing solenoid placed in a magnetic field with its axis perpendicular to the field experiences a torque which is equal to the resultant of the torques acting on each of the turns of the solenoid. These turns can be regarded as a series of individual coaxial coils. The resulting magnetic moment of the solenoid is NIA, where N is the total number of turns, I the current, and A the cross-sectional area of the solenoid.

If we place a small bar magnet (magnetic needle) with its axis perpendicular to a magnetic field (Fig. 41.1), it experiences a torque in a direction such as to align the axis of the magnet with the direction of **B**. As defined in Sec. 40.5, the magnetic moment **M** is the ratio of the torque **L** to the field strength **B**. Since the *apparent* magnetic properties of the magnet are associated with the poles at the ends, it is often convenient to think of the torque as arising from the forces acting on the north and south poles, which are separated by a distance equal roughly to the length of the magnet l. Let us define the pole strength p of this magnetic needle as the ratio of the magnetic moment to the length.

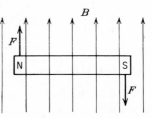

Fig. 41.1. A small bar magnet with its axis perpendicular to a uniform magnetic field is subject to a torque in a direction to align the magnet with the field.

$$p = \frac{M}{l} \qquad (41.1)$$

Since the dimensions of the magnetic moment are ampere-meters², the dimensions of pole strength are ampere-meters. The force **F** on a pole p placed in the magnetic field of strength **B** is given by

$$F = Bp \qquad (41.2)$$

487

A pole has a strength of one ampere-meter if the force acting on it is one newton when the pole is placed in a magnetic field of intensity one newton per ampere-meter.   Observe that the force on the north pole of the magnet is in the direction of **B** while the direction of the force on the south pole is opposite to that of **B**.

If the axis of the magnet makes an angle θ with the magnetic field, the torque is less than if the magnet were perpendicular to the field.   In general, the torque **L** is given by

$$L = BM \sin \theta = Bpl \sin \theta \qquad (41.3)$$

as can be seen from Fig. 41.2.

In many problems regarding magnets it is convenient to consider the forces and torques on the magnet as arising from the interaction between magnetic field

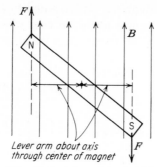

Lever arm about axis
through center of magnet

Fig. 41.2. A bar magnet with its axis making an angle θ with a uniform magnetic field.

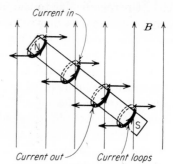

Fig. 41.3. The torque on a bar magnet can be considered to be the resultant of many torques exerted on small current loops.

and point poles.   However, it should be remembered that the pole picture is a simplication of the more general point of view that there are forces on current elements in magnetic fields.   The torque on the magnet of Fig. 41.2 can be explained in terms of torques acting on elementary current loops as is shown in the Fig. 41.3.   The magnetic moment **M** of the magnet is just that which would be produced by a current $I = M/A$ (where A is the cross-sectional area of the magnet) flowing as a current sheet around the magnet.   The point of view of the current loops is rigorous and universally acceptable, but for many problems the force-on-pole concept is simpler and more convenient.

Magnets never have single poles.   The magnetic field arises from currents and, as we have seen in Chap. 40, magnetic lines of force are always continuous.   The pole of a magnet is a region where a large fraction of lines of force enter or leave the magnet.   Since every line of force which enters a magnet also leaves, it is clear that no magnet can have a single pole.

41.2. Coulomb's Law.   When the poles of bar magnets are brought into the vicinity of one another, there are interactions between them.

Like poles repel one another and unlike poles attract. Coulomb studied the interaction between magnetic needles with small torsion balances and found that the force between two poles varies as the product of the pole strengths and inversely as the square of the distance between the poles.

$$F = k\,\frac{p_1 p_2}{r^2} \tag{41.4}$$

When the force is in newtons, pole strengths in ampere-meters, and r in meters, k is 10^{-7} newton/amp^2, the same constant which appears in Ampère's law.

Coulomb's law is applicable whenever one can regard the magnetic properties of the needle as concentrated in point poles. This, in turn, requires that the distance between the two magnets be substantially greater than the thickness of either magnet, since otherwise a pole of a magnet cannot be correctly approximated by a point pole. If one wishes to calculate the force which one magnetic needle exerts on another, it is ordinarily necessary to calculate not only the forces between nearest poles but also the forces between the other poles. The N pole of one magnet exerts a force on both the N and S poles of the second magnet; similarly the S pole exerts a force on both poles of the other magnet. Therefore, to calculate the total force exerted on one magnet by another, it is necessary to compute four forces and add them vectorially.

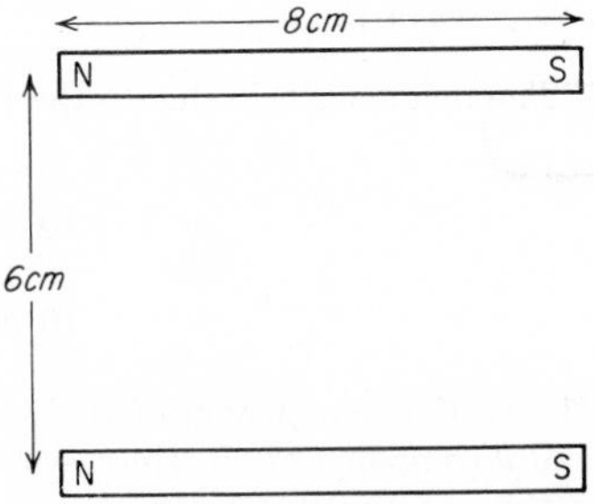

Fig. 41.4. It is possible to make one small magnet "float" above another.

Example. Two small identical magnets are 8 cm long and have pole strengths of 60 amp-m. When they are restrained so they cannot rotate, it is possible to make one "float" 6 cm above the other (Fig. 41.4). Find the force which the lower magnet exerts on the upper one (which is the weight of the upper magnet, of course).

$$F_{NN} = k\,\frac{p_1 p_2}{r^2} \qquad\qquad F_{NS} = 10^{-7}\frac{60 \times 60}{(0.1)^2}$$

$$= 10^{-7}\frac{60 \times 60}{(0.06)^2} \qquad = 0.036 \text{ newton}$$

$$= 0.100 \text{ newton}$$

Similarly $F_{SS} = 0.100$ newton and $F_{SN} = 0.036$ newton. The vertical component of F_{NS} is $0.036 \times 0.6 = 0.0216$ newton and the horizontal component is

$$0.036 \times 0.8 = 0.0288 \text{ newton}.$$

The horizontal component of F_{SN} exactly balances the horizontal component of F_{NS}. If we take the upward direction as positive, the vertical force on the upper magnet is given by

$$F = 0.100 + 0.100 - 0.0216 - 0.0216 = 0.1568 \text{ newton, or } 16 \text{ g-wt}$$

Any pole or group of poles has a magnetic field associated with it.   To determine the field intensity **B** at any point, we may imagine we bring a

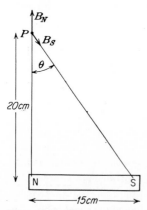

test pole p_t to the point in question and measure the force **F** on this pole.   The intensity **B** is given by $\mathbf{F}/p_t$.   If we wish to calculate the magnetic intensity due to any group of poles, we find the magnetic intensity which each pole would produce by itself and add all these fields together vectorially.   The magnetic field due to one pole p can be calculated readily by Coulomb's law.   The force on a test pole p_t at a distance r from the pole p is given by $F = pp_t/10^7r^2$ and

$$B = \frac{F}{p_t} = \frac{p}{10^7r^2} \qquad (41.5)$$

Fig. 41.5. The magnetic field at P is the resultant of the fields due to the two poles of the magnet.

Example. A magnet 15 cm long with poles of strength 250 amp-m lies on a table. Find the magnitude of the magnetic intensity B at a point P 20 cm directly above the N pole of the magnet (Fig. 41.5).

The magnetic field due to the N pole is given by

$$B_N = \frac{p_N}{10^7r^2} = \frac{250}{10^7(0.2)^2} = 6.25 \times 10^{-4} \text{ newton/amp-m}$$

$$B_S = \frac{p_S}{10^7r^2} = \frac{250}{10^7(0.25)^2} = 4.00 \times 10^{-4} \text{ newton/amp-m}$$

The vertical component of B_S is $B_S \cos\theta = 3.2 \times 10^{-4}$ newton/amp-m and the horizontal component is $B_S \sin\theta = 2.4 \times 10^{-4}$ newton/amp-m. The vertical component of the resultant intensity is

$(6.25 - 3.2) \times 10^{-4} = 3.05 \times 10^{-4}$

and the horizontal component is 2.4×10^{-4}.

The resultant B is

$\sqrt{(3.05)^2 + (2.4)^2} \times 10^{-4}$
$= 3.9 \times 10^{-4}$ newton/amp-m

41.3. The Magnetic Field of the Earth.

The usefulness of the compass as a device for determining direction arises from the fact that the earth has a

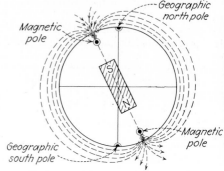

Fig. 41.6. The earth as a magnet.

magnetic field which aligns the compass needle. The earth's field is approximately that which would be obtained from a tremendous magnet (Fig. 41.6) near the center of the earth with its axis making an

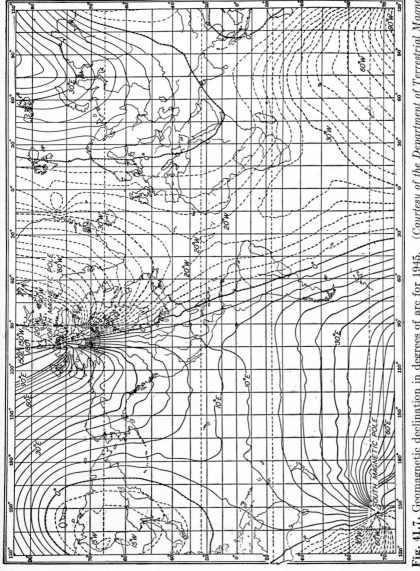

Fig. 41.7. Geomagnetic declination in degrees of are for 1945. (*Courtesy of the Department of Terrestrial Magnetism, Carnegie Institution of Washington.*)

angle of roughly 15° with the earth's axis of rotation.   (Of course, there is no such magnet buried in the earth!)   The south-seeking pole of the earth is located near Hudson Bay at approximately 94° west longitude, 73° north latitude, while the north-seeking pole is in Antarctica at approximately 82° east longitude, 72° south latitude.

In view of the fact that the earth's magnetic axis does not coincide with its axis of rotation, a compass needle points true north at relatively few regions on the earth's surface.   The angle between a free horizontal compass needle and true north is called the *angle of declination*.   Figure 41.7 shows the declination at various places in the United States.   A line on the earth's surface along which a compass needle points true north is called an *agonic line*.   At points east of the agonic line in the United States, the declination is west; at points west of the agonic line, the declination is east.   In New York City the declination is about 11.5°W, while in San Francisco it is roughly 18°E.

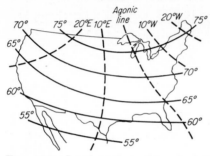

Fig. 41.8. Isoclinic lines (heavy) and isogonic lines (dashed) in the United States.

When a compass needle is free to orient itself along the lines of magnetic force, it is found that the needle points downward as well as to the north.   The angle between the free magnetic needle and the horizontal plane is called the *inclination* or *angle of dip*.   Figure 41.8 shows lines of constant dip, which are called *isoclinic* lines.   The inclination in various parts of the United States varies from about 50 to 80°.

The earth's magnetic field is a relatively weak one.   The horizontal component varies from approximately 25×10^{-6} newton/amp-m in the southern part of the United States to roughly 15×10^{-6} newton/amp-m in the northern part.   The vertical component varies similarly from about 40×10^{-6} to 55×10^{-6} newton/amp-m as one goes from south to north.

The magnetic isogonic and isoclinic lines, shown in Figs. 41.7 and 41.8 as smooth regular lines, actually have many local irregularities and variations.   One would expect the magnetic lines of the earth to be significantly altered by large deposits of iron ores and other magnetic materials, and indeed they are.   One method of prospecting involves the careful measurement of the earth's magnetic field over large areas.   The vertical component of the earth's field sometimes increases sharply above a body of magnetic ore and is often weaker than normal above an oil deposit.

The magnetic field at a given point varies from time to time during a day.   Further, there are sporadic variations which can be correlated with sunspots and solar flares and with the northern lights and similar phenomena on the earth.   The earth's magnetic field is not static.   Over a period of years the declination at a given point changes substantially.   Since 1580 it has varied between 11°E and 24°W at London.

41.4. Magnetic Materials.   Relatively few materials possess strong magnetic properties.   Iron, nickel, and cobalt are the only common elements which ordinarily interact appreciably with a small magnet.   Gadolinium and liquid oxygen are also strongly magnetic; so are a substantial number of alloys.   All materials which interact strongly with magnets are classed as *ferromagnetic*.

For the vast majority of materials the magnetic effects are exceedingly small.   However, when they are carefully studied in a strong nonuniform magnetic field, each material falls into one of two classes: Some become very feebly magnetized in the direction of the field.   If a needle of such a material is placed in the field, it aligns itself with the field.   Such materials are called *paramagnetic* (*para* means "parallel").   Examples are palladium, manganese, and many metallic salts.   Other materials become very feebly magnetized in the direction opposite to the field.   A needle of bismuth aligns itself at right angles to a strong nonuniform magnetic field.   Such a material is called *diamagnetic* (*dia* means "across").   Most elements and chemical compounds are slightly diamagnetic.   Bismuth is the most diamagnetic element.

For most practical purposes paramagnetic and diamagnetic materials can be regarded as magnetically inactive.   They are not useful for magnets.   Ferromagnetic materials are of very great practical importance and utility.   They are vital for transformers, electric motors, electric generators, and electromagnets.

41.5. Origin of Ferromagnetism.   Why some materials are magnetic and others are not is a complex question.   However, a qualitative answer can be given in fairly simple terms.   Magnetic effects are always associated with moving electric charges.   As long ago as 1820, Ampère suggested that within magnetized iron there are circulating currents.   It is obvious that these currents cannot be due to flow of charges around the circumference of the iron core, since such currents would necessarily dissipate heat in the iron as a result of the resistance.   Instead, the currents are due to the motions of the atomic electrons.   The electrons associated with any given atom are in constant motion and a moving charge always produces a magnetic field.

An electron may establish a magnetic field for either of two reasons.   First, we may picture the electron as traveling around the nucleus of the atom in an orbit analogous to the orbit in which the earth rotates about the sun.   Second, the electron may be thought of as revolving about its own axis, much as the earth revolves once each day about its axis.   A single electron may establish a magnetic field by virtue of its orbital and its spin motions.   In almost all atoms the *net* effects of the magnetic field set up by various electrons is exceedingly small or zero, because the magnetic field set up by one electron counterbalances the fields set up by other electrons.   However, in iron, nickel, and cobalt the magnetic fields due to the spinning of the electrons do not cancel for certain of the electrons in an unfilled (M) shell.   In these metals, individual atoms act as tiny magnets.

It must be emphasized that, although magnetic properties are associated with individual atoms of iron, not all materials containing iron are magnetic.   The reason is that in the chemical combination the sharing of electrons may give rise to a situation in which the magnetic fields add to zero.   Whereas many of the compounds and alloys of iron are magnetic, a number, including stainless steel, are not.   On the other hand, the Heusler alloys, containing aluminum, copper, and manganese, are ferromagnetic although none of the component elements are.

41.6. Magnetization by Induction.   In a ferromagnetic material it is sometimes individual atoms which are the elementary magnets, sometimes combinations or groups of atoms.   Although the net magnetic field outside a piece of unmagnetized soft iron is zero, over small volumes of the order 10^{-6} cm^3 most of the elementary magnets are aligned with their N poles in the same direction.   There is no field outside the iron because these tiny *domains* are oriented at random.   If this iron is placed in a magnetic field, it is magnetized *by induction*.   This magnetization occurs through two processes: (1) Domains which are magnetized in the direction of the inducing field grow at the expense of neighboring domains which are magnetized in less favorable directions.   (2) The direction of magnetization of an entire domain may be shifted by the simultaneous rotation of the elementary magnets which make up the domain.

Further evidence confirming that the nature of the magnetizing process is the alignment of elementary magnets are the following observations:

1. When a piece of soft iron lies in a weak field, its magnetization is increased by tapping the iron.   Tapping gives the elementary magnets a better chance to align themselves with the magnetizing field.   On the other hand, if a piece of material is already magnetized and is no longer in a field, tapping usually disaligns some of the domains and thereby reduces the strength of the magnet.

2. Increasing the temperature of the magnet tends to demagnetize it, because giving additional kinetic energy to the molecules by thermal agitation produces the same effects as tapping or dropping the magnet. Iron heated above 760°C loses its magnetic properties.   Indeed, all magnetic materials have a temperature above which they lose their magnetism.   The temperature at which the magnetic properties of a given material disappear is called the *Curie point* for that material.

3. If a long permanent magnet is cut into two equal shorter pieces, the magnetized domains remain aligned.   There are now two magnets, each half as long as the original.   The pole strength of each remaining magnet is roughly equal to that of the original magnet.   The reason that magnetic effects seem to be concentrated at the ends or poles is readily

understood when one remembers that throughout the body of the magnet the arrangement of elementary magnets (Fig. 41.9) leaves a N pole close to each S pole so that their effects cancel one another. At one end of the magnet there is a concentration of elementary N poles and at the other end of S poles. Consequently, the magnetic effects are strong at the ends.

When the N pole of a bar magnet is brought near an unmagnetized needle, the elementary magnets in the needle align themselves in the

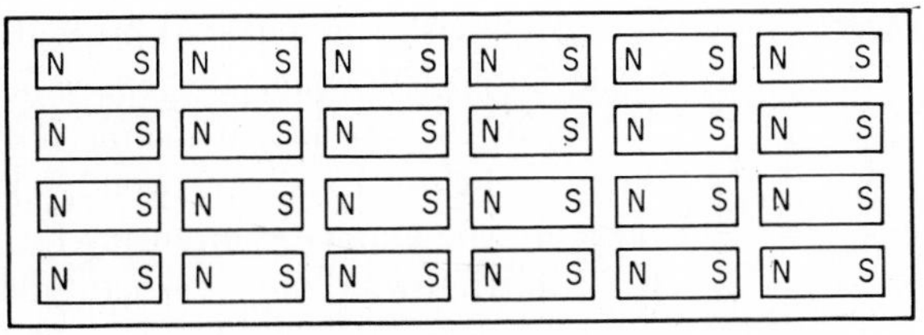

N	S	N	S	N	S	N	S	N	S	N	S
N	S	N	S	N	S	N	S	N	S	N	S
N	S	N	S	N	S	N	S	N	S	N	S
N	S	N	S	N	S	N	S	N	S	N	S

Fig. 41.9. Arrangement of elementary magnets in an idealized magnet.

field. Thus, a S pole is produced near the N pole of the bar magnet. Since the attractive force between the S pole of the needle and the N pole of the bar magnet is greater than the repulsive force between the two N poles, there is a net attractive force. It should be noted that *this attractive force arises only in a nonuniform magnetic field.* In a uniform field the forces on opposite poles are equal and opposite.

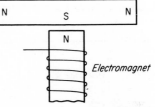

Fig. 41.10. A magnet (above) with two N poles and a single S pole.

While most common magnets have two poles, it is entirely possible for a magnet to have three or more. For example, if the middle of a piece of soft iron is brought up to the strong N pole of an electromagnet, it develops a N pole at both ends and a stronger S pole at the middle (Fig. 41.10). When steel gas or water pipes are explored with a small compass needle, several N and S poles are often found along a few feet of the pipe. Such poles are called *consequent* poles.

41.7. Permeability and the Magnetizing Field. If a long solenoid is bent in the form of a circle until the two ends touch (Fig. 41.11), we have a ring solenoid or *toroid*. Consider a toroid which has n turns per meter of length and bears a current I. Bending a long solenoid to form a toroid does not change the magnetic field inside; thus the magnetic field in a toroid is given by $B = 4\pi nI/10^7$, according to Eq. (40.10).

Suppose that the entire core of the toroid is now filled with iron, and a current I sent through the windings. How is the value of **B** inside the toroid affected by adding this iron?   A measurement[1] of **B** shows that it is now several hundred times greater than before the iron was added.

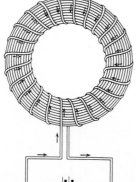

The magnetic field in the iron may be written

$$B = \frac{4\pi K_m n I}{10^7} \qquad (41.6)$$

where K_m is called the *relative permeability*. For any material it is the ratio of the magnetic intensity with the material present to the magnetic intensity when the space is evacuated. If we fill the toroid with some other material, such as bismuth, silver, wood, or nickel and measure the magnetic intensity for a given current in the windings, we can determine the relative permeability of each.   Table 1 shows the relative permeabilities of several materials.

Fig. 41.11. A toroid or ring solenoid. The magnetic lines of force are entirely within the toroid.

Those with relative permeability less than unity are diamagnetic, those with permeability slightly greater than unity are paramagnetic, and those with permeabilities much larger than unity are ferromagnetic.

Table 1

RELATIVE PERMEABILITIES OF VARIOUS SUBSTANCES

(Vacuum = 1.000 by definition)

Material	Relative permeability	Material	Maximum relative permeability
Bismuth......... ...	0.99983	Cobalt...............	250
Silver................	0.99998	Nickel................	600
Copper...............	0.99999	Mild steel............	2,000
Water................	0.99999	Iron (0.2% impurity)....	5,000
Air..................	1.0000004	Silicon iron*..........	7,000
Aluminum..............	1.00002	Permalloy............	100,000
		Supermalloy..........	1,000,000

* Used in power transformers.

The magnetic intensity in a toroid depends on two factors: (1) the properties of the medium in the toroid and (2) the influences which are

[1] The measurement of **B** in the solid material may be made without disturbing the material in any way by wrapping a few turns of wire around the solenoid as indicated in Fig. 42.3 and observing the induced emf as the field is changed.   The operation of such a measuring device, known as a fluxmeter, is described in detail in Chap. 42.

inducing the magnetization of the material.   In this case the inducing field is provided by the current through the turns of the toroid.   In other situations it may be provided by magnetic poles or other kinds of current distributions.   It is called the *magnetizing field* and is represented by **H**.   In the special case of the uniformly filled toroid we have continuous magnetization and no poles; the magnetizing force is the product of the current and the number of turns per unit length; thus we have

$$H = nI \tag{41.7}$$

If nI is replaced by H in Eq. (41.6), we obtain

$$B = \frac{4\pi}{10^7} K_m H = \mu H \tag{41.8}$$

Here μ stands for $4\pi K_m/10^7$.   It is called the *absolute permeability* of the material Since the relative permeability K_m of a vacuum is unity, the absolute permeability is $4\pi/10^7$ for a vacuum (and for air for practical purposes).   It is usually represented by μ_0 and called the *permeability of free space*.

The reason that **B** is different inside the toroid when it is filled with iron is the magnetization of the iron which occurs when we apply the magnetizing field. We have seen (Sec. 41.1) that the magnetic moment M of a bar magnet of cross-sectional area A and length l is that which would exist if we have a current M/A flowing around the surface, i.e., a surface current M/lA per unit length.   The ratio M/lA is the magnetic moment per unit volume which we shall indicate by M_v.   With magnetic material in the toroid the total magnetic intensity **B** comes from two contributions; $\mu_0 H$ due to the conduction currents in the windings and $\mu_0 M_v$ due to the internal currents in the magnetic material.

$$\mathbf{B} = \mu_0(\mathbf{H} + \mathbf{M}_v) \tag{41.9}$$

In an *ideal* magnetic material $\mathbf{M}_v$ is proportional to the magnetizing field **H**. From the equation $\mathbf{B} = \mu\mathbf{H} = \mu_0(\mathbf{H} + \mathbf{M}_v)$, we obtain the relation

$$\mu = \mu_0\left(1 + \frac{M_v}{H}\right) = \mu_0 K_m \tag{41.10}$$

For a material such as permalloy, which has K_m of the order of 100,000, this equation shows that $\mathbf{M}_v$, the magnetic moment per unit volume due to the "internal currents," is about 99,999 times as great as the magnetizing field due to currents in the external windings.

Only when $\mathbf{M}_v$ is proportional to **H** is the permeability μ a constant.   We shall see in Sec. 41.8 that for ferromagnetic materials μ is not constant over any large range of values of **H**.

If we solve Eq. (41.9) for **H**, we obtain

$$\mathbf{H} = \frac{\mathbf{B}}{\mu_0} - \mathbf{M}_v \tag{41.11}$$

This is the defining equation[1] for **H** in the general case.

[1] **B**, **H** and $\mathbf{M}_v$ are all vectors, and do not always have the same direction.

41.8. The Magnetization Curve and Hysteresis. If a toroid is wound around an iron core and a fluxmeter is provided to measure changes in magnetic intensity in the core, we can measure **B** as a function of **H** by starting with an unmagnetized core and no current in the windings and increasing the current in the windings step by step. If this is done, we obtain a so-called magnetization curve in which the magnetic intensity B is plotted as a function of the magnetizing field $H = nI$. For a typical iron sample, a curve similar to that of Fig. 41.12a is obtained.

The permeability μ is the ratio of B to H by definition. Figure 41.12b shows how μ varies with H for the particular magnetization curve of Fig. 41.12a. Observe that the permeability is not constant for a ferromagnetic substance, as it is for an ideal magnetic material. Rather it varies over a considerable range. It is not difficult to understand qualitatively

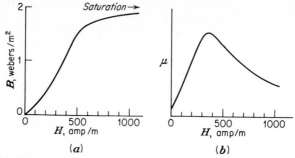

Fig. 41.12. (a) The magnetic intensity as a function of the magnetizing field and (b) the permeability as a function of magnetizing field for a sample initially unmagnetized.

why this is true. The iron core is composed of a large number of magnetic domains originally oriented at random. When a tiny current is passed through the windings, the magnetizing field H has a small effect on these domains compared with the influence of neighboring domains; therefore relatively small changes in magnetization occur. As the current is increased, the more favorably aligned domains grow at the expense of the others. The number of elementary magnetic dipoles oriented in the direction of the magnetizing field increases rapidly as is shown by the steep portion of the magnetization curve. Once most of the elementary magnets are aligned, the region of "hard magnetization" begins. Here the magnetizations of the unaligned domains undergo rotations which bring them into more exact alignment with the applied field. When essentially all the elementary magnets are aligned, the iron is said to be *saturated*. From this point on, increases in H result in small increases in B. When the iron has become saturated, the permeability (B/H) falls off rapidly as H is increased.

If one observes a portion of the magnetization curve with instruments of great sensitivity, he finds that the curve is not perfectly smooth but that it is made up of a number of tiny jumps, called *Barkhausen steps*, which are due to the fact that a large number of neighboring elementary magnets along a domain boundary align themselves with the applied field simultaneously, thereby producing sharp little jumps in the magnetization.

Although this picture of magnetism is a simplified one, it does present the qualitative features in reasonable perspective. During magnetization the sizes of domains change and domains are reoriented. There may even be an observable change in the length of the magnet. Such a change in length that takes place during magnetization is known as *magnetostriction*. Magnetostriction oscillators are used to produce sound waves of very high frequency, particularly in liquid mediums.

If an iron core is saturated and the magnetizing field is removed, the magnetization does not fall to zero, because the magnetic domains have been aligned by the magnetization process and help to keep one another

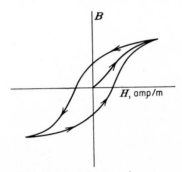

Fig. 41.13. A hysteresis curve.

aligned. If one wishes to demagnetize the specimen completely, a magnetizing field in the opposite direction must be applied. If one magnetizes a specimen first in one direction and then in another, the relationship between B and H is shown in the curve of Fig. 41.13, which is called a *hysteresis curve*.

If a material is good for permanent magnets, it must have a very broad hysteresis loop, since one wants to have a high retention of magnetism when the magnetizing field is removed. Such a sample of material would not be good for an electromagnet, which should lose its magnetic properties when the magnetizing field is eliminated. Figure 41.14 shows a hysteresis loop for a material which would be suitable for a permanent magnet and another which would be satisfactory for an electromagnet. In a-c transformers, motors, etc., one ordinarily desires a magnetic material with a hysteresis loop of small area. The reason is that it takes energy to reverse the direction of the magnetization. The area of the hysteresis loop is a measure of the energy lost per cycle per unit volume of the material.   A transformer made of steel with a broad hysteresis loop would be unsatisfactory because of the large energy losses required in magnetizing and demagnetizing the iron many times each second.

Soft iron demagnetizes rapidly when the magnetizing field is removed. Such iron is desirable for electromagnets and transformers.   On the other hand, the alloy *alnico*, made of aluminum, nickel, and cobalt steel, is particularly high in its retentivity and therefore makes a fine permanent magnet.

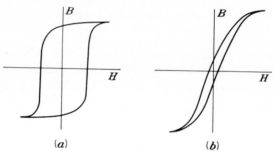

Fig. 41.14. Hysteresis curves for (*a*) a material good for permanent magnets and (*b*) a material suitable for a power transformer.

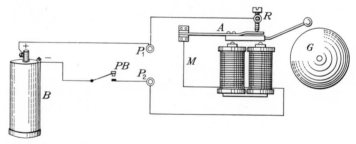

Fig. 41.15. Electromagnet in a doorbell.

41.9. Applications of Electromagnets.   If a solenoid is wound around a soft-iron core, the iron becomes strongly magnetized when a current is passed through the solenoid and loses most of its magnetism when the current is stopped. There are many uses for electromagnets.   Large ones can pick up rails and operate switches on railroads as well as lift and move scrap iron and other magnetic materials.   At the other extreme small ones have been developed for extracting particles of iron from the eye and to open or close switches in telephone and automobile circuits.

A common use of electromagnetism is in the doorbell.   Here a soft-iron vane *A* (Fig. 41.15) is attracted by the electromagnet when the switch *PB* is closed. When the iron moves toward the poles of the electromagnet, the clapper strikes the bell and the connection at *R* is broken by the movement of the iron vane. The current ceases and spring action moves the vane *A* back toward its original position.   Contact at *R* is reestablished, the electromagnet is activated once more, and another cycle begins. The same basic idea is also utilized in the electric horn except that a diaphragm is set into vibration instead of a clapper.

PROBLEMS

1. The magnetic declination in Oregon is 20°E. How far from a true north course would a flier be after traveling 100 miles following the compass without making a correction for declination? Would he be east or west of his course?

Ans. 34.2 miles east

2. A magnet has a winding 40 cm long, with 80 turns to the centimeter. What is H near the center of the winding if the current is 4 amp?

3. Two magnetic poles have strengths of 40 and 90 amp-m, respectively. At what distance in air will the force of attraction between them be 10^{-3} newton? *Ans.* 0.6 m

4. A long bar of cobalt steel with a mass of 35 g when placed horizontally over a similar bar, both being equally magnetized, remains suspended at a distance of 0.8 cm above it. What is the pole strength at each end of each bar? (10.5)

5. At a place where the horizontal component of the earth's field is 2×10^{-5} newton/amp-m, a bar magnet 10 cm long with a pole strength of 3.6 amp-m is placed horizontally at right angles with the earth's field, with its N pole pointing toward the west. Find the direction and intensity of the field at a point 10 cm west of the N pole of the magnet. *Ans.* 3.36×10^{-5} newton/amp-m 36.5°N of W

6. A bar magnet 12 cm long and with a pole strength of 4.8 amp-m is placed horizontally at right angles to the earth's magnetic field with its N pole pointing west. Find the intensity and direction of the magnetic field at a point 20 cm west of the N pole. Take the horizontal component of the earth's magnetic field as 2×10^{-5} newton/amp-m.

7. The poles of a magnet are 20 cm apart and each has a strength of 60 amp-m. What is the magnitude of the magnetic intensity at a point that is 15 cm from one pole and 25 cm from the other pole? *Ans.* 2.22×10^{-4} newton/amp-m

8. A N pole of 15 amp-m is placed at a distance of 12 cm from a S pole of 60 amp-m. How far from the N pole, on a line drawn through the two poles, will the combined field be zero?

9. Find the force on a pole of 120 amp-m placed at the center of a circular loop with a radius of 8 cm when a current of 5 amp is flowing through the loop.

Ans. 0.0047 newton

10. A bar magnet is 10 cm long, and each pole has a strength of 25 amp-m. Find the intensity of the magnetic field at a point 20 cm from the S pole, the distance from the pole to be measured at right angles to the axis of the magnet.

11. A magnet with poles of 48 amp-m separated by a distance of 5 cm is placed in a uniform field with an intensity of 0.3 newton/amp-m, so that the magnet is at right angles to the lines of force. What torque does the field exert on the magnet?

Ans. 0.72 newton-m

12. What is the intensity of the magnetic field at a point 50 cm from the center of a magnet that is 12 cm long? The pole strength of the magnet is 160 amp-m and the point lies on the perpendicular bisector of the line joining the poles.

13. What torque is necessary to hold the axis of a magnet at an angle of 60°with the magnetic meridian where the horizontal component of the earth's magnetic field is 2×10^{-5} newton/amp-m? The length of the magnet is 20 cm and its pole strength is 40 amp-m. *Ans.* 1.39×10^{-4} newton-m

14. A magnet has a pole strength of 35 amp-m. It is placed at right angles to the earth's magnetic field of 2×10^{-5} newton/amp-m, and a torque of 7×10^{-5} newton-m acts on it. Find the distance between the poles.

15. A solenoid that is 60 cm long is wound with 1,200 turns of copper wire. An iron rod having a relative permeability of 450 is placed along the axis of the solenoid. What is the magnetic intensity in the rod when a current of 1.5 amp is flowing through the turns of wire in the solenoid? What is the magnetizing force?

Ans. 1.7 newton/amp-m; 3,000 amp-turns/m

16. An iron ring has a cross section of 0.6 cm² and a diameter of 18 cm. It is wound with 450 turns of copper wire. If the iron in the core has a relative permeability of 650, what is the magnetic intensity in the iron when a current of 2 amp flows through the windings?

17. An iron anchor ring is wound with a solenoid having 800 turns. If the current in the solenoid is 0.1 amp and the relative permeability of the iron core is 250, what is the magnetic induction *B*, assuming that the toroid has a cross section of 12 cm² and a mean diameter of 40 cm? What is the magnetizing force *H*?

Ans. 0.02 newton/amp-m; 63.6 amp-turns/m

Induced Electromotive Forces

42.1. The Discovery of Induced Emfs. The discovery by Oersted in 1819 that a current has an associated magnetic field led a number of physicists to search for some means by which a magnetic field might produce a current. The first observation of such a phenomenon was made in 1830 by Joseph Henry. He used a horseshoe-shaped electromagnet around which he wound a second coil, the terminals of which were connected to a galvanometer (Fig. 42.1).

Henry found that when the current of the electromagnet is changed, either increased or decreased, there is a deflection of the galvanometer coil. When the current in the electromagnet is steady, there is no current through the galvanometer. When the current in the magnet is turned on, the deflection of the galvanometer is in one direction; when the current is stopped, the deflection is in the opposite direction.

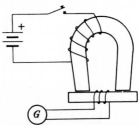

Fig. 42.1. Schematic diagram of apparatus used by Henry in discovering electromagnetic induction.

Several months later Michael Faraday independently discovered the deflection of a galvanometer connected to one coil when the current in an adjacent coil was started or stopped. Faraday published his findings first and is therefore usually credited with the discovery.

Faraday made a thorough study of the phenomenon. He found that the galvanometer in series with the second coil deflected not only when the current in the first coil was started and stopped, but also when the first coil carried a steady current and was moved nearer to or farther from the second. He brought a magnet near the second coil and then withdrew it. The galvanometer needle deflected during the motion of the magnet. When the north pole of a magnet was brought near the coil, the current was in one direction. When this pole was withdrawn, the current was in the opposite direction. If a south pole was brought

503

near the coil, the deflection was in the same direction as when the north pole was withdrawn. Whenever the magnetic lines of force linking the second coil were changed, there was an induced emf which produced a current through the galvanometer. This phenomenon is called *electromagnetic induction*. To develop quantitative relations between change in magnetic field and induced emf, we must become familiar with the meaning of the term *magnetic flux*.

42.2. Magnetic Flux—The Weber. Consider an area A (Fig. 42.2a) with its plane perpendicular to a uniform magnetic field of intensity B. The magnetic flux Φ through this area is defined to be the product of B and A.

$$\Phi = BA \tag{42.1}$$

The flux Φ is given in *webers* when B is in newtons per ampere-meter and A is in square meters. The weber is thus dimensionally equivalent

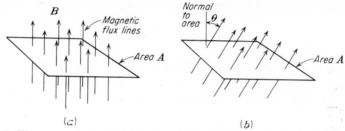

Fig. 42.2. The magnetic flux linking an area is the product of the area and the component of the magnetic intensity perpendicular to the area.

to the newton-meter per ampere. It is named in honor of W. E. Weber (1804–1891), German physicist.

In many situations it is easier to measure the flux through a coil than it is to measure B directly. If Φ and the area are known, the average value of B is given by Φ/A webers/m². (The weber per square meter and the newton per ampere-meter are equivalent units. Sometimes it is convenient to express B in webers per square meter; other times in newtons per ampere-meter.)

If B is not perpendicular to the plane of the area through which the flux is desired, $\Phi = BA \cos \theta$, where θ is the angle between B and the normal to the area (Fig. 42.2b). When B is not constant over the area, Eq. (42.1) is still applicable if we take the *average* flux density for B.

An alternative point of view toward flux was developed by Faraday. We have seen in Sec. 40.3 that a magnetic field may be represented by drawing lines of force. If we draw many lines of force in regions where the field is strong and correspondingly fewer where the field is weak, we have a plot which shows not only the direction of the magnetic field at various points but also its intensity.   If we agree to limit the number of lines of force so that we draw one line per square meter where **B** is 1 w/m², two lines per square meter where **B** is 2 w/m², etc., the number of lines through any large area is just equal to the magnetic flux through that area.   Let us call lines drawn according to this convention lines of flux to distinguish them from lines of *force*, which give only the direction of the field.   In terms of this physical picture, the *flux* through any area is equal to the number of *flux lines* which pass through the area.

42.3. Faraday's Law of Electromagnetic Induction.   Faraday found experimentally that the magnitude of the induced emf in a coil was directly proportional to the rate at which the flux linking the coil changed.

$$e = -N \frac{\Delta\Phi}{\Delta t} \qquad (42.2)$$

where N is the number of turns in the coil and $\Delta\Phi$ is the change in flux occurring in the time Δt.   The emf e† is given in volts when $\Delta\Phi/\Delta t$ is in webers per second.   Actually an emf $\Delta\Phi/\Delta t$ is induced in each turn of the coil.   The N turns are connected in series; consequently, the total emf in the coil is N times that induced in a single loop.   The significance of the minus sign is discussed in Sec. 42.5.

42.4. The Fluxmeter.   In Sec. 41.7 it was assumed that we can measure **B** inside a toroid without cutting any holes in the material.   We are now in a position to see how this can be done.   Consider the iron-filled toroid shown in Fig. 42.3.   Assume the iron is originally unmagnetized and the current in the winding is zero.   If N turns of wire are wound around this toroid and are connected to a suitable galvanometer, we can measure **B** as follows: We pass a small current through the toroid windings.

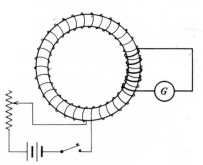

Fig. 42.3. A toroid filled with iron with a fluxmeter to measure changes in the magnetic flux.

This changes the magnetic intensity in the iron from zero to some value **B**.   If A is the cross-sectional area of the iron core, the flux in the iron goes from zero to BA in a time t.   According to Faraday's law of induction, there is an induced emf e in the fluxmeter windings given by

$$e = \frac{-N\Delta\Phi}{\Delta t} = \frac{-NAB}{t}$$

There is a current in the fluxmeter given by $i = e/R = NAB/Rt$.   It follows that $it = NAB/R$.   Now it is just the charge q passing through the fluxmeter.

† Note that we have used e rather than $\mathcal{E}$ to indicate the induced emf in this case. In general, we use $\mathcal{E}$ and I to represent constant values and the lower-case letters e and i to indicate emfs and currents which are varying in time.

If we use a suitable galvanometer, we obtain a deflection proportional to this charge and we can measure q. If we know q, N, and A, we can calculate **B**.

42.5. Lenz's Law. The direction of the induced emf is readily predicted by an application of a rule due to Lenz. *The direction of an induced emf is always such that any current it produces opposes through its magnetic effects the change inducing the emf.*

To illustrate Lenz's law, consider an N pole that is being pushed (Fig. 42.4) toward a coil. The current induced in the coil is in such a direc-

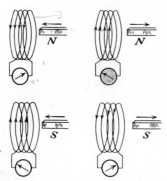

tion that its magnetic field opposes the motion of the magnet. In this case, it is directed toward the north pole of the magnet, which requires that the current be counterclockwise. When the N pole is withdrawn, the directions of induced emf and current reverse, since the induced magnetic effect opposes the act which creates it.

Actually, Lenz's law represents one of the many forms in which conservation of energy appears in physics. That this law follows from the conservation of energy may be seen by this reasoning: Changing a magnetic field induces an emf and a corresponding current if there is a conducting path. Thus, electrical energy appears as

Fig. 42.4. The induced emf is such that the resulting current opposes by its magnetic field the act which induces the emf.

the result of this act. It is the work done against the opposing magnetic field which is transformed into electrical energy.

42.6. Motional Electromotive Force. If a wire of length **l** is moved with a velocity **v** perpendicular to a magnetic field of flux density **B** (Fig. 42.5), there is induced in this wire an emf

$$\mathcal{E} = vBl \qquad (42.3)$$

The origin of this emf is in the force exerted on each individual charge moving through the magnetic field. This force we saw in Sec. 40.4 is qvB. The electric field strength $E = F/q = vB$. The potential difference across a wire of length l is given by the product of the field strength and the length.

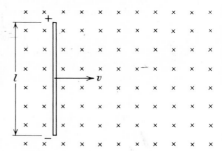

Fig. 42.5. A motional emf is induced by moving a wire through a magnetic field. In this case **B** is into the paper and the upper end of the wire becomes positive.

Therefore, $\mathcal{E} = El = vBl$. (In the event that **B**, **v**, and **l** are not mutually perpendicular, $\mathcal{E}$ is numerically equal to the volume of a parallelepiped with sides in the directions of **B**, **v**, and **l** and of lengths proportional to the magnitudes of the respective quantities.)

In electric generators the emf is ordinarily induced by moving wires through a magnetic field at a high speed. The direction of the induced emf is such that the force on the resulting current opposes the movement of the wire across the field. From this it follows immediately that the magnetic field of the current produced by the induced emf strengthens the field on the side toward which the wire is moving and weakens it on the opposite side. Once we know the direction of the magnetic field associated with the induced current, we can let the fingers of the right hand curve along the lines of force and the right thumb then points in the direction of the induced emf (see Sec. 40.2). In the situation shown in Fig. 42.6 the induced emf produces a current into the paper when the wire is moved as indicated.

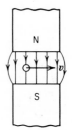

Fig. 42.6. The emf induced produces a current into the paper when the wire is moved to the right.

42.7. Mutual Inductance. Consider the neighboring circuits of Fig. 42.7. When the key is pressed, the current in coil A rises and the associated magnetic lines of flux produce a change in the magnetic flux linking coil B. As a consequence, there is an induced emf and a resulting current in coil B. The current in B lasts only while the current in A is changing. In such a circuit, coil A is called the primary and coil B the secondary. When the current in the primary is increasing, the

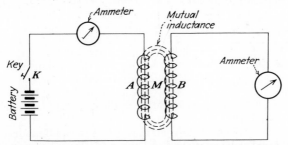

Fig. 42.7. Mutual inductance between two circuits.

induced emf in the secondary produces a current which by its magnetic effect opposes the rise of current in the primary. Note that it is always the *change in current in the primary* which is opposed, not the current itself. Thus, when the current is at its maximum value and is being reduced, the magnetic effect due to the induced current in coil B is such as to keep the primary current at its previous value. The effect which results in an emf being produced in one circuit due to a changing current in another circuit is called *mutual induction*.

The emf e_2 induced in the secondary coil is directly proportional to the rate of change of current in the primary.

$$e_2 = M \frac{\Delta i_1}{\Delta t} \tag{42.4}$$

where the constant M is called the *coefficient of mutual inductance*.

From this equation we may define the *coefficient of mutual inductance between two circuits* as *the ratio of the emf induced in the second circuit to the rate of change of current with time in the first circuit*. When an emf of 1 volt is induced in a secondary coil by a current change of 1 amp/sec in the primary, the coefficient of mutual inductance is said to be 1 *henry*.

Example. The mutual inductance between two circuits is 0.4 henry. Find the emf induced in the secondary at an instant when the current is changing at the rate of 90 amp/sec in the primary.

$$e_2 = M \frac{\Delta i_1}{\Delta t}$$
$$= 0.4 \times 90$$
$$= 36 \text{ volts}$$

42.8. The Induction Coil. An illustration of mutual inductance is found in the induction coil, which is constructed as shown in Fig. 42.8. There is an iron core around which is wound a primary coil made of a few turns of heavy copper wire. Insulated from this primary coil is the secondary coil, which is wound on the outside of the primary. The secondary contains a large number of turns of fine, well-insulated wire. By making or breaking the current in the primary, an emf is induced in the secondary. In order to make and break the current in the primary, an interrupter similar to that of the doorbell (Sec. 41.9) is connected in the primary circuit.

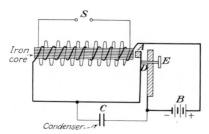

Fig. 42.8. The induction coil.

When the primary circuit is broken, the current is rapidly reduced to zero and an emf is induced in the secondary. This emf is large because the number of turns in the secondary is very large and the time in which the primary current is stopped is short. To get the greatest induced emf, the primary current must be stopped as quickly as possible. To effect this, a capacitor C is connected across the gap in the primary. It acts as a storage place into which the charge surges when the circuit is broken. Without this capacitor an arc would be established at the contacts when the circuit is opened. Such an arc pits the contacts and results in a slower stopping of primary current. There is also an emf induced in the secondary when the primary current is rising. This emf is much smaller because the time required for the current to build up to its maximum value is long compared with the time required to stop the current. The primary current and the induced emf in the secondary are plotted as a function of time in Fig. 42.9.

The spark coil of an automobile is an induction coil similar to the one just described except that, instead of using a mechanical vibrator to open and close the primary circuit, there is a cam on the distributor shaft which opens the

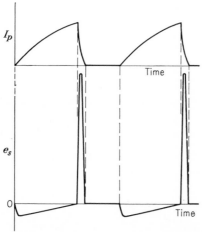

Fig. 42.9. Current I_p in the primary coil and emf e_s induced in the secondary as a function of time for an induction coil.

"points" at the instant a high potential is needed to make a spark between the terminals of a spark plug. The secondary potential is many thousand volts, although only 12 volts are available in the primary.

42.9. Self-inductance. When the current through a circuit such as that in Fig. 42.10 is changing, the magnetic flux linking this same circuit is also changing. Consequently, there is an induced emf e proportional to $\Delta\Phi/\Delta t$, which in turn is proportional to the rate of change of current with time $\Delta i/\Delta t$.

$$e = -L\frac{\Delta i}{\Delta t} \qquad (42.5)$$

where L is a constant known as the *coefficient of self-inductance*. The negative sign appears in Eq. (42.5) because, by Lenz's law, the direction of the induced emf is always such as to oppose the change in current.

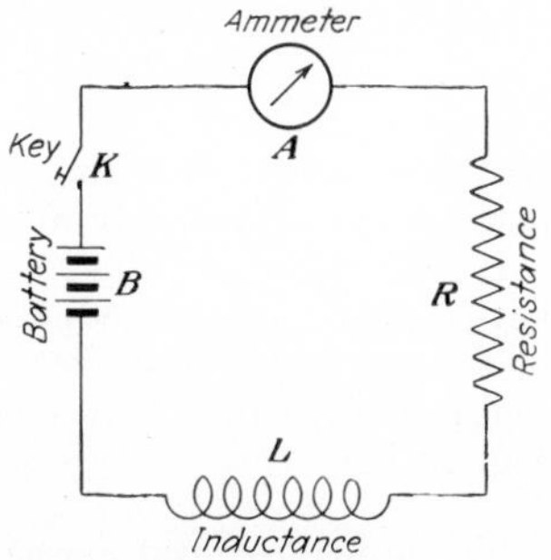

Self-inductance is ordinarily measured in

Fig. 42.10. Circuit containing an inductor. The flux linking the inductor changes when the current changes.

henrys. *The self-inductance of a circuit or component is one henry when there is induced an emf of one volt in that circuit or component at an instant the current is changing at the rate of one ampere per second.*

The self-inductance of many d-c circuits is negligibly small, but a coil with many turns, a large solenoid, or an electromagnet may have a large self-inductance. In a-c circuits inductance is of great practical importance, since the current is constantly changing. The emf resulting from self-inductance always opposes the *change of current;* it operates to hold down the current when it is rising and to maintain the current when it is decreasing.

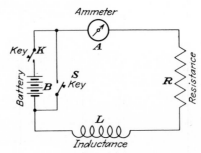

Fig. 42.11. Circuit for observing the rise and fall of current in an inductor.

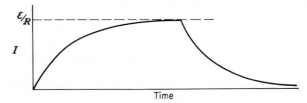

Fig. 42.12. Rise and decay of current in an inductive circuit.

Consider the circuit of Fig. 42.11. When the key K is closed, the current in the circuit begins to rise. If we apply Kirchhoff's second law to the circuit at any instant, we obtain

$$\mathcal{E} - Ri - L\frac{\Delta i}{\Delta t} = 0 \tag{42.6}$$

At the instant the switch is closed, i is zero and $\mathcal{E} = L\,\Delta i/\Delta t$. As time goes on, i increases and eventually reaches the value $I = \mathcal{E}/R$ (Fig. 42.12).

If the battery in Fig. 42.11 is suddenly shorted out of the circuit by closing the key S, the emf of self-induction keeps a current passing through the circuit until all the energy stored in the magnetic field of the inductor is dissipated. The current in the circuit is shown as a function of time after closing S in the right half of Fig. 42.12.

When a current I passes through an inductor L, the energy W stored in the magnetic field is given by

$$W = \tfrac{1}{2}LI^2 \tag{42.7}$$

as can be readily shown by the application of integral calculus (see Appendix, Sec. E.2). The energy calculated from Eq. (42.7) is expressed in joules when L is in henrys and I in amperes.

PROBLEMS

1. The secondary of an induction coil has 30,000 turns. If the flux linking the coil changes from 6×10^{-4} to 5×10^{-5} weber in 0.0002 sec, how great will the induced emf be?   *Ans.* 82,500 volts

2. Find the emf induced in a coil having 400 turns when it is removed from the air gap between the poles of a magnet that produces a magnetic intensity of 1.2 w/m². It is assumed that the plane of the coil is originally perpendicular to the lines of force and that it is removed from the magnetic field in 0.025 sec. The area of the coil is 2 cm².

3. A small "search" coil with an area of 2 cm² has 50 turns of very fine wire. This coil is placed between the pole pieces of a small magnet and then suddenly jerked out. If the average induced emf is 0.3 volt when the coil is pulled to a field-free region in 0.05 sec, what is the magnetic intensity between the poles?

    Ans. 1.5 w/m² (newton/amp-m)

4. A coil of 300 turns with an area of 380 cm² is placed with its plane perpendicular to the earth's field and is rotated in $\frac{1}{60}$ sec through a quarter turn, so that its plane is parallel to the earth's field. What is the average emf induced if the earth's field has an intensity of 8×10^{-5} newton/amp-m (w/m²)?

5. The axle of a truck is 2.5 m long. If the truck is moving due north 30 m/sec at a place where the vertical component of the earth's magnetic field is 9×10^{-5} w/m², find the potential difference between the two ends of the axle. Which end is positive?

    Ans. 0.0068 volt; west

6. A wire 250 cm long moves across a magnetic field with a velocity of 8 m/sec. Find the voltage induced in the wire if the field intensity is 0.5 newton/amp-m (w/m²).

7. An emf of 4 volts is obtained by moving a wire 1.2 m long at a rate of 15 m/sec across a uniform magnetic field. What is the intensity of the field?   *Ans.* 0.22 w/m²

8. Calculate the emf which is induced in the axle of a car which is moving with a speed of 30 m/sec, where the vertical component of the earth's magnetic field is 6×10^{-5} newton/amp-m. Assume that the length of the axle is 110 cm.

9. The coefficient of mutual inductance between two coils is 0.24 henry. What emf is induced in the second coil if the current is changing at the rate of 5,000 amp/sec in the first coil?   *Ans.* 1,200 volts

10. Two circuits have a coefficient of mutual induction of 1.4 henrys. What emf is introduced in the secondary by a change from 0 to 20 amp in 0.008 sec in the primary?

11. When the current in the primary of a transformer is changing at the rate of 500 amp/sec the induced emf in the secondary is 30 volts. What is the coefficient of mutual inductance?   *Ans.* 0.06 henry

12. A coil has inductance of 4 henrys and carries a current of 8 amp. What time must be allowed for the current to die out in order that the average induced emf may be 450 volts?

13. What back emf is induced in a coil of self-inductance 0.004 henry when the current in the coil is changing at the rate of 225 amp/sec?   *Ans.* 0.9 volt

14. The coefficient of self-inductance of a coil is 4 henrys and the current in it is 10 amp. If the current is reduced to zero in 0.003 sec, what is the average emf set up in the coil?

15. An electromagnet has a self-inductance of 6 henrys. How much energy is stored in the magnetic field when a current of 3 amp exists in the coil?   *Ans.* 27 joules

16. How much energy is stored in a circuit of 16 henrys self-inductance when a current of 0.12 amp has been built up?

17. The current in a circuit changes from 20 amp to zero in 0.004 sec.   If the average induced emf is 4,800 volts, what is the coefficient of self-induction of the circuit?

Ans. 0.96 henry

18. Find the coefficient of self-induction of a coil of wire, if an emf of 0.75 volt is generated in it when the current is changing at the rate of 25 amp in 2 sec.

19. A coil has a resistance of 5 ohms and a self-inductance of 0.008 henry.   A constant potential difference of 75 volts is suddenly applied to the coil.   At what rate does the current begin to rise?   What is the current at the instant the current is changing at the rate of 1,000 amp/sec?   What is the final current?

Ans. 9,375 amp/sec; 13.4 amp; 15 amp

20. Find the emf which will be produced in a coil of wire which has an inductance of 0.6 henry when the current in the coil is changing at the rate of 40 amp/sec.

21. A galvanometer with a resistance of 800 ohms gives a full-scale deflection for 8×10^{-5} coulomb of electricity.   A coil of 120 turns and 80 ohms resistance is to be constructed to study fields up to 0.9 newton/amp-m by observing deflections produced when the coil is suddenly removed from the field.   What is the maximum radius allowable for the coil?

Ans. 1.44 cm

22. A coil of 80 turns with a radius of 6 mm and a resistance of 20 ohms is placed between the poles of an electromagnet and suddenly removed.   A charge of 9×10^{-6} coulomb is sent through a galvanometer connected to the coil.   The resistance of the galvanometer is 1,200 ohms.   What is the intensity of the magnetic field?

CHAPTER 43

important know - back emf, and all power relationships of shunt motors and series motors, also transformers. (some of this is in chapt 44)

Generators and Motors

Two of the most important applications of our knowledge of electricity are the generator, which produces electrical energy from some other form of energy, and the motor, which transforms electrical energy into mechanical work. In many situations the same combination of wires and magnetic fields may be used either as a generator or as a motor.

43.1. The EMF in a Revolving Loop. When a rectangular loop of wire revolves in a uniform magnetic field (Fig. 43.1), the conductors move through the field and a motional emf is induced. The conductors AB and CD cut across the flux lines, while the conductors AD and BC do not. In the conductors AB and CD there is induced an instantaneous emf

$$e = vBl \sin \theta = \mathcal{E}_{max} \sin \theta \qquad (43.1)$$

where θ is the angle between the velocity **v** of the wire and **B**. The direction of the induced emf is from B toward A as the side AB moves downward. At the same time, in the side DC there exists an emf directed from D to C. These emfs are in series aiding; therefore, a current flows around the loop in the direction $BADC$.

The net emf induced in the coil varies as the angle θ changes. It is zero when the plane of the coil is vertical, since in this position the wires in the coil move parallel to the magnetic intensity **B** and $\sin \theta = 0$. When the plane of the coil is horizontal, the wires move perpendicular to the lines of flux, $\sin \theta = 1$, and the induced emf is maximum. The relation between the position of the coil and the induced emf is evident from Fig. 43.2.

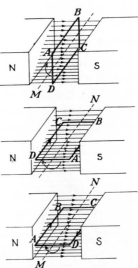

Fig. 43.1. Induced emf in a revolving loop of wire in a magnetic field. The direction of the emf reverses twice in each revolution.

513

When side AB begins to move upward and side DC to move downward the emf reverses, since the component of the velocity of each wire perpendicular to the field is reversed in direction. Thus, as the loop is rotated in the magnetic field, the direction of the induced emf changes twice during each revolution.

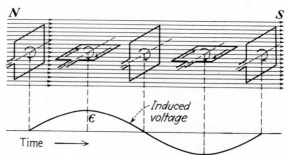

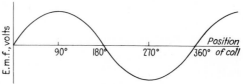

Fig. 43.2. Motional emf is greatest when conductors are moving perpendicular to the magnetic intensity.

Fig. 43.3. Sine curve of emf. In commercial circuits the frequency is 60 cycles/sec.

43.2. Sine Curve of Electromotive Force. If the angle through which the coil has rotated is measured from the vertical position with AB on top, the plane of the coil is horizontal for angles of 90° and 270°. At these positions the emf is maximum. Figure 43.3 shows the relationship between the induced emf and the angle through which the coil has

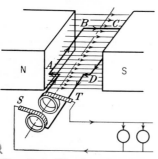

Fig. 43.4. Slip rings for an a-c generator.

rotated. The curve shows that the emf generated rises from zero to maximum value at 90°, decreases to zero again at 180°, reverses its direction, and reaches its largest negative value at 270°. Once again it decreases in magnitude and reaches zero when the revolution is completed. This cycle of events occurs during each complete revolution of the coil. The emf induced in the coil is an *alternating emf*.

43.3. Collecting Rings. If the loop of Fig. 43.1 is opened at the axis and an outside circuit is connected continuously to the two ends of the revolving coil, the induced emf may be applied to an external circuit. In order to make continuous connection to the outside circuit, the ends of the wire forming the coil may be fastened to rings (Fig. 43.4) which are mounted on the axis of the revolving loop. Connections between the outside circuit and these rings are ordinarily made by sliding connectors, called "brushes." As the coil revolves, the slip rings revolve with it. The brushes are pressed against the slip rings and connect the rotating coil to the external circuit.

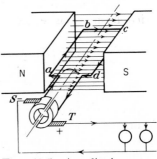

43.4. The Commutator. We have

seen that the emf induced in a loop rotating in a magnetic field is an alternating one. To obtain a current which is always in the same direction through the external circuit, the terminals of the rotating loop are joined to a commutator, which is a ring divided into two segments, as shown in Fig. 43.5.

Fig. 43.5. A split-ring commutator gives unidirectional current in an external circuit.

Against this divided ring press two brushes which are connected to the external circuit and so placed that they slip from one segment of the commutator to the other at the instant the emf of the revolving coil passes through zero.

If the loop of Fig. 43.5 is rotating clockwise, the wire cd which is moving downward has an emf in the direction of the arrow, while the current

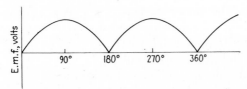

Fig. 43.6. The potential difference between the brushes of the commutator of Fig. 43.5 as a function of the angular position of the coil when a negligibly small current is drawn.

in the wire ab is in the opposite direction. Hence, current leaves the brush T and passes through the external circuit in the direction of the arrow from T to S. When the loop has made one-half revolution, the segment of the commutator which was in contact with brush T makes contact with brush S, and the other segment makes contact with brush T. The wire cd is now moving upward and current in it is reversed. The wire ab is moving down and the current in it is also reversed. However, the segments of the commutator have reversed their positions. The current still leaves by the brush T and flows through the external circuit in the same direction in which it flowed originally. By this means the current in the external circuit continues in the same direction. In the revolving coil the current alternates; in the external circuit the current is pulsating, but *unidirectional*. The potential difference between the brushes is shown in Fig. 43.6.

43.5. Practical Generators. In most practical generators, both alternating and direct current, several coils are rotated simultaneously

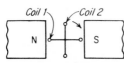

Fig. 43.7. A generator with two coils which are mutually perpendicular.

in a magnetic field. These several coils are connected in such a way as to give the desired emf and current capacity.

Consider a d-c generator with two coils whose planes are mutually perpendicular (Fig. 43.7). If the coils are connected in series through a suitable commutator arrangement, the fluctuation in the output emf is much smaller than are the fluctuations in output of each coil separately as is shown in Fig. 43.8. By adding more coils the resultant output can be made constant except for small fluctuations known as the *commutator ripple*.

The wires which rotate past the poles of a generator are ordinarily embedded in slots in an iron core. The rotating system involving the iron core and the wires is known as the *armature*. The purpose of the iron core is to increase the magnetic intensity **B** and thereby to increase the emf induced. There are emfs induced, not only in the copper wires of the armature, but in any material which moves in the magnetic field, including the iron of the armature. If the armature were a solid piece of iron, these induced emfs would

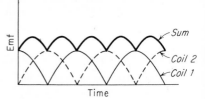

Fig. 43.8. Connecting the two coils of Fig. 43.7 in series leads to a steadier output emf than either coil produces by itself.

lead to large currents circulating in the iron and much energy would be dissipated as heat by these current whirlpools which are called *eddy currents*. To reduce the eddy currents, the iron core is constructed from thin sheets or *laminations* with a thin insulating layer between them to make the resistance high.

Not only does the practical generator have several coils mounted on the same armature, but these coils often pass several magnetic poles during each revolution. Four- and six-pole generators are common; in some applications as many as twenty-four poles are passed in a single revolution. In a six-pole generator one complete cycle is induced for each third of a revolution, or three cycles in each revolution.

An emf may equally well be induced in a stationary coil by the varying of a magnetic field. The rotating magnetic poles of two revolving magnetic field generators are shown in Fig. 43.9.

43.6. Excitation of the Fields of Generators. Generators and motors are sometimes classified with regard to the manner in which their magnetic fields are produced. In the simplest type of generator the magnetic field may be due to a permanent magnet. An example of such a generator is the *magneto*, shown in Fig. 43.10.

Most large generators have fields which are produced by electromagnets. Such generators may be classified as self-excited or separately excited, depending on whether the generator produces its own magnetic field or uses some other source to excite the electromagnet. Self-excited generators may be divided into series-, shunt-, and compound-wound generators.

In the series-wound generator (Fig. 43.11) the current to the external circuit goes through the field coil, which consists of a few turns of heavy wire. When the generator is not delivering current, the only magnetic field is that due to residual magnetism. The greater the current drawn by the external circuit, the greater is the current in the field coils and therefore the greater the magnetic field in which the armature rotates. When the generator is operated at constant

Fig. 43.9. Revolving magnetic field of a generator.

speed, the greater the current, the greater the emf generated. Series-wound generators are relatively uncommon because one does not ordinarily desire an emf which increases rapidly as the current drawn is increased.

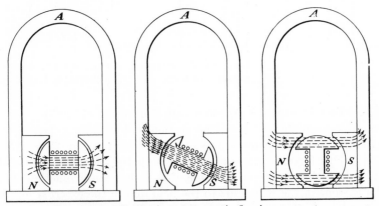

Fig. 43.10. Distribution of magnetic flux in a magneto.

In the shunt-wound generator the field coils are in parallel with the external circuit (Fig. 43.12). When such a generator is operated at constant speed and the current in the external circuit is increased, the terminal potential difference V_t of the generator decreases for the following reason: The terminal potential is the induced emf $\mathcal{E}$ minus Ir, where r is the resistance of the armature and I the armature current. As I increases, the terminal potential decreases and so does the current in the field coils (given by V_t divided by the resistance of the field coils). This reduces the magnetic field and the induced emf. Therefore, a shunt-wound generator provides a potential which decreases as the current drawn is increased. Such a current-voltage response is not commonly desired.

When the terminal potential supplied by a generator is to be essentially independent of the current load, a compound-wound generator (Fig. 43.13) is used. Such a generator has field coils which are composed of a series-wound part and a shunt-wound part. The characteristic of a series-wound field to give an increased emf with increasing current demand and the characteristic of a shunt-wound generator to give a terminal potential which decreases with load current may be combined to design a generator with almost any desired variation of terminal potential with load current.

43.7. The Efficiency of Generators. The efficiency of a generator is defined as the ratio of the electrical energy output of the generator to the energy input, or alternatively, as the ratio of the electric power output to the power input. The power output of the generator is the product of the terminal potential and the current to the external circuit. The power input is greater, of course; it is equal to the power output plus the various losses which occur such as the I^2R heat loss in the armature and the field coils, the hysteresis losses, eddy-current losses, and frictional losses.

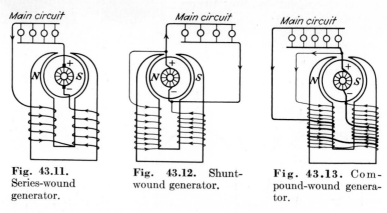

Fig. 43.11. Series-wound generator.

Fig. 43.12. Shunt-wound generator.

Fig. 43.13. Compound-wound generator.

43.8. Electric Motor. When a wire bearing an electric current I is placed in a magnetic field **B** so that the length **l** of the wire is perpendicular to the field, the wire experiences a force given by $F = IlB$ [Eq. (40.2)]. This force is perpendicular to both the magnetic field and to the length of the wire. On one side of the wire, the magnetic field due to the current in the wire adds to the field due to the external magnetic circuit, while on the opposite side the two fields oppose, as indicated in Fig. 43.14. The force on the wire is from the stronger toward the weaker field. If the current is reversed, the force is reversed.

Figure 43.15 shows the cross section of a single current-bearing loop of wire in a uniform magnetic field. Assume that the current enters at A and leaves at B. There results a force downward on wire A and upward on wire B. Thus, there is a torque in a direction to produce a counterclockwise rotation about the axis of the coil. In an electric motor there are ordinarily many conductors bearing currents perpendicular to a magnetic field. The resulting torque produces rotation of the motor.

There are many kinds of electric motors. Or, to put it in another way, there are many ways to convert electrical energy to mechanical energy. The underlying principle in most motors is that a current-bearing conductor experiences a force in a magnetic field.

43.9. Back EMF in a Motor. When the conductors in the armature of a motor rotate in a magnetic field, an emf is induced which opposes the current in the conductors. For this reason it is called a *back emf*, or a *counter emf*.

If an incandescent lamp is connected in series with a small shunt-wound motor while the armature is held stationary, the lamp glows as if the motor were absent, since the armature resistance is small. When the armature is allowed to revolve, the lamp becomes dim. This is because the emf generated in the armature opposes the impressed emf and thereby reduces the current in the circuit. In a constant magnetic field, the faster the armature revolves, the greater is the back emf and the smaller the armature current.

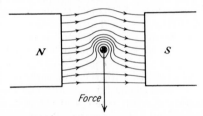

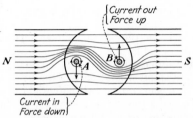

Fig. 43.14. The force on a conductor carrying a current into the plane of the paper.

Fig. 43.15. Torque on a current-bearing coil in a magnetic field.

For shunt-wound motors the potential difference across the armature is just the potential V_t applied to its terminals. The terminal potential of the armature is equal to the back emf plus the potential drop across the armature resistance r_a due to the armature current I_a.

$$V_t = \mathcal{E}_b + I_a r_a \qquad (43.2)$$

A motor is analogous to a battery under charge, except that electrical energy is transformed into mechanical energy rather than to chemical energy. If Eq. (43.2) is solved for the armature current, it yields

$$I_a = \frac{V_t - \mathcal{E}_b}{r_a} \qquad (43.2a)$$

The electrical work done against the back emf appears as mechanical energy output of the motor. Indeed, the mechanical power output P of the motor is equal to the product of the back emf $\mathcal{E}_b$ and the armature current.

$$P = \mathcal{E}_b I_a \qquad (43.3)$$

This follows directly from the fact that $\mathcal{E}_b$ is the electrical work per unit charge performed to produce motion of the conductors and I_a is the charge per second passing through the conductors.

Since the armature current of a motor depends on the difference between the terminal potential and the back emf, the current is largest when the armature is at rest, for in this case the back emf is zero.   In order to keep the current in a large motor from being excessive at the start, it is customary to introduce a series resistor that reduces the current flowing in the circuit.   As the speed of the motor increases and the back emf becomes appreciable, this resistance is removed from the circuit.   Such a resistance is called a "starting resistance" or a "starting box."

43.10. Series-wound and Shunt-wound Motors.   If large starting torques are required, motors having field coils which are in series with the armature are used.   With such a series-wound motor the back emf is small when the motor is starting and the current drawn is large.   Since this same current passes through the series field coils, the magnetic field is also large.   The starting torque is proportional to IlB, the force on an individual conductor.   As the motor gains speed, the back emf increases and both armature current and field strength decrease.   Therefore, the torque is much smaller at high speeds.   Series-wound motors are often used for rock crushers and other machines in which particularly large starting torques are desired.

In shunt-wound motors the field coils are in parallel with the armature coils.   For a constant applied potential difference, the field strength is constant and the torque is directly proportional to the armature current, whereas in the series-wound motor the torque is more nearly proportional to the square of the current.   Most common small electric motors are shunt-wound.

The efficiency of a motor may be obtained by dividing the mechanical power output of the motor by the electric power input.   For a d-c motor the electric power input is just the product of the applied potential and the current drawn, while the mechanical power output is the product of the back emf and the armature current.   The difference between the input and output power is dissipated in heating, air friction, and so forth.

43.11. Dynamos.   The fundamental components of many motors are identical to those of corresponding generators.   The single term *dynamo* describes an electric device which can function as either motor or generator.   When a dynamo is supplied with a potential difference and energy by an electrical source and does mechanical work, it is a motor.   When it is driven by a mechanical torque, it develops electrical energy and acts as a generator.   Not every motor can be operated as a generator but many can.   There are many applications for a dynamo operating part time as a motor and the rest of the time as a generator.

An example is the dynamo used in diesel-electric locomotives.   When the train is set in motion, diesel engines drive generators to supply current to the dynamos on the axles of the driving wheels.   These dynamos exert large torques on the wheels and put the locomotive in motion.   When it is desired to reduce the speed of the train, the dynamo may be disconnected from its power supply, leaving the armature rotating in a magnetic field as long as the wheels turn.   An emf is induced in the armature; if the terminals are connected to a resistor, a current flows.   The dynamo is now operating as a generator, converting kinetic energy of the train into electrical energy, and thus braking the train.   In diesel-electric locomotives the electrical energy is dissipated in heat, but in electric locomotives it may be fed back into the power lines.

43.12. Watt-hour Meter. The Thomson form of recording watt-hour meter (Fig. 43.16) consists of a little shunt motor whose armature turns at a speed which is proportional to the power that is supplied to it. The armature is geared to dials which record the energy in kilowatt-hours. The stationary field coils L and M are connected in series with the generator supplying the current to the external circuit. The field strength of the motor is therefore proportional to the current to the load. The armature is connected across the line, as a voltmeter would be connected. The potential difference across the armature is the potential supplied to the load and the armature current is proportional to this potential. The torque which turns the motor is proportional to the product of the current in the armature and the magnetic field in which the armature turns. Hence, the torque which turns the armature is proportional to the product of

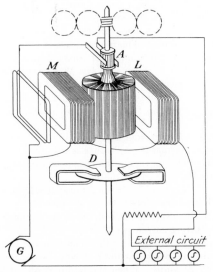

Fig. 43.16. A watt-hour meter.

current supplied to the load and the potential at which it is supplied, i.e., to the power received.

In order that the motor may not run too fast and in order also that it may stop as soon as the current ceases to flow, an electromagnetic brake D is attached to it. This brake consists of an aluminum disk rotating between the poles of a permanent magnet. The eddy currents induced in the disk by its rotation between the poles of the magnet retard its motion and cause it to stop as soon as the current ceases to flow. This type of watt-hour meter can be used with either direct or alternating currents.

PROBLEMS

1. Part of the windings of an electric motor is a segment of wire 20 cm long which lies perpendicular to the magnetic field of 1.2 newtons/amp-m. Find the force on this segment when it bears a current of 5 amp. *Ans.* 1.2 newtons

2. The flux density between the poles of a certain motor is 1.5 w/m². A conductor carrying 5 amp lies in this magnetic field so that it is perpendicular to the field. Find the force on it per centimeter of length.

3. Find the torque produced on a rectangular loop of wire ot one turn when its plane is parallel to the magnetic lines of a field with an intensity of 1.2 newtons/amp-m, when a current of 8 amp is sent through the loop. The dimensions of the loop are 18 cm parallel to the lines and 24 cm at right angles to them.

Ans. 0.415 newton-m

4. A generator that develops 120 volts at no load furnishes only 114 volts when a current of 40 amp is drawn. What is the resistance of the armature?

5. The armature of a shunt generator has a resistance of 0.12 ohm. The terminal voltage of the generator is 118 volts when the armature current is 60 amp. Find the emf of the generator and the power dissipated in heat in the armature.

Ans. 125.2 volts; 432 watts

6. A motor running at full load on a 115-volt line develops a back emf of 107 volts and draws a current of 6 amp through the armature. What is the mechanical power output of the motor, disregarding frictional losses?

7. A series-wound motor has an armature with a resistance of 0.40 ohm and field coils with a resistance of 5 ohms. The motor draws 8 amp at 120 volts. Find the power supplied to the motor, the number of watts transformed into heat, and the mechanical power output.   *Ans.* 960 watts; 345.6 watts; 614.4 watts

8. The armature of a generator has a resistance of 0.12 ohm. When run at its rated speed, it yields 115 volts on open circuit and 112 volts on full load. What is the current when it is running on full load? How much power is delivered to the external circuit?

9. A shunt motor draws 5 amp from a 110-volt line. The field coils have a resistance of 220 ohms and the armature resistance is 0.4 ohm. Find the armature current and the back emf. What is the mechanical power output of the motor? How much power is dissipated in heat in the motor?

Ans. 4.5 amp; 108.2 volts; 487 watts; 63 watts

10. A shunt motor has an armature with a resistance of 0.6 ohm. It operates on a 120-volt circuit. Find the resistance which must be connected in series with the armature to limit the starting current to 24 amp.

11. A shunt motor has an armature with a resistance of 0.4 ohm. If this motor operates from a 220-volt line, what starting resistance is required if the armature current must be limited to 25 amp? When the motor is operating normally with the starting resistor shorted out, it draws 10 amp. Find the back emf and the mechanical power output.   *Ans.* 8.4 ohms; 216 volts; 2,160 watts

12. A shunt generator delivers 100 amp at a brush potential of 120 volts. If the stray-power loss is 1,200 watts, what is the efficiency of the generator? The field coils have a resistance of 40 ohms, and the armature has a resistance of 0.15 ohm.

13. How much work is done in moving a wire 30 cm long in which there is a current of 20 amp across a magnetic field which is at right angles to the wire? The intensity of the magnetic field is 0.9 newton/amp-m, and the wire is moved a distance of 25 cm.   *Ans.* 1.35 joules

14. What horsepower is necessary to drive a generator which supplies 40 amp at 220 volts, if the efficiency of the generator is 90 per cent?

15. The armature of a motor connected to a 220-volt line draws 50 amp at the instant the connection is made, when the motor is at rest, through a starting resistance of 3 ohms. What is the resistance of the armature? What is the counter emf when the current drawn is 35 amp (with the starting resistance disconnected)?

Ans. 1.4 ohms; 171 volts

16. The armature of a generator has a resistance of 0.09 ohm. When the current through the armature is 9 amp, the terminal potential is 119 volts. What will be the terminal potential when the current is 85 amp, assuming that the field strength and the speed remain unchanged?

17. The brush potential of a generator when delivering 10 amp is 540 volts. When the generator delivers 45 amp, the difference of potential across the brushes falls to 535 volts. What is the resistance of the armature?   *Ans.* 0.14 ohm

18. A shunt motor takes a total current of 40 amp from 120-volt mains. The resistance of the armature is 1.6 ohms, and that of the field is 80 ohms. Find the current in the field coils and in the armature and the power used in heating the armatues and the field coils.

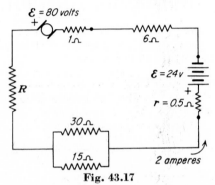

Fig. 43.17

19. Consider the circuit of Fig. 43.17. (*a*) Find the terminal potential differences of the generator and the battery. (*b*) Find *R* and the power dissipated in *R*. (*c*) Find the charge passing through the 15-ohm resistor in one minute. (*d*) Find the mechanical energy converted to electrical energy and the electrical energy converted to chemical energy in 10 sec.

Ans. (*a*) 78 volts, 25 volts; (*b*) 10.5 ohms, 42 watts; (*c*) 80 coulombs; (*d*) 1,600 joules, 480 joules

20. The resistance of the field coils of a shunt motor is 180 ohms, and the resistance of its armature is 0.06 ohm. What back emf is developed when the motor takes 9 amp from a 120-volt battery?

Alternating Currents

44.1. Alternating Currents. When a rectangular loop revolves in a magnetic field, the current reverses its direction at regular intervals. Such a current is called an alternating current. When the current rises from zero to a maximum, returns to zero, then rises to a maximum in the opposite direction, and returns to zero again, it has completed one cycle.

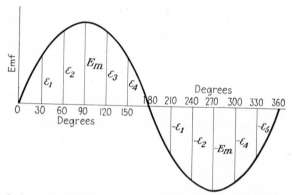

Fig. 44.1. Variation of emf with angular position (or time) for a coil rotating with constant angular velocity.

This cycle is repeated over and over again; the number of times the cycle is repeated each second is known as the frequency. The frequency ordinarily used in electric power production in the United States is 60 cycles/sec, although some power generated at Niagara Falls is at 25 cycles/sec and there is common use of 50 cycles/sec in Europe.

44.2. Instantaneous Electromotive Force. If the armature of a generator consists of a single coil of wire revolving in a horizontal magnetic field, the instantaneous emf induced in it can be represented by a sine curve (Fig. 44.1), in which the angle through which the coil has turned from its vertical position is plotted on the horizontal axis and the

524

corresponding induced emf on the vertical axis.   The equation which connects the instantaneous emf e with the angle through which the coil has turned is

$$e = \mathcal{E}_{max} \sin \theta = \mathcal{E}_{max} \sin 2\pi ft \qquad (44.1)$$

where $\mathcal{E}_{max}$ is the maximum emf induced in the coil, θ is the angle through which the coil has turned from the position in which the wires are moving parallel to the magnetic field, f is the frequency, and t is the time.   In this equation and subsequent ones we continue to use lower-case letters to represent the instantaneous value of quantities which vary in time and capital letters to indicate quantities which are constant.

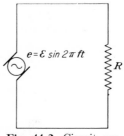

Fig. 44.2. Circuit containing a source of alternating emf and pure resistance.

44.3. Relation of Current to Potential Difference in a Resistance.   When an alternating emf is applied to a circuit (Fig. 44.2) which contains resistance R without any inductance, the curve representing the variation of the current with the time has the same form as the corresponding curve for the impressed potential.   The current and the potential both reach their maximum value at the same instant (Fig. 44.3) and their zero value at the same instant.   The current is said to be "in phase" with the potential.   Ohm's law in its simplest form applies so that

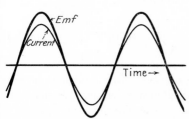

Fig. 44.3. Relation of current to applied emf in a circuit containing resistance only.

$$i = \frac{v}{R} \quad \text{and} \quad I_{max} = \frac{V_{max}}{R}$$

The current and the potential are then given by

$$\begin{aligned} i &= I_{max} \sin \theta = I_{max} \sin 2\pi ft \\ v &= V_{max} \sin \theta = V_{max} \sin 2\pi ft \end{aligned} \qquad (44.2)$$

44.4. Effective Value of Alternating Current.   The power dissipated in heat in a resistor by a d-c current is $I^2 R$.   For a direct current the maximum value, the average value, and the instantaneous value are all the same.   For an alternating current, the average value of current over a whole cycle is zero; the current fluctuates between maximum value in one direction and same maximum value in the opposite direction.   Nevertheless, an alternating current is effective in producing heat in a resistor.

The effective value of an alternating current is the value of that direct current which would produce heat at the same rate in a given resistance.   An alternating current is said to have an effective value of two amperes when it generates heat in a one-ohm resistor at the rate of four watts—the same rate at which a direct current of two amperes produces heat in a one-ohm resistor. Since the heating effect depends on the square of the current, this is equivalent to saying that the average value of the square of the alternating current is the same as the square of the corresponding direct current. The effective value of an alternating current is found by taking the average of the square of the instantaneous current and then extracting the square root of this average square. Sometimes the effective value of the alternating current obtained in this way is called the *root-mean-square* (rms) current.

The effective value of a sine wave current is given by (Appendix E, Sec. E.3)

$$I_{\text{eff}} = \frac{I_{\text{max}}}{\sqrt{2}} = 0.707 I_{\text{max}} \tag{44.3}$$

where I_{max} is the maximum value of the current. Similarly, the effective value of an alternating potential difference is 0.707 times the maximum, i.e.,

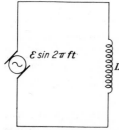

$$V_{\text{eff}} = \frac{V_{\text{max}}}{\sqrt{2}} = 0.707 V_{\text{max}} \tag{44.4}$$

Fig. 44.4. Circuit containing a source of alternating emf and an inductor of negligible resistance.

Ordinary a-c ammeters and voltmeters are calibrated to read effective values. When we speak of a 110-volt a-c circuit or a current of 5 amp alternating current, it is effective values which are being specified. Hereafter, we shall use V and I without subscripts to denote effective values.

44.5. Current in an Inductive Circuit. When an alternating potential of frequency f is applied to a large inductor with negligible resistance (Fig. 44.4), the current is limited by the inductance. This limitation is due to the fact that, as the current changes, a back emf is induced in the inductance. At every instant this emf opposes the *change in the current.* If we apply Kirchhoff's second law to this situation, we have

$$v = V_{\text{max}} \sin 2\pi f t = L \frac{\Delta i}{\Delta t}$$

By the use of calculus (Appendix E, Sec. E.4) it can be readily shown that

$$i = -\frac{V_{\text{max}}}{2\pi f L} \cos 2\pi f t = -I_{\text{max}} \cos 2\pi f t \tag{44.5}$$

The maximum current is V_{max} divided by the quantity $2\pi fL$, which is called the *inductive reactance* of the inductor and is indicated by X_L. The effective current is just $I = V/2\pi fL = V/X_L$. The dimensions of X_L are volts per ampere or ohms.

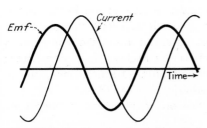

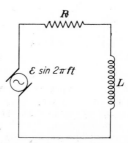

Fig. 44.5. In the circuit of Fig. 44.4 the current lags behind the applied emf by 90°.

Fig. 44.6. Series circuit containing source of alternating emf, resistance, and inductance.

When a potential difference is applied across a pure inductance, the current is not in phase with the potential difference. It reaches its maximum value when the potential is passing through zero; the current is zero when the potential is at its maximum value as is shown in Fig. 44.5. The current in this case lags 90° behind the potential.

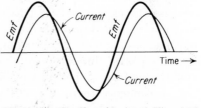

Fig. 44.7. In the circuit of Fig. 44.6 the current lags behind the applied emf by an angle θ given by

$$\tan \theta = 2\pi fL/R$$

If a circuit (Fig. 44.6) contains both resistance and inductance, the current lags behind the potential by some angle less than 90° (Fig. 44.7). Kirchhoff's second law applied to the circuit yields

$$e = \mathcal{E}_{max} \sin 2\pi ft = Ri + L \frac{\Delta i}{\Delta t}$$

It can be shown (Appendix E, Sec. E.4) that in this case

$$I = \frac{\mathcal{E}}{\sqrt{R^2 + (2\pi fL)^2}} \tag{44.6}$$

and that the current lags behind the potential by an angle θ such that $\tan \theta = 2\pi fL/R$. The quantity by which $\mathcal{E}$ must be divided to get I is called the *impedance* of the circuit and is represented by Z. In this case $Z = \sqrt{R^2 + (2\pi fL)^2}$. It can be computed as the resultant of R and $2\pi fL$, where R and $2\pi fL$ are drawn as vectors at right angles to one another as shown in Fig. 44.8a. The angle θ by which the current lags behind the emf is the angle between Z and R.

An a-c voltmeter connected across the resistor R would read IR. Con-

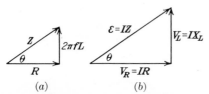

Fig. 44.8. (a) Vector diagram for finding the angle by which current lags behind applied emf in an a-c series circuit containing inductance and resistance. (b) The vector sum of the potential difference IR and IX_L add up to the applied emf.

nected across the inductor L, it would read IX_L. The arithmetical sum $IR + IX_L$ is not equal to the applied effective emf $\mathcal{E}$, since when the potential difference is maximum across the resistor, it is zero across the inductor. Rather, if we add the potentials vectorially with IX_L 90° ahead of IR, as shown in Fig. 44.8b, we obtain $\mathcal{E}$. Obviously, the triangle in this figure is similar to the impedance triangle of Fig. 44.8a;

each side is just I times the corresponding side in the impedance diagram.

44.6. The Capacitive Circuit. If an alternating emf is applied across a capacitor, the current is zero when the applied emf is maximum because the capacitor is charged to the maximum potential difference. As the potential decreases, the capacitor begins to discharge. The current increases and reaches it maximum value when the emf passes through zero. Thus, the current and the emf are out of phase. In the case of a *pure capacitance* there is a 90° phase difference between the two, with the current leading the emf. The effective current I is given by

$$I = \frac{\mathcal{E}}{1/2\pi f C} = \frac{\mathcal{E}}{X_C} \qquad (44.7)$$

where C is the capacitance and the quantity $1/2\pi f C = X_C$ is called the *capacitive reactance*.

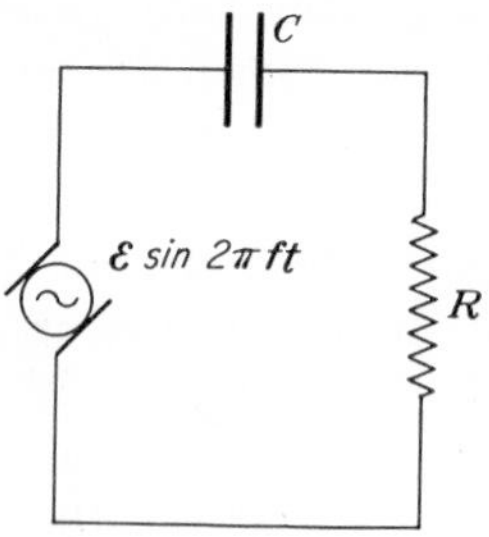

Fig. 44.9. Series circuit containing capacitance and resistance.

When a circuit (Fig. 44.9) contains both capacitance and resistance, the current is given by

$$I = \frac{\mathcal{E}}{\sqrt{R^2 + (1/2\pi f C)^2}} \qquad (44.8)$$

In this case the current leads the emf (Fig. 44.10) by the angle θ ($\tan \theta = X_C/R$). The effective potential difference across the resistance is given by IR, while the effective potential across the capacitor is given by IX_C. The vector sum of IR and IX_C gives the applied emf $\mathcal{E}$.

44.7. Circuit Containing Inductance, Capacitance, and Resistance. In a series a-c circuit containing inductance, capacitance, and resistance (Fig. 44.11), the current is given (Appendix E, Sec. E.4) by

$$I = \frac{\mathcal{E}}{\sqrt{R^2 + (2\pi fL - 1/2\pi fC)^2}} = \frac{\mathcal{E}}{Z} \tag{44.9}$$

Note that the impedance may be considered as the *geometric sum* of the resistance, the inductive reactance, and the capacitive reactance with due

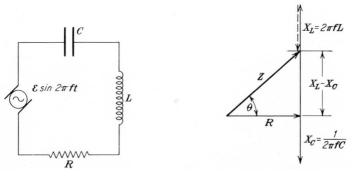

Fig. 44.10. In a capacitive circuit the current leads the applied emf.

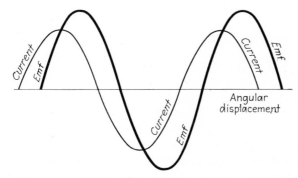

Fig. 44.11. Series circuit containing resistance, inductance, and capacitance.

Fig. 44.12. Impedance diagram for the circuit of Fig. 44.11.

regard to the fact that the inductive reactance and the capacitive reactance shift the phase in opposite directions. The impedance can be computed by drawing a vector diagram, such as the one in Fig. 44.12. The angle by which the current lags behind the emf is θ. Clearly, $\tan \theta = (X_L - X_C)/R$, $\sin \theta = (X_L - X_C)/Z$, and $\cos \theta = R/Z$. When X_C is larger than X_L, θ is negative and the current leads the applied emf.

Example. In the circuit of Fig. 44.11 $\mathcal{E}$ is 24 volts, the total resistance $R = 10$ ohms, $L = 0.05$ henry, and $C = 10^{-4}$ farad. If the frequency is 60 cycles/sec, find the impedance of the circuit and the current. What would an a-c voltmeter connected across R read? across L? across C?

$$X_L = 2\pi fL = 6.28 \times 60 \times 0.05 = 18.9 \text{ ohms}$$
$$X_C = \frac{1}{2\pi fC} = \frac{1}{377 \times 10^{-4}} = 26.5 \text{ ohms}$$
$$Z = \sqrt{R^2 + (X_L - X_C)^2} = \sqrt{(10)^2 + (18.9 - 26.5)^2}$$
$$= \sqrt{100 + 57.8} = 12.5 \text{ ohms}$$
$$I = \frac{\mathcal{E}}{Z} = \frac{24 \text{ volts}}{12.5 \text{ ohms}} = 1.9 \text{ amp}$$
$$V_R = IR = 19 \text{ volts} \qquad V_L = IX_L = (1.9 \times 18.9) = 36 \text{ volts}$$
$$V_C = IX_C = (1.9 \times 26.5) = 51 \text{ volts}$$

In this circuit the current leads the emf by an angle given by $\cos\theta = R/Z = 10/12.5 = 0.8$; $\theta = -37°$. (The minus sign means the current leads the emf.)

44.8. Resonance in Series Circuits. When $X_C = X_L$, the total reactance is zero and the current is given by $I = \mathcal{E}/R$. In these circumstances the current is in phase with the applied emf and the circuit is said to be resonant. The current under these conditions is greater than it is for either a higher or a lower frequency. Resonant circuits are discussed further in Chap. 47.

The frequency for which a circuit is resonant can be obtained readily from the requirement that $X_L = X_C$. This gives $2\pi fL = 1/2\pi fC$, or

$$f = \frac{1}{2\pi \sqrt{LC}} \tag{44.10}$$

Physically, the thing which is happening in a circuit at resonance is that energy is stored during part of the cycle in the magnetic field of the inductor. A quarter cycle later this energy is stored in the electric field of the capacitor. In another quarter cycle it is once again stored in the magnetic field of the inductor. Thus energy is transferred back and forth between inductor and capacitor. The current is in phase with the applied emf because the effects of inductance and capacitance cancel one another. The only net energy supplied to the circuit is that dissipated as heat in the resistor.

44.9. Power in A-C Circuits. The power supplied at any instant in an a-c circuit is obtained by multiplying the instantaneous current by the emf at the same instant.

$$p = ei \tag{44.11}$$

where p is the instantaneous power, i the instantaneous current, and e the instantaneous emf. The power varies from instant to instant, since both the current i and the applied emf e change with time.

The curves in Fig. 44.13 are drawn for the case in which the current and applied emf are in phase with each other. Here the power is always positive, although the current and emf are negative during one-half cycle. The current and emf change signs at the same time, so that their product

is always positive.   The average power over one or more cycles is given
(Appendix E, Sec. E.5) by the prod-
uct of the effective current and the
effective potential difference.

When the current and potential
difference are out of phase, the power
is no longer given by IV.   When an
emf is applied across a capacitor, the
power is negative as much as it is
positive and there is no *net* supply of
energy by the generator; the generator
supplies energy to charge the capacitor, and then the capacitor returns the
energy.   For a circuit in which the
reactance is primarily inductive, the
power curve is similar to that in Fig.
44.14.   In this case, the instantaneous power is negative during part of

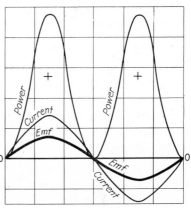

Fig. 44.13. Power supplied to a circuit
in which the applied emf and the
current are in phase.

the cycle, which means that some of the energy stored in the inductance
is being returned to the power source.   In the general case, the power

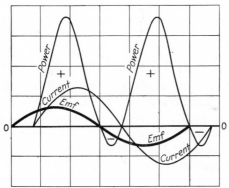

Fig. 44.14. Power supplied to a current in which applied emf and current are not in
phase.

dissipated in a series a-c circuit is given (Appendix E, Sec. E.5) by the
relation

$$P = \mathcal{E}I \cos \theta \tag{44.12}$$

where θ is the angle by which the current lags behind the applied emf.
The vector diagram from which θ may be found is shown in Fig. 44.12.
Cosine θ is called the *power factor* of the circuit.

Power companies are eager to have a power factor as near unity as possible,
because in those cases in which the power factor is far different from unity, energy

is supplied by the power company and then part of it is returned each cycle. Since the power company has to provide the I^2R line losses which occur in delivering the power to the customer, this results in a disadvantageous situation.   Most power companies charge higher rates to any consumer whose power factor is appreciably different from unity.   By the suitable use of additional inductors or capacitors, it is possible to bring the power factor of most loads fairly close to unity.

44.10. The Transformer.   One of the major reasons for the widespread use of alternating currents is that it is possible to change from one potential difference to another simply and efficiently.   This is very desirable since it is most economical to transmit electric power at potentials which are much too high to be used safely in a home or factory.

To illustrate why it is desirable to transmit power at high potentials, consider the following practical problem: A power company must deliver 1,100 kw to a distant city over a transmission line which has a resistance of 2 ohms.   How much power is dissipated in the line for delivery at the city at 110,000 volts and at 1,100 volts?   From $P = VI$ it is clear that the line must deliver 10 amp at 110,000 volts or 1,000 amp at 1,100 volts.   The I^2R power loss in this line is 200 watts at 110,000 volts and 2,000,000 watts at 1,100 volts.   In the latter case more power would be dissipated in the line than is delivered to the ultimate consumer!

If these arguments were the only ones involved, it would be desirable to transmit power at potentials of many million volts.   However, as the potential increases, there are serious power losses due to corona (Chap. 35) and the difficulties of insulation become severe.   For these reasons 330,000 volts is the highest potential difference used for power transmission in the United States.

The change from one a-c potential difference to another can be made very efficiently by means of a *transformer*.   Although a little power is dissipated in the transformer because of hysteresis and eddy currents, the efficiency of a large transformer may be 99 per cent, while even smaller transformers have efficiencies well over 90 per cent.

If an iron core (Fig. 44.15) of any form is wound with two separate coils which are insulated from each other and an alternating current is maintained in one of them, an alternating emf of the same frequency is induced in the other.   The first coil is called the *primary* and the other the *secondary*.   Power is transferred from the primary to the secondary by mutual inductance.   In an idealized transformer the small losses in

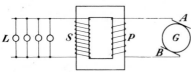

Fig. 44.15. A transformer showing primary windings P and secondary windings S.

the iron core can be neglected and the power supplied the primary circuit is equal to the power delivered by the secondary.   If V_p and V_s are the primary and secondary potentials and I_p and I_s are the corresponding currents,

$$V_p I_p \geq V_s I_s \tag{44.13}$$

Further, since the same magnetic flux links both the primary and the secondary windings, the ratio of the emf in the secondary to that in the primary is equal to the ratio of the number of turns in the secondary N_2 to the number in the primary N_1.

$$\frac{\mathcal{E}_2}{\mathcal{E}_1} = \frac{N_2}{N_1} \qquad (44.14)$$

For an ideal transformer there are no losses and the induced emfs in the primary and secondary are equal to the corresponding terminal potentials V_1 and V_2. From $\mathcal{E}_1 = V_1$, $\mathcal{E}_2 = V_2$, and Eqs. (44.13) and (44.14), we can write

$$\frac{V_2}{V_1} = \frac{\mathcal{E}_2}{\mathcal{E}_1} = \frac{N_2}{N_1} = \frac{I_1}{I_2} \qquad (44.15)$$

Where the emf is large, the current is small; and where the emf is small, the current is large. By means of a transformer, a small emf and a large current may be transformed into a large emf and a small current, or vice versa.

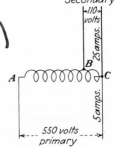

Fig. 44.16. An autotransformer designed to step down the potential difference from 550 to 110 volts.

In an ordinary transformer, when no current is being drawn in the secondary, the current in the primary is limited by the inductive reactance of the primary. Since the primary of a large transformer ordinarily has a low resistance, the current is controlled almost entirely by the self-inductance when the secondary circuit is open and by the self-inductance and the mutual inductance when there is a current in the secondary.

For small transformers where the ratio of transformation is not large, economy of construction and efficiency of operation are obtained by using the same coil for both primary and secondary. Such a transformer is known as an *autotransformer*. The arrangement and connections of the coil are shown in Fig. 44.16. The entire coil AC is the primary of the transformer, and the part between B and C is the secondary. Equation (44.15) is applicable to autotransformers as well as to other types, provided always that heat losses are negligible.

PROBLEMS

1. Most household electric equipment is designed to operate on 110 volts alternating current. Find the maximum value of the potential difference between the terminals of a 110-volt a-c source. *Ans.* 156 volts

2. The effective value of an alternating emf applied to a capacitor is 6,000 volts. What is the maximum value?

3. An alternating emf of frequency 60 cycles/sec has a peak value of 300 volts. Find the instantaneous value of the emf at the instants $\frac{1}{360}$ and $\frac{1}{240}$ sec after it passes through its zero value. *Ans.* 259.8 volts; 300 volts

4. An alternating emf has a frequency of 60 cycles/sec and an effective value of 110 volts. What is the instantaneous value of the emf at an instant $\frac{1}{360}$ sec after it passes the zero value?

5. An alternating current flowing through a resistance of 11 ohms produces heat at the rate of 396 watts. What is the effective value of the current? of the voltage? What are the maximum values?   *Ans.* 6 amp; 66 volts; 8.48 amp; 93.3 volts

6. Find the reactance of a 0.3-henry inductor and of a 20-μf capacitor at 60 cycles/sec.

7. At what frequency would a 50-μf capacitor have a reactance of 80 ohms? What inductance would have this same reactance at this frequency?

Ans. 39.8 cycles/sec; 0.32 henry

8. Find the reactance of a 0.2-μf capacitor at 10 cycles/sec, 10 kc/sec, 10 megacycles/sec, and 1,000 megacycles/sec. Note that a capacitor passes high frequencies readily and offers high reactance to low frequencies.

9. A transformer has 1,000 turns on the primary and 50 turns on the secondary. What is the output voltage if the input voltage is 4,400? If the transformer is assumed to have an efficiency of 100 per cent, what primary current is required if 2,000 watts are drawn from the secondary?   *Ans.* 220 volts; 0.45 amp

10. The secondary of a transformer has 200 times as many turns as the primary. It is used on a 110-volt circuit. What is the voltage across the secondary?

11. A choke has an inductance of 0.5 henry and a resistance of 50 ohms. What is its reactance and its impedance at 120 cps?   *Ans.* 377 ohms; 380 ohms

12. What resistance must be connected in series with the choke of Prob. 11 to give a total impedance of 500 ohms at 120 cycles/sec?

13. An inductor has a resistance of 10 ohms and an inductive reactance of 80 ohms at 60 cycles/sec. It is connected in series with an emf of 120 volts and a resistor of 50 ohms. Find the current, the voltage across the inductor (do not forget its resistance), and the voltage across the resistor.   *Ans.* 1.2 amp; 96.7 volts; 60 volts

14. A pure inductance of 0.3 henry and a 100-ohm resistor are connected in series across a 220-volt 60 cycle/sec source. Find the current and the angle by which it lags behind the source potential.

15. A 10-μf capacitor and a 20-ohm resistor are connected in series with a 2-volt 1,000 cycles/sec emf. Find the current, the angle by which the current leads the emf, and the power dissipated.   *Ans.* 0.078 amp; 38.5°; 0.123 watt

16. A current of 0.5 amp is drawn from a 110-volt 60 cycle/sec line when a 40-ohm resistor is connected in series with a capacitor. Find the capacitance.

17. In the a-c circuit shown in the Fig. 44.11, the effective emf is 200 volts, the inductance is 0.160 henry, the resistance is 80 ohms, and the capacitance is 10 μf. The frequency is $500/\pi$ cycles/sec. (a) Find the inductive reactance, the capacitive reactance, and the impedance. (b) Find the current and the voltage across each part of the system. (Note that it is the *vector* sum of the voltages which adds to 200. The voltage across an inductance or capacitance may exceed the applied voltage!) (c) Find the angle by which the current lags behind the emf. (d) Find the power dissipated in the circuit.

Ans. (a) 160 ohms, 100 ohms, 100 ohms, (b) 2 amp, $V_R = 160$ volts, $V_L = 320$ volts, $V_C = 200$ volts; (c) 37°; (d) 320 watts

18. An a-c series circuit contains resistors, an inductor, and a variable capacitor. If the frequency is constant, will increasing the capacitance increase or decrease the current? Explain carefully.

PART VI

Electronics

The rest of the book is not covered

CHAPTER 45

Electrons and Gaseous Ions

45.1. Gaseous Conduction. Air and other gases are composed of molecules which are normally electrically neutral. Under these conditions air is an excellent insulator. The leaves of an electroscope may hold their charge many hours (Fig. 45.1). However, when electrons are removed from molecules of a gas, the ionized gas is a good conductor of electricity. There are many ways in which a gas may be ionized. Among them are the following.

Ionization by an Electric Field. Air at atmospheric pressure ordinarily "breaks down" under electric fields of about 30,000 volts/cm. At lower pressures the breakdown occurs at lower field strengths. The corona glow from a lightning rod is an example of ionization by a strong electric field. Once such ionization begins, other ions may be produced by collisions and a conducting path between two charged objects created.

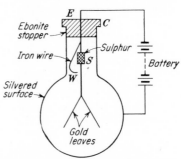

Fig. 45.1. Electroscope for measuring the conductivity of air. The leaves slowly collapse, owing to ionization by cosmic rays and residual radioactivity.

Ionization by Flames. Gases drawn from a bunsen flame contain many ions which permit the gas to conduct electricity (Fig. 45.2). Ordinarily, the ions exist for only a short time before the positive and negative ions neutralize each other. The ionization produced by flame is greatly increased if the flame is fed with some volatile salt such as sodium chloride, which readily breaks into ion pairs (Fig. 45.3). The flame of a match similarly produces an abundant supply of ions.

Ionization by Electromagnetic Radiation. When gamma rays, x-rays, or ultraviolet radiation pass through gases, electrons are ejected from atoms and thus produce positive gas ions and negative free electrons. Figure 45.4 shows an apparatus for observing the conductivity of gas pro-

537

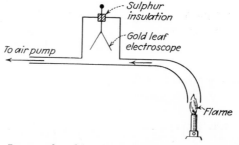

Fig. 45.2. Ions produced by the flame discharge the electroscope.

duced by x-rays.   The gas remains ionized for some time after the x-ray tube has been turned off, although the conductivity of the gas diminishes once the ionizing agent has been removed.

Ionization by Collisions.   When a high-speed ion collides with a neutral atom, an electron may be knocked off and the atom ionized.   This proc-

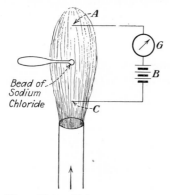

Fig. 45.3. Enhancement of flame ionization by salts.

ess is the dominant one in fluorescent lamp bulbs, neon tubes, and similar devices. Positive ions are accelerated toward the negative electrode and negative ions toward the positive electrode. If the ions have enough energy when they collide with neutral atoms, additional ion pairs are produced.

45.2. The Ionization Chamber.   An ionization chamber is a device for measuring the number of ion pairs produced in a gas.   A simple type of ionization chamber is shown in Fig. 45.5 where two charged metal plates are used to collect ions produced by a beam of x-rays.   If the plates are connected in series with a sensitive galvanometer to the terminals of a battery, a current passes from one plate to another.

The current through the conducting gas does not obey Ohm's law. As the potential difference between the plates is increased, the current

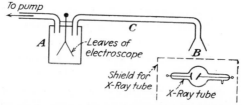

Fig. 45.4. Apparatus for showing the persistence of the conductivity of a gas.

through the galvanometer increases roughly as shown in Fig. 45.6.   At
first the increase is rapid, but eventually the current assumes a value
which is practically independent of potential difference.   This latter situation exists when all the ions formed
by the x-ray beam are being collected
by the plates.   At this point the
current is independent of the applied
field and is called the *saturation
current*.   Except for cases of very
intense ionization, an electric field
of 20 to 30 volts/cm is sufficient to
produce saturation.   Once saturation
has been reached, a further *moderate*
increase in field results in no significant change in the current.

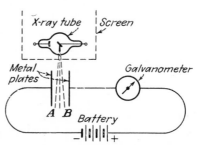

Fig. 45.5. A simple ionization chamber.

If the potential gradient is increased far above the value required for
saturation, the current begins to increase again, as shown in Fig. 45.7.
As the electric field strength is raised still higher, the current increases

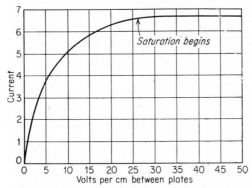

Fig. 45.6. Saturation current in an ionization chamber.

rapidly.   Eventually, a discharge occurs between the plates.   The rapid
increase is due to ionization by collision.

45.3. Discharge in Gases at Low Pressures.   When an electric discharge is maintained between two electrodes in a long glass tube filled
with air (Fig. 45.8), some beautiful and interesting effects are observed
as the air is pumped out of the tube.   If the potential difference between
the electrodes is not much greater than is necessary to maintain the discharge, sparks jump between the electrodes at atmospheric pressure.   As
the pressure in the tube is lowered, a narrow pink streamer appears
between the electrodes.   As the pressure is reduced further, the streamer
expands until it fills almost the entire volume of the tube.   By the time
the pressure is reduced to 1 mm Hg, the entire gas glows.

As the pressure is reduced still further, one reaches the stage of discharge indicated in Fig. 45.8. A velvety glow, known as the *cathode glow*, covers the surface of the negative electrode. Outside of this glow is a region called the *Crookes dark space*. Beyond this is a luminous region, known as the *negative glow*, and then a second dark region called the *Faraday dark space*. Then follows another luminous region, known as the *positive column* which reaches to the positive electrode. The positive column is not perfectly continuous, but may show alternate light

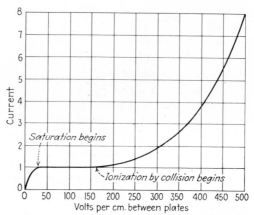

Fig. 45.7. Ionization by collisions in a gas.

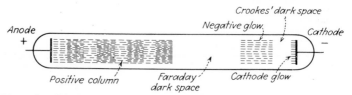

Fig. 45.8. Discharge of electricity through a gas at reduced pressure.

and dark layers called *striations* across the path of the discharge. If the distance between the electrodes is increased, the appearance of the cathode region is not much changed; the positive column increases in length to fill the added volume. Practically all the potential difference across the discharge tube occurs between the cathode and the negative edge of the positive column.

The potential difference required to maintain the discharge in a tube depends sensitively upon the pressure. When the air is at atmospheric pressure, a high potential difference is required. As the pressure is reduced, the potential difference required to maintain the discharge decreases steadily (Fig. 45.9). At some relatively low pressure, a minimum in the curve is reached; then as the pressure is decreased still further, the potential difference required to maintain the discharge increases sharply. Practically all the ionization of the air in the discharge tube occurs as the result of impacts. At high pressure the few residual ions (which may be formed by cosmic rays or by radioactivity) are accelerated by the electric field in the tube, but they travel short distances between collisions and attain relatively low energies. In order to produce more ionization they must have a certain minimum energy. If an ion is to attain this minimum energy between collisions at high pressure, it is necessary that a high electric field be maintained. As the pressure is reduced, the distance an ion travels between collisions is increased and the ion has a greater distance over which to acquire the energy needed to produce ionization by collision. Eventually the pressure becomes so low that ions may go all the way to the collecting electrode without having a collision. Then a higher potential difference is required to maintain

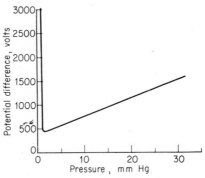

Fig. 45.9. The potential required to maintain a discharge as a function of pressure for a particular discharge tube.

the discharge; the ions may eject electrons and other ions when they collide with the electrode. These *secondary ions* aid in supporting the discharge.

45.4. Cathode Rays. As the pressure in a discharge tube is reduced beyond the stage pictured in Fig. 45.8, the Faraday dark space lengthens and the positive column shrinks. Eventually, a greenish glow is observed at the glass. As the pressure is reduced, this greenish glow may spread over almost the entire tube. The glow is due to fluorescence of the glass as it is bombarded by rays which Crookes showed originated at the cathode of the tube. These particles were given the name *cathode rays*. We now

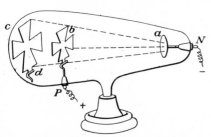

Fig. 45.10. Cathode rays travel in straight lines and cast sharp shadows.

know that cathode rays are high-speed electrons. Before these rays were identified as electrons (indeed, before electrons were "discovered"), they were known to have the following properties:

1. *The rays travel in straight lines.* This fact is shown by inserting in the path of the rays some obstacle such as the Maltese cross shown in Fig. 45.10. The geometric shadow of the cross on the tube no longer shows fluorescence, because the cross has intercepted the rays.

2. *The rays emerge normally from the surface of the cathode.* If the cathode is made with a concave surface, the cathode rays come to a focus near the geometric center of the concave surface. If the anode of the discharge tube is shielded by some obstruction or is off at one side of the tube, the cathode rays strike at points which one would expect would be hit if the rays left perpendicularly from the surface of the cathode.

3. *The rays penetrate small thicknesses of matter.* If a thin window of aluminum is inserted in the tube (Fig. 45.11), the cathode rays pass through the aluminum and make themselves evident by luminous streamers in the air beyond the window.

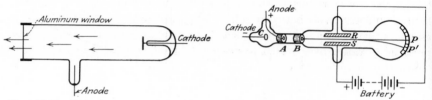

Fig. 45.11. Cathode rays pass through a thin aluminum foil.

Fig. 45.12. Cathode rays are deflected by an electric field.

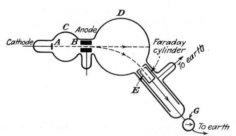

Fig. 45.13. Cathode rays are deflected by a magnetic field, directed in this case into the paper.

4. *The rays are deflected by a magnetic field.* If a bar magnet is held near the discharge tube, the magnetic field causes a deflection of the rays from the original path as is shown by the displacement of the brightly fluorescent region on the far end of the tube.

5. *The rays are deflected by an electrostatic field.* By applying a potential difference between the plates R and S in the discharge tube of Fig. 45.12, it is possible to deflect the beam of cathode rays.

6. *The rays carry negative electric charge.* If a beam of cathode rays is produced by the arrangement shown in Fig. 45.13, a bright spot is produced on the wall of the sphere D. By applying a suitable magnetic field, the cathode-ray beam can be bent so that it enters the small cylindrical vessel at E which is insulated from the glass bulb, but is connected to a galvanometer G. When the cathode rays are deflected into cylinder E, negative charge is collected, as is shown by the galvanometer.

45.5. The Ratio of Electronic Charge to Mass. By using a tube similar to that in Fig. 45.12, J. J. Thomson was able to measure the velocity of the cathode rays (electrons). If the plate S of this cathode-ray tube is made positive, the beam is deflected downward. Now if a magnetic field uniform over the area between the plates R and S is applied out of the plane of the paper, it exerts an upward force on the moving electrons. It is possible to choose magnetic and electric fields in such a way that their effects exactly balance, the upward force due to the magnetic field being equal to the downward force due to the electrostatic field. Let e represent the charge on one electron. The force due to the electric field is then Ee, where E is the intensity of the electric field. Similarly, the force on this charge due to the magnetic field is given by evB, where B is the magnetic intensity and v the speed of the particles. When the beam is undeflected, these two forces are equal.

$$Ee = evB \qquad (45.1)$$

From this equation, $v = E/B$. Thomson measured the electric and magnetic field intensities and calculated the speed of the cathode rays. For a potential difference between anode and cathode of 25 kilovolts (kv), the speed is about 8×10^7 m/sec, almost one-third the speed of light.

If the electric field is reduced to zero while the magnetic field is maintained, the cathode-ray beam is deflected upward. While the particles are in the magnetic field, they follow a circular path of radius r. The force due to the magnetic field provides the necessary centripetal force perpendicular to the path. Therefore

$$\frac{mv^2}{r} = evB \qquad (45.2)$$

or

$$\frac{e}{m} = \frac{v}{Br} \qquad (45.2a)$$

By measuring the radius of curvature of this electron path from the deflection of the cathode-ray beam and then using the values of the velocity and magnetic intensity previously determined, the ratio of the charge to the mass of the electron can be computed. It is found to be

$$\frac{e}{m} = 1.759 \times 10^8 \text{ coul/g}$$

Thomson's pioneering experiments in deflecting beams of high-speed electrons by electric and magnetic fields laid the foundations for modern cathode-ray oscilloscopes and television-picture tubes.

In Chap. 39 we learned that it takes 96,520 coulombs to deposit electrolytically 1 gram-equivalent weight of any element, which in the case of hydrogen is 1.008 g.   If the cathode rays in a discharge tube bear the same magnitude of charge as a monovalent ion, we can calculate the ratio of the mass M of a hydrogen atom to that of the electron.   For the hydrogen atom $e/M = 96,520/1.008 = 9.575 \times 10^4$ coul/g, from which we have

$$\frac{\text{Mass of hydrogen atom}}{\text{Mass of electron}} = \frac{M}{m} = \frac{1.759 \times 10^8}{9.575 \times 10^4} = 1,837$$

45.6. The Charge on the Electron.   Millikan measured the charge on the electron and produced evidence that every electron carries the same charge.   Millikan's apparatus is shown schematically in Fig. 45.14. Two horizontal plates B and C are placed a few centimeters apart.   An atomizer A shoots a fine spray of oil into the space above these plates. The drops of oil are so small that they do not settle for a long time.

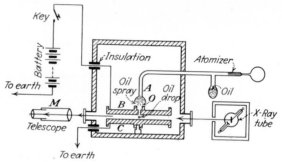

Fig. 45.14. Millikan's apparatus for determining the charge on the electron.

Eventually one or more of the drops finds its way through the opening O in the upper plate.   A telescope is focused on this drop so that its movements can be observed over a long period of time.   The rate at which the drop falls can be measured by means of a micrometer eyepiece in the telescope.

A beam of x-rays is next sent into the air between the horizontal plates. By means of these x-rays electrons are detached from the atoms of air. One or more of these electrons may be captured by oil drops.   If the upper plate B is charged positively and the lower C negatively, there is an upward force on a negatively charged oil drop.   If the electric field is sufficiently strong, this upward force may equal or exceed the weight of the drop.   Under such conditions the drop may be made to hang in the air for a substantial time.   If the downward pull of gravity and the upward pull of electrostatic field leave the oil drop essentially at rest, we may write

$$W = Eq = \frac{Vq}{d}$$

where W is the weight of the drop, q the charge on the drop, E the electric field strength, V the potential difference between the plates, and d their separation.   By measuring W, V, and d it is possible to calculate the charge q.   Frequently, a number of electrons may be attached to the drop and as a result q is several times the charge on a single electron. Careful observations show that whatever charges are present, their magnitudes are always integer multiples of a single elementary charge.   This charge e is the smallest known unit of electricity.   It is the fundamental unit of electric charge and is borne by all electrons.

$$e = 1.602 \times 10^{-19} \text{ coulomb}$$

The procedure just described is an oversimplification of the method used by Millikan, who actually measured the velocity of the oil drop as it moved upward under the influence of the electric field and the velocity of the same drop as it moved downward due to gravity with the electric field turned off.   The calculations are straightforward, but somewhat involved; they lead to the result quoted above.

45.7. The Mass of the Electron.   Once the charge on the electron is known, the mass can be calculated from the fact that the ratio e/m ($= 1.759 \times 10^8$ coul/g) is known.   The mass of the electron is 9.1085×10^{-31} kg.

Early measurements on the ratio e/m for cathode rays showed that the value depended somewhat on the energy of the electrons; the higher the energy, the smaller e/m.   Some years later Einstein developed his famous theory of relativity, which predicts that the mass of a body depends on its velocity according to the relation

$$m = \frac{m_0}{\sqrt{1 - v^2/c^2}} \tag{45.3}$$

where m_0 is the mass of the body at rest, c the speed of light *in vacuo*, and v the speed of the body.   For ordinary objects and speeds, the change of mass with velocity is too small to be observed, but for electrons which fall through potential differences of many thousand volts, the change in mass with velocity becomes an important consideration.

According to the theory of relativity, no energy can be transmitted with a velocity which exceeds the speed c of light in vacuum.   If an electron which is moving with almost the speed of light is acted upon by an accelerating electric field, the velocity is increased very little and the work done on the electron goes into an increase in mass.   This is an example of the celebrated discovery of Einstein that *mass is a form of energy.* The kinetic energy of an ordinary body is given by $mv^2/2$.   This is an approximation derived on the assumption the mass remains constant. It is valid whenever the speed is small compared with c.   Einstein's theory shows that when the speed of a body is comparable with c the kinetic energy is given by

$$\text{Kinetic energy} = (m - m_0)c^2 \qquad (45.4)$$

Since high-energy electrons are usually produced by accelerating them through a large potential difference, it is convenient to measure their energies in electron volts. *One electron volt is the energy attained by an electron in falling through a potential difference of one volt.* Modern accelerators produce electrons with energies of many million electron volts (Mev).

Example. A Van de Graaff generator accelerates electrons to a kinetic energy of 2 Mev. Find the mass of these electrons. Calculate the speed of the 2-Mev electrons.

$$2 \text{ Mev} = 2 \times 10^6 \text{ ev} \times 1.602 \times 10^{-19} \text{ joule/ev} = 3.2 \times 10^{-13} \text{ joule}$$
$$3.2 \times 10^{-13} \text{ joule} = (m - m_0)c^2 = (m - m_0)9 \times 10^{16}$$
$$m - m_0 = 35.6 \times 10^{-31} \text{ kg}$$
$$m = (35.6 + 9.1) \times 10^{-31}$$
$$= 44.7 \times 10^{-31} \text{ kg (almost 5 times the rest mass)}$$
$$44.7 \times 10^{-31} = \frac{9.11 \times 10^{-31}}{\sqrt{1 - v^2/c^2}}$$

Squaring both sides and transposing yields

$$2{,}000 \left(1 - \frac{v^2}{c^2}\right) = 83$$
$$\frac{v^2}{c^2} = \frac{1{,}917}{2{,}000} = 0.959 \frac{m^2}{\text{sec}^2}$$
$$v = 0.98c$$
$$= 2.94 \times 10^8 \text{ m/sec}$$

Table 1 shows how the ratios v/c and m/m_0 vary with the kinetic energy of an electron. In a modern synchrotron in which electrons are given kinetic energies of 1 billion electron volts, the mass of the moving electron is greater than the mass of the hydrogen atom at rest!

Table 1

Kinetic energy of electron		$\dfrac{v}{c} = \dfrac{\text{speed of electron}}{\text{speed of light}}$	$\dfrac{m}{m_0}$
ev	joules		
0	0	0	1
10^2	1.6×10^{-17}	0.0198	1.0002
10^3	1.6×10^{-16}	0.0625	1.001
10^4	1.6×10^{-15}	0.195	1.02
10^5	1.6×10^{-14}	0.550	1.20
10^6	1.6×10^{-13}	0.938	2.96
10^7	1.6×10^{-12}	0.992	20.6
10^8	1.6×10^{-11}	0.999+	197
10^9	1.6×10^{-10}	1.000−	1,960

45.8. Positive Rays and the Mass Spectrometer. We have not yet considered the positive ions passing through a gas-discharge tube. Since electrons are negatively charged and a gas molecule is originally neutral, the residue after the removal of an electron carries a *positive* charge. The residue has a mass large in comparison with that of the electron. When a potential difference is applied between the electrodes of the discharge tube, positive ions move to the cathode. If a hole is made in the cathode normal to its surface, some of these positive ions stream through it. These ions, often called *positive rays*, can be deflected by electric and magnetic fields. In this way their masses and charges may be determined.

The discharge tube (Fig. 45.15) used by J. J. Thomson for this purpose consists of a large bulb C in which the cathode A is pierced by a small hole through which comes a fine pencil of positive rays. These ions pass

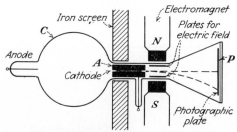

Fig. 45.15. Positive rays passing through the hole in the cathode are deflected by both an electric and a magnetic field.

between the poles N and S of an electromagnet and then fall on a photographic plate P where they produce blackening. By means of an electrostatic field in the same direction as the magnetic field, a second deflection is produced at right angles to the first. Positive rays of different masses and charges are deflected to different positions on the photographic plate (Fig. 45.16). The ratio of charge to mass can be determined from the shape and location of the spots on the photographic plate. In this way J. J. Thomson showed in 1907 that neon is composed of atoms with two different mass numbers, 20 and 22. This was the first positive proof that atoms of a given chemical element may have different masses. Atoms of the same element which have different masses are called *isotopes*.

In recent years very accurate instruments known as mass spectrometers (Fig. 45.17) have been developed for measuring the masses of isotopes and complex ions. In all these instruments streams of charged particles are deflected by magnetic (and electric) fields and the ratio of charge to mass for the particles determined from a knowledge of the path they follow. Figure 45.18 shows the circular paths into which beams of ions of three different masses are bent by a uniform magnetic field directed into the paper.

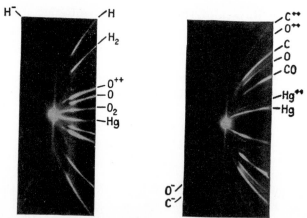

Fig. 45.16. Photographs of positive rays after deflection by parallel electric and magnetic fields.

Fig. 45.17. A mass spectrograph for separating positive ions of different masses. (*Westinghouse Electric Corp.*)

45.9. Avogadro's Number and the Masses of Atoms. We now consider how we find Avogadro's number, the number of atoms in a gram-atomic weight. If we assume that a monovalent atomic ion is a neutral atom with a single electron missing, the positive charge on the ion is the same as the electronic charge, 1.602×10^{-19} coulomb. Since it takes 96,520 coulombs to deposit 1-atomic weight of any monovalent element, Avogadro's number N becomes

$$N = \frac{96,520}{1.602 \times 10^{-19}} = 6.025 \times 10^{23}$$

The atomic weight of chlorine is 35.5 and the average mass of chlorine atoms is given by $35.5/(6.025 \times 10^{23}) = 5.89 \times 10^{-23}$ g $= 5.89 \times 10^{-26}$ kg. Similar reasoning permits us to calculate the average masses of atoms of any other element. These average masses do not, of course, represent the masses of all the

Fig. 45.18. Paths of atomic beams of three different masses in a mass spectrograph. (*Westinghouse Electric Corp.*)

atoms of the element, since many elements have atoms of several different masses. For example, chlorine is roughly three-fourths atoms of mass 5.8×10^{-26} kg and one-fourth atoms of mass 6.14×10^{-26} kg.

45.10. The Electron Microscope. An important application of electric and magnetic fields in controlling the trajectories of moving charged particles is found in the electron microscope. The resolving power of an optical microscope is limited by the wavelength of the light that can be used. In order to recognize two neighboring particles as separate particles, light of very short wavelength must be used if the particles are very close together.

Electrons also have wave properties. The wavelength λ of an electron moving with a velocity v is (Sec. 49.12)

$$\lambda = \frac{h}{mv} \qquad (45.5)$$

where m is the mass of the electron and h is a universal constant known as Planck's constant (Sec. 46.1). When accelerated through potential differences in the neighborhood of 100,000 volts, electrons have wavelengths as short as those found in x-rays. With such wavelengths, particles that are as close as 10^{-9} m can be separated and photographed by an electron microscope (Fig. 45.19).

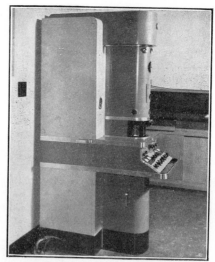

Fig. 45.19. An electron microscope. (*Radio Corp. of America.*)

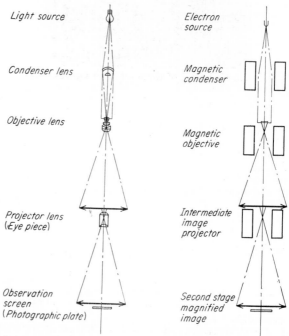

Fig. 45.20. Schematic drawing of an electron microscope and an optical microscope. (*Radio Corp. of America.*)

A comparison of an optical microscope and an electron microscope is shown in Fig. 45.20.   The lenses of the optical microscope are replaced by magnetic lenses, which consist of coils of wire carrying currents.   The magnetic fields produced by these coils are used to focus the electrons that are emitted by the hot filament. The object to be examined is on a thin collodion film.   The electrons penetrate this film with some decrease in velocity.   Below the object to be investigated is another magnetic lens which serves the same purpose as the objective lens in an optical microscope.   It produces an enlarged image of the original object.   This image is further magnified when the electrons pass through a second magnetic

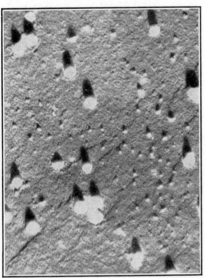

Fig. 45.21. An electron micrograph of influenza virus shadowed with gold to make it appear in relief.   (*Courtesy of R. W. G. Wyckoff and R. C. Williams.*)

lens.   Finally, an enlarged image is formed on a fluorescent screen or on a photographic plate.   Figure 45.21 shows the image of an influenza virus formed by an electron microscope.

PROBLEMS

1. The current in the plate circuit of a vacuum tube is 50 ma.   How many electrons are arriving at the plate each second?   *Ans.* 3.1×10^{17}

2. A device for measuring very small currents has been designed, which measures a current of 60 electrons per second.   How many amperes is that?

3. Find the kinetic energy in joules of an electron which has been accelerated through a potential difference of 200 volts.   *Ans.* 3.2×10^{-17} joule

4. A 10-watt lamp is turned on for a period of 6 hr.   How many electrons pass through in that time?   (The source of current is a 110-volt d-c line.)

5. Find the speed of an electron with an energy of 25 ev.   *Ans.* 2.97×10^6 m/sec

6. Two small spheres, equally charged with negative electricity, at a distance of 2 cm repel each other with a force of 10^{-4} newton.   How many excess electrons does each sphere carry?   What is the mass of these electrons?

7. Find the mass of an electron traveling at 0.8 times the speed of light (2.4 × 10⁸ m/sec). How many times as great as the rest mass is this value?

Ans. 1.52 × 10⁻³⁰ kg; 1.67

8. In Millikan's oil-drop experiment, the charge on the oil drop is equal to the charge on 3 electrons. The oil drop is in an electric field arising from a difference of potential of 5,000 volts between two plates that are at a distance of 0.75 cm from each other. Find the force acting on the oil drop.

9. The plates of a cathode-ray tube are parallel and 0.5 cm apart. The potential difference between these plates is 15,000 volts. Find the force on an electron passing between the plates. *Ans.* 4.8 × 10⁻¹³ newton

10. An electron is moving perpendicular to a magnetic field with one-eighth the speed of light. If the intensity of the magnetic field is 0.06 newton/amp-m, what force acts on the electron?

11. In determining the speed of electrons by Thomson's method it is found that a magnetic field of 8 × 10⁻³ newton/amp-m is just adequate to compensate for an electric field of 5 × 10⁵ newton/coul. Find the speed. *Ans.* 6.25 × 10⁷ m/sec

12. Find the mass of a fluorine atom if the atomic weight of fluorine is 19.0.

13. In Millikan's oil-drop experiment an oil drop of 4.9 × 10⁻¹¹ g mass is "balanced" by applying a potential difference of 4,000 volts between plates which are 0.8 cm apart. How many elementary charges are on the oil drop? *Ans.* 6

14. Show [starting with Eq. (45.2)] that, if two ions of the same charge and energy but different mass are passing through a uniform magnetic field, the radii of the paths are proportional to the square roots of the masses.

15. Find the speed of an electron when its mass is ten times its rest mass.

Ans. 2.98 × 10⁸ m/sec

16. The gas between two parallel plates is ionized by a constant x-ray beam. If the voltage between the plates is increased from zero to a very high value, what happens to the current? Explain carefully. Is Ohm's law obeyed?

17. List five properties of cathode rays.

CHAPTER 46

Photoelectricity
and Thermionic Emission

46.1. The Photoelectric Effect. In 1887 Hertz was doing pioneering work in the study of radio waves. In this work he used spark gaps and observed that when ultraviolet light fell on the electrodes of the gap, a spark passed at a substantially lower potential difference. A little later it was found that a negatively charged sheet of zinc lost its charge when it was exposed to ultraviolet light, but retained its charge when positive. It was several years before this phenomenon received adequate explanation.

When ultraviolet light falls on a metallic surface, electrons are liberated from the metal. The energy required to eject an electron is provided by the incident electromagnetic radiation. If the metal is charged negatively, these "photoelectrons" are repelled. When the metal is positive, the photoelectrons are attracted back to the plate and thus there is no loss of charge.

In the case of zinc, photoelectrons are emitted when ultraviolet light falls on the zinc, but none for visible light (Fig. 46.1). On the other hand, there are several elements from which light in the visible spectrum can produce photo-

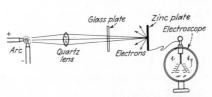

Fig. 46.1. When ultraviolet light falls on the zinc plate, photoelectrons are emitted. If the glass plate is inserted, photoemission ceases.

electrons. To explain this, we accept a hypothesis advanced by Planck in 1900 to account quantitatively for black-body radiation curves (Fig. 23.9). Planck suggested that radiation comes in small packets which we call *photons* or *quanta*. The energy associated with each photon is given by

$$\text{Energy of photon} = hf \tag{46.1}$$

553

where f is the frequency of the radiation and h is a universal constant equal to 6.625×10^{-34} joule-sec. In honor of its discoverer, h is called Planck's constant.

In order to eject a photoelectron from a surface, a photon must have enough energy to free the electron from the atom or material with which it is associated. If it requires an energy W to remove an electron from the metal and if the photon brings up an energy hf which is greater than W, the difference in energy appears as kinetic energy of the ejected photoelectron. This explanation of the photoelectric effect in terms of quanta was made by Einstein in 1905 and was one of the early triumphs of the quantum idea. If we let W_{min} represent the smallest energy which can free an electron from the solid, the maximum kinetic energy of ejected electrons is given by Einstein's photoelectric relation

$$\tfrac{1}{2}mv_{max}^2 = hf - W_{min} \qquad (46.2)$$

Many careful experiments have shown that the Einstein relationship is correct. If the frequency of the incident light is increased, the maximum kinetic energy of the ejected photoelectrons increases correspondingly (Fig. 46.2). Similarly, if the frequency of the incident photons is decreased, the energy of ejected photoelectrons decreases until the frequency $f_{min} = W_{min}/h$ is reached. For any lower frequency no photoelectrons are emitted.

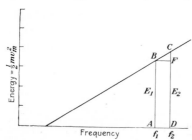

Fig. 46.2. Relation between frequency of light and energy of emitted electrons.

If the frequency of the incident light is kept constant while the intensity is changed by increasing the number of photons incident, the number of photoelectrons emitted increases. For a given frequency of radiation the number of photoelectrons ejected per second is directly proportional to the intensity of the incident radiation.

Among the metals from which photoelectrons may be ejected by visible light are barium, cesium, lithium, potassium, sodium, and rubidium. These are elements from which it is particularly easy to remove an electron in chemical reactions. Both chemical and photoelectric properties of electropositive elements depend on the ease with which an electron may be removed.

Example. Light of wavelength 700 mμ is required to cause the emission of electrons from a potassium surface. What is the energy necessary to remove one of the least firmly bound electrons? Find the kinetic energy and velocity of such an electron if the potassium surface is bombarded with light of wavelength 500 mμ.

Energy of a 700-mμ photon $= hf = hc/\lambda$

$$= 6.6 \times 10^{-34} \text{ joule-sec} \times \frac{3 \times 10^8 \text{ m/sec}}{700 \times 10^{-9} \text{ m}}$$

$$= 2.83 \times 10^{-19} \text{ joule}$$

Since this is the lowest-frequency photon which causes photoemission, $W_{min} = 2.83 \times 10^{-19}$ joule.

Energy of a 500-mμ photon $= 6.6 \times 10^{-34} \times \dfrac{3 \times 10^8}{500 \times 10^{-9}}$

$$= 3.96 \times 10^{-19} \text{ joule}$$

$$\tfrac{1}{2}mv_{max}^2 = hf - W_{min} = (3.96 - 2.83) \times 10^{-19} \text{ joule}$$

$$= 1.13 \times 10^{-19} \text{ joule}$$

$$\tfrac{1}{2}(9.1 \times 10^{-31})v_{max}^2 = 1.13 \times 10^{-19}$$

$$v_{max}^2 = 24.6 \times 10^{10}$$

$$v_{max} = 5 \times 10^5 \text{ m/sec}$$

46.2. Photoelectric Cells. Devices which utilize the photoelectric effect have many important applications. One is the exposure meter used by the photographer. Here the rate of photoelectron ejection by the incident light is a measure of the illumination. Photocells are used to open store doors when people cut off a light beam, to sound burglar alarms, and to turn on street lights

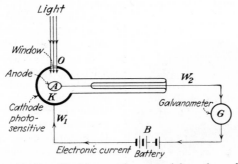

Fig. 46.3. Photoelectric cell with sensitive material on the walls of the tube.

whenever the sun fails to provide adequate illumination. Photocells are used in physics, biology, and medicine for measuring the intensity of various kinds of electromagnetic radiation. In the television studio it is variations in light intensity on a photosensitive surface which are used to convert the picture into electric signals in the image orthicon tube.

The sound track of motion-picture films permits varying amounts of light to pass through when the film is run between a light source and a photoelectric cell. The photoelectric cell converts the variations in light intensity into variations in electric current.

There are several different types of photoelectric cells. In some there is a light-sensitive surface which emits electrons and a second electrode, usually maintained at a fairly high positive potential, which collects the electrons. A circuit for such a photocell is shown in Fig. 46.3 with a galvanometer to measure the relative light intensity.

A second type is the *photovoltaic* or *barrier layer* photocell in which incident light produces an emf between two terminals. A typical photovoltaic cell (Fig. 46.4) contains a thin metal disk A on which there is a film of light-sensitive material *B*. In contact with *B* is a conducting ring or layer *C*. In one common type *A* is an iron plate and *B* is a thin film of selenium over which a thin gold coating is produced to serve as the conductor *C*. Another cell uses a copper plate as *A*, cuprous oxide as *B*, and a thin layer of silver as *C*. When the sensitive surface is illuminated with light, an emf is generated between the sensitive layer *B*

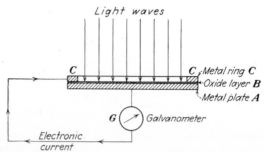

Fig. 46.4. Barrier-layer photoelectric cell. The incident light develops a potential difference.

and the metal disk *A*. The electrons produced flow from the sensitive layer of the tube to the metal plate across their surface of separation. This type of cell

Fig. 46.5. A barrier-layer photocell used for measuring illuminances. (*Weston Electrical Instrument Corp.*)

is used for exposure meters (Fig. 46.5) since the light produces the emf required to deflect the galvanometer.

A third type utilizes the photoconductivity effect. When photons are absorbed in a material, relatively few photoelectrons leave the material. Other electrons which have been freed are available for conduction through the material itself. If the material was initially a poor conductor, these electrons reduce the resistivity. The resistance of a piece of germanium, for example, decreases greatly when it is subjected to high illumination. The conductivity of a selenium cell may be twenty-five or more times as great in bright light as in the dark. Thallium sulfide cells have their conductivity changed by an even larger factor.

46.3. Thermionic Emission.

In the photoelectric effect we have energy of incident photons ejecting electrons from a material. The energy required to eject an electron may be supplied in other ways. For example, when high-speed electrons or ions collide with a material, electrons may be knocked out in the collision. When a beam of electrons ejects other electrons from a surface, the phenomenon is described as *secondary emission.*   Another means of giving electrons enough energy to escape is by heating a material to a high temperature.

In 1883, when Thomas Edison was developing the incandescent lamp, he made an important discovery. He observed that if he had a third electrode (Fig. 46.6) in one of his lamps, there was a current to this electrode when it was *positive* relative to the incandescent filament, but not when it was *negative*. *When materials are heated to a high temperature, there are electrons emitted.* In Edison's experiments these electrons were attracted to the positive electrode and a current was registered. When the third electrode was negative, the electrons were repelled. The emission of electrons from heated surfaces is *thermionic emission;* it is sometimes called the *Edison effect.*

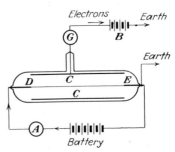

Fig. 46.6. Apparatus for observing the electron discharge from a hot wire.

The qualitative explanation of thermionic emission is relatively simple. In every material there are some electrons which are less tightly bound

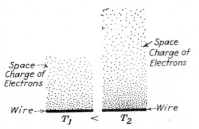

Fig. 46.7. Space charge of electrons near a wire increases as the temperature is raised.

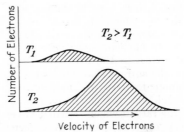

Fig. 46.8. Schematic diagram showing the number of electrons emitted and their average speeds increase as the temperature is raised.

than others.   In metals, for instance, there are electrons which are free to move about.   These electrons cannot leave the surface of the metal unless they are given sufficient energy.   One of the ways in which these electrons can receive enough energy to escape from the surface is by raising the temperature.   As the temperature goes up, an occasional electron receives enough energy to escape.   At higher temperatures more electrons escape.   Some of the electrons have not only enough energy to escape, but have relatively high speeds after they break free from the material.   Figures 46.7 and 46.8 show schematically that both the number and the average speed of the escaping electrons increase as the temperature is raised.

Thermionic emission is analogous in many ways to evaporation from the surface of a liquid. In both cases, particles which happen to obtain an unusually large amount of energy when they are at the surface may escape. The theoretical

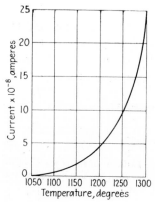

work of Richardson showed that the current density J (current I emitted per unit area A) from a heated surface should be given by the relation

$$J = \frac{I}{A} = aT^2e^{-b/T} \qquad (46.3)$$

where a and b are constants, T is the absolute temperature, and e is the base of the natural system of logarithms. The constant a is the same for all pure metals. The constant b varies from metal to metal and has particularly low values for those elements which are good thermionic emitters.

Fig. 46.9. Increase in thermionic emission with temperature.

The number of electrons emitted per unit area per second increases rapidly as the temperature is increased (Fig. 46.9). In order to measure the total emitted current, it is necessary that the potential difference between the emitting surface and the positive collecting plate be fairly high. If it is not, there is a cloud of electrons around the emitting surface which repels additional electrons and drives many of them back to the filament. This electron cloud is called *space charge*. If the collecting plate is made only slightly positive, the current is limited by this space charge and bears no simple relation to the total number of electrons emitted from the filament, since some emitted electrons are repelled by the space charge and return to the filament. Figure 46.10 shows how the current collected by the plate depends on the potential for three temperatures of the filament. In each case the maximum current is determined by the rate at which electrons are emitted. When every electron emitted is collected, the current has reached its *saturation* value. As the temperature of the emitting surface is raised, the saturation current increases. At low plate potentials the current is *space-charge limited* and does not depend on the temperature so long as the temperature is sufficiently high. Clearly, the current to the collecting plate does not obey Ohm's law.

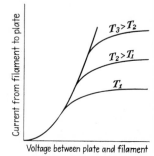

Fig. 46.10. Current to collecting plate as a function of potential difference between filament and plate for different filament temperatures.

The oxides of barium and strontium are copious electron emitters at relatively low temperatures. Many radio tubes and other electronic devices which operate at low plate potentials use a cathode coated with such oxides. Where high potentials are required, the bombardment of the negative cathode by positive ions may destroy the oxide surface. If the potentials used are not particularly high, a thoriated tungsten filament is the common emitter. It is produced by adding a small amount of thorium oxide to tungsten. When this material is heated, a layer of thorium is formed on the surface of the tungsten and provides an excellent emitting surface.   Where the filament is subject to bombardment by high-energy positive ions, thoriated tungsten fails and pure tungsten emitters are used.

46.4. The Diode.   A two-element vacuum tube containing an electron emitting cathode and a plate is called a *diode*.   Such a tube conducts electricity freely when the plate is positive, but not when the plate is negative.   A diode is useful for changing an alternating current to a direct one.   When it is used in this way, it is called a *rectifier*.

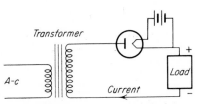

Suppose we wish to charge a battery, but we have available only an alternating potential difference.   The direct application of an alternating potential difference to the battery results in no useful charging, since

Fig. 46.11. Use of a diode as a rectifier. The load may be a battery to be charged.

the electrical energy stored during one-half cycle is returned during the second half.   However, if we provide a circuit like that of Fig. 46.11, there is a current through the battery only when the plate of the rectifier

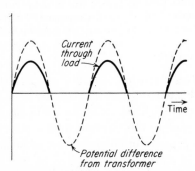

Fig. 46.12. Potential difference applied to the rectifier of Fig. 46.11 and the resulting current through the load.

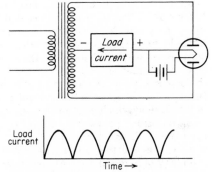

Fig. 46.13. Circuit to provide full wave rectification. The load current is shown below.

tube is positive.   Thus there is a current in the direction to charge the battery.   Figure 46.12 shows the alternating potential difference provided for the circuit and the current.   In this circuit current exists only during half a cycle.   This is therefore called *half-wave rectification*.

The circuit shown in Fig. 46.13 provides *full-wave rectification*.   When the upper terminal of the a-c transformer is positive, electrons go from the cathode to the upper plate of the tube and then through the load.   Conversely, when the lower end of the transformer is positive, electrons go to the lower plate.   The current through the load is always in the same direction.

If it is desired to make the current a steady one, one can introduce a filter consisting of one or more capacitors in parallel with the load and one or more inductors (called *chokes* when used in this way) in series with the load (Fig. 46.14). By suitable choice of capacitors and inductors it is possible to provide almost any

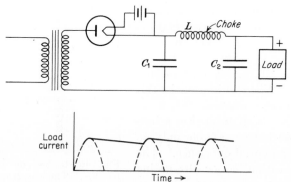

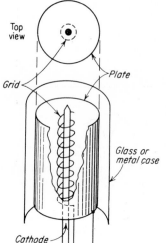

Fig. 46.14. A rectifier using a filter to keep the load current almost constant. The dotted curve shows how the load current would vary if the filter were eliminated.

desired degree of constancy in the current. The general action of the capacitors is to store energy in the electrostatic field when the output from the tube is at its maximum and to release this energy to maintain the current as the output from the tube falls to zero. An inductor connected in series with the load stores energy in its magnetic field when the current is maximum and releases this energy to maintain the current as the current decreases.

46.5. The Triode. In 1907 De Forest had the brilliant idea of introducing a *grid* between the cathode and the plate of a diode to control the current to the plate. This grid consists of an open mesh or helix

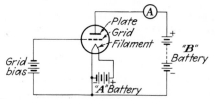

Fig. 46.15. Schematic structure of a simple triode.

Fig. 46.16. Simple circuit utilizing a triode.

around the filament, as shown in Fig. 46.15. By keeping the grid at a potential slightly negative relative to the cathode, it is possible to prevent it from collecting electrons (Fig. 46.16). Because the grid is close to the electron-emitting cathode, a small change in the grid potential makes a significant change in the number of electrons which pass the grid and reach the plate.

If the plate potential of a triode is kept constant and the grid potential is varied, the plate current varies as a function of grid potential as shown

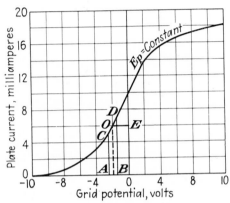

Fig. 46.17. Relation between plate current and grid potential in a triode.

in Fig. 46.17.   (Note that all potential differences are measured relative to the filament.)   If the grid is made sufficiently negative, the current to the plate may be cut off entirely.

Figure 46.18 shows the plate current of a typical triode as a function of plate potential for three different values of the grid potential.   Note that at points x and y in this figure the plate current is exactly the same.   In going from x to y the grid potential has been decreased from -2 to -5 volts, while the plate potential has been increased from 90 to 140 volts.   Thus, an increase in the plate potential of 50 volts has compensated for a decrease in grid potential of 3 volts, so far as the plate current is concerned.   To put it another way, a reduction in the grid potential of 3 volts requires an increase of 50 volts in plate potential to keep the plate current constant.   Under these conditions of operation, the

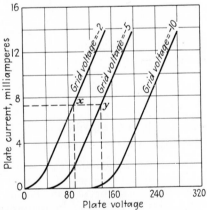

Fig. 46.18.   The plate current as a function of plate potential for three different grid potentials.

grid is 5% or 16.7 times as effective in controlling the plate current as is the plate.   We say that the *amplification factor* is 16.7.

If, when the grid potential of a triode is changed by a small amount $-\Delta V_g$, it requires a change in plate potential ΔV_p to keep the plate current constant, the amplification factor μ of the triode is defined to be $\Delta V_p/(-\Delta V_g)$.

$$\mu = \frac{\Delta V_p}{-\Delta V_g} \qquad I_p \text{ kept constant} \qquad (46.4)$$

46.6. The Triode as an Amplifier. The fact that small changes in the grid potential can produce large changes in the plate current in a triode permits us to obtain large potential variations in the plate circuit when the grid potential is changed by small amounts. Consider the circuit shown in Fig. 46.19. If we apply to the grid a small alternating signal, the plate current changes as indicated in Fig. 46.20. As a result

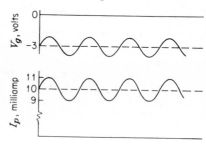

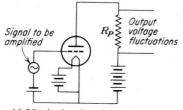

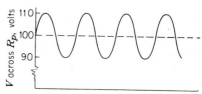

Fig. 46.19. A circuit using a triode to amplify alternating potential differences.

Fig. 46.20. Variation of grid potential, plate current, and potential difference across the load resistor R_p.

of this change in plate current, the potential difference across the plate resistor R_p varies. For such a circuit we define the *voltage gain* by

$$\text{Voltage gain} = \frac{V_{out}}{V_{in}} = \frac{R_p \Delta i_p}{\Delta e_g} \qquad (46.5)$$

where R_p is the resistance of the plate resistor and Δi_p and Δe_g are the variations in plate current and in grid potential, respectively.

It is possible to take the changes in potential across the plate (or load) resistor and apply them to the grid of a second amplifier tube. In this way signals may be amplified by factors of many hundred.

46.7. Rectifiers Using Semiconductors. It is possible to rectify alternating currents by suitable semiconductors as well as by use of vacuum tubes. A *semiconductor* is a material which has a conductivity intermediate between that of metals and of insulators. Aluminum oxide, silicon, germanium, copper oxide, and selenium are examples. In semiconductors relatively few electrons are free to move about. The current produced in a semiconductor by an applied voltage does not follow Ohm's law; rather it depends on such factors as what impurities are present, what type of contacts are used, how much light is falling on it, and what mechanical stresses it is under.

Consider a thin layer of aluminum oxide formed on an aluminum plate on the other side of which is a solution of boric acid. If an alternating potential difference is applied to such a system, the resistance is low when the aluminum is negative, high when it is positive. The aluminum oxide layer can accept electrons readily from the aluminum and transfer them to the solution. However, when the aluminum is positive, the oxide layer cannot supply many electrons. As a consequence, the current is high in one direction and low in the other. The rectification is not perfect, but the current is so low when the aluminum is positive that this combination of materials is used in electrolytic capacitors (Sec. 36.7).

One of the cheapest and most satisfactory types of rectifiers uses a thin layer of copper oxide as the semiconductor. Selenium rectifiers have also found wide use. In the early days of radio a "cat-whisker" detector was often used to rectify small high-frequency currents. It consisted of a tungsten point touching a crystal of galena or germanium. Electrons passed readily from the crystal to the point, but not in the opposite direction.

A particularly important type of rectifier is the *p-n junction*. Such a rectifier may be made primarily of germanium, an element which is normally tetravalent.

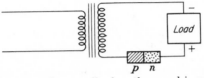

Fig. 46.21. A *p-n* junction conducts well when the *p* end is made positive and very little when the *p* end is negative.

If a few atoms of some pentavalent element such as arsenic are introduced into molten germanium, the crystal formed when the melt solidifies contains some arsenic atoms in the crystal structure. Each of these atoms "uses" four of its valence electrons to form bonds with the neighboring germanium atoms, but the fifth electron is not used in the binding. As a consequence, there is roughly one free electron for each arsenic impurity atom which acts as *donor* of electrons. This crystal structure is of the *n-type* since it has free negative charges.

If indium or some other trivalent atoms are introduced into molten germanium, these *impurity* atoms have one too few valence electrons to form bonds with the four neighboring germanium atoms and we have an electron *hole* in the structure. This hole may be filled by some other electron, but this only means there is a hole somewhere else. In such a crystal we may have conduction by motion of the *holes* which behave like positive charges. A crystal with electron holes is a *p-type* since conduction is by movement of positive holes. The indium atoms in a *p-type* crystal serve as *acceptors* for electrons.

It is possible to form single crystals which are *n-type* over a part of the volume and then become *p-type* (Fig. 46.21). Such a crystal conducts readily when the *n* region is made negative and the *p* region positive, but it offers high resistance when the potentials are reversed. Rectifiers using semiconductors such as germanium are rapidly finding use in a wide variety of electronic circuits.

Transistors with *n*-type ends and a thin *p*-type layer between can be used to amplify much like a triode vacuum tube. In many applications transistors are replacing vacuum tubes. Transistors need no heating supply for the filament, are inherently more rugged than vacuum tubes, have potentially longer lives, and can be made much smaller. Some transistors have volumes less than a cubic millimeter.

PROBLEMS

1. Determine the energy of a photon of yellow radiation whose wavelength is 5,890 A. *Ans.* 3.37×10^{-19} joule

2. A photon has an energy of 5×10^{-19} joule. Find its wavelength.

3. It requires 4×10^{-19} joule to remove one of the least tightly bound electrons from a surface. Find the longest wavelength which will be effective in producing photoelectrons. What is the maximum energy of photoelectrons ejected from this surface by ultraviolet radiation of $\lambda = 2,000$ A? *Ans.* 4,960 A; 4.9×10^{-19} joule

4. Electrons with a maximum energy of 2 ev are emitted from a surface radiated with light of $\lambda = 3,000$ A. Find W_{min}, the smallest energy which can free an electron from the surface.

5. On a clear day, about 2 cal of radiant energy from the sun strikes an area of 1 cm² each minute if that area is perpendicular to the direction of the sun. If this energy were all in the form of photons of yellow-green light whose wavelength is 5,500 A, how many photons would arrive per square centimeter in 1 sec?

Ans. 3.91×10^{17} photons/sec

6. Draw a circuit showing how a simple diode can be used as a rectifier to charge a battery.

7. A vacuum tube has an amplification factor of 15. If the grid voltage is decreased 0.3 volt, how much must the plate potential be raised if the plate current is to remain constant? *Ans.* 4.5 volts

8. Explain, using curves, how a triode can be used to amplify a small signal.

9. The plate current of a vacuum tube is 2 ma when the grid potential is -1.5 volts and the plate potential 120 volts. It is also 2 ma when the grid potential is -2.8 volts and the plate potential is 136 volts. What is the amplification factor? *Ans.* 12.3

10. Draw a diagram of a full-wave rectifier using a transformer as a power source to charge a battery.

11. A triode is used as an amplifier. If the grid is biased at -4 volts and a plate resistor of 10,000 ohms is used, the plate current is 0.010 amp. If the grid potential is varied from -4.2 to -3.8 volts, the plate current varies from 9 to 11 ma. Find the maximum and minimum potential difference across the plate resistor and the voltage gain. *Ans.* 90 volts; 110 volts; 50

12. A triode amplifier uses a plate resistor of 20,000 ohms. When no signal is applied to the grid, the plate current is 5 ma. If the voltage gain is 20, find the amplitude of the potential fluctuations across the plate resistor when a signal of amplitude 0.004 volt is applied to the grid. Between what limits does the plate current fluctuate?

13. The signal available from an antenna has an amplitude of 3 μv. If this signal is passed through two stages of amplification, each with a voltage gain of 40, what is the amplitude of the potential fluctuations in the output circuit? *Ans.* 0.0048 volt

14. Through how many more stages of the same voltage gain would the signal of Prob. 13 have to be passed to obtain an output voltage in excess of 5 volts?

CHAPTER 47

Electronics

47.1. Oscillatory Discharge. In Chap. 46 we have seen how simple diode and triode vacuum tubes operate. We now consider how vacuum tubes may be used in simple radio and television circuits. Since the detailed operation of a radio transmitter or receiver involves many complexities, we emphasize only the basic physics of their operation.

All radio and television stations send out electromagnetic waves at frequencies varying from many thousand to many million vibrations per second. Let us first consider how high-frequency alternating currents may be produced and sustained.

Consider the circuit of Fig. 47.1 in which we have a capacitor and an inductor. If we close key K_1, the capacitor is charged to a potential difference $\mathcal{E}$ and energy is stored in the capacitor. Let us now open K_1 and close K_2. The capacitor C begins to discharge and a current is established through the inductor L. Energy is transferred from the electric field of the capacitor to the magnetic field of the inductor. When C is completely discharged, energy is stored in the inductor which sustains the current until the capacitor has been charged oppositely to its original condition. Now the capacitor discharges by a current in the opposite direction, thereby transferring energy to the inductor, which in turn uses this energy to recharge the capacitor to the condition in which it was when K_2 was closed.

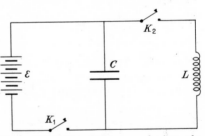

Fig. 47.1. Circuit for producing the oscillatory discharge of a capacitor through an inductor.

If there were no resistance in this circuit, the capacitor would be charged to the same potential difference with which it started. However, some of the energy is dissipated in heat in the inevitable resistance of the circuit; thus the potential difference does not attain the value $\mathcal{E}$.

The capacitor discharges again and again. The current rises and falls, as shown in Fig. 47.2. There are a number of oscillations before all the energy originally stored in the capacitor is dissipated.

The frequency of oscillation is the frequency to which the circuit is resonant. That is the frequency at which the inductive and capacitive

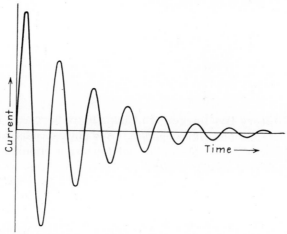

Fig. 47.2. Damped oscillations produced when a capacitor is discharged through an inductor.

reactances are equal, provided the resistance of the circuit is small compared with the reactances. By Eq. (44.10) the frequency of oscillation is given by

$$f = \frac{1}{2\pi \sqrt{LC}} \tag{47.1}$$

Example. The oscillating circuit of a radio station has an inductance of 5×10^{-6} henry and a capacity of 0.01 μf. Neglecting the effect of resistance, find the natural frequency and the wavelength of the electromagnetic waves.

$$f = \frac{1}{2\pi \sqrt{LC}}$$

$$= \frac{1}{2\pi \sqrt{5 \times 10^{-6} \times 1 \times 10^{-8}}}$$

$$= 720,000 \text{ cycles/sec}$$

$$\text{Wavelength} = \frac{\text{velocity}}{\text{frequency}}$$

$$= \frac{3 \times 10^{8} \text{m/sec}}{720,000/\text{sec}}$$

$$= 417 \text{ m}$$

47.2. The Triode as an Oscillator. The oscillations described in Sec. 47.1 are damped because energy is dissipated in heat and no energy is being supplied to the circuit.   Steady oscillations of constant amplitude can be maintained in such a circuit if energy is provided to compensate for energy losses.   It is possible to use a triode to produce such stable oscillations by providing energy to the oscillating circuit from the plate potential supply of the triode.   One of the ways in which this can be done is indicated in Fig. 47.3.

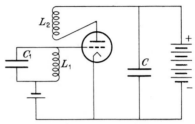

Here the condenser C_1 and the inductor L_1 form the oscillating circuit.   The oscillations produce variations in the potential of the grid.   This, in turn, results in variations of the plate current.   The varying plate current passes through the inductor L_2 and induces by mutual induction an emf in the coil L_1, thereby supplying energy to the oscillating grid circuit.

Fig. 47.3. A simple oscillator using a triode.

The energy is fed back into the grid circuit in such a way as to provide for the losses in the grid circuit.   In this way there are maintained oscillations of constant amplitude and of frequency determined by the grid-circuit elements.

If one wishes the oscillation frequency to remain very constant, one uses for C_1 a capacitor which has as dielectric between its plates a carefully cut crystal of quartz.   In an oscillating electric field, such a crystal undergoes mechanical vibrations (see Sec. 36.3), the frequency of which depends on the thickness of the quartz.   If the oscillating circuit and the crystal are resonant to essentially the same frequency, the oscillator assumes the frequency of the mechanical vibrations of the quartz.   In such a case the oscillator is *crystal controlled*.

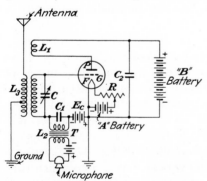

Fig. 47.4. A simplified radio transmitter.

47.3. Radio Transmitter. A very primitive type of radio transmitter is shown in Fig. 47.4.   It consists of an oscillator, an antenna, and a *modulator*.   The oscillator has a frequency determined by the resonant grid circuit.   For the standard radio band, frequencies range from 550 to 1,600 kc/sec.

The oscillations in the grid circuit produce through mutual induction an oscillating current in the inductor L_3 which is a part of the antenna circuit.   The oscillator thus "drives" the antenna, setting up in it an alternating current of frequency characteristic of the oscillator.   The current surging back and forth in the antenna produces the rapidly changing electromagnetic field which can be detected at great distances from the transmitter.

To understand the origin of the electromagnetic field sent out by the antenna, consider a single electron performing simple harmonic motion in an antenna (Fig. 47.5). When this electron moves from A to B, a magnetic field is produced at P directed into the paper. Simultaneously, the electric field at P changes in direction by the radiation vector ΔE. As the electron moves from B back to A, both the electric and magnetic

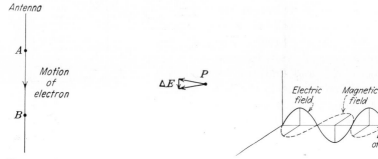

Fig. 47.5. An oscillating charge produces an electromagnetic field. As an electron moves from A to B, the electric field changes by ΔE and a magnetic field directed into the paper is produced. When the electron moves from B to A, these fields are reversed.

Fig. 47.6. Relation between electric and magnetic radiation fields some distance from an antenna when the charges oscillate parallel to the vertical axis.

radiation fields reverse. Both fields describe sinusoidal variations in phase with one another (Fig. 47.6).

As described thus far, this transmitter would send out a constant amplitude signal at a very high frequency, called the *carrier frequency*. If we wish to convey intelligence by such a signal, we must interrupt it or modify it in some way. The most primitive method of doing this is to turn the oscillator on and off, and thus send a series of dots and dashes. Early radio communication was carried on in this way. However, it is possible to send information which leads to accurate reproduction of sound waves. If we speak into the microphone of Fig. 47.4, there are set up in the grid circuit additional small voltage fluctuations which vary the amplitude of the oscillations. If we wish to send a 1,000-cycle note over the transmitter, we "modulate" (i.e., vary the amplitude) of the carrier wave at a frequency of 1,000 times a second. Since the carrier frequency is many thousand times as high as the highest sound frequency we wish to transmit, the carrier wave makes many thousands of oscillations for one period of the sound wave. The general appearance of the unmodulated carrier wave, of the sound frequency with which we modulate this wave, and of the modulated wave which is sent out by the transmitter are all shown in Fig. 47.7. This particular method of transmitting intelligence is called *amplitude modulation*. There are of course other ways in which the carrier wave can be modified to convey intelligence. One of the possibilities is to introduce fluctuations in the frequency, keeping the amplitude constant. This is *frequency modulation*.

47.4. The Radio Receiver. The electromagnetic waves sent out by a radio transmitter fall upon the antenna of the receiver shown schematically in Fig. 47.8. These electromagnetic waves set up oscillations in the antenna which induce small potential variations in the grid circuit of the receiver. There are many transmitters from which signals may

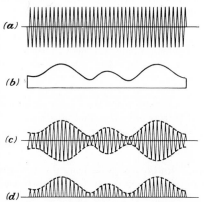

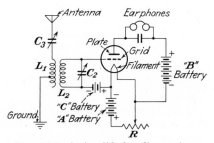

Fig. 47.7. (*a*) Unmodulated carrier wave, (*b*) audiofrequency wave, (*c*) modulated carrier wave, and (*d*) rectified wave.

Fig. 47.8. A simplified radio receiver.

be received. It is in the grid circuit L_2C_2 that the selection of which signal will be heard is made. By varying the capacitance of C_2, the grid circuit L_2C_2 can be made resonant to any desired carrier frequency. Then oscillations in the antenna corresponding to that particular frequency establish appreciable changes in potential in the grid circuit, while oscillations of all other frequencies produce negligible effects because the impedance of the circuit is large for other frequencies.

The oscillations in potential across C_2 in the resonance circuit are applied to the grid of the triode in Fig. 47.8. If this grid is made sufficiently negative, the plate current increases substantially when the grid potential changes in the positive direction, but decreases relatively little (or not at all) when the changes are in the negative direction. In this case the output of the plate circuit looks like that of Fig. 47.7*d*. The variations in plate current at radio frequency are such that the human ear cannot detect them; however, the average plate current over many carrier-wave oscillations fluctuates with the modulation frequency.

Thus, the current through the earphones oscillates with the modulation frequency and sound is heard.

If one wishes to drive a loudspeaker, much more energy must be provided than can be expected from the output of a single triode of the type indicated. In a modern radio receiver several more tubes may be used to provide this additional power. First of all, the signal coming into the initial resonant circuit is amplified before the detection process is performed. Then the audio frequency may be amplified several times before it is finally supplied to a *power amplifier* which drives the loudspeaker.

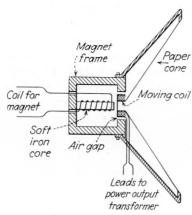

Fig. 47.9. A dynamic loudspeaker.

47.5. The Loudspeaker. A loudspeaker is a device which transforms audio-frequency variations in electric currents into sound waves. Figure 47.9 shows schematically the principal parts of a dynamic loudspeaker. A light thin coil of wire is attached to the apex of a light cone. The coil is placed in a magnetic field. Current from the power amplifier is fed to this coil; the fluctuating current produces fluctuating forces upon the coil, causing it to vibrate. The cone vibrates with the coil and produces waves in the surrounding air.

47.6. The Kennelly-Heaviside Layers. Radio reception from distant stations is usually superior at night. Sometimes reception is excellent at distances

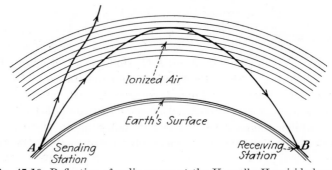

Fig. 47.10. Reflection of radio waves at the Kennelly-Heaviside layers.

of several thousand miles when a receiving station only a few hundred miles away may not be able to detect the signal. In order to explain these phenomena it was suggested by Kennelly and also by Heaviside that there are layers of ionized air in the upper atmosphere which act as refractors and reflectors of radio waves (Fig. 47.10). Ions are produced in the outer layers by a variety of processes, chiefly by ultraviolet light from the sun. The height of the ionized layers changes from time to time; as a result, the transmission of electrical waves varies with time. In general, the ionizing layers occur at different altitudes at night than during the day, being higher and more uniform at night.

47.7. The Cathode-ray Oscilloscope. One of the most useful of all types of vacuum tubes is the so-called *cathode-ray tube.* A heated cathode (Fig. 47.11) emits electrons. These electrons are accelerated to a cylindrical anode, which has a hole in its center through which the cathode rays pass. The electron beam may be controlled by the grid G. Beyond the anode we now have a beam of rapidly moving electrons of well-defined energy.

This beam passes between a pair of flat plates P_1 whose plane is horizontal. If a potential difference is applied between these plates, an electric field is created which may move the beam of electrons up or down. Next the beam passes between the pair of plates P_2 whose plane is vertical. If a potential difference is applied between these plates, the beam may be moved to right or left. If no potential difference is applied between the plates, the beam of electrons strikes the center of a screen coated with a fluorescent material that emits light where the electron

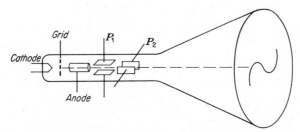

Fig. 47.11. Schematic diagram of a cathode-ray tube.

beam strikes. The position of the point on the screen at which electrons strike may be controlled by the potentials applied to the deflecting plates.

In one common application of the oscilloscope the horizontal deflectors P_2 have applied to them a saw-tooth potential variation which sweeps the beam at a constant rate from left to right and then suddenly switches the beam back to the left edge. If a sinusoidal potential difference is applied to the deflecting plates P_1, the beam traces a sine-wave curve on the face of the oscilloscope. If some other type of potential variation is applied to the plates P_1, the picture on the oscilloscope screen reproduces the fluctuations in potential across the deflecting plates.

When a cathode-ray tube is combined with electronic circuits for amplifying signals and applying potentials to the horizontal and vertical deflecting plates, the unit is called a *cathode-ray oscilloscope.* The cathode-ray oscilloscope is one of the most convenient, versatile, and powerful tools of modern physics.

47.8. Television. In the television receiver a cathode-ray tube, in which horizontal and vertical deflections are usually produced by magnetic, rather than electric fields, is used. The magnetic deflection is obtained by having a pair of coils, one on each side of the picture tube, that produce a horizontal magnetic field and another pair, one above and one below the neck of the tube, that produce a vertical field.   By sending high-frequency alternating currents through these coils it is possible to make the cathode-ray beam move back and forth across the tube, producing the familiar lines of the television picture.

If one moves the cathode-ray beam across the face of the oscilloscope and then down a little and across the screen, etc., there would be drawn on the face of the screen only a number of white lines.   However, by controlling the intensity of the beam by means of the grid in the cathode-ray tube, it is possible to draw lines which vary in their lightness, depending on the potential applied to the grid at the particular instant the spot is drawing a given segment of the line.   Thus the cathode-ray beam draws lines of varying brightness.   There are 525 horizontal lines drawn to make a complete picture.   In order to transmit pictures of moving objects, it is necessary that the picture be "redrawn" many times a second.   In

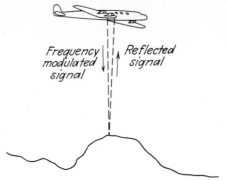

Fig. 47.12. Diagram of the use of a radio altimeter.

current television practice the even numbered lines are drawn in $\frac{1}{60}$ sec and the odd-numbered lines in the next $\frac{1}{60}$ sec.   Thus, 30 complete pictures or "frames" are drawn each second.

At the sending station the information transmitted is obtained in roughly the following way: An image of the picture to be transmitted is produced by lenses on the photosensitive screen of a tube known as an *image orthicon tube*.   Each element of the sensitive surface emits photoelectrons, the number of which depends upon the intensity of the incident light.   By a complex process the number of photoelectrons emitted from each of the tiny sensitive elements is determined and is converted into information which can be used to modulate the carrier wave.   At the receiver this information is used to control the grid potential at the instant the corresponding element of the picture is to be reproduced on the receiving screen.

47.9. Radar.   The wavelengths of ordinary radio waves are of the order of a thousand feet.   Such waves bend readily around obstacles such as buildings or airplanes.   If radio waves of much higher frequency, and therefore shorter wavelength, are produced, the waves are readily reflected by aircraft and other objects of comparable size.   Further, these waves can be focused into sharp beams by a reasonably small antenna.   If a sharply focused beam of high-frequency waves is used to scan the sky, it is reflected by airplanes or other objects in the sky.   By measuring the time lapse between the transmission of a pulse and the reception of the reflected pulse, one can determine the distance of the object from the transmitter, since radio waves are transmitted with the speed of light.

It is possible to scan a relatively large area by means of a radar transmitter and show on an oscilloscope screen the areas from which there is substantial reflection and those from which the reflection is much smaller. In this way one can make a radar map of an area which is not visible because of clouds, fog, or darkness.

One of the earliest and simplest examples of the use of radio waves to measure distance is found in the radio altimeter (Fig. 47.12). If a radio wave is sent down from an airplane, it is reflected by the earth. If this radiation is sent in pulses and it is possible to measure the time it takes the wave to go to the earth and return, the altitude of the plane above the terrain can be calculated.

PROBLEMS

1. WOSU broadcasts on an assigned frequency of 820 kc/sec. Find the wavelength of the radio waves sent out.   *Ans.* 366 m

2. Signals with a frequency of 600 kc/sec are sent out by a radio station. Find the wavelength, assuming that the waves travel with the speed of light.

3. What capacitance is required to be used with an inductance of 0.004 henry to have the combination resonant to a frequency of 820 kc/sec?   *Ans.* 9.4 $\mu\mu$f

4. What inductance is needed with a capacitance of 4 $\mu\mu$f to tune a circuit to a frequency of 5 megacycles/sec?

5. A radar unit sends out waves 40 cm in wavelength. What is the frequency of the radiation?   *Ans.* 750 megacycles/sec

6. What capacitance is required with an inductance of 2 μh to form a resonant circuit for a wavelength of 30 cm?

7. A television station operates at a frequency of 200 megacycles/sec. What inductance is needed with a capacitance of 4 $\mu\mu$f to form a circuit resonant to this frequency?   *Ans.* 1.58 $\times$ 10^{-7} henry

8. Radios are ordinarily tuned to various stations by changing the capacitance of an air condenser by varying the effective area of the plates. If one wishes to tune to a station with a higher frequency, must the effective area be increased or decreased? Explain.

9. The twelve standard TV channels are located in the 54 to 72, 76 to 78, and 174 to 216 megacycle bands, while the standard radio band is 550 to 1,600 kc. With this in view give at least one reason why switching TV channels is done by changing inductors while switching radio stations is done by changing a single variable air condenser.

PART VII

Atomic and Nuclear Physics

CHAPTER 48

Atomic Structure

48.1. Thomson's Atomic Model. Evidence from the discharge of electricity through gases, from the photoelectric effect, and from thermionic emission all suggest that the electron is one of the building blocks from which atoms are constructed. The fact that an atom is electrically neutral requires that it have equal amounts of positive and negative charge. Toward the end of the nineteenth century Thomson suggested that the positive electricity of an atom is distributed uniformly throughout a sphere which has the same radius as the atom (about 1A). Inside this sphere he proposed that there were a number of electrons which would correspond roughly to plums in a plum pudding. Photons of light, collisions with other atoms, or thermal collisions could eject an electron from such an atom. Fairly soon, however, it became evident that atoms must be constructed in a way very different from Thomson's model.

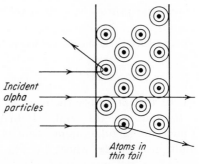

Incident alpha particles

Atoms in thin foil

Fig. 48.1. The fact that some alpha particles are scattered backward by a thin foil requires very large repulsive forces, which Rutherford explained by assuming all the positive charge is concentrated in a small nucleus.

48.2. The Rutherford Model of the Atom. In 1911 Rutherford fired positively charged alpha particles from radioactive materials at and through thin metal foils and observed how the alpha particles were deflected (Fig. 48.1). According to the Thomson model, one would expect only small deflections because the positive and negative electricity in the atom would be distributed over a relatively large volume. As a consequence, there should be no tremendously great forces deflecting the alpha particles. Rutherford's experiments showed that a surprisingly large number of the alpha particles were actually scattered backward by the foil. The alpha particles which went through had much

577

larger changes in direction than could be explained on the basis of the Thomson model. Rutherford showed that, if all the positive electricity of the atom were concentrated at almost a point, such significant scattering at large angles was to be expected. He calculated how the number of alpha particles scattered should depend on angle for various kinds of foils and for alpha particles of different energies. His predictions were in excellent agreement with measurements made by Geiger and Marsden.

In the Rutherford model all the positive electricity is concentrated in a very small volume called the *nucleus*. Surrounding this core are the electrons, held to the nucleus by electrostatic attraction. The radius of even the largest nucleus is only about 10^{-14} m, while the radius of a typical atom is nearer to 10^{-10} m. Thus all the positive charge and almost all the mass of the atom is concentrated in about one million millionth of the volume of the atom.

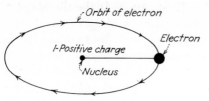

Fig. 48.2. Bohr picture of the hydrogen atom.

48.3. The Bohr Atom.

In 1913 Niels Bohr made a great forward stride in explaining the structure of the atom. Bohr imagined that a hydrogen atom was composed of a nucleus called a *proton* and a single electron which revolves about the proton in a circular orbit (Fig. 48.2). The centripetal force required to keep the electron in this orbit is provided by the Coulomb electrostatic attraction between the proton and electron.

$$\frac{mv^2}{r} = 9 \times 10^9 \frac{e^2}{r^2} \tag{48.1}$$

where m, v, and e are the mass, velocity, and charge of the electron and r is the radius of the orbit. Bohr further postulated that the only values which the angular momentum of the electron could have were integer multiples of $h/2\pi$, where h is Planck's constant.

$$mvr = n \frac{h}{2\pi} \tag{48.2}$$

where n is an integer. This condition Bohr adopted from the radiation laws which Planck had developed several years earlier.

Solving Eqs. (48.1) and (48.2) simultaneously for r yields

$$r = \frac{n^2 h^2}{4\pi^2 (9 \times 10^9) m e^2} \tag{48.3}$$

The smallest orbit in which the electron can exist is that given by $n = 1$. If $n = 1$ and the other constants are given their proper values, we find that $r_1 = 5.28 \times 10^{-11}$ m. This agrees well with measured values of the radius of the hydrogen atom. The next smallest allowed radius is four times as great, the third possible radius is nine r_1, and so forth. Normally, the hydrogen electron is in the orbit corresponding to $n = 1$, but on occasions it may be "excited" and find itself in one of the larger orbits.

The total energy of the hydrogen electron is the sum of the kinetic and potential energies. The kinetic energy $mv^2/2$ is, by Eq. (48.1),

$$\text{Kinetic energy} = \tfrac{1}{2}mv^2 = \frac{9 \times 10^9 e^2}{2r}$$

while the potential energy, assumed to be zero when proton and electron are an infinite distance apart, is given by Eq. (35.1),

$$\text{Potential energy} = Ve = -\frac{9 \times 10^9 e^2}{r}$$

from which

$$\text{Total energy} = \text{kinetic} + \text{potential energy} = -\frac{9 \times 10^9 e^2}{2r}$$

$$= -\frac{2\pi^2 (9 \times 10^9)^2 m e^4}{n^2 h^2} \tag{48.4}$$

The negative sign means the electron is bound to the nucleus and cannot escape.

The hydrogen electron has its lowest possible energy when it is in the orbit characterized by $n = 1$. If the electron is in any other orbit, it may be expected to jump to an orbit of lower energy (Fig. 48.3). When it makes such a jump a photon of radiation is emitted. The energy of the emitted photon is hf, where f is the frequency. It is equal to the energy lost by the electron as it goes from a level A characterized by the integer n_A to another level B characterized by n_B.

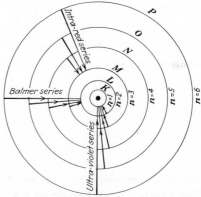

Fig. 48.3. Circular orbits and transitions for the hydrogen atom (not to scale).

$$\text{Energy radiated} = hf = \frac{2\pi^2 (9 \times 10^9)^2 m e^4}{h^2} \left(\frac{1}{n_B^2} - \frac{1}{n_A^2} \right) \tag{48.5}$$

Combining Eq. (48.5) with the relation $c = f\lambda$, we obtain

$$\frac{1}{\lambda} = \frac{f}{c} = \frac{2\pi^2(9 \times 10^9)^2me^4}{h^3c}\left(\frac{1}{n_B^2} - \frac{1}{n_A^2}\right)$$

$$= R\left(\frac{1}{n_B^2} - \frac{1}{n_A^2}\right) \tag{48.6}$$

where R is called the Rydberg constant. It has the value 1.0968×10^7 m^{-1}.

48.4. Spectral Series in Hydrogen. Many years before Bohr's work it was known that the visible spectrum of hydrogen consists of a

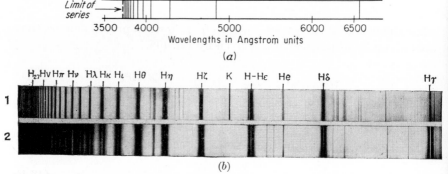

Fig. 48.4. The visible spectrum of hydrogen consists of the Balmer series. (*a*) Diagram of Balmer series lines. (*b*) Spectrum of the star ζ Tauri showing the Balmer series of hydrogen. (*Photographed by R. H. Curtiss, University of Michigan.*)

number of lines (Fig. 48.4) which become closer together as the wavelength decreases, until finally at a certain minimum wavelength called the *series limit*, the lines cease. In 1885 Balmer showed that the wavelengths of these lines are predicted accurately by

$$\lambda = 3.6456 \times 10^{-7}\left(\frac{m^2}{m^2 - 4}\right) \qquad \lambda \text{ in meters}$$

where m is an integer taking the values 3, 4, 5, . . . This group of lines is known as the Balmer series.

According to Bohr's formula [Eq. (48.6)], the wavelengths of the series of lines produced when electrons jump from outer orbits to that characterized by $n_B = 2$ are given by the relation

$$\frac{1}{\lambda} = R\left(\frac{1}{4} - \frac{1}{n_A^2}\right)$$

or

$$\lambda = \frac{1}{R}\left(\frac{4n_A^2}{n_A^2 - 4}\right) = 3.65 \times 10^{-7}\left(\frac{n_A^2}{n_A^2 - 4}\right)$$

This agrees with Balmer's formula if we let $n_A = m$.

Thus, we explain the Balmer series as follows: In a discharge of electricity through hydrogen, electrons are torn free from hydrogen atoms. Eventually, the electrons and the hydrogen nuclei recombine and in this recombination the electron may be captured in any one of the many possible orbits whose radii are given by Eq. (48.3). Atoms with electrons in these higher orbits are said to be *excited*. The electron of an excited hydrogen atom normally makes transitions to lower states until it finally reaches the stable orbit corresponding to $n = 1$. When it makes jumps from one orbit to another, radiation is emitted. The Balmer series arises when electrons from higher orbits jump to the orbit corresponding to $n = 2$, as is shown schematically in Fig. 48.3. Figure 48.5 shows the

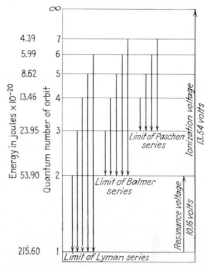

Fig. 48.5. Energy-level diagram for hydrogen (not to scale).

energy levels of the hydrogen atom and the transitions which lead to the Balmer series and to other series.

We expect electrons eventually to make transitions to the orbit $n = 1$, since this is the normal state for the electron to occupy. For such a transition Eq. (48.5) shows that the emitted frequencies should be in the ultraviolet region. Lyman studied the ultraviolet spectrum of hydrogen and found, just as the Bohr theory predicts, a series of lines corresponding to electron jumps from excited levels to the level $n = 1$. This series we call the *Lyman* series in honor of its discoverer.

What should happen if electrons in higher excited states make transitions to levels $n = 3$? Once again Eq. (48.5) reveals that the frequencies expected would be in the infrared region of the spectrum. Such a series had been found by Paschen. Later another series in the far infrared was discovered by Brackett. The wavelengths of the lines in these series are accurately given by Eq. (48.6) when $n_B = 3$ for the Paschen series and $n_B = 4$ for the Brackett series, while n_A takes on all larger integer values.

Sommerfeld extended Bohr's theory to include elliptic orbits (Fig. 48.6) as well as circular ones. For each value of n in Bohr theory there are n allowed orbits, one circular (the Bohr orbit) and $(n - 1)$ elliptic orbits. However, the energies of all orbits for a given n are given *almost* exactly by Eq. (48.4). In modern wave mechanics the ideas of sharp orbits and well-defined velocities at each point of the electronic motion are abandoned, but the allowed electron energies remain virtually unchanged.

In 1925 Uhlenbeck and Goudsmit discovered that many features of atomic spectra could be explained by assuming that the electron not only goes around a nucleus in an orbit but also rotates or "spins" around its own axis. This spin produces a magnetic moment of great importance in atomic spectra.

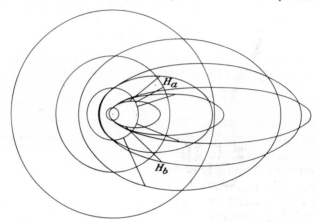

Fig. 48.6. Circular and elliptic orbits of the hydrogen atom.

48.5. The Atomic Number and Characteristic X-rays. Consider an *ionized* helium atom. Here we have a nucleus with a charge of two fundamental units and a single electron. If we apply the Bohr theory to this system, the relations developed for hydrogen are applicable, provided we put $2e$ for the nuclear charge. The energies become four times as large in magnitude, and the predicted frequency of the line emitted for any given transition is four times that for hydrogen. Experiments reveal that this is indeed the case, except for very small shifts which can be explained readily.

In general, if we have a nucleus with positive charge Ze and a *single* electron, the force between electron and nucleus is $9 \times 10^9 Ze^2/r^2$ and the radius of an allowed circular orbit is found by the method of Sec. 48.3 to be

$$r = \frac{n^2 h^2}{4\pi^2 (9 \times 10^9) m Z e^2} \tag{48.3a}$$

while the energy becomes

$$\text{Total energy} = -\frac{2\pi^2 (9 \times 10^9)^2 m Z^2 e^4}{n^2 h^2} \tag{48.7}$$

Suppose that a single electron circling a nucleus of charge Ze in the orbit characterized by $n_A = 2$ were to make a transition to the $n_B = 1$ orbit. The Bohr theory predicts for such a transition that a photon of energy W should be emitted where, by Eqs. (48.5) and (48.7),

$$W = hf = \frac{2\pi^2(9 \times 10^9)^2 mZ^2 e^4}{h^2}\left(\frac{1}{n_B^2} - \frac{1}{n_A^2}\right)$$

$$= \frac{2\pi^2(9 \times 10^9)^2 mZ^2 e^4}{h^2}\left(\frac{1}{1^2} - \frac{1}{2^2}\right) \tag{48.8}$$

If this equation is solved for f with the known values of h, m, and e inserted, we obtain

$$f = 2.46 \times 10^{15} Z^2 \text{ per sec} \tag{48.9}$$

The English physicist Moseley found in the x-ray spectrum of many elements a line of frequency given by the empirical relation

$$f = 2.52 \times 10^{15}(Z - 1.13)^2 \text{ per sec} \tag{48.9a}$$

This line is called $K\alpha$ and it is the line at the right for each of the elements whose x-ray spectrum is shown in Fig. 48.7. Subsequent work

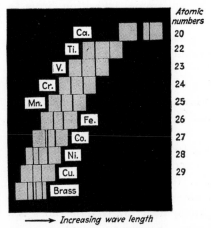

Increasing wave length

Fig. 48.7. Moseley's photographs of K x-ray spectra.

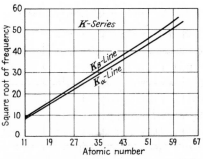

Fig. 48.8. Relationship between the square root of the frequency (arbitrary units) of K lines and the atomic number of the emitting element.

has shown that this line is indeed associated with the transition of an electron from a level with $n = 2$ to that with $n = 1$. A plot of the square root of the frequency as a function of atomic number for this line is shown in Fig. 48.8.

Moseley also observed a line called $K\beta$ associated with the transition $n_A = 3$ to $n_B = 1$. This line has a frequency which corresponds well to what one would expect if he places $n_A = 3$ in Eq. (48.8). The square root of the frequency of $K\beta$ as a function of atomic number is also shown in Fig. 48.8.

Both the slight difference in the constants of Eqs. (48.9) and (48.9a) and the correction to the atomic number in Eq. (48.9a) can be explained quantitatively as well as qualitatively in terms of the effects due to other electrons. The energies of the levels characterized by $n = 1$ are somewhat affected by the addition of other electrons in atoms. (The radii of the other circular orbits are at least four times the radius of the first orbit.) An orbit characterized by $n = 1$ is called a K orbit and the associated electron a K electron. A K electron moves in a force field which is not far from that of the nuclear charge Ze alone. The energy, however, is affected significantly by the other K electron in particular and to a smaller extent by the other electrons. The net effect of all the other electrons is to make the effective nuclear charge appropriate to Eq. (48.8) about $(Z - 1)$ rather than Z.

The lines which Moseley studied have very short wavelengths and belong to the x-ray region of the electromagnetic spectrum. The frequencies observed are characteristic of the material which emits them and are for this reason called *characteristic x-rays*. X-rays involving an electronic transition from a state of higher n to the $n = 1$ level are called K series lines. Other families of x-ray lines have also been observed. Those corresponding to transitions from higher n to a level with $n = 2$ are called L lines and electrons with $n = 2$ are known as L electrons. Lines corresponding to transitions to levels characterized by $n = 3$ are called M lines, etc. (see Fig. 49.7). Figure 48.9 shows the wavelengths at which the principal K, L, and M lines are found for various elements.

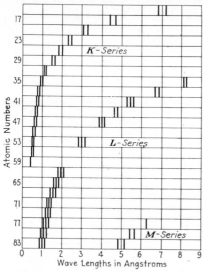

Fig. 48.9. Wavelengths of the characteristic x-ray lines of elements of various atomic numbers.

The x-ray spectra of elements permit us to make an unambiguous assignment of atomic number to every element. At one time there was uncertainty as to whether potassium or argon had the higher atomic number. Argon is heavier, but the chemical properties suggest potassium has the higher atomic number. X-rays have shown clearly that argon has atomic number 18, while potassium has 19. X-rays resolved a similar paradox in connection with cobalt and nickel.

48.6. The Optical Spectra of Other Atoms. After hydrogen, the next simplest atom is helium. It consists of a nucleus bearing two elementary positive charges and two electrons. Like that of hydrogen, the spectrum of helium consists of several series of lines. However, it is much more complicated than that of hydrogen, and the calculation of the allowed energy levels is more difficult. The reason is that there are three interacting charged particles (nucleus and two electrons) in the helium atom.

The optical spectra of helium and all other atoms arise from the excitation of one or more electrons to a higher energy state than the normal one. Indeed, in the normal state each electron has the smallest energy it is allowed to have. Even for the most complicated atoms it is possible by use of quantum mechanics to make fairly accurate calculation of what energies electrons can have and what the wavelengths of the spectral

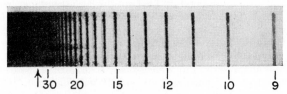

Fig. 48.10. One of the series of the sodium spectrum.

lines are. The observed values agree well with predictions. For all elements the lines arrange themselves into series, although not as simply as for hydrogen. In some atoms, the energy associated with a given "orbit" has two values, depending on the direction of the spin of the excited electron. Such a splitting of energy levels may give rise to series in which the lines are double when examined under high resolution. The sodium *D* lines are examples of such a "doublet"; they have wavelengths of 5,890 and 5,896 A. Figure 48.10 shows part of one of the series in the sodium spectrum; the lines are doublets so close together that they look like single lines. In other atoms the lines may be triple; in some cases as many as 15 lines have been observed where only one appears in a spectroscope of low resolving power.

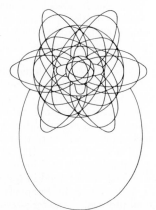

48.7. The Pauli Exclusion Principle. In dealing with the energy levels of atoms it is possible to think of each electron having its own orbit about the nucleus. Such a picture is an oversimplification, since each electron interacts constantly with the other electrons and the motion of any one electron is highly complex. However, the orbit picture is a reasonable approximation in the

Fig. 48.11. Orbit picture of a copper atom magnified 240 million times.

sense that it represents a statistical "average" of the positions of the electrons. Figure 48.11 is a diagram, based on the orbit model, of an atom of copper with its 29 electrons.

If we treat complex atoms from the point of view of such orbits, it turns out that we must specify four numbers, called *quantum numbers*, which describe the state of the electron. One of these is a measure of the orbital angular momentum of the electron about the nucleus, the second specifies the orientation of the angular momentum associated with the spin of the electron about its own axis, and the third specifies how the orbit is oriented in space relative to some direction prescribed by a magnetic field or some other field. The fourth, or *principal*, quantum number is the n which appears in Eq. (48.7). The various possible values of the other three quantum numbers are determined by the value of the principal quantum number.

According to an important principle enunciated by Pauli, no two electrons associated with any given atom may have the same four quantum numbers. It can be shown that for any given atom the largest number of electrons which can have principal quantum number $n = 1$ is two; the largest number which can have $n = 2$ is eight; the largest number with $n = 3$ is eighteen. In general, the maximum for any given n is $2n^2$.

48.8. The Periodic Table. According to the Pauli exclusion principle, only 2 electrons in any atom can have $n = 1$ and they form a "closed shell." The element lithium is characterized by 3 electrons. The third of these electrons cannot be in the $n = 1$ shell; it must seek an "orbit" with higher n. Of these available the lowest energy corresponds to $n = 2$. A grand total of 8 electrons can be added with $n = 2$. When we reach neon, both the $n = 1$ and $n = 2$ shells are completely filled with a total of 10 electrons. If we wish to add still another electron, it goes in an $n = 3$ level. The element sodium is characterized by 11 electrons; it represents the beginning of the filling of the third shell.

Each time we have a single electron alone in a new shell (as we do in hydrogen, lithium, sodium, etc.) we find that this electron is relatively easy to detach from the atom. In potassium, rubidium, and cesium we are beginning shells characterized by $n = 4$, 5, and 6, respectively. In every case these elements have their outer electron easily detachable. They are all electropositive elements with similar chemical properties. In general, we add 1, 2, 3, etc., electrons above the closed shell, we find that the atoms have rather similar chemical and physical properties to those elements with the same number of additional electrons in another shell.

After 8 electrons have been added to the $n = 3$ shell, we reach the element *argon*. In the next element *potassium*, the outer electron has $n = 4$, although several levels with $n = 3$ (but higher energy) remain empty. However, as we proceed up the periodic table, the $n = 3$ shell is quickly filled and this gives rise to the first long period in the periodic table (Appendix F). In this table the period is the principal quantum number n of the outermost electrons.

A detailed explanation of why shells of higher n begin to fill before all the possible "orbits" of lower n are filled is beyond the scope of this text. It is, however, understood in terms of the general picture outlined here.

48.9. Periodic Properties of the Elements. There are many chemical and physical characteristics of the elements which can be correlated with the way in which electrons are added to fill the various shells. One such characteristic is the ionization potential, or the energy required to remove one of the least tightly bound electrons from an atom, which is shown graphically in Fig. 48.12. Note that for hydrogen, sodium, lithium, etc., the ionization potential is exceptionally low compared with that of neighboring atoms. This arises from the fact that in each case there is a single electron in a new outer shell. On the other hand, after 8 electrons have been provided in any given shell, a peculiarly stable electronic configuration occurs in which the element is chemically inert. This is the situation which pertains to the noble gases, neon, argon, krypton, and xenon.

Many other properties show a similar periodicity. Among them should be mentioned the atomic diameter. One might at first think that the atoms should get larger as Z is increased. However, a glance at Eq. (48.3a) shows that the radius of an orbit is proportional to n^2, but inversely proportional to Z. The radii of the outer orbits are decreased about as much by the increase in effective

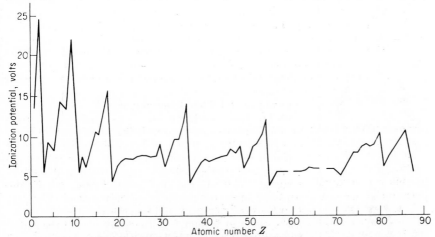

Fig. 48.12. Ionization potentials of the elements.

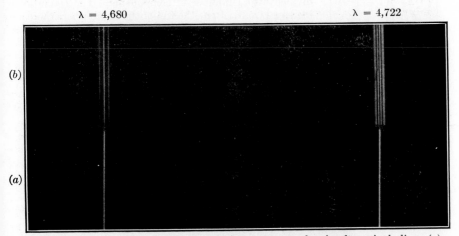

$\lambda = 4,680$ $\lambda = 4,722$

Fig. 48.13. Zeeman effect in lines of the zinc spectrum, showing how single lines (*a*) are split by application of a magnetic field (*b*). (*Courtesy of J. B. Green.*)

Z as they are increased by higher values of n. Other properties which show the characteristic periodicity are compressibility, melting point, and coefficient of thermal expansion.

48.10. The Zeeman Effect. When a source of light is placed between the poles of a powerful electromagnet, a single spectral line breaks up into several components (Fig. 48.13). This separation of a spectral line into components by the action of a magnetic field is known as the *Zeeman effect*. The number of components depends on the particular spectral line that is examined, and this number is not the same when the light is viewed in the direction of the magnetic field as it is when the light is viewed at right angles to the direction of the magnetic lines of force.   Figure 48.13 gives two examples of the Zeeman effect for the zinc

lines ($\lambda = 4{,}722$ A and $\lambda = 4{,}680$ A) when the light is viewed perpendicular to the magnetic field.   The single spectral line has been replaced by three in one case and by six lines in the other.   In some cases, a large number of components is observed.   Because of the interaction between the magnetic field due to the magnet and the magnetic fields due to the electrons in the atom, the energy levels in the atom are split up into a number of additional levels.   Transitions between these new levels give rise to additional spectral lines.

48.11. The Stark Effect.   An electric as well as a magnetic field causes the splitting up of spectral lines.   In a sufficiently large electric field, a single spectral line is replaced by a number of components.   The greater the electric field, the greater is the separation of these components.   This separation of spectral lines into components by an electric field is known as the *Stark effect* after its discoverer.   Figure 48.14 shows an example of the Stark effect in helium.   In the lower part of the figure, where the electric field is strong, the spectral line has been divided into a number of components.   The separation increases from zero at the top of the figure where there is no electric field to its greatest value at the bottom where the electric field is largest.   Data on the amount of this separation for different spectral lines give valuable information about the structure of the atoms emitting the lines.

Fig. 48.14. Stark effect for a line of the helium spectrum showing splitting due to an electric field. (*After Foster.*)

48.12. Molecular Spectra.   In the preceding sections it has been seen that line spectra are emitted by atoms as a result of energy changes which take place when an electron changes its position in the system of electrons surrounding the nucleus of the atom.   There is another important type of spectra, known as

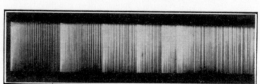

Fig. 48.15. Bands in the spectrum of cyanogen.

molecular spectra, due to changes in the energy of molecules rather than to changes inside the atom.   These spectra appear both as emission spectra and as absorption spectra.

The series of bands in the far infrared known as the pure-rotation spectrum arise from the rotation of the molecule.   In the case of HCl, the mass of the hydrogen atom is small in comparison with the mass of the chlorine atom, and the center of gravity of the two atoms forming the molecule is very near the chlorine atom.   The molecule as a whole rotates about an axis through the center of gravity.   Because of changes in the rotation of the molecule about this axis, the molecule emits a pure-rotational spectrum that lies in the region around 200 μ.   The near infrared spectrum, lying between 1 and 23 μ, known as the rotation-vibration spectrum, arises from vibratory motions of the atoms in the molecule combined with the rotation of the molecule about an axis.   The simplest case is that of a diatomic molecule, which may be thought of as a small dumbbell that is both rotating and vibrating.   The forces holding the atoms together in such a molecule are known to be large, and two nuclei in a diatomic molecule performing oscillations along a line joining their centers may have a frequency of about 10^{14} oscillations per second.

The changes in energy which give rise to molecular spectra may be made up of three parts: (1) *changes in the rotational energy* of the molecule about its axis of rotation; (2) *changes in the vibrational energy* of two or more molecules with respect to each other; (3) *changes in the energy of the electronic system* which is associated with the molecule.   These changes in energy give rise to groups of lines called *bands*.   Figure 48.15 shows typical bands in cyanogen.

PROBLEMS

1. Use the Balmer formula to calculate the wavelengths of the first four lines of the Balmer series of hydrogen.   *Ans.* 6,562 A; 4,861 A; 4,340 A; 4,102 A

2. Find the number of waves per centimeter for the light of the first line of the Balmer series of hydrogen.

3. Compute the wavelengths of the longest and shortest spectral lines possible in the Lyman series.   *Ans.* 1,216 A; 912 A

4. Calculate the wavelengths of the first three lines of the Paschen series for the hydrogen atom.

5. Calculate the radius of the first Bohr orbit in the case of singly ionized helium.
            Ans. 2.64 × 10^{-11} m

6. Through what difference of potential, in volts, must an electron fall in order to have an amount of energy equal to that emitted when an atom radiates the first line of the Lyman series?

7. The orbital electron of a singly ionized helium atom is attracted by the nucleus which has a positive charge twice that of the electron.   Find the speed of an electron in the first Bohr orbit of ionized helium.   *Ans.* 4.4 × 10^{6} m/sec

CHAPTER 49

X-rays

49.1. The Discovery of X-rays. In 1895 Röntgen was studying the conduction of electricity through partially evacuated tubes when he observed a mysterious radiation which was able to penetrate thin layers of material. He called this radiation *x-rays*, with the "x" standing for "unknown." He found that x-rays produce fluorescence in a large number of materials and that all materials are transparent to x-rays, though in very different degrees. Paper, wood, and aluminum are almost transparent, while lead and gold are comparatively opaque. He found that photographic emulsions are sensitive to x-rays, although the eye is not. He was unable to concentrate x-rays with lenses or mirrors and was unable to find any evidence of interference or diffraction of x-rays. The rays were not deflected by magnetic fields and showed no evidence of bearing electric charges. He found that x-rays are produced wherever a beam of cathode rays strikes matter.

We now know that x-rays are electromagnetic radiation similar to light and ultraviolet radiation, except that the wavelength is much shorter. Although the lines of demarcation between the various kinds of electromagnetic radiation are not sharp, we may think of x-rays as including radiation of wavelengths shorter than about 100 A.

Among the earliest x-ray photographs were pictures of the human hand and forearm similar to the one of Fig. 49.1. Soon pictures of this kind were utilized in studying fractures and similar abnormalities. Only three months after Röntgen's discovery x-rays were used in connection with a surgical operation.

The news that rays had been discovered which could take pictures through walls was tremendously exciting. X-rays were front-page news all over the world in 1896. Grossly exaggerated claims and absurd statements made some people feel that privacy was lost forever. A London firm advertised the sale of x-ray-proof underclothing. A bill was introduced in one of the state legislatures "to prohibit the insertion of x-rays, or any device for producing the same into, or their use in connection with, opera glasses, or similar aids to vision."

49.2. Applications of X-rays. X-rays have found many important applications. They have given the diagnostic methods of physicians, surgeons, and dentists an exactitude that formerly was impossible.   X-rays possess valuable properties in the treatment of certain diseases.   Malignant cells are somewhat more readily killed by x-rays than are normal ones.   Under x-ray treatment inflamed glands shrink in size, and various morbid conditions of the blood and skin clear up.   By means of x-rays, the metallurgist determines the effect of heat-treatment, tempering, rolling, and aging on metals and alloys.   Hidden defects in objects and concealed cracks in metals may be revealed by means of x-rays, which are a major tool in the nondestructive testing of materials.

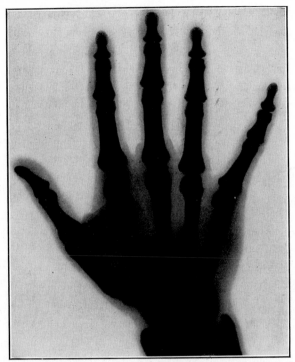

Fig. 49.1. X-ray photograph of the human hand.   (*Ewing Galloway.*)

49.3. The Production of X-rays. Electromagnetic radiation is emitted when electric charges are accelerated (Sec. 47.3).   This radiation appears in the form of photons (Sec. 46.1), the energy of which is given by the product of Planck's constant h and the frequency f.   For a typical x-ray photon, λ may be 1 A and the corresponding energy 12,400 ev.

The most common means of producing x-rays is to accelerate electrons through high potential differences in vacuum tubes and allow them to strike a target of some heavy element.   In Röntgen's original experiments he applied a high potential difference between two elements in a partially evacuated tube.   The electrons accelerated came from the ionization of the residual gas molecules and from secondary electrons ejected from the cathode by impact of positive ions.   Gas tubes (Fig. 49.2), operating on the same principle as Röntgen's, are still used for producing x-rays.

In 1913 Coolidge developed an x-ray tube which was easier to control than the gas type. In the Coolidge tube (Fig. 49.3) the electrons are emitted from a heated filament F placed in a highly evacuated chamber.

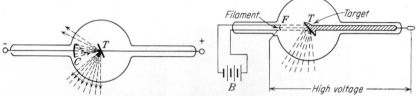

Fig. 49.2. Gas-type x-ray tube. The electrons accelerated are derived from the ionization of the residual gas in the tube.

Fig. 49.3. Coolidge x-ray tube. A hot filament is the source of the electrons.

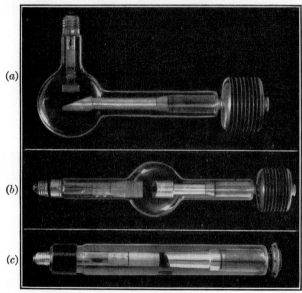

Fig. 49.4. Coolidge x-ray tubes adopted for different uses. (*a*) Air-cooled tube for dental radiology; (*b*) tube for general use; (*c*) tube in a protective lead-glass shield with "window" under the anode.

By varying the temperature of the filament the number of electrons emitted can be controlled. These electrons are accelerated and strike a target T from which the x-rays are emitted. The x-rays go out in every direction, but those which travel into the target are readily absorbed. Many different forms of Coolidge tubes (Fig. 49.4) are used.

49.4. The Continuous X-ray Spectrum. When a beam of high-energy electrons strikes a target, the wavelengths of the x-rays emitted vary widely. (In Sec. 49.7 we shall describe how the wavelengths may be measured.) If the intensity associated with a given wavelength is plotted as a function of wavelength for different values of the applied potential across the tube, curves similar to those of Fig. 49.5 are produced. Since every wavelength over a wide range is present, the spectra are *continuous*. There are three features of these curves which are immediately apparent:

1. The intensity radiated increases at all wavelengths when the potential difference across the tube is raised.

2. The shortest wavelength emitted at a given potential is sharply defined and decreases as the voltage across the tube increases.

3. As the potential difference

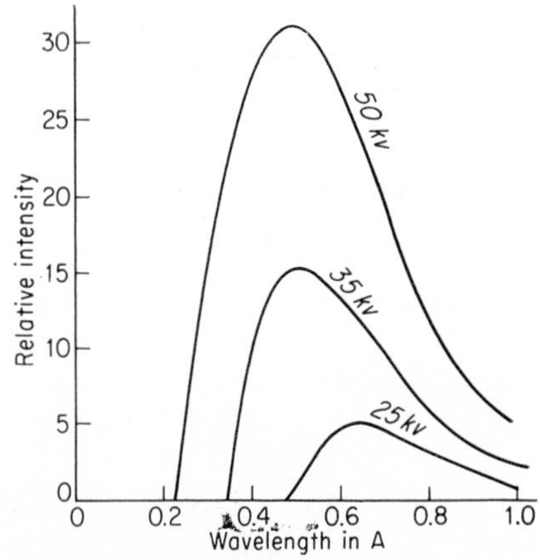

Fig. 49.5. Intensity curve for x-rays from an aluminum target.

across the tube is increased, the wavelength at which the maximum energy is radiated shifts toward shorter wavelengths.

The reason that the spectrum is continuous is easy to understand. The x-rays are emitted when the incident electrons lose energy through collisions with the atoms of the target. Some of these collisions are head-on; an electron loses all of its energy at once. Many more are glancing collisions in which some fraction of the energy is lost. Some electrons have several collisions and produce several x-ray photons.

These collisions in which the electron loses all its energy are relatively rare and these are the ones which produce the x-rays at the *short wavelength limit*. Clearly, the most energy an electron can lose is all it has. This corresponds to Ve, where V is the potential difference across the tube and e the electronic charge. If we equate this energy to that of the most energetic photon, we obtain

$$Ve = hf_{\max} = \frac{hc}{\lambda_{\min}} \tag{49.1}$$

where c is the speed of light. Solving for $\lambda_{\min}$ yields

$$\lambda_{\min} = \frac{hc}{Ve} \tag{49.1a}$$

This relationship is known as the *Duane-Hunt law*.

In many respects the process of x-ray emission is the inverse of the photoelectric effect. In producing an x-ray photon the kinetic energy of the incident electron is converted into radiant energy; in the photoelectric effect the radiant energy of a photon is converted, at least in part, into kinetic energy of the electron.

The amount of energy available for radiation of each electron is increased as the potential difference across the tube is increased. Therefore, we should expect more energy radiated per electron, which explains why the ordinates increase as the potential difference across the tube is increased. The area under the curve is proportional to the amount of energy radiated in the form of x-rays. The rest of the energy of the incident electrons appears as heat in the target.

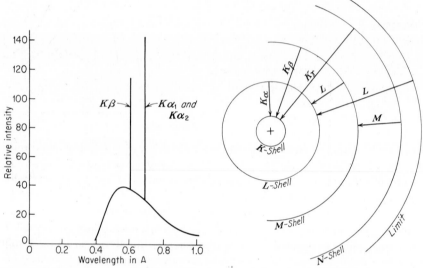

Fig. 49.6. Intensity curve for x-rays from a molybdenum target showing characteristic lines superimposed on the continuous spectrum.

Fig. 49.7. Representation of the transitions involved in the emission of characteristic x-ray lines.

The shorter the wavelength of the x-rays, the more penetrating they are. Increasing the potential difference across the tube results in a reduced average wavelength. X-rays from a high-voltage tube are called *hard* x-rays, while those emitted from a tube operating at low potentials are readily absorbed and are known as *soft* x-rays.

49.5. Characteristic X-ray Spectra. If a molybdenum target replaces the aluminum target for which data are plotted in Fig. 49.5, the curves for a given potential difference and tube current are similar except that (1) there is more energy radiated at every wavelength longer than λ_{min}, and (2) at certain sharp wavelengths large amounts of energy are radiated (Fig. 49.6). The first difference comes about as the result of the fact that the efficiency for producing the continuous x-ray spectrum is proportional to the atomic number of the target material. The second arises because we are exciting the *characteristic* x-ray spectra of molybdenum (Sec. 48.5). The position of the sharp "lines" depends on the atomic number of the target. For this reason they are called *characteristic lines.* A characteristic photon is emitted when a vacancy in an inner shell is filled by an electron making a transition from some other level (Fig. 49.7). No characteristic lines appear in the aluminum curves of Fig. 49.5, because all of them are at wavelengths greater than those shown.

49.6. The Detection and Measurement of X-rays. There are three properties of x-rays, all discovered by Röntgen, which are ordinarily used to detect x-rays and to measure their intensity. These are:

1. *X-rays eject electrons from atoms and thereby produce ionization in a gas.* By collecting the ions in an ionization chamber (Fig. 49.8) one can measure the intensity. The ionization chamber may be made of a metal cylinder closed at both ends except for windows through which the x-rays pass. A metal collector AC is insulated from the main cylinder and charged positively. When x-rays pass through the chamber, electrons are collected by AC and positive ions by the chamber itself. The current read by the galvanometer G is a measure of the intensity of the x-ray beam.

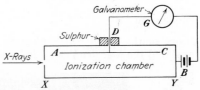

Fig. 49.8. Apparatus for measuring the intensity of x-rays by observing the ionization they produce.

Ionization measurements are used to determine dosages of x-rays and gamma rays. The unit dose, as adopted by the International Congress of Radiology, is called the *roentgen,* which may be defined as follows: *The roentgen is that quantity of x- or gamma radiation which produces in dry air a total ionization of* 3.33×10^{-10} *coulomb/*0.001293 *g of air.* A dosage of about $400 \ r$ (r is the symbol for *roentgen*) over the entire body is fatal to about 50 per cent of a random sample of human beings. This quantity, called the *median lethal dose,* is of considerable interest in connection with atomic weapons. Dosages far smaller than the median lethal dose are dangerous; one should never expose oneself needlessly to substantial radiation doses.

2. *X-rays affect photographic plates.* Over a fairly wide range the blackening of a photographic plate is proportional to the amount of x-ray energy of a given wavelength absorbed in the emulsion.

3. *X-rays produce fluorescence in many materials.* The detection of x-rays by fluorescent screens is widely used in medical diagnostics. For example, a fluorescent screen can be used to observe the shadow of a mass of bismuth salt as it passes through the digestive tract of a patient.

When x-rays fall on certain crystals, the fluorescence produced is a direct measure of the energy absorbed (Sec. 50.15).

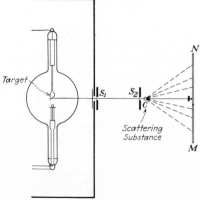

Fig. 49.9. Apparatus for studying the diffraction of x-rays.

49.7. Measuring the Wavelengths of X-rays. When x-rays fall on a body, the atoms scatter radiation in all directions. In a crystalline substance the atoms are arranged in a regular way and definite phase relationships exist between the scattered rays from the atoms. If a narrow pencil of x-rays falls on a crystal C (Fig. 49.9), there are certain directions in which the scattered x-rays reinforce one another by constructive interference. If a photographic plate is present at the proper location, a series of spots is formed (Fig. 49.10) where constructive interference occurs. The theory of this effect was worked out by Laue. The discovery of Laue spots presented the first definite evidence that x-rays have wave properties.

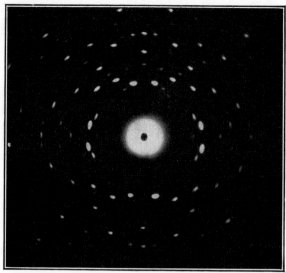

Fig. 49.10. A Laue photograph of iron pyrites. (*Courtesy of P. M. Harris.*)

The diffraction of x-rays by crystals can be used to measure the wavelengths of the x-rays. Consider a cubic crystal such as one of sodium chloride (Fig. 49.11). If x-rays are incident on a single plane of this crystal (Fig. 49.12), each particle scatters the x-rays. By Huygens' principle the condition for constructive interference from every atom lying in this plane is that the angle of incidence be equal to the angle of reflection. To form a Laue spot, it is necessary to have not only constructive interference of all scattered wavelets from a given plane of atoms but also to have constructive interference of the radiation scattered from adjacent planes. In order that the radiation scattered by the second plane of Fig. 49.13 interfere constructively with that scattered by the first plane, it is necessary that the path difference be an integral number of wavelengths. It can be seen from the figure that the difference in path is AOB. Let the distance between adjacent planes be d. Since $AO = OB = d \sin \theta$, it follows immediately that

$$n\lambda = 2d \sin \theta \qquad (49.2)$$

where n is an integer, λ the wavelength of the x-rays, and θ is the glancing angle. Equation (49.2) is known as *Bragg's law*.

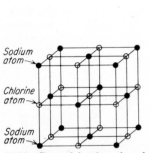

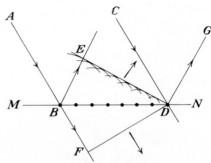

Fig. 49.11. Crystal lattice of rock salt (NaCl).

Fig. 49.12. Scattering of x-rays from atoms in a plane.

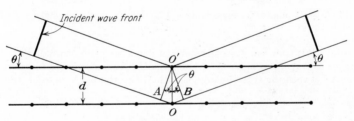

Fig. 49.13. There is constructive interference of the waves scattered from adjacent planes of a crystal if $n\lambda = d \sin \theta$.

To measure the wavelengths of x-rays, Bragg developed the x-ray spectrometer (Fig. 49.14) in which x-rays are incident upon a crystal C mounted on a rotating table so the glancing angle θ can be varied. An ionization chamber is mounted on a movable arm. The ionization chamber is positioned in such a way that the angle of "reflection" is equal to the angle of incidence for the crystal face. The wavelength of the x-rays which enter the chamber can be calculated from Eq. (49.2) if θ is measured and d is known.

Bragg calculated the grating space d for NaCl as follows: If M is the molecular weight of the NaCl, the number of atoms in a mass M is $2N$, where N is Avogadro's number. The number of atoms per gram is $2N/M$. To obtain the number of atoms per cubic centimeter, we multiply by the density ρ and have

$$\text{Number of atoms per cubic centimeter} = \frac{2N\rho}{M}$$

The volume per atom is therefore $M/2N\rho$. For a cubic crystal we can think of each atom occupying a cube of length d on a side; thus $d^3 = M/2N\rho$ or

$$d = \sqrt[3]{\frac{M}{2N\rho}} \qquad \text{for a cubic crystal} \qquad (49.3)$$

For NaCl the molecular weight is 58.45 and the density is 2.16 g/cm³. Since $N = 6.02 \times 10^{23}$, $d = 2.81 \times 10^{-8}$ cm $= 2.81$ A.

Bragg measured the wavelengths of many x-ray lines, using sodium chloride crystals. Once the wavelengths of lines are known, it is possible by Bragg's equation to determine the separations between planes (i.e., the grating spaces) for crystals of more complicated structure. Figure 49.15 shows how gold atoms are arranged in a gold crystal.

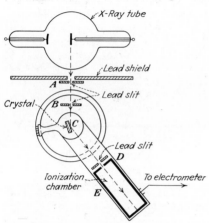

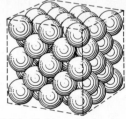

Fig. 49.14. A spectrometer for measuring the wavelengths of x-rays.

Fig. 49.15. Gold crystal magnified 30 million times.

Example. With an x-ray spectrometer using a rock-salt crystal, the glancing angle for the first reinforcement ($n = 1$) for the Cu Kα line is found to be 15.8°. If the distance between the crystal planes is 2.81 A, find the wavelength of this line.

$$n\lambda = 2d \sin \theta$$
$$n = 1 \quad \text{and} \quad d = 2.81 \text{ A}$$
$$\sin \theta = 0.273$$
$$\lambda = 2 \times 2.81 \times 0.273 = 1.54 \text{ A}$$

49.8. The Absorption of X-rays. If a sheet of any substance is placed in the path of an x-ray beam, the intensity of the beam is diminished. Let I_0 be the initial intensity of a homogeneous beam and I its intensity after passing through a thickness z of the material. Then

$$I = I_0 e^{-\mu z} \qquad (49.4)$$

where μ is called the *absorption coefficient* of the material for the particular wavelength incident and e is the base of the natural logarithms. The absorption coefficient varies with the wavelength of the x-rays, usually increasing as the wavelength increases. It is found experimentally that the absorption depends only on the number and kinds of atoms present in the absorbing layer; it is independent of their physical or chemical state.

A thickness of absorber which is adequate to cut the intensity to one-half is called the *half-value layer*. When a beam of homogeneous x-rays falls on an absorber just thick enough to remove half of the beam, a second absorber of the same thickness removes half of what is left so that one-fourth the initial intensity is transmitted. However, if a nonhomogeneous beam is incident, the second absorber removes less than half of what was transmitted by the first. With a nonhomogeneous beam the half-value layer removes more than half of the less penetrating and less than half of the more penetrating wavelengths. Therefore, the radiation which strikes the second absorber is more penetrating on the average than that which struck the first. Thin layers of copper or aluminum are used with x-ray tubes to remove the softer components of the x-rays. If the x-rays are used to treat a deep tumor, these soft x-rays would only produce burns near the skin.

X-rays with photon energies of less than a million electron volts (Mev) are absorbed or removed from the beam by photoelectric absorption and by scattering. Photons with energy above 1.02 Mev may be absorbed by pair production as well.

49.9. Photoelectric Absorption.
In photoelectric absorption the incident x-ray photons eject photoelectrons from the atoms of the absorbing material. For penetrating x-rays the probability of ejecting a K electron is far greater than that of ejecting any one of the other electrons. As the wavelength of the incident radiation is increased, the absorption increases rapidly up to the point at which photons no longer have enough energy to eject K electrons. At this point the absorption drops sharply (Fig. 49.16). As the wavelength is increased still further, the absorption increases rapidly until we reach the three absorption discontinuities for the L shell. At still longer wave-

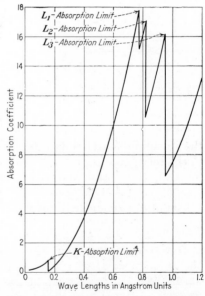

Fig. 49.16. Variation of photoelectric absorption coefficient with wavelength (in this case for lead).

lengths there are five discontinuities associated with the M shell and seven with the N shell.

49.10. Scattering and the Compton Effect.
The second process by which x-rays are removed from a beam is scattering. In this process photons strike atoms or electrons and are deflected out of the beam

(Fig. 49.17). Compton showed that when a beam of monochromatic x-rays is scattered, the beam of scattered rays gives two spectral lines instead of one. One of these lines has the wavelength of the primary beam, the other a longer wavelength. Figure 49.18 shows the scattered radiation from carbon when it was irradiated by the $K\alpha$ line of molybdenum. The vertical line AB shows the wavelength of the primary radiation, and the vertical line CD shows the wavelength of the modified line produced by the scattering.

Compton found that the change in wavelength $\Delta\lambda$ was independent of

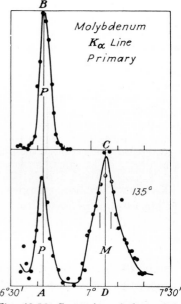

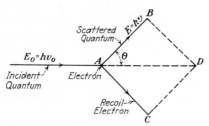

Fig. 49.17. Illustration of the scattering of a photon through an angle θ.

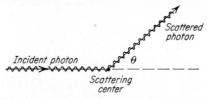

Molybdenum
$K\alpha$ Line
Primary

135°

6°30'   A   7° D   7°30'

Fig. 49.18. Scattering of the molybdenum $K\alpha$ line by carbon leads to two lines, one of which has a longer wavelength than the primary.

the scattering material, but depended on the scattering angle θ according to the relation

$$\Delta\lambda = 0.024\,(1 - \cos\theta) \qquad \text{in angstroms} \qquad (49.5)$$

Compton explained the shift in the wavelength in the scattering of x-rays by assuming that the incident beam of x-rays consists of a stream of photons of energy hf. These photons possess momentum hf/c as well as energy. When they collide with an electron (Fig. 49.19), the collision may be described in terms of the law of conservation of momentum and the law of conservation of energy. Applying these laws to the collision, Compton calculated the change in wavelength associated with such a collision and found

Fig. 49.19. Elastic collision of a photon with an electron. The frequency of the incident quantum is ν_0 and that of the scattered quantum is ν.

$$\Delta\lambda = \frac{h}{mc}(1 - \cos\theta) = 0.024(1 - \cos\theta) \qquad \text{in angstroms} \quad (49.5a)$$

where m is the mass of the electron and c the speed of light.

Compton's experiments were a clear indication that electromagnetic radiation has particle as well as wave properties. The Compton effect is convincing evidence that radiation in the x-ray region comes in photons or quanta which behave like particles in collisions with electrons.

49.11. Pair Production and the Positron. When photons with energy greater than 1.02 Mev pass through matter, a third absorption process called *pair production* takes place. In this process the photon

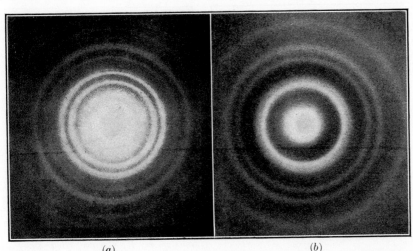

(a)   (b)

Fig. 49.20. (a) Diffraction of x-rays by aluminum. (*Hull.*) (b) Diffraction of electrons by a thin gold foil. (*G. P. Thomson.*)

interacts with the nucleus of the atom and is transformed into two particles, an *electron* and a *positron*. The *positron* (Sec. 50.13) is a particle identical to an electron, except that it bears a positive charge. The higher the energy of a photon, the more probable pair production becomes. It requires a minimum energy of 1.02 Mev to provide the mass of the electron and the positron (Sec. 51.3). The positron and electron share whatever energy is left over from the energy of the incident photon. Thus, if pairs are produced by a 4.02-Mev photon, the electron and positron each have 1.5 Mev of kinetic energy.

Positrons exist for a very short time. As they move through matter, they lose energy rapidly. As soon as they are stopped, an electron and a positron interact to annihilate each other. Two electron masses vanish and 1.02 Mev of energy is released. This usually appears in the form of two 0.51-Mev photons moving in opposite directions. The reason there are two photons of 0.51-Mev energy rather than a single 1.02-Mev photon is that it is not possible to conserve both energy and momentum for a single photon (unless some additional particle is involved).

49.12. Wave Properties of the Electron. If a pencil of monochromatic x-rays passes through a *powdered* crystalline substance placed at C in Fig. 49.9, the x-rays produce a diffraction pattern on the photographic plate MN. This pattern consists of a series of concentric circular fringes produced by interference of the scattered x-rays (Fig. 49.20a). If a stream of electrons, all having the same velocity, is allowed to pass through a thin film of metal, a similar set of interference

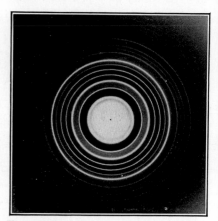

Fig. 49.21. An electron diffraction camera. (*Bell Telephone Laboratories, Inc.*)

Fig. 49.22. Electron diffraction pattern of a thin film of caesium iodide. (*Courtesy of L. H. Germer, Bell Telephone Laboratories, Inc.*)

fringes is produced (Fig. 49.20b). The fringes produced in the case of the beam of x-rays are explained on the basis that x-rays are waves of short wavelength which reinforce or destroy each other. It would also seem necessary to interpret the results on the beam of electrons as showing that electrons have a wavelength and that they also produce interference fringes. This remarkable result confirms de Broglie's conjecture that an electron has wave properties and a wavelength

$$\lambda = \frac{h}{mv} \tag{49.6}$$

where m is the mass of the electron, h is Planck's constant, and v is the speed of the electron.

Figure 49.21 shows an electron-diffraction camera and Fig. 49.22 shows the kind of diffraction pattern it provides.

Example. What is the de Broglie wavelength of an electron traveling at a speed of 10^4 m/sec?

$$\lambda = \frac{h}{mv} = \frac{6.62 \times 10^{-34} \text{ joule-sec}}{9.1 \times 10^{-31} \text{ kg} \times 10^4 \text{ m/sec}}$$
$$= 7 \times 10^{-8} \text{ m}$$

PROBLEMS

1. The shortest wavelength emitted by an x-ray tube arises when all the kinetic energy of the incident electron is converted into radiant energy. Find the shortest wavelength produced in a tube across which a potential difference of 60,000 volts is maintained. *Ans.* 0.206 A

2. What is the shortest wavelength of x-rays produced by a tube working at a potential of 40,000 volts?

3. Two energy levels differ from each other by 1,200 ev. What is the wavelength of the x-ray radiation that is emitted when an electron makes a transition from the higher to the lower energy level? *Ans.* 10.3 A

4. A Coolidge x-ray tube is operating at 150,000 volts. With what velocity do the electrons strike the anode? (Relativity correction for change of mass of electron with speed must be made.)

5. Fifty per cent of a homogeneous beam of x-rays from a 180-kv source is absorbed by a copper sheet 0.25 cm thick. What fraction of the beam will pass through 0.5 cm of copper? Through 1 cm of copper? *Ans.* 25 per cent; 6.25 per cent

6. An x-ray beam is studied by means of aluminum plates. It is found that 0.6 cm of Al passes 50 per cent of the beam, 1.2 cm passes 30 per cent, and 2.4 cm passes 10 per cent. Explain in detail how this result can be reconciled with the results of Prob. 5.

7. The grating space of calcite is 3.04 A. Find the wavelength for which the first-order Bragg reflection occurs at 20°, i.e., when the incident and the emergent radiation are inclined 20° with respect to the surface of the calcite. *Ans.* 2.08 A

8. Find the angle for first-order Bragg reflection of Cu Kα radiation (1.54 A) from a calcite crystal with a grating space of 3.04 A.

9. Find the de Broglie wavelength associated with an electron traveling at a speed of 10^6 m/sec. *Ans.* 7.28 A

CHAPTER 50

Radioactivity
and Nuclear Physics

50.1. Natural Radioactivity. Röntgen's discovery of x-rays in 1895 stimulated others to search for new kinds of rays. In 1896 Becquerel found that the compounds of uranium emitted radiations that produced a shadow picture on a photographic plate covered with black paper. These radiations had many of the properties of x-rays in that they could produce ionization in gases, affect photographic plates, and pass through thin sheets of substances which are opaque to light.

It was soon found that the property of emitting penetrating radiations is not confined to uranium and its compounds. Minerals containing thorium and several other elements have this same property. Such substances are said to be *radioactive*. A few years after Becquerel's discovery of radioactivity Pierre and Marie Curie were able to isolate the highly radioactive element *radium* from the mineral pitchblende. Many other radioactive elements were discovered later.

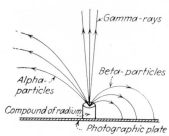

When the rays from a radioactive material are passed through a strong magnetic field, some are bent in one direction, some deflected in the opposite direction, and some are undeviated (Fig. 50.1). Thus, three different types of radiation are emitted by radioactive substances. These radiations were named *alpha, beta,*

Fig. 50.1. Alpha and beta particles are deflected in opposite directions by a magnetic field into the plane of the paper. Gamma rays are undeviated.

and *gamma rays.* The bending of alpha and beta rays in a magnetic field shows that alpha rays carry positive charge and beta rays negative charge, while gamma rays are electrically neutral.

50.2. The Nature and Properties of Alpha Rays. The alpha particle is the nucleus of the helium atom. This fact was established by separating an alpha emitter from an evacuated region by a thin wall through which alpha particles could pass.   After a few hours enough gas collected in the evacuated region so that its spectrum could be excited. This showed that the gas was helium.   Alpha particles have been found to bear a double elementary positive charge, so they are helium nuclei.

Fig. 50.2. Apparatus for measuring the range of alpha particles in air.

Alpha particles are easily absorbed by metal foils or by a few centimeters of air.   They affect a photographic plate, cause many materials to fluoresce brilliantly, and they ionize the air through which they pass. When alpha particles strike screens of fluorescent material, they produce tiny flashes of light called *scintillations*.   Many of the early researches on alpha particles were carried out in darkened rooms by patient observers who sat for hours counting these flashes.   If an alpha emitter is placed at R in Fig. 50.2, a fluorescent screen S receives many scintillations each second when it is close to the source.   As the screen is moved away from the alpha emitter, the number of scintillations per second remains roughly constant over a considerable distance.   Then the number drops off

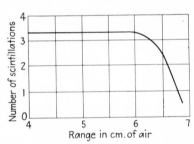

Fig. 50.3. Range of alpha particles in air.

sharply (Fig. 50.3).   As the particles move through the gas, they lose energy by ionizing the gas.   In passing through the first few centimeters of air, the alpha particles are slowed down significantly, but few are lost. This type of range curve is characteristic for particles which lose energy gradually as they pass through matter. A curve like that of Fig. 50.3 suggests that all the alpha particles from the source had the same energy.   For any given alpha emitter we find that most (and sometimes all) of the alpha particles have essentially the same energy.

50.3. Beta Emission.   Beta particles are electrons ejected from nuclei with high speeds, which may exceed $0.9c$, where c is the speed of light.   These electrons have a penetrating power far greater than that of alpha particles.

The energies of the beta rays from a given radioactive nucleus vary continuously from very low energy to a maximum (Fig. 50.4).   There is a *continuous energy spectrum of the beta rays*.   This is in sharp contrast with the energy spectrum of the alpha particles, which have at most a few discrete energies.   If beta rays were the only particles coming out of a given kind of nucleus, one would expect the energies of the beta rays to be discrete.   However, if some other particle were emitted simultaneously with the electron, this particle would share in the total energy available and the electron energy spectrum would be continuous.   There is substantial evidence that another particle is ejected from beta emitters along

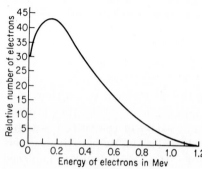

Fig. 50.4. Beta-ray spectrum of RaE. The ordinate represents the relative number of electrons emitted with each energy.

with the electron.   It is the *neutrino*, a particle of essentially zero mass and no electric charge.   The word *neutrino* means "little neutral one."

50.4. Gamma   Rays. High-energy electromagnetic rays are called gamma rays when they are emitted   by   radioactive   nuclei. The properties of gamma rays are identical to those of x-rays of the same wavelength.

When   a   radioactive   nucleus emits an alpha or beta particle, it is likely that the residual nucleus will be left not in its most stable arrangement, but in an excited state. Ordinarily, when the nucleus goes to a more stable configuration, the energy released is radiated as a gamma ray.   Like the alpha particles, the gamma rays from a given radioactive species have discrete energies.

50.5. The Uranium–Radium Series.   The most abundant of radioactive nuclei in nature is that of the uranium isotope of mass 238 atomic units, which we abbreviate U^{238}.   This material decays by the emission of an alpha particle with a half-life of 5 billion years.   *The half-life is the time required for one-half of the nuclei to disintegrate.*   For example, for radon the half-life is 3.85 days.   If one has a sample of radon, one half of it disappears in 3.85 days.   At the end of 7.7 days three-quarters of it will have disappeared, and one-fourth remains.   After 15.4 days, only one-sixteenth of the original radon is present.

When U^{238} emits an alpha particle, the reaction may be written

$$_{92}U^{238} \rightarrow {}_2He^4 + {}_{90}Th^{234}$$

Note that the emission of an alpha particle reduces the atomic number (left subscript) by 2 and the mass number (right superscript) by 4.   The Th^{234} decays by beta emission to protactinium 234, which in turn emits a beta ray and becomes U^{234}.

$$_{90}Th^{234} \rightarrow {}_{-1}\beta^0 + {}_{91}Pa^{234}$$
$$_{91}Pa^{234} \rightarrow {}_{-1}\beta^0 + {}_{92}U^{234}$$

U^{234} is an alpha emitter with the daughter Th^{230}. Ultimately the decay series ends with lead 206. The detailed list of reactions and their half-lives for the uranium-radium series is presented in Table 1.

Table 1
THE URANIUM-RADIUM SERIES

Nuclide	Element	Early name	Half-life	Energy of rays, Mev		
				α	β	γ
$_{92}U^{238}$	Uranium	Uranium I	4.5×10^9 yr	4.18		
$_{90}Th^{234}$	Thorium	Uranium X_1	24.1 days		0.103	0.09
$_{91}Pa^{234}$	Protactinium	Uranium X_2	1.18 min		2.32	0.8
$_{92}U^{234}$	Uranium	Uranium II	2.35×10^5 yr	4.76		
$_{90}Th^{230}$	Thorium	Ionium	8×10^4 yr	4.66		
$_{88}Ra^{226}$	Radium	Radium	1,620 yr	4.79		0.19
$_{86}Rn^{222}$	Radon	Ra emanation	3.8 days	5.49		
$_{84}Po^{218}$	Polonium	Radium A	3.05 min	6.00		
$_{82}Pb^{214}$	Lead	Radium B	26.8 min		0.65	0.29
$_{83}Bi^{214}$	Bismuth	Radium C	19.7 min	5.5	3.15	1.8
$_{84}Po^{214}$	Polonium	Radium C'	1.5×10^{-4} sec	7.68		
or						
$_{81}Th^{210}$	Thallium	Radium C''	1.32 min		1.80	
$_{82}Pb^{210}$	Lead	Radium D	22 yr		0.026	0.047
$_{83}Bi^{210}$	Bismuth	Radium E	5.0 days		1.17	
$_{84}Po^{210}$	Polonium	Radium F	138 days	5.3		0.8
$_{82}Pb^{206}$	Lead	Radium G	Stable			

In addition to the uranium-radium series three other natural radioactive series exist. The longest-lived member of the *thorium series* is Th^{232} and the final stable nucleus formed is again lead, but this time Pb^{208}. The *neptunium series* has Np^{237} as its longest-lived member and the radioactive chain ends with bismuth 209, while the *actinium series* has U^{235} as its longest-lived member and Pb^{207} as its final stable nucleus.

50.6. Age of the Earth. Since each alpha particle is a helium nucleus, helium is in the process of formation in all minerals containing alpha-emitting radioactive substances. The number of alpha particles given out by 1 g of uranium in equilibrium with its radioactive products has been found to be 9.7×10^4 per second. If this helium were all occluded and retained by the mineral, the ratio of the amount of helium to the amount of uranium would give an estimate of the age of the mineral. Without doubt some of the helium escapes and this estimate of the age of the mineral would be too low. A determination of the uranium and helium in different kinds of rocks has shown that the ratio of the amount of helium to the amount of uranium is largest in those formations which from geological considerations are known to be the oldest.

50.7. Heat from Radioactivity. Since the various radiations from radioactive substances are emitted with very high speeds, it is evident that radioactive substances give off energy in considerable quantities. One gram of radium in equilibrium with its short-lived products liberates 140 cal/hr and over 3 billion calories over its complete decay time. The heat generated by a radioactive substance can be determined by means of the apparatus of Fig. 50.5 in which the heat generated in radioactivity in A is matched by measured heat produced electrically in B. The energy liberated by the radioactive substance is derived from the conversion of mass to energy (Sec. 51.4).

50.8. The First Artificial Transmutation.
In 1919 Rutherford found that when alpha particles from radium C passed through air, a penetrating charged particle was produced which had a range as great as 40 cm, although the range of the alpha particles was only 7 cm. The more penetrating particles were not observed when the alpha particles

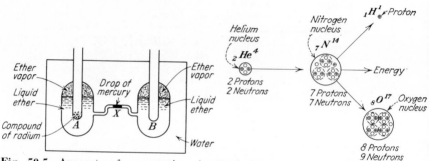

Fig. 50.5. Apparatus for measuring the heating by radium.

Fig. 50.6. Nitrogen bombarded with alpha particles yields oxygen 17 and a proton. Nuclei are composed of protons and neutrons.

passed through oxygen or carbon dioxide, but they were observed whenever nitrogen was present. Rutherford showed that the penetrating particles were high-energy protons, produced by the capture of alpha particles by nitrogen nuclei (Fig. 50.6).

When an alpha particle is captured by a nitrogen nucleus, a highly excited fluorine 18 nucleus is produced. This excited nucleus has too much energy to remain together; it breaks up by ejecting one of the protons, leaving a residual $_8O^{17}$ nucleus. We write the reaction

$$_2He^4 + _7N^{14} \rightarrow _9F^{18*} \rightarrow _8O^{17} + _1H^1 + \text{energy}$$

Here the asterisk is placed with the F^{18} nucleus to indicate that it is excited.

Rutherford's discovery of artificial transmutation suggested that physicists could change one element into another by shooting high-speed particles into nuclei. In Rutherford's day alpha particles from radioactive materials were the only convenient high-energy projectiles available. Only high-energy charged particles can enter nuclei, because positive charges repel one another and these repulsive forces become exceedingly great before the two particles are close enough for the attractive nuclear forces to become dominant. Rutherford's discovery was a great stimulus toward the development of accelerators to produce high-energy charged particles. Until such high-voltage machines could be developed, there was always the possibility of using alpha particles from radioactive materials as bombarding projectiles. Here again Rutherford's discovery provided a major stimulus.

50.9. The Discovery of the Neutron. In 1930 Bothe and Becker observed that several of the lighter elements emitted a very penetrating radiation when bombarded by alpha particles from polonium. They thought this radiation consisted of gamma rays, since it was not affected by magnetic fields and was therefore uncharged. The radiation was so penetrating that, when alpha particles bombarded beryllium, it required 2 cm of lead to cut the intensity in half.

Two years later the Joliots found that these penetrating rays were fairly readily absorbed in paraffin, water, or cellophane. They concluded

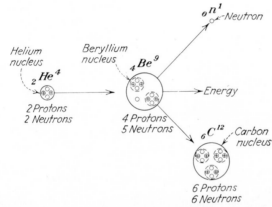

Fig. 50.7. Beryllium bombarded by alpha particles gives carbon and neutrons.

that the penetrating radiation was absorbed through some reaction which resulted in the ejection of protons from hydrogenous materials.

Later that same year Chadwick repeated the Joliot experiment and measured the energy of the ejected protons. He concluded that the energy of the protons was much too high to have been received in any sort of gamma-ray reaction. He recalled that 12 years earlier Rutherford had suggested that there might be a neutral particle with approximately the mass of the proton. If the penetrating radiation consisted of high-speed particles of this kind, they should produce not only recoil protons, but also recoils in other nuclei. Feather had previously measured the recoil velocities of nitrogen nuclei when they were struck by this penetrating radiation, using a cloud chamber for his work. Chadwick took his own data on the energy of the recoil protons and that of Feather for the energy of the nitrogen nuclei which recoiled from collisions. When he applied the laws of conservation of energy and conservation of momentum, he found that the recoil velocities were consistent with the idea that the penetrating radiation consisted of neutral particles of mass slightly greater than the mass of the proton. These particles are called *neutrons*. The reaction by which neutrons are produced when beryllium is bombarded with alpha particles (Fig. 50.7) is

$$_4Be^9 + {_2}He^4 \rightarrow {_6}O^{13*} \rightarrow {_6}C^{12} + {_0}n^1 + \text{energy}$$

50.10. Charged Particle Accelerators. Soon after Rutherford's discovery of artificial transmutation, physicists in several countries began to build accelerators to produce high-energy protons. The first device which was successful in accelerating charged particles artificially to produce nuclear reactions was put into operation by Cockcroft and Walton

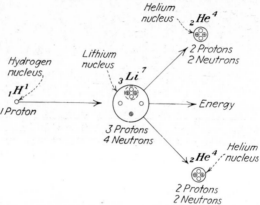

Fig. 50.8. Lithium 7 bombarded with protons gives two alpha particles.

in England in 1930. Their accelerator produced a beam of protons of 0.5-Mev energy by utilizing high-voltage transformers, rectifiers, and capacitors.

Cockcroft and Walton found that when lithium was bombarded with protons of 150-kev energy, alpha particles were emitted with energies of about 8.6 Mev (Fig. 50.8). The following reaction occurred:

$$_3Li^7 + {_1}H^1 \rightarrow {_4}Be^{8*} \rightarrow {_2}He^4 + {_2}He^4 + 17.3 \text{ Mev energy}$$

The energy released is shared equally by the alpha particles since this is the only way in which momentum can be conserved.

Shortly after Cockroft and Walton made their great discovery, other types of accelerators were put into operation. Among the many kinds which have been developed are those described below.

The Van de Graaff Generator. The Van de Graaff electrostatic generator makes use of the simple electrostatic fact that the charges go to the outside of a conductor. The high potential element is a metal sphere or

Fig. 50.9. A 4-Mev Van de Graaff generator. (*Courtesy of High Voltage Engineering Corporation.*)

rounded shell (Fig. 50.9). A belt made of insulating material carries charge at high speed from a charging source into the sphere (Fig. 50.10) where the charge is picked off and goes to the outside of the sphere. Of course, some charges are lost from the sphere. The potential of the high-voltage electrode builds up until charges are lost and gained at exactly the same rate. Often the entire system is placed in a large tank and the pressure raised to several atmospheres to reduce the loss of charge by sparks and corona.

If the Van de Graaff generator is to be useful for nuclear experiments, one must utilize the high potential in accelerating some kind of particle. Many generators accelerate electrons, but protons and deuterons are the most common nuclear projectiles. These are produced in an ion source

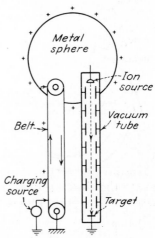

Fig. 50.10. Schematic diagram of a Van de Graaff electrostatic generator.

Fig. 50.11. A general view of the giant Berkeley cyclotron which has pole pieces 184 in. in diameter. The magnet weighs 4,000 tons. (*Courtesy of Radiation Laboratory, University of California.*)

in the high potential electrode and are accelerated down an evacuated tube to the grounded end of the generator, where they are focused upon a target.

The Cyclotron. A major contribution to nuclear physics was the devel-

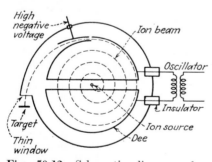

Fig. 50.12. Schematic diagram of a cyclotron showing the path of a charged particle in the vacuum chamber of the cyclotron.

opment of the cyclotron by Lawrence and Livingston (Fig. 50.11). The key parts of the cyclotron are a large electromagnet which provides a constant magnetic field over a large area and an oscillating electric field between two semicircular hollow elements called *dees*, because they have the shape D. Ions are produced at the center of the magnetic field between the two dees, as shown in Fig. 50.12. A charged particle which is accelerated toward the lower dee gains energy as it crosses the gap between the dees. Once in the lower dee its path is circular, since

$$qvB = \frac{mv^2}{r} \qquad (50.1)$$

Soon the particle finds itself in the region between the two dees once more. If now the upper dee is negative and the lower dee positive, the particle is accelerated across the gap and enters the upper dee with a higher velocity, where it traverses a semicircular arc of greater radius. When it again reaches the gap between the dees, the electric field has reversed and the particle is accelerated downward. At each passing of the gap it gains energy and the radius of its path in the magnetic field becomes greater, until eventually the particle has a very high energy and its orbit approaches the circumference of the magnetic poles. It is then removed from the cyclotron and directed against a target. The time $T_{\frac{1}{2}}$ required for the particle to make the half circle in one of the dees is

$$T_{\frac{1}{2}} = \frac{\pi r}{v}$$

In this time the accelerating field should be reversed; therefore this is the time for one-half cycle of the alternating potential difference applied to the dees. The number of complete revolutions made per second is

$$f = \frac{v}{2\pi r} \qquad (50.2)$$

Substituting the ratio v/r from Eq. (50.1), we have

$$f = \frac{Bq}{2\pi m} \qquad (50.3)$$

If we apply a constant frequency given by Eq. (50.3) to the dees, ions are accelerated each time they pass the gap.

The time required for a charged particle to make half a revolution in the cyclotron is independent of radius only so long as the mass of the particle is constant. As we have seen in Sec. 45.7, the mass of any particle varies rapidly with velocity when v approaches c, the speed of light. If one wishes to use the cyclotron to accelerate particles to a velocity which is more than a few per cent of the speed of light, the mass of the particle increases with time. By Eq. (50.3) the accelerating field can be kept in step with the particles only by decreasing the frequency as the mass increases. In very large cyclotrons the speed of the particles becomes great enough so that relativistic effects are important. Then the frequency of the cyclotron must be varied during an acceleration cycle. A cyclotron operated in such a way is said to be *frequency modulated* and is sometimes called a *synchrocyclotron*.

The Betatron. The betatron is used to produce high-speed electrons. It consists essentially of a large electromagnet (Fig. 50.13) between the

Fig. 50.13. A 300-Mev betatron.   D. W. Kerst, who built the first betatron, stands in front of the accelerator.   (*Courtesy of Physics Research Laboratory, University of Illinois.*)

poles of which is placed an evacuated tube in the form of a doughnut (Fig. 50.14).   Alternating current is applied to the coils of the electro-magnet and the accelerating potential difference is induced by the changing magnetic field, which acts on the electrons in the vacuum tube as if the tube were the secondary of a transformer.   The electrons previously injected into the tube are whirled around in circular paths.   As the electrons gain energy, the magnetic field is increasing at such a rate that it is just strong enough to keep the electrons rotating in the same circular path.   While the magnetic field builds up

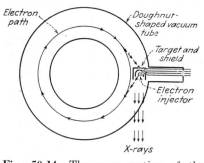

Fig. 50.14. The cross section of the doughnut vacuum tube of a betatron showing the electron injector and the orbit of the electrons.

to its maximum value, the electrons travel around the vacuum tube many thousand times.   During this time they acquire a velocity which closely approaches the speed of light.

The Synchrotron.   In a synchrotron particles are accelerated at essentially constant radius in a doughnut-shaped evacuated tube.   The acceleration is produced by a radio-frequency electric field applied across one or more gaps, as in the cyclotron.   The magnetic field serves to keep the particle traversing the same circular path as it goes around.   As the speed of the particle increases, the strength of the magnetic field must be increased so that the particle does not hit the walls of the doughnut and

Fig. 50.15. View of the 6-Bev Bevatron while under construction.   (*Courtesy of Radiation Laboratory, University of California.*)

the frequency applied across the gap is increased so that each time the particle crosses the gap it is properly accelerated.   Synchrotrons may be used for accelerating either electrons or protons.   A 3-Bev (billion electron volt) proton synchrotron is in operation at the Brookhaven National Laboratory where it is called the *cosmotron* and a 6-Bev proton synchrotron is operating at the University of California, Berkeley, where it is known as the *bevatron* (Fig. 50.15).   Higher energy accelerators are under construction.

50.11. Artificial Transmutations.   The development of high-voltage accelerators has made it possible to bombard atomic nuclei with swiftly moving protons, deuterons, alpha particles, and other projectiles. When one of these particles is captured by a nucleus, the residual nucleus

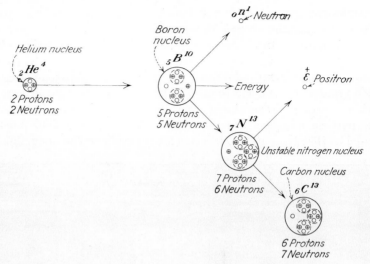

Fig. 50.16. Boron 10 bombarded with alpha particles gives neutrons and unstable nitrogen 13, which decays to carbon 13 with the ejection of a positron.

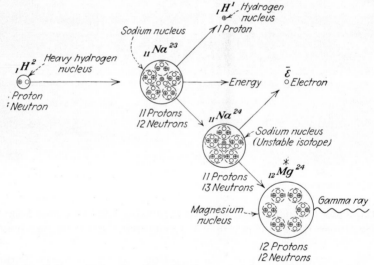

Fig. 50.17. Sodium 23 bombarded with deuterons gives sodium 24 and protons. The sodium 24 is unstable and changes to magnesium 24 with the emission of an electron.

is usually formed in a state of high excitation. It may get rid of its excess energy by emitting one or more particles, gamma rays, or both. Hundreds of artificial transmutations have been produced. Table 2 lists typical reactions which can be produced and Figs. 50.16 and 50.17 show two reactions in schematic form. A reaction in which a proton is

Table 2

SOME TYPICAL NUCLEAR TRANSMUTATIONS

Kind	Example	Kind	Example
(α,p)	$_{13}Al^{27} + _2He^4 \rightarrow _1H^1 + _{14}Si^{30}$	$(d,2n)$	$_1H^3 + _1H^2 \rightarrow 2_0n^1 + _2He^3$
(α,n)	$_{13}Al^{27} + _2He^4 \rightarrow _0n^1 + _{15}P^{30}$	(n,α)	$_{13}Al^{27} + _0n^1 \rightarrow _2He^4 + _{11}Na^{24}$
(p,α)	$_9F^{19} + _1H^1 \rightarrow _2He^4 + _8O^{16}$	(n,p)	$_{48}Cd^{106} + _0n^1 \rightarrow _1H^1 + _{47}Ag^{106}$
(p,n)	$_5B^{11} + _1H^1 \rightarrow _0n^1 + _6C^{11}$	$(n,2n)$	$_{47}Ag^{107} + _0n^1 \rightarrow 2_0n^1 + _{47}Ag^{106}$
(p,γ)	$_{15}P^{31} + _1H^1 \rightarrow _{16}S^{32} + \gamma$	(n,γ)	$_{48}Cd^{113} + _0n^1 \rightarrow _{48}Cd^{114} + \gamma$
(d,α)	$_{13}Al^{27} + _1H^2 \rightarrow _2He^4 + _{12}Mg^{25}$	(γ,n)	$_4Be^9 + \gamma \rightarrow _0n^1 + _4Be^8$
(d,p)	$_7N^{14} + _1H^2 \rightarrow _1H^1 + _7N^{15}$	(γ,p)	$_{13}Al^{27} + \gamma \rightarrow _1H^1 + _{12}Mg^{26}$
(d,n)	$_{12}Mg^{25} + _1H^2 \rightarrow _0n^1 + _{13}Al^{26}$		

captured and a neutron is emitted is called a (p,n) reaction for short, etc. In this shorthand the entering particle appears first and the emitted one after the comma.

If a target is bombarded by protons (or some other particle), it is common to find that protons of one energy are strongly captured, while protons of slightly higher or lower energy are rejected. We say that such capture reactions show *resonances*. A proton is likely to be captured if it brings in just the right energy and angular momentum to form a compound nucleus in one of its allowed energy states. A proton with more or less energy than this required amount is not captured.

Quite a few nuclei created by transmutations are unstable and eventually decay. In some cases these unstable nuclei have relatively long half-lives. When a proton is captured by carbon 12, nitrogen 13 is formed. This nitrogen nucleus is unstable with a half-life of 10.1 min. It decays to C^{13} by the emission of a positron. When tellurium 130 is bombarded with neutrons, Te^{131} is formed which decays by electron emission to iodine 131. I^{131} is also a beta emitter; its half-life is 8 days. This radioactive isotope is used in treating hyperthyroid conditions.

Hundreds of artificially radioactive nuclei have been formed by bombarding stable nuclei with x-rays, neutrons, and charged particles such as protons, deuterons, alpha particles, and carbon nuclei.

50.12. The Detection of Nuclear Reactions. In nuclear reactions the target nuclei, the bombarding particle, and the resulting products are far too small to see and too light to weigh on the most sensitive balance. The problem of studying a reaction is a difficult one, since all judgments as to what has happened must be inferred from indirect evidence. However, scientists have developed a number of ingenious methods for studying nuclear reactions and detecting the products of the reactions.

The first detector for nuclear reactions was the photographic plate. Gamma rays striking such a plate produce blackening just as does visible light or x-rays. By using exceedingly fine-grained emulsions the path of a high-energy proton, alpha particle, or electron may be visible in the emulsion. Since the tracks of such particles are very short, they are observed in a microscope.

50.13. The Cloud Chamber. The *Wilson cloud chamber* consists of a cylinder with a glass top and a movable piston at the bottom (Fig. 50.18). The volume of the chamber is filled with air and saturated water vapor or alcohol. When the piston is moved downward quickly, an adiabatic expansion of the mixture occurs, the temperature falls, and the formerly saturated vapor becomes supersaturated. Vapor molecules condense on any tiny particle which is present to serve as nucleus for a droplet. In particular, droplets form readily on charged ions. If a charged particle is moving through the chamber when the expansion occurs, droplets form on the ions produced by the passage of this charged particle and a *track* is produced. Figure

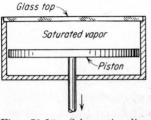

Fig. 50.18. Schematic diagram of a Wilson cloud chamber.

(a)   (b)

Fig. 50.19. Cloud-chamber tracks made by alpha particles colliding with atoms in the gas. (*a*) Collisions with helium atoms. (*b*) Collisions with oxygen atoms in which the recoiling oxygen ion makes the shorter track. (*After Blackett.*)

50.19 shows cloud-chamber pictures of collisions between alpha particles and atoms. The atom which is struck is ionized in the collision and its track is also visible.

When a strong magnetic field is impressed on a cloud chamber, charged particles moving across the magnetic field are deflected in circular paths. By observing the tracks made by these particles, it is possible to determine the mass and the charge of the particles responsible for each track. Figure 50.20 shows the track of a positron moving upward in a magnetic field directed into the paper. The track below the plate has a curvature corresponding to a charged particle with the rest mass of an electron and an energy of 63 Mev. The track above the plate has a curvature expected for a particle of the same mass, but with an energy of only 23 Mev. Since the particle could not have gained energy in passing through the plate, it must have passed upward rather than downward through the plate. It is this which convinces us that the track was made by a positron moving upward rather than by an electron moving downward. It was by precisely this type of experiment that Anderson discovered the positron. Figure 50.21 shows a positron-electron "pair" detected in a cloud chamber.

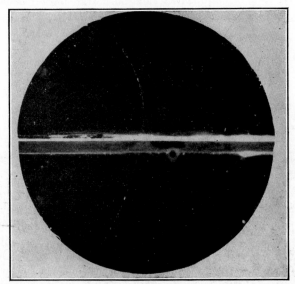

Fig. 50.20. The track of a positron passing upward through a lead plate in a cloud chamber. There was a magnetic field directed away from the camera when this photograph was taken. (*Courtesy of Carl D. Anderson, California Institute of Technology.*)

50.14. The Geiger-Mueller Counter. A common detector of beta and gamma rays is the Geiger-Mueller counter. An elementary counter can be made by stretching an insulated wire along the axis of a conducting metal cylinder (Fig. 50.22). This chamber is evacuated and then filled to a pressure of about 10 cm Hg with a mixture of argon and methyl alcohol. The central wire is made positive about 1,000 volts relative to the metal cylinder. When an ionizing particle passes through this counter, electrons are ejected from atoms. The electrons move to the central wire, while the positive ions move outward. The electric field near the wire is sufficiently great so that the gas breaks down and an avalanche results during which a large instantaneous current is drawn. As the current rises, the potential difference across the Geiger counter falls and that across the resistance rises.   Soon the potential difference across the Geiger counter becomes too low to maintain the discharge.   The current drops to zero and the potential difference across the counter again rises to a thousand volts so that the counter is once more ready to detect an incident particle.   Each time the gas breaks down in the Geiger counter, the potential difference across the resistor R rises sharply, and this rise can be made to trigger a scaling circuit, which automatically counts how many pulses occur.

50.15. The Scintillation Detector.   A detector which is becoming of increasing importance is the scintillation counter.   When either a charged particle or a gamma ray falls on a transparent crystal, part of

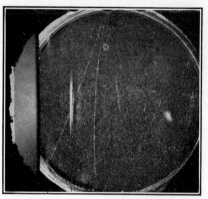

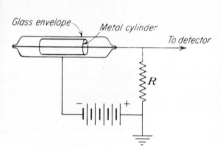

Fig. 50.21.   A positron-electron pair produced in a magnetic field.   The positron and the electron are deflected in opposite directions.   (*Courtesy of J. C. Street and E. C. Stevenson, Harvard University.*)

Fig. 50.22.   Schematic diagram of a Geiger-Muller counter.

the energy absorbed is reemitted in the form of visible and ultraviolet light.   If this radiation falls on a photosensitive surface, electrons are emitted.

When gamma rays fall on a crystal of sodium iodide with a little thallium impurity, the absorption of the gamma rays results in the fluorescent emission of ultraviolet and visible light.   In the scintillation detector shown in Fig. 50.23, the gamma-ray energy is absorbed in the crystal, producing light which falls on the photosensitive surface of the cathode of an *electron multiplier tube*.   Electrons are ejected by the photoelectric effect.   These electrons are accelerated by a potential difference of the order of 200 volts to electrode 1 which is made of material which has the property of copious secondary emission.   When they strike this electrode, several secondary electrons are ejected for each incident electron. The electrons from electrode 1 are accelerated to electrode 2 where a further multiplication is produced, and so forth. At the final collector an electron pulse is collected which may be a million times as great as that from the photocathode. Each time a gamma ray strikes and is absorbed in the crystal, a charge pulse is delivered to the anode. The charge collected is a measure of the energy of the gamma ray. The

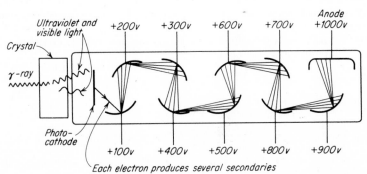

Fig. 50.23. Schematic diagram of a scintillation detector with a photomultiplier tube.

scintillation counter has the great advantage over the Geiger counter that it not only tells when a gamma ray has been absorbed in the crystal, but it also yields a charge pulse which is a measure of the energy.

PROBLEMS

1. The half-life of iodine 131 is 8 days. What fraction of a given sample of I^{131} remains after 16 days? after 32 days? *Ans.* 25 per cent; 6.25 per cent

2. The half-life of carbon 11 is 20.35 min. What fraction of a sample of C^{11} remains after a time of 61.05 min?

3. How many protons are associated with the nucleus $_{92}U^{238}$? How many neutrons? *Ans.* 92; 146

4. At the end of 2 days one-sixteenth of a sample of radioactive material remains. What is the half-life?

5. After a series of alpha and beta decays plutonium 239 ($_{94}Pu^{239}$) eventually becomes lead 207 ($_{82}Pb^{207}$). How many alpha and beta particles are emitted in the complete decay scheme? *Ans.* 8; 4

6. A nucleus of thorium 232 ($_{90}Th^{232}$) eventually becomes lead 208 ($_{82}Pb^{208}$). In the series of alpha and beta decays by which this occurs how many alpha and beta particles are emitted?

7. The first observed artificial transmutation was reported by Rutherford in 1910. He bombarded $_7N^{14}$ with alpha particles and protons came out of the reaction. What nucleus remained? *Ans.* $_8O^{17}$

8. Complete the following nuclear reactions:

$$_{88}Ra^{226} \rightarrow {_{86}}Po^{222} +$$
$$_{19}K^{40} \rightarrow {_{20}}Ca^{40} +$$
$$_{6}C^{11} \rightarrow {_{5}}B^{11} +$$
$$_{11}Na^{23} + {_1}H^1 \rightarrow {_2}He^4 +$$

9. An alpha particle with a speed of 3×10^7 m/sec is moving perpendicular to a uniform magnetic field of 1.2 w/m² in a cyclotron.   Find the force on the alpha particle and the radius of the circular path which it follows.   What frequency must be applied to the dees to accelerate this alpha particle?

Ans. 1.15×10^{-11} newton; 0.52 m; 9.2 megacycle/sec

10. Show that for a cyclotron the maximum kinetic energy which can be given an ion is $q^2B^2r^2/2m$, where B is the magnetic intensity and r the maximum allowed radius.

11. A cyclotron has pole faces with a diameter of 1.2 m and operates at a frequency of 20 megacycles/sec.   Find the time required for a proton to traverse a semicircle in one dee, the magnetic field required to accelerate protons, and the maximum kinetic energy which protons can receive under these conditions.

Ans. 2.5×10^{-8} sec; 1.31 w/m²; 29.5 Mev

CHAPTER 51

Nuclear Structure
and Nuclear Energy

51.1. The Building Blocks of Nuclei. Protons and neutrons are the fundamental building blocks out of which we may construct any nucleus. The number of protons in a nucleus determines the atomic number Z, which is the positive charge on the nucleus in elementary units and also the number of electrons associated with the neutral atom. The number of protons plus the number of neutrons gives us the *mass number A*, which is the integer nearest to the atomic weight. Protons and neutrons in a nucleus are referred to as *nucleons*. The mass number A is then the number of nucleons in the nucleus. The chemical behavior of any atom is determined primarily by its atomic number Z. All atoms which have $Z = 1$ are hydrogen atoms, all with $Z = 8$ are oxygen, and all with $Z = 92$ are uranium. However, atoms with the same number of protons may have different numbers of neutrons (Fig. 51.1). Atoms with the same atomic number, but different mass numbers are *isotopes* (Sec. 45.8).

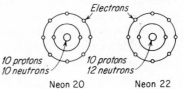

Fig. 51.1. Neon has two stable isotopes with mass numbers 20 and 22.

Most elements have at least two stable isotopes. Zinc has eight, the largest number for any element. In addition to stable isotopes one or more unstable isotopes are known for every element.

51.2. The Deuteron. In 1932 Urey and his collaborators discovered that there is a stable isotope of hydrogen which has mass number 2. Such a hydrogen atom is known as *heavy hydrogen,* or *deuterium.* The *deuteron,* the nucleus of deuterium, has 2 nucleons, 1 proton and 1 neutron. Measurements of the masses of the proton, neutron, and deuteron reveal that the mass of the deuteron is slightly less than the sum of the masses of proton and neutron. In dealing with atoms, it is convenient to measure masses in atomic mass units (amu) based on the isotope O^{16} as 16. One atomic mass unit corresponds (Sec. 45.7) to $1/(6.025 \times 10^{23}) = 1.67 \times 10^{-24}$ g $= 1.67 \times 10^{-27}$ kg. On this scale the masses of the proton, neutron, and deuteron are, respectively, 1.007593, 1.008982, and 2.014176. When a proton and a neutron combine to form a deuteron, 0.00238 amu $(1.007593 + 1.008982 - 2.014176)$ disappear as mass and are transformed to another form (a gamma photon).

According to Einstein's theory of relativity, the mass-energy equivalence is expressed by the equation

$$\text{Energy} = E = mc^2 \tag{51.1}$$

By Eq. (51.1)

$$1 \text{ amu} = mc^2 = (1.66 \times 10^{-26})(3 \times 10^8)^2 = 1.49 \times 10^{-10} \text{ joule}$$

Since 1 ev $= 1.6 \times 10^{-19}$ joule,

$$1 \text{ amu} = 931 \text{ Mev}$$

The mass which disappears when the deuteron is formed corresponds to 2.2 Mev. If we break a deuteron into a proton and a neutron, we must supply 2.2 Mev. Indeed, one of the best methods of measuring the neutron mass involves finding the lowest-energy photon which can break up the deuteron. This process is called *photodisintegration*.

The fact that energy is released in the reaction $_1H^1 + _0n^1 \rightarrow {}_1H^2$ and is required to break up the deuteron is analogous to the situation in chemical reactions. When carbon and oxygen unite to form carbon dioxide, energy is released. If we wish to decompose carbon dioxide into carbon and oxygen, we must add this amount of energy to the system. In the case of nuclei the total energy which would be released if we could perform a series of operations to build a nucleus from neutrons and protons is called the *binding energy* of the nucleus. For the deuteron it is 2.2 Mev. Alternatively, the binding energy is the energy required to tear the nucleus apart into protons and neutrons.

There is a third isotopic form of hydrogen which has a mass of 3 and is called *tritium*. Its nucleus, the *triton*, is composed of 1 proton and 2 neutrons. It is unstable with a half-life of 12 years. H^3 decays by beta emission to He^3.

51.3. The Binding Energy of Nuclei. The nuclear forces are so great and the amount of energy involved when nucleons are brought together to form a new nucleus is so tremendous that we can observe the difference in masses before and after. We have called the difference between the mass of the component nucleons from which a nucleus is composed and the actual mass of the nucleus the *binding energy* of the nucleus. In practice, mass spectrometers determine the masses of heavy atoms (or ions) rather than the masses of nuclei directly. It is convenient to think of any neutral atom of mass number A and atomic number Z as being composed of Z hydrogen atoms plus $(A - Z)$ neutrons. The hydrogen atoms bring in the protons for the nucleus and the electrons for the shells. Then the binding energy is given by the difference between the mass of Z hydrogen atoms plus $A - Z$ neutrons and the mass of the neutral atom.

$$\text{Binding energy} = Zm_\text{H} + (A - Z)m_n - M \qquad (51.2)$$

where m_H, m_n and M are the masses of the hydrogen atom, the neutron, and the neutral atom, respectively. Table 1 lists the masses of a number of common atoms.

Table 1

MASSES OF ATOMS IN AMU
(Based on 0^{16} as 16.00000)

Element	Z	A	Mass	Element	Z	A	Mass
(Neutron)	0	1	1.008982	Nitrogen	7	14	14.0076
Hydrogen	1	1	1.008146	Oxygen	8	16	16.0000
		2	2.014741	Sodium	11	23	22.9965
		3	3.016997	Sulfur	16	32	31.9823
Helium	2	3	3.016977	Nickel	28	58	57.9538
		4	4.003873	Copper	29	63	62.9493
Lithium	3	6	6.01702	Tin	50	120	119.941
		7	7.01822	Lead	82	208	208.042
Carbon	6	12	12.00384	Uranium	92	238	238.124

To obtain the mass of the nucleus from the known atomic mass, one subtracts the mass of the Z electrons.

One electron mass $= 0.00054876$ amu $= 0.511$ Mev

The binding energy increases with the mass number A. For purposes of comparison it is convenient to divide the total binding energy by the number of nucleons and thus obtain the *binding energy per nucleon*. A plot of the binding energy per nucleon for many stable nuclei is shown in Fig. 51.2.

Example. Find the binding energy and the binding energy per nucleon for Li^7; Li^7 is composed of 3 hydrogen atoms + 4 neutrons.

$$3 \times 1.008146 = 3.024438$$
$$4 \times 1.008982 = 4.035928$$
$$\overline{ 7.060366}$$
$$\text{Li}^7 \qquad 7.01822$$
$$\text{Binding energy} = \overline{0.042146} \text{ amu}$$
$$0.0421 \times 931 = 39.3 \text{ Mev binding energy}$$
$$\text{Binding energy per particle} = \frac{39.3}{7} = 5.6 \text{ Mev/nucleon}$$

51.4. Stability Criteria. We do not know the exact nature of the forces which hold nucleons together, but we do know what stable nuclei exist in nature and some of the conditions which must be satisfied if a nucleus is to be stable. Among the light elements we never find stable nuclei which have radically different numbers of protons and neutrons. For example, oxygen has three stable isotopes with masses 16, 17, and 18. The 8 protons of the oxygen nucleus form stable configurations with 8, 9, or 10 neutrons, but not with 4 neutrons nor with 20 neutrons. As we go up the periodic table, the number of neutrons increases more rapidly than the number of protons until in U^{238} there are almost 1.6 neutrons for every proton.

The increase in binding energy per nucleon for light elements (Fig. 51.2) is associated with the fact that on the average each nucleon has more neighbors to

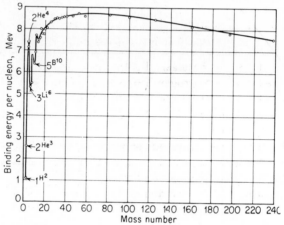

Fig. 51.2. The binding energy per nucleon as a function of mass number for stable nuclei.

which it is bound. However, as we add protons, the disruptive energy due to Coulomb repulsion between protons increases. As the mutual electrostatic repulsion of the protons becomes more serious, the binding energy per nucleon falls off. To the Coulomb repulsion we attribute the fact that the number of neutrons exceeds the number of protons for stable nuclei heavier than Ca^{40} and the instability of the heavy nuclei which emit alpha particles.

In general, a nucleus is unstable against alpha decay if its mass exceeds that of an alpha particle plus that of the residual nucleus. In the reaction

$$_{88}Ra^{226} \rightarrow {}_{86}Rn^{222} + {}_2He^4 + energy$$

the energy released is the difference between the mass of the radium (226.10309 amu) and the sum of the masses of the radon (222.09397) and the helium (4.00387). This is 0.00525 amu, or 4.9 Mev.

When a nucleus contains too many neutrons for the number of protons present, this unbalance is corrected by the transformation of a neutron into a proton with emission of a beta ray and a neutrino.

$$_0n^1 \rightarrow {}_1H^1 + {}_{-1}\beta^0 + neutrino$$

This is the beta-decay process which results in a final nucleus of the same mass number A, but one higher atomic number Z. Beta decay is expected when the mass of the product nucleus is less than that of the original nucleus. As an example, the C^{14} nucleus has a mass greater than that of N^{14} and

$$_6C^{14} \rightarrow {}_7N^{14} + {}_{-1}\beta^0 + \text{neutrino}$$

When elements of low-to-moderate mass have too many protons for the number of neutrons, a transmutation occurs which results in the changing of a proton into a neutron. This may happen in one of two ways: (1) a positron may be emitted or (2) an orbital electron may be captured. In either case a neutrino is also involved. An example of a positron emitter is carbon 11 which decays by the reaction

$$_6C^{11} \rightarrow {}_5B^{11} + {}_1\beta^0 + \text{neutrino}$$

where $_1\beta^0$ represents a positron.

51.5. Fusion. The alpha particle is composed of 4 nucleons, 2 protons and 2 neutrons. The mass of a He^4 atom is 4.00387 amu, while the sum of the masses of 2 hydrogen atoms and 2 neutrons is 4.03416 amu. The binding energy is 0.0304 amu, or 28.2 Mev.

If we could build helium nuclei from protons and neutrons, we would have a source of tremendous energy. Actually, the probability of getting 2 protons and 2 neutrons simultaneously in so small a volume that they would interact to form an alpha particle is small. However, we might well carry on the process by having first a proton and a neutron combine to form a deuteron. Then two deuterons might be brought close enough together to interact. When we do this, so much energy is available that the four particles do not ordinarily stick together. Rather, either a high-energy proton is emitted, leaving us a triton, or a neutron is emitted, leaving us with a He^3 nucleus. The reactions are

$$_1H^2 + {}_1H^2 \nearrow \; {}_2He^3 + {}_0n^1 + 3.28 \text{ Mev energy}$$
$$\searrow \; {}_1H^3 + {}_1H^1 + 4.04 \text{ Mev energy}$$

The energy released in a nuclear reaction such as this is calculated by subtracting the mass of the reaction products from the mass of the interacting particles. One of the many ways in which we can get an alpha particle from these products is to bring a deuteron and a triton together. The resulting reaction is

$$_1H^2 + {}_1H^3 \rightarrow {}_2He^4 + {}_0n^1 + 17.6 \text{ Mev energy}$$

The process of building helium from hydrogen is called *fusion*. As we have seen, 28.2 Mev of energy is released for each helium nucleus built from the building blocks. If we produce fusion reactions on a large scale, we have a colossal release of energy in a very short time and thus create a great explosion. The hydrogen bomb is an example of a fusion device. If deuterons and tritons are to come in contact with each other in spite of the repulsion between the positive charges, they must have high speeds. In a hydrogen bomb these speeds may be achieved by bringing the particles to an exceedingly high temperature, thereby producing *thermonuclear reactions*. One way to produce temperatures of this magnitude is by a nuclear explosion utilizing fission.

The release of energy by means of the combination of nucleons into heavier particles (fusion) is directly analogous to the release of chemical energy by the combination of atoms. In the nuclear case one may release energy by combining a proton and a neutron to form a deuteron. In the analogous chemical situation one may combine an atom of sodium with an atom of chlorine to form sodium chloride. One great difference between these two reactions lies in the amount of energy released per interacting particle. In the case of proton and neutron the energy resulting from the combination is 2.2 Mev per proton, while in the case of the sodium chlorine reaction the energy is about 4 ev per sodium atom.

51.6. Fission. One can obtain energy from chemical reactions, not only by combining atoms of various substances to form molecules, but

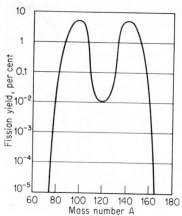

Fig. 51.3. Fission yield as a function of mass number for the fission of U^{236} produced by capture of a slow neutron in U^{235}.

also by taking very large and complex molecules, such as trinitrotoluene molecules, and causing them to break up into smaller and more tightly bound units. Similarly, heavy and complex nuclei can be made to break up with the release of energy.

When any heavy nucleus is highly excited it may break up into two roughly equal parts. This process is called *fission*. Some heavy nuclei fission readily; others do not. The excitation can be achieved in several ways. For example, gamma rays may induce fission. The most familiar method is by introducing a neutron into a nucleus of uranium 235. When a slow neutron collides with a U^{235} nucleus, it may be captured. The resulting U^{236} nucleus breaks up into two roughly equal parts, plus a few additional neutrons. A typical reaction is:

$$_{92}U^{235} + _{0}n^{1} \rightarrow _{92}U^{236} \rightarrow _{56}Ba^{145} + _{36}Kr^{88} + 3_{0}n^{1} + \text{energy}$$

The mass of the products is less than that of the fissioning nucleus; thus energy is released, on the average about 200 Mev per fission. The excited U^{236} nucleus may break up in many different ways. Figure 51.3 shows the relative fission yields of the many mass numbers which may be created as fission fragments.

When heavy nuclei fission, the two product nuclei usually have several too many neutrons for stability. For example, one common fission product is strontium 95. The heaviest stable isotope of strontium is Sr^{88}. The radioactive Sr^{95} nucleus undergoes three successive beta decays and finally reaches stability as a columbium 95. Some fission products transmute through beta decays of long half-life and produce serious contamination after a nuclear explosion.

51.7. Chain Reactions and the Reactor. Since two to three neutrons are released in a typical fission, two or three other atoms may be fissioned if these neutrons are captured by U^{235} nuclei. The neutrons released in these fissions can produce four or five more fissions and a *chain reaction* is set off if a sufficient supply of U^{235} atoms is present in a small volume. Such a chain reaction does not occur in ordinary uranium because a large fraction of the neutrons are captured by U^{238} nuclei which are 140 times as abundant in natural uranium as U^{235} nuclei. Few of the U^{238} nuclei fission.

To produce the first nuclear weapons, U^{235} was separated from U^{238} so a large fraction of the neutrons emitted by fissioning nuclei would be captured by U^{235} nuclei and thereby produce additional fissions. How-

Fig. 51.4. Nuclear explosion over Bikini Lagoon, July 1, 1946. (*Acme Newspictures, Inc.*)

ever, even pure U^{235} does not support a chain reaction unless an amount known as a *critical mass* is present because too large a fraction of the neutrons escape from the surface of a subcritical mass. If two almost critical masses are brought together, the system becomes critical and an explosion (Fig. 51.4) occurs.

The neutrons released in fission are *fast* with energies of several Mev. They are quickly slowed down by collisions with nuclei. U^{235} does not capture fast neutrons readily, but it captures slow neutrons (energy less than 1 ev) very effectively. On the other hand, U^{238} captures neutrons of intermediate energies more readily than slow ones. If the neutrons from fissions in natural uranium are slowed down in some other material so the U^{238} does not capture them while they have intermediate energies, a sustained reaction using natural uranium can be maintained in a nuclear *reactor* (or *pile*). Figure 51.5 shows a reactor in which carbon is used to slow down or *moderate* the neutrons. (Heavy water, containing deuterium, is another material which is an excellent *moderator*.) Fissions produce fast neutrons which enter the carbon where they have many collisions and slow down to thermal velocities before they reach another

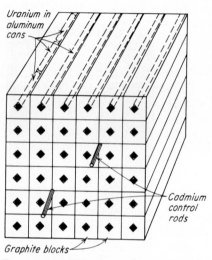

Uranium in aluminum cans

Cadmium control rods

Graphite blocks

Fig. 51.5. A uranium-graphite reactor using uranium "slugs" canned in aluminum. The cadmium rods are used to control the power level at which the reactor operates.

uranium slug. The probability that a slow neutron will be captured by a U^{235} nucleus is much greater than the probability it will be captured by a U^{238} nucleus, even though there are 140 times as many of the latter. Cadmium control rods are moved into or out of the reactor to regulate the power level of the pile and keep it from blowing up. Cadmium 113 is an excellent capturer of slow neutrons.

Each fission in a reactor releases about 200 Mev of energy and the total energy transformed from mass to thermal energy in a large reactor is great. Nuclear energy is being used for generating electric power, for heating, for propelling submarines, and for nuclear weapons. Nuclear power plants for aircraft promise to extend the range and revolutionize the operation of airplanes. In the next century it is likely that an ever-increasing fraction of our total energy requirements will be supplied from nuclear sources.

51.8. Plutonium. When neutrons are captured in U^{238}, fission sometimes occurs, but usually the U^{239} formed does not split up. However, it does emit a beta particle (half-life 23 min) and becomes neptunium 239 (Fig. 51.6). Np^{239} is a beta emitter with a half-life of 2.3 days and becomes plutonium 239. Pu^{239} is an alpha emitter with a half-life of 24,400 years. This plutonium fissions readily. Practically no plutonium exists in natural materials. Substantial quantities have been produced for use in nuclear weapons. It is produced in reactors which use natural uranium as fuel.

51.9. The Size of Nuclei. Although nuclei are exceedingly small, several types of measurements have been devised to determine nuclear radii. While there are minor differences in the values, all methods agree on the order of magnitude. The volumes of all nuclei are roughly proportional to the number of nucleons A. Assuming a roughly spherical shape, we find that the radius of a nucleus of mass number A is given by

$$r = 1.2 \times 10^{-15} \sqrt[3]{A} \qquad m \qquad (51.3)$$

The heaviest of all common nuclei is that of uranium 238, for which $\sqrt[3]{A}$ is slightly over 6 and the nuclear radius as given by Eq. (51.3) is a little less than 10^{-14} m. On the other hand, atoms have radii of the order of 10^{-10} m. If we imagine a typical atom expanded until its nucleus has a radius of 1 mm, the atom itself would have a radius of about 10 m. The nucleus occupies a small fraction

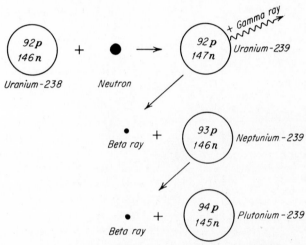

Fig. 51.6. The production of plutonium from U^{238}.

(about 10^{-12}) of the volume of the atom, which must be regarded as a loose structure composed largely of empty space.

The density of nuclei of all kinds is roughly the same, about 2×10^{14} g/cm³. A pint of packed nucleons would weigh 100 billion tons!

51.10. Cosmic Rays. In addition to the alpha particles from radioactive nuclei and the charged particles from high-energy accelerators there is another source of high-energy charged particles which has been of great importance in studying nuclear reactions. This source is the *cosmic radiation*. The primary cosmic rays consist of charged particles, primarily protons, with energies as great as 10^{18} ev. These particles come from sources outside the earth. Very few primary cosmic rays reach the surface of the earth. As they pass through the upper atmosphere, they collide with atmospheric nuclei and blast them apart. At the earth's surface the progeny of the primaries are high-energy photons, electrons, positrons, and mesons (Sec. 51.11) which we call the *secondary* cosmic rays. A single proton may initiate a "shower" containing thousands of these secondaries.   Figure 51.7 shows a shower of 19 secondary particles produced by a single electron which itself was only one of many secondaries from a single primary particle.

51.11. Mesons and Hyperons.   When a primary cosmic-ray proton collides with a nucleus in the upper atmosphere, *pi mesons* are created. The term *meson* is used to signify any particle of mass intermediate between the masses of the electron and the proton.   Several kinds of mesons exist (Table 2), but pi mesons are most closely linked with interactions between nucleons and are the ones most copiously produced.   Pi

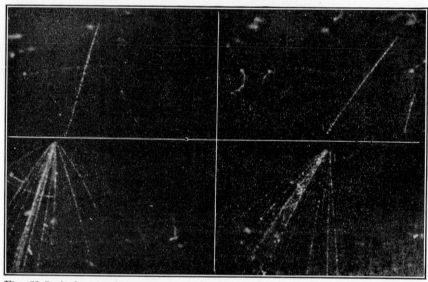

Fig. 51.7. A shower of 19 secondary rays apparently produced by a single electron. These tracks were photographed in a cloud chamber. (*Courtesy of J. C. Street and E. C. Stevenson, Harvard University.*)

mesons may be positive, negative, or neutral.   Positive and negative pi mesons have a mass 273 times that of an electron, while the neutral pi meson is slightly lighter, probably 264 electron masses.   In high-energy nuclear collisions all three kinds of pi mesons are created.   Neutral mesons disappear with the emission of 2 photons which share the 134 Mev of energy released.   Negative pi mesons are strongly attracted to nuclei and are captured quickly.   Positive pi mesons are repelled by nuclei and are less likely to be captured.   Charged pi mesons exist for a very short time.   If they are not captured, they undergo a sudden decay in which a *mu meson* of the same charge and a neutrino appear.   Mu mesons have a mass 207 times that of the electron.   They, in turn, are short-lived and decay into an electron (+ or −) and two neutrinos.

When protons with energies of several Bev collide with nuclei. occasionally a *negative proton* is produced.   This particle is like the ordinary proton except that it bears the opposite charge.   A negative proton and a proton in some nucleus promptly annihilate one another, thereby producing several pi mesons and tearing many of the other nucleons out of the nucleus.

Table 2
MESONS AND HYPERONS

Name	Symbol	Rest mass in electron masses	Mean life, sec	Decay
Mu meson........	$\mu^{\pm}$	207	2×10^{-6}	$\mu^{\pm} \to e^{\pm} + 2$ neutrinos + 105 Mev
Pi meson..........	$\pi^{\pm}$	273	3×10^{-8}	$\pi^{\pm} \to \mu^{\pm} +$ neutrino + 34 Mev
Neutral pi meson...	π^0	264	10^{-14}	$\pi^0 \to 2\gamma$ rays
K meson..........	K_{μ}^{+}	940	10^{-8}	$K_{\mu}^{+} \to \mu^{+} +$ neutrino + 373 Mev
Theta meson.......	$\theta^{\pm}$	953	10^{-9}	$\theta^{\pm} \to \pi^{\pm} + \pi^0 + 215$ Mev
Neutral theta meson	θ^0	966	10^{-10}	$\theta^0 \to \pi^{+} + \pi^{-} + 214$ Mev
Tau meson........	$\tau^{\pm}$	966	10^{-8}	$\tau^{\pm} \to \pi^{\pm} + \pi^{+} + \pi^{-} + 75$ Mev or $\pi^{\pm} + 2\pi^0 + 84$ Mev
Kappa meson.......	κ	(1,000)	$10^{-9}(?)$	
Chi meson........		(1,000)		
Neutral hyperon....	Λ^0	2,181	4×10^{-10}	$\Lambda^0 \to p + \pi^{-} + 37$ Mev
Charged hyperon....	$\Sigma^{\pm}$	2,329	10^{-10}	$\Sigma^{+} \to p + \pi^0 + 117$ Mev $\Sigma^{\pm} \to n + \pi^{\pm} + 111$ Mev
Charged hyperon....	Ξ^{-}	2,583	10^{-10}	$\Xi^{-} \to \Lambda^0 + \pi^{-} + 66$ Mev

A number of other particles have been discovered, some lighter than the proton and others heavier.   The heavier particles are called *hyperons* (Table 2).   All these particles have exceedingly short half-lives, usually less than a billionth of a second.   Their discovery in recent years has created great interest.   We have no way of knowing whether or not there are dozens more such particles.   Physicists are hard at work determining the properties of the particles and studying their decay schemes.   These new particles open new vistas in physics, a field in which every discovery raises many new questions.

PROBLEMS

1. Find the binding energy and the binding energy per nucleon for the triton.

Ans. 8.46 Mev; 2.82 Mev/nucleon

2. Find the binding energy and the binding energy per nucleon for oxygen 16.

3. In a typical fission reaction a neutron is captured by a $_{92}U^{235}$ nucleus and three neutrons and two fission fragments are formed.   If one of the fragments is a $_{55}Cs^{140}$ nucleus, what must the other fragment be?   *Ans.* $_{37}Rb^{93}$

4. When a U^{238} nucleus captures a slow neutron, uranium 239 with a half-life of 23 min is produced.   If a sample of radioactive material from a nuclear reactor contains 10 g of U^{239}, find what fraction of this uranium has decayed at the end of 115 min.

5. Uranium 238 decays to thorium 234 by the emission of an alpha particle of energy 4.18 Mev.   Assuming that essentially all the energy released in this decay goes to the alpha particle, calculate how much the mass of uranium 238 exceeds the sum of the masses of thorium 234 and helium 4.   *Ans.* 4.18 Mev, or 0.0045 amu

6. When two deuterons interact, a triton and a proton may be produced.   Find the energy released in this reaction.

7. Calculate the energy released in the beta decay of tritium to helium 3.

Ans. 18.6 kev

8. One of the alternative processes which occur when two deuterons interact is the formation of He^3 and a neutron.   Find the energy released.

9. The first transmutation by artificially accelerated particles was produced by Cockcroft and Walton who bombarded $_3Li^7$ with protons to form two helium atoms. Find the energy released (Sec. 50.10).   *Ans.* 17.3 Mev

10. When a deuteron and a triton interact, He^4 and a neutron may result.   Calculate the energy released.

11. Free neutrons are unstable and decay to proton plus an electron (and also a massless neutrino) with a half-life of about 11 min.   Calculate the energy associated with the beta decay of the neutron.   *Ans.* 0.78 Mev

12. How much energy would be released if a carbon 12 atom were assembled from 6 hydrogen atoms and 6 neutrons?

13. When a slow neutron is captured by a U^{235} nucleus, a fission releasing 200 Mev results.   How much mass disappears?   What fraction of the mass of the reacting particles is converted into energy?   *Ans.* 0.217 amu; 0.1 per cent

14. When one atomic weight (12 g) of carbon is oxidized to CO_2, 406,000 joules of heat energy is released.   Using the Einstein mass-energy relation, find how much mass disappears in burning one atomic weight of carbon.

15. It is estimated that the energy released in the atomic bomb explosion at Hiroshima was about 7.6×10^{13} joules, equivalent to 20,000 tons of TNT.   If an average of 200 Mev was released per fission and if all fissions were by neutron capture in U^{235}, find the number of U^{235} atoms fissioned and the mass of U^{235} consumed.

Ans. 2.38×10^{24}; 926 g

16. How many fissions per day are required if a reactor is to develop electric power at the rate of 100 megawatts if 10 per cent of the energy released in fission is converted to electrical energy?

Appendixes

Trigonometric Formulas
and Functions

In a right triangle ABC (Fig. A.1), it is convenient to define the relations between the sides in the following way. Consider the angle at A. Divide the side BC, opposite A, by the hypotenuse AB and call the ratio, for brevity, *sine A*. Now divide the side AC, adjacent to A, by the

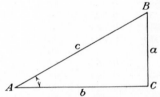

Fig. A.1. A right triangle useful for defining the trigonometric functions.

hypotenuse AB and call this ratio *cosine A*. Then divide the side BC, opposite A, by the side AC, adjacent to A, and call this ratio *tangent A*.

$$\sin A = \frac{\text{side opposite}}{\text{hypotenuse}} = \frac{BC}{AB}$$

$$\cos A = \frac{\text{side adjacent}}{\text{hypotenuse}} = \frac{AC}{AB}$$

$$\tan A = \frac{\text{side opposite}}{\text{side adjacent}} = \frac{BC}{AC}$$

Let c = the hypotenuse, b = the adjacent side, and a = the opposite side.

$$\sin A = \frac{a}{c} \qquad a = c \sin A$$

$$\cos A = \frac{b}{c} \qquad b = c \cos A$$

$$\tan A = \frac{a}{b} \qquad a = b \tan A$$

Table A.1
TRIGONOMETRIC FUNCTIONS

Angle θ, deg	sin θ	cos θ	tan θ	Angle θ, deg	sin θ	cos θ	tan θ
0	0.000	1.000	0.000	46	0.719	0.695	1.04
1	0.017	0.999	0.017	47	0.731	0.682	1.07
2	0.035	0.999	0.035	48	0.743	0.669	1.11
3	0.052	0.999	0.052	49	0.755	0.656	1.15
4	0.070	0.998	0.070				
5	0.087	0.996	0.087	50	0.766	0.643	1.19
6	0.105	0.995	0.105	51	0.777	0.629	1.23
7	0.122	0.993	0.123	52	0.788	0.616	1.28
8	0.139	0.990	0.141	53	0.799	0.602	1.33
9	0.156	0.988	0.158	54	0.809	0.588	1.38
10	0.174	0.985	0.176	55	0.819	0.574	1.43
				56	0.829	0.559	1.48
11	0.191	0.982	0.194	57	0.839	0.545	1.54
12	0.208	0.978	0.213	58	0.848	0.530	1.60
13	0.225	0.974	0.231	59	0.857	0.515	1.56
14	0.242	0.970	0.249				
15	0.259	0.966	0.268	60	0.866	0.500	1.73
16	0.276	0.961	0.287	61	0.875	0.485	1.80
17	0.292	0.956	0.306	62	0.883	0.469	1.88
18	0.309	0.951	0.325	63	0.891	0.454	1.96
19	0.326	0.946	0.344	64	0.898	0.428	2.05
20	0.342	0.940	0.364	65	0.906	0.423	2.14
				66	0.914	0.407	2.25
21	0.358	0.934	0.384	67	0.921	0.391	2.36
22	0.375	0.927	0.404	68	0.927	0.375	2.48
23	0.391	0.921	0.424	69	0.934	0.358	2.61
24	0.407	0.914	0.445	70	0.940	0.342	2.75
25	0.423	0.906	0.466				
26	0.438	0.898	0.488	71	0.946	0.326	2.90
27	0.454	0.891	0.510	72	0.951	0.309	3.08
28	0.469	0.883	0.532	73	0.956	0.292	3.27
29	0.485	0.875	0.554	74	0.961	0.276	3.49
30	0.500	0.866	0.577	75	0.966	0.259	3.73
				76	0.970	0.242	4.01
31	0.515	0.857	0.601	77	0.974	0.225	4.33
32	0.530	0.848	0.625	78	0.978	0.208	4.70
33	0.545	0.839	0.649	79	0.982	0.191	5.14
34	0.559	0.829	0.675	80	0.985	0.174	5.67
35	0.574	0.819	0.700				
36	0.588	0.809	0.727	81	0.988	0.156	6.31
37	0.602	0.799	0.754	82	0.990	0.139	7.12
38	0.616	0.788	0.781	83	0.993	0.122	8.14
39	0.629	0.777	0.810	84	0.995	0.105	9.51
40	0.643	0.766	0.839	85	0.996	0.087	11.43
				86	0.998	0.070	14.30
41	0.656	0.755	0.869	87	0.999	0.052	19.08
42	0.669	0.743	0.900	88	0.999	0.035	28.64
43	0.682	0.731	0.933	89	0.999	0.017	57.28
44	0.695	0.719	0.966	90	1.000	0.000	Infinity
45	0.707	0.707	1.000				

Tables are prepared giving the values of sin A, cos A, and tan A for all values of A. With such a table at hand it is easy to find any side of a right triangle when an acute angle and one of the sides are given.

Example. In a right triangle ABC (Fig. A.1) the angle A is 30°, and the side BC is 2 ft. Find the hypotenuse.

$$\sin A = \frac{BC}{AB}$$
$$\sin 30° = 0.500$$
$$0.500 = \frac{2}{AB}$$
$$AB = 4 \text{ ft}$$

NOTE. For numerical values of trigonometric functions, see Table **A.1**.

Important Physical Constants

Speed of light	c	2.9979×10^8 m/sec
Electronic charge	e	1.6021×10^{-19} coulomb
Electron rest mass	m	9.108×10^{-31} kg
Avogadro's number of particles per mole	N	6.0247×10^{23}
Volume of one mole under STP		$22,421$ cm^3
Universal gas constant	R	8.3166 joules/(mole)(K°)
		$= 1.9870$ cal/(mole)(K°)
Faraday		$96,520$ coulombs
Gravitational constant	G	6.670×10^{-11} newton-m^2/kg^2
Mechanical equivalent of heat	J	4.1855 joules/cal
Standard atmosphere		$101,325$ newtons/m^2
Density of mercury (STP)		13.595 g/cm^3
Planck's constant	h	6.6252×10^{-34} joule-sec
Electron volt	ev	1.6021×10^{-19} joule
Stefan-Boltzmann constant	σ	5.6686×10^{-8} watt/(K°)^4(m^2)
Wien's constant		2.8979×10^{-3} (m)(K°)
Atomic mass unit	amu	1.6597×10^{-27} kg
Rest energy of 1 amu		931.2 Mev
Atomic mass of natural oxygen on physical scale		16.0044

THE GREEK ALPHABET

A	α	Alpha	H	η	Eta	N	ν	Nu	T	τ	Tau
B	β	Beta	Θ	θ	Theta	Ξ	ξ	Xi	Υ	υ	Upsilon
Γ	γ	Gamma	I	ι	Iota	O	o	Omicron	Φ	ϕ	Phi
Δ	δ	Delta	K	κ	Kappa	Π	π	Pi	X	χ	Chi
E	ϵ	Epsilon	Λ	λ	Lambda	P	ρ	Rho	Ψ	ψ	Psi
Z	ζ	Zeta	M	μ	Mu	Σ	σ	Sigma	Ω	ω	Omega

APPENDIX C

Conversion Factors

Length
1 m = 39.37 in. = 3.281 ft = 6.214 × 10^{-4} mile
1 ft = 30.48 cm; 1 mile = 1.609 km

Area
1 m^2 = 10.76 ft^2 = 1,550 $in.^2$
1 ft^2 = 929 cm^2

Volume
1 m^3 = 35.31 ft^3 = 6.102 × 10^4 $in.^3$
1 ft^3 = 0.02832 m^3; 1 U.S. gallon = 231 $in.^3$

Velocity
1 km/hr = 0.2778 m/sec = 0.9113 ft/sec = 0.6214 mi/hr
1 mi/hr = 1.467 ft/sec = 1.609 km/hr = 0.8684 knot

Mass
1 kg = 2.205 lb mass = 0.06852 slug
1 lb mass = 0.4536 kg

Density
1 g/cm^3 = 1,000 kg/m^3 = 62.43 lb mass/ft^3 = 1.940 slug/ft^3
1 lb mass/ft^3 = 0.03108 slug/ft^3 = 27,680 kg/m^3 = 27.68 g/cm^3

Force
1 newton = 10^5 dynes = 0.1020 kg-wt = 0.2248 lb
1 lb (force) = 4.448 newtons = 0.4536 kg-wt = 32.17 poundals

Pressure
1 newton/m^2 = 9.869 × 10^{-6} atm = 1.450 × 10^{-4} lb/$in.^2$ = 0.02089 lb/ft^2
$\qquad$ = 7.501 × 10^{-4} cm Hg = 4.015 × 10^{-3} in. of water
1 lb/$in.^2$ = 144 lb/ft^2 = 6,895 newtons/m^2 = 5.171 cm Hg = 27.68 in. of water
1 atm = 406.8 in. of water = 76 cm Hg = 1.013 × 10^5 newtons/m^2
$\qquad$ = 10,330 kg-wt/m^2 = 2,116 lb/ft^2 = 14.70 lb/in^2

Work, Energy, Heat
1 joule = 0.2389 cal = 9.481 × 10^{-4} Btu = 0.7376 ft-lb = 10^7 ergs
1 cal = 4.186 joules = 0.003968 Btu = 3.087 ft-lb
1 amu = 1.492 × 10^{-10} joule = 931 Mev

Power
1 hp = 2545 Btu/hr = 550 ft-lb/sec = 745.7 watts
$\qquad$ = 178.2 cal/sec

Electric Charge
1 coulomb = 0.1 abcoulomb = 3 × 10^9 statcoulombs (esu)
1 faraday = 96,520 coulombs; one electronic charge = 1.602 × 10^{-19} coulomb

Electric Potential and Electromotive Force
1 abvolt = 10^{-8} volt; 1 statvolt (esu) = 300 volts
Capacitance
1 statfarad (esu) = 1 cm = 1.113×10^{-12} farad
Magnetic Flux
1 weber = 10^8 maxwells = 10^5 kilolines
Magnetic Intensity B
1 newton/amp-m = 1 w/m² = 10,000 gauss = 10^9 gamma
Magnetizing Force H
1 amp-turn/m = 0.01257 oersted

APPENDIX D

Tables of Data

Table D.1

HEAT CONSTANTS OF SOLIDS

Substance	Melting point, °C	Coefficient of linear expansion per C°	Specific heat cal/(g)(C°)	Heat of fusion cal/g	Heat of fusion Btu/lb
Aluminum	657	0.0000255	0.22	76.8	140
Bismuth	268	0.0000157	0.030	12.6	22.7
Brass	......	0.0000193	0.090		
Copper	1084	0.0000167	0.093	43	77
Glass	......	0.0000083	0.20		
Gold	1063	0.0000139	0.030		
Ice	0	0.000051	0.50	79.8	144
Iron	1503	0.0000119	0.11	30	54
Lead	327	0.0000276	0.030	5.4	9.7
Mercury	−38.8	....	0.033	2.8	5.4
Nickel	1452	0.0000128	0.109	4.6	8.3
Platinum	1756	0.0000089	0.032	27	48.6
Silver	960	0.0000188	0.056	22	39
Steel	......	0.0000132	0.11		
Tungsten	3360	0.0000044	0.034		
Zinc	418	0.0000263	0.092	28.1	50.6

Table D.2
HEAT CONSTANTS OF LIQUIDS

Substance	Boiling point, °C	Cubical expansion per C°	Specific heat, cal/(g)(C°)	Heat of vaporization cal/g	Heat of vaporization Btu/lb
Ammonia.........	−34	....	....	294	529
Aniline...........	184	....	0.514	110	198
Alcohol (ethyl).....	78.1	0.0011	0.55	205	369
Benzine...........	80.3	0.00124	0.34	94.4	170
Chloroform........	61	0.00126	0.232	58	106
Ether (ethyl).......	34.5	0.00163	0.56	88.4	159
Gasoline..........	70–90	0.0012	....	71–81	128–146
Glycerin..........	290	0.00053	0.58		
Mercury..........	358	0.000182	0.0332	68	122
Turpentine........	159	0.00094	0.42	70	126
Water............	100	0.00030	1.00	540	970

Table D.3
BOILING POINT OF WATER

(Boiling points of water at pressures near standard atmospheric pressure. The pressures are given in millimeters of mercury at 0°C.)

Pressure, mm	Temperature, °C	Pressure, mm	Temperature, °C	Pressure, mm	Temperature, °C	Pressure, mm	Temperature, °C
733	98.99	745	99.44	757	98.89	769	100.33
735	99.07	747	99.52	759	99.96	771	100.40
737	99.14	749	99.59	761	100.04	773	100.47
739	99.22	751	99.67	763	100.11	775	100.55
741	99.29	753	99.74	765	100.18	777	100.62
743	99.37	755	99.82	767	100.26	779	100.69

Table D.4
PROPERTIES OF SATURATED WATER VAPOR

Temperature, °C	Pressure		Volume		Heat units per unit mass		
	kg/cm²	lb/in.²	m³/kg	ft³/lb	Of water	Latent heat	Total heat of vapor
0	0.0063	0.089	204.970	3283.00	0	594.7	594.7
10	0.0125	0.178	106.620	1707.60	10	589.4	599.4
20	0.0236	0.336	58.150	931.48	20	584.1	604.1
30	0.0429	0.61	33.132	530.72	30	578.8	608.8
40	0.0747	1.06	19.650	314.77	40.1	573.4	613.5
50	0.125	1.78	12.091	193.68	50.1	567.9	618
60	0.202	2.88	7.695	123.26	60.1	562.4	622.6
70	0.317	4.51	5.050	80.89	70.2	556.8	627
80	0.482	6.86	3.4085	54.60	80.3	551	631.5
90	0.714	10.16	2.3592	37.79	90.4	545.2	635.6
100	1.033	14.70	1.6702	26.754	100.5	539.6	639.7
110	1.462	20.79	1.2073	19.339	101.7	532.9	643.6
120	2.027	28.83	0.8894	14.247	120.9	526.6	647.4
130	2.760	39.26	0.6664	10.675	131.1	520	651
140	3.695	52.56	0.5071	8.123	141.3	513.2	654.5
150	4.868	69.24	0.3917	6.274	151.6	506.2	657.8
160	6.323	89.93	0.3065	4.91	161.9	498.9	660.8
170	8.104	115.27	0.2429	3.891	172.2	491.4	663.7
180	10.258	145.90	0.1945	3.116	182.6	483.7	666.3
190	12.835	182.56	0.1575	2.523	193.1	475.7	668.8
200	15.890	226.00	0.1288	2.063	203.6	467.5	671.1
210	19.490	277.20	0.1063	1.703	214.1	459.1	673.2

APPENDIX E

Derivations

E.1. Velocity of Waves in a Cord. Suppose that a transverse wave is traveling toward the right in the cord (Fig. A.2).

Let T = the tension

m_l = the mass per unit length

V = the velocity of the wave

Now assume that while the pulse, or wave, is moving toward the right with a velocity V, the cord is made to move toward the left with an equal velocity. As a result of

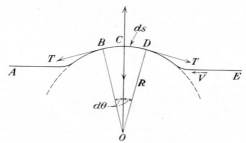

Fig. A.2. Transverse wave in a stretched string.

these superposed velocities, the wave appears to stand still. For simplicity, assume that the pulse is circular in form, and consider a small segment ds of the cord. The components of the tension T along the radius CO are

$$F = 2T \sin d\theta = 2T \, d\theta \text{ (approx.)}$$

Since $2 \, d\theta = ds/R$ and $d\theta = ds/2R$,

$$F = 2T \, d\theta = 2T \frac{ds}{2R} = T \frac{ds}{R}$$

The centrifugal force on the element ds of the cord of mass $m_l \, ds$ is

$$f = m_l \, ds \frac{V^2}{R}$$

Since the cord is in equilibrium, the force F due to tension and the centrifugal force f must be equal.

646

Hence

$$m_l \, ds \, \frac{V^2}{R} = T \frac{ds}{R}$$

$$V^2 = \frac{T}{m_l}$$

$$V = \sqrt{\frac{T}{m_l}}$$

E.2. Energy Stored in an Inductive Circuit. The energy stored in the magnetic field associated with a circuit for which the coefficient of self-induction is L is equal to the work required to establish the current in the circuit or the energy which will be released when the current is eliminated. The back emf due to the self-inductance in the circuit is

$$e = -L \frac{di}{dt}$$

The work done against this back emf in the time dt is

$$ei \, dt = Li \frac{di}{dt} \, dt = Li \, di$$

The whole work is

$$W = \int_0^I ei \, dt = \int_0^I Li \, di$$
$$= \tfrac{1}{2}LI^2$$

E.3. Effective Value of an Alternating Current. By definition the effective value of an alternating current is the steady current which dissipates heat in a resistor at the same average rate as the alternating current. Let the alternating current be $i = I_{max} \sin 2\pi ft$. The power developed instantaneously in a resistor R is $I_{max}^2 R \sin^2 2\pi ft$. The heat developed during one cycle is

$$I_{eff}^2 RT = \int_0^T I_{max}^2 R \sin^2 2\pi ft \, dt$$

where T is the period $(T = 1/f)$. Therefore,

$$I_{eff}^2 T = I_{max}^2 \int_0^T \sin^2 \frac{2\pi}{T} t \, dt = \frac{I_{max}^2 T}{2}$$

from which

$$I_{eff} = \frac{I_{max}}{\sqrt{2}} = 0.707 I_{max}$$

E.4. Alternating-current Series Circuits. Application of Kirchhoff's second law to the circuit of Fig. 44.4 yields

$$v = V_{max} \sin 2\pi ft = L \frac{di}{dt}$$

from which

$$i = \int \frac{V_{max} \sin 2\pi ft \, dt}{L} = -\frac{V_{max} \cos 2\pi ft}{2\pi fL}$$

and

$$I_{max} = \frac{V_{max}}{2\pi fL}$$

Similarly, when an alternating potential difference $V_{max} \sin 2\pi ft$ is applied across a capacitor, $V_{max} \sin 2\pi ft = q/C$. Since $i = dq/dt$,

$$\frac{i}{C} = \frac{d(V_{max} \sin 2\pi ft)}{dt} = 2\pi f V_{max} \cos 2\pi ft$$

Therefore
$$i = \frac{V_{max} \cos 2\pi ft}{1/2\pi fC} \quad \text{and} \quad I_{max} = \frac{V_{max}}{1/2\pi fC}$$

If we have an a-c series circuit containing a source of emf $e = \mathcal{E}_{max} \sin 2\pi ft$, resistance, inductance, and capacitance (Fig. 44.11), application of Kirchhoff's second law at any instant leads to

$$e = \mathcal{E}_{max} \sin 2\pi ft = Ri + L\frac{di}{dt} + \frac{q}{C}$$

If we differentiate with respect to time,

$$2\pi f\mathcal{E}_{max} \cos 2\pi ft = R\frac{di}{dt} + L\frac{d^2i}{dt^2} + \frac{i}{C}$$

The solution of this differential equation is

$$i = \frac{\mathcal{E}_{max} \sin (2\pi ft - \theta)}{\sqrt{R^2 + [2\pi fL - (1/2\pi fC)^2}}$$

where
$$\tan \theta = \frac{2\pi fL - 1/2\pi fC}{R}$$

and
$$I = \frac{\mathcal{E}}{\sqrt{R^2 + [2\pi fL - (1/2\pi fC)]^2}}$$

If either the inductor or capacitor is removed from the circuit and the circuit is completed once more, the appropriate term vanishes from the equations above. This leads to Eq. (44.6) if the capacitor is removed and to Eq. (44.8) if there is no inductance.

E.5. Power in the Alternating-current Circuit. The instantaneous power supplied to an a-c circuit is given by $p = ei$ [Eq. (44.11)]. The average power over a complete cycle is

$$P = \frac{1}{T}\int_0^T p\, dt = \frac{1}{T}\int_0^T ei\, dt = \frac{1}{T}\int_0^T \mathcal{E}_{max} \sin 2\pi ft\, I_{max} \sin (2\pi ft - \theta)\, dt$$

where T is the period $(T = 1/f)$. Since $\sin (2\pi ft - \theta) = \sin 2\pi ft \cos \theta - \cos 2\pi ft \sin \theta$, P becomes

$$P = \frac{\mathcal{E}_{max}I_{max}}{T}\int_0^T \left(\sin^2 \frac{2\pi t}{T} \cos \theta + \sin \frac{2\pi t}{T} \cos \frac{2\pi t}{T} \sin \theta\right) dt$$

$$= \frac{\mathcal{E}_{max}I_{max} \cos \theta}{2} = \mathcal{E}I \cos \theta$$

which is Eq. (44.12).

The Periodic Table
of the Elements

The Periodic Table of the Elements

Period	I	II	III	IV	V	VI	VII	VIII
1	1 H 1.008							2 He 4.003
2	3 Li 6.940	4 Be 9.013	5 B 10.82	6 C 12.01	7 N 14.008	8 O 16.000	9 F 19.000	10 Ne 20.183
3	11 Na 22.997	12 Mg 24.32	13 Al 26.98	14 Si 28.06	15 P 30.98	16 S 32.06	17 Cl 35.457	18 A 39.944
4	19 K 39.096	20 Ca 40.08	21 Sc 45.10	22 Ti 47.90	23 V 50.95	24 Cr 52.01	25 Mn 54.93	26 Fe 55.84 27 Co 58.94 28 Ni 58.69
	29 Cu 63.57	30 Zn 65.38	31 Ga 69.72	32 Ge 72.60	33 As 74.91	34 Se 78.96	35 Br 79.916	36 K 83.7
5	37 Rb 85.48	38 Sr 87.63	39 Yt 88.92	40 Zr 91.22	41 Cb 92.91	42 Mo 96.0	43 Tc 99	44 Ru 101.1 45 Rh 102.91 46 Pd 106.7
	47 Ag 107.9	48 Cd 112.41	49 In 114.8	50 Sn 118.7	51 Sb 121.8	52 Te 127.6	53 I 126.9	54 Xe 131.3
6	55 Cs 132.9	56 Ba 137.4	57 La 138.9	72 Hf 178.6	73 Ta 180.88	74 W 184.0	75 Re 186.3	76 Os 190.2 77 Ir 192.2 78 Pt 195.2
	79 Au 197.0	80 Hg 200.6	81 Tl 204.39	82 Pb 207.18	83 Bi 209.00	84 Po 210	85 At 211	86 Rn 222
7	87 Fr 223	88 Ra 226	89 Ac 227					

Period														
6	58 Ce 140.2	59 Pr 140.9	60 Nd 144.3	61 Il 146.0	62 Sa 150.4	63 Eu 152.0	64 Gd 156.9	65 Tb 159.0	66 Ds 162.5	67 Ho 164.9	68 Er 167.6	69 Tm 169.0	70 Yb 173.0	71 Lu 175.0
7	90 Th 232	91 Pa 231	92 U 238	93 Np 237	94 Pu 242	95 Am	96 Cm	97 Bk	98 Cf	99 E	100 Fm			

650

APPENDIX G

Suggestions for Further Reading

General

Dampier, W: *A History of Science*, Macmillan, New York.
 Historical treatment with emphasis on philosophical and mathematical aspects of science.
Lindsay, R. B., and H. Margenau: *Foundations of Physics*, Wiley, New York.
 Emphasizes the logical structure of physics.
Magie, W. F.: *Source Book in Physics*, McGraw-Hill, New York.
 Quotations from the writings of great physicists.
Moulton, F. R., and J. J. Schifferes: *The Autobiography of Science*, Doubleday, New York.
 Excerpts from the writings of great scientists.
Taylor, L. W.: *Physics, the Pioneer Science*, Houghton Mifflin, Boston.
 A general physics text with emphasis on the history of physics.

Color

Hardy, Arthur C.: *Handbook of Colorimetry*, The Technology Press, Massachusetts Institute of Technology, Cambridge, Mass., 1936.
 An authoritative discussion of colorimetry with detailed treatment of ICI chromaticity diagram.
Evans, R. M.: *An Introduction to Color*, Wiley, New York: 1948.
 Excellent and readable discussion of color.
Judd, D. B.: *Color in Business, Science and Industry*, Wiley, New York: 1952.
 Clear, readable description of color vision and color in practical life.
Committee on Colorimetry, Optical Society of America: *The Science of Color*, Crowell, New York: 1953.
 Beautifully illustrated and readable.
Eastman Kodak Company: *Color as Seen and Photographed*, Eastman Kodak Co., Rochester, N.Y.: 1950.
 Well-illustrated and well-written booklet with emphasis on color in photography.

Mechanics

Mach, E.: *The Science of Mechanics*, Open Court, La Salle, Ill.
 The authoritative treatise on the development of mechanics.

Modern Physics

Gamow, G.: *Mr. Tomkins in Wonderland*, Macmillan, New York.
   Delightful treatment of relativity in modern physics.
Hecht, S.: *Explaining the Atom*, Viking, New York.
   Readable treatment of the structure of atoms.
The Effects of Atomic Weapons, U.S. Government Printing Office, Washington, D.C.
   Excellent descriptions of nuclear explosions and the associated phenomena.

Biophysics

Glasser, O.: *Medical Physics*, Year Book Publishers, Inc., Chicago.
   An authoritative book on applications of physics in medicine.
Schroedinger, E.: *What Is Life?* Macmillan, New York.
   A stimulating, speculative book by a great physicist.

Index

653